Mr. Heisey in Biology: "Can _____ _____ _____ without tails by cutting off the tail _____ _____ _____

Class: No.

Mr. Heisey: What do you call that.

Nelson Weigert: Amputation

Man and the Biological World

MAN AND THE BIOLOGICAL WORLD

J. Speed Rogers
Director, Museum of Zoology, University of Michigan

Theodore H. Hubbell
Curator of Insects, Museum of Zoology, University of Michigan

C. Francis Byers
University of Florida

With illustrations by

William L. Brudon
Artist, Museum of Zoology, University of Michigan

SECOND EDITION

New York   Toronto   London

McGRAW-HILL BOOK COMPANY, Inc.

1952

MAN AND THE BIOLOGICAL WORLD

Library of Congress Catalog Card Number: 51-12946

III

MAPLE PRESS COMPANY, YORK, PA.

PREFACE TO THE SECOND EDITION

Nine years' use has shown many needs for revision of the original text, and we are grateful to the numerous teachers who have pointed out errors or omissions of details and suggested changes in emphasis, arrangement, and treatment. The discussions of mitosis and meiosis and the whole section on evolution have been completely rewritten and brought up to date. The portions dealing with the structure and functioning of the human body and of the plant have been considerably revised in the light of recent studies, particularly as concerns hormones, vitamins, and physiology of blood, photosynthesis, and the transport of water and solutes in plants. There has been some rearrangement of chapters to present a more unified treatment of reproduction, and a short summary chapter has been added.

Our thanks are extended to all the numerous persons who have aided us in the task of revision. We are especially indebted to the following: Profs. Edwin B. Mains and Alexander H. Smith for contributing many photographs of plants; Prof. Wm. Randolph Taylor for advice on botanical matters; and Profs. Robert J. Braidwood, Emerson F. Greenman, Volney H. Jones, and Leslie A. White for reading and criticizing the chapters dealing with prehistoric man and the biological significance of culture.

The chief merit of the new edition, we feel, lies in the carefully planned and skillfully drawn illustrations by William L. Brudon. We believe that these not only make the book far more attractive as a volume, but contribute much to the hoped-for clarity of presentation and integration of subject matter. Many of the illustrations are original; acknowledgment of source is made in the captions of the others. Gray's *Anatomy of the Human Body* and Spalteholz's *Atlas of Human Anatomy* served as reference works to ensure accuracy in representation of the human body.

We have not changed the over-all plan of the book. Its treatment is still frankly selective, aiming at a one-course presentation of biological principles that seem to us both pertinent to the student's basic education and capable of being presented as a related whole.

J. Speed Rogers
Theodore H. Hubbell
C. Francis Byers

Ann Arbor, Mich.
Gainesville, Fla.
June, 1952

PREFACE TO THE FIRST EDITION

The past ten years have witnessed the introduction of numerous survey courses in the various sciences. Such courses owe their development to the feeling that the usual freshman course of a particular discipline is at once too technical and too limited for the student who desires a general cultural knowledge of the subject rather than a professional training. Although nearly all educators will agree that some appreciation of the findings and problems of the biological sciences should form a part of a liberal education, the great majority of college students cannot afford time for more than a single course in this field. For them some integrated account of the contributions that biology has made to man's understanding of himself and his environment seems more pertinent than the more detailed and more restricted preparation for the advanced courses they will not take.

If it be granted that a survey course has a place, the question of what viewpoints and what subject matter can and should be presented still remains. The authors are part of a group that was requested to organize a "comprehensive" or "survey" course in the biological sciences for underclassmen at the University of Florida. Now, after some six years of experiment with and modification of subject matter and presentation, with classes of first- or second-year students, they are convinced that a presentation of biological principles that stresses an appreciation of the data and reasoning on which such principles are based is practicable as a single-year course and provides a definite contribution to the student's knowledge of himself and of the world in which he lives.

In order to adapt the survey course to the needs of those students who decide to major or take further work in biology at the University of Florida, laboratory courses that more or less parallel Part I of this book are elective in biology.

It is impossible for the authors to acknowledge all of their indebtedness to other biologists. Perhaps it is not inappropriate to quote from Kipling's introduction to *Barrack Room Ballads:*

> When 'Omer smote 'is bloomin' lyre,
>   He'd 'eard men sing by land an' sea;
> An' what he thought 'e might require,
>   'E went an' took—the same as me!

ix

The authors are grateful to the various publishers and to the General Biological Supply Company whose loans of figures are specifically acknowledged under the reproductions of the illustrations in question. They are greatly indebted to Messrs. Joseph C. Moore and William Brudon, students in the Department of Biology, and to Dr. Albert M. Laessle, instructional staff, University of Florida, for the original drawings and diagrams. Gratitude is expressed also to Prof. A. E. Hooton, of Harvard University, who very kindly read and commented on the preliminary draft of Chaps. XXX and XXXI; to Prof. A. F. Shull, of the University of Michigan, both for reading an earlier draft of the entire manuscript and for his courses and publications; to Dr. Georg Neumann, of Indiana University, for assistance in preparing Chap. XXXI; and to the authors' colleagues in developing and teaching Man and the Biological World at the University of Florida—Prof. H. B. Sherman and Drs. A. F. Carr, H. H. Hobbs, and H. K. Wallace—who have provided many pertinent suggestions and criticisms. Finally the authors wish to acknowledge the unvarying cooperation of Dean W. W. Little, of the General College of the University of Florida, and the freedom he has granted and maintained for them in choosing the viewpoints and materials for the biological part of a "General College" curriculum.

J. SPEED ROGERS
T. H. HUBBELL
C. FRANCIS BYERS

GAINESVILLE, FLA.
  October, 1942

CONTENTS

PART III. THE CHANGING GENERATIONS: THE EVOLUTION OF LIFE IN TIME AND SPACE

CHAPTER I

INTRODUCTION: THE FIELD AND PROBLEMS OF BIOLOGY

Whatever else man may be—a rational, a social, or a religious being—he is also a living organism. Along with more than a million other kinds of living things, he is composed of the intricate stuff called *protoplasm*. Like them he is subject to the peculiar laws that govern the existence and functioning of this living substance. Underlying such aspects of human conduct as are the special concern of history, sociology, and economics are the fundamental attributes, capacities, and limitations that are inherent in man's organic make-up and his membership in the company of living things. This book is concerned with some of the basic principles that have been found to apply to living things and that help us better to understand ourselves and the world in which we live.

The field of knowledge that relates primarily to life processes and living things as such, is known as *biology*.[1] This science seeks to discover and describe all the phenomena associated with living things and the state of being alive. It has amassed a huge content of facts, hypotheses, and principles that give us an insight into the conditions of man's existence, his limitations, and his potentialities. But even if our only interest in biology were to discover the principles that govern human existence and welfare, we could not profitably or efficiently confine our attention to man. He is one of the most complex of all organisms; he is unavailable for many kinds of experiment and observation; and much of his biological make-up is modified or concealed by his intellectual and social attainments. Most of our surest knowledge of man has been gained, and can best be tested, by turning to other forms of life that are more available for experiment and safer for objective observation. Indeed, we cannot adequately understand man's biological heritage and background without some appreciation of the whole living world—in which he lives, of which he is a part, and which he must in some measure control and exploit.

[1] This word comes from the Greek *bios*, meaning "life," and *logos*, which literally meant "the word," "a discourse," or "the discussion of," and which has come to mean "the science of."

Perhaps the best way to get an idea of the scope and content of biology and the light it can throw on many aspects of human function and behavior is to look at some of the problems we encounter in attempting to comprehend a single living organism. No matter what one we choose—man, or one of the familiar domesticated animals or plants, or any of the innumerable "wild" forms that live all about us—we shall encounter a series of broader and broader problems as we examine our selected organism from various points of view.

The organism as an isolated individual. Considered from the simplest possible viewpoint, as an isolated individual, without question as to its origin or possible relations to other individuals, our organism still presents two closely related problems: How is it constructed? And how does it work? Neither question has yet been completely answered for even the most familiar organism. The partial answers that have been obtained, however, form a large part of the subject matter of biology. They are fundamental to any understanding and appreciation of the still more complicated problems of organic interrelationships.

The answer to the query "How is this individual constructed?" will be found to require an analysis of its component parts. Scrutiny of its outward form and structure will show it to be made up of diverse parts. These, together with a variety of concealed but equally gross internal structures, will be found to be fabricated from smaller parts; and these in turn from still smaller ones, until the analysis reaches the limits of microscopic detail. Similarly, the attempt to discover "how it works" reveals the same high degree of organization. Such major processes as motion and locomotion, digestion, respiration, coordination, and appropriate behavior resolve themselves, step by step, into the coordinated functioning of minute individual cells, and finally into the physical and chemical activities of protoplasm.

The parts that are involved and the way in which they are organized differ widely from one type of organism to another. Nevertheless, in any terrestrial animal large enough to be seen and handled we shall find a high degree of differentiation of parts and much division of labor. We shall find that the individual comprises a number of closely interrelated structural and functional systems, that each system is composed of diverse but coordinated organs, that the organs are built of tissues, and that the tissues are made up of cells and cell products.

The organism as a link in a sequence of generations. The second viewpoint from which we shall examine the organism relates to its role as a temporary unit in a succession of similar individuals. We find that our individual was produced by parents (rarely by a single parent) very much like itself. We find also that each individual organism has but a limited life span and eventually ceases to exist. In spite of this, however, the race to which it belongs continues. The organism is thus more than an individual; it also functions as a member of its race—a link in a continuing sequence of individuals.

Here we encounter a new group of problems. How is a new individual produced? To what extent and by what means are the characteristics of the parent reproduced in the offspring and in the offspring's progeny? Does the role of the organism as an individual conflict or fit in with its role as a member of the race, or are these two aspects of the organism wholly unrelated? The answers to these questions are not only fundamental to a comprehension of the living world in general but also the basis for an understanding of many important human problems—sex and reproduction, the role of biological inheritance in relation to stability and change in populations and societies, and the individual man or woman's potential value as a contributor to the next generation.

The organism as the product of evolution. From a third and still broader viewpoint we shall compare an organism with other forms of life about it. We find that its individual pattern of structure and function and the details of its reproductive processes differ more or less from those of other organisms. We find not only that the individual is a member of a sequence of generations but that it also belongs to a much larger assemblage of closely similar individuals that we recognize as a kind or *species.* Most species comprise many thousands or millions of similar individuals. We find that this species is, in turn, a member of a still larger assemblage of several or many similar species, termed a *genus;* that *genera* (plural of genus) can be grouped into *families*, families into *orders*, orders into *classes*, etc.—progressively larger and larger groups that include forms having less and less closely similar structures.

All told, more than a million different kinds of organisms are known to exist. They are grouped into two great kingdoms, animal and plant, and these are subdivisible into phyla, classes, orders, families, genera, and species. When we seek to account for this tremendous variety in the forms of life and for their graduated degrees of likeness and difference, we are led to the conclusion that organisms are all related by blood ties. Their similarities are caused by descent from common ancestors; their differences are due to the remoteness of such common ancestors in the immensity of past time. This is the broad concept; deciphering the details of relationship is still in its initial stages, so that the study of organisms from this viewpoint is still largely a program for the future. But the more data we gather, the more certain seems the conclusion. We see the organism before us as the end product of a long history of survival and change. We see that much of its structure and functioning and its reproductive processes bear the impress of former adaptations for existence. This concept applies to man and to all other organisms and provides the only rational explanation of many human attributes that are inexplicable on any other grounds.

The organism as a unit in a socioeconomic complex. Our fourth viewpoint is concerned with another sort of relationship among organisms. No animal or plant "liveth unto itself." Instead it is a member of a complex society of often diverse kinds of organisms brought together by more or less similar responses to particular intensities of heat, light, moisture, etc. These organisms exhibit various kinds of interdependencies in the competition for the necessities of existence. Much of this interdependence is based upon the fact that the whole organic world is a huge "energy cycle." Energy from the sun, captured by the photosynthesis of green plants, provides the driving power upon which all forms of life are directly or indirectly dependent. The competition for this energy and its transfer from organism to organism involve a host of reciprocal actions—finding food, competition for food, avoiding being eaten, and cooperation for mutual aid, as well as many less direct relationships.

Regarded from this viewpoint, the organism presents a number of new problems. What role does it play in the economy of nature? How does its existence affect the other members of its society? What other organisms affect its own welfare? These are far from simple questions, and to answer them requires a multitude of difficult and subtle observations and many quantitative data. From such observations and such data comes much of man's ability to utilize and conserve the living world for his own needs and purposes. Medicine, agriculture, and forestry are dependent upon our knowledge of such relationships, and hope for the conservation of natural biotic resources—fish, game, and other wildlife—rests upon their adequate understanding.

These four aspects of the organism—its roles as an individual, as a member of its race, as a product of evolution, and as a unit in a competitive and in part cooperative society—form the four chief subdivisions of this book. It must be emphasized that all are related aspects of each and every organism. Each individual and the niche that it occupies in the organic world have been shaped by evolution, and this evolution, in turn, has been the result of the functioning of the individual organism's ancestors—members of successive races that lived and competed with other organisms in the world about them.

BIOLOGY AS A SCIENCE: THE SCIENTIFIC METHOD AND ITS LIMITATIONS

It is important to keep in mind that biology, in attempting to answer the various questions confronting it, has adopted the methods and technique of a science. Any science is a body of knowledge concerning some particular "field," or group of phenomena, in the universe in which we live. It assumes that the phenomena with which it is concerned are more or less interrelated, and sets out to analyze and precisely describe them and to discover their relationships. Observation and experiment establish facts (*i.e.*, result in agreed-upon descriptions of isolated phenomena); but science is much more than a compilation of such observations. It attempts to summarize and classify its observations and establish relationships among them. Here it utilizes one of its most valuable devices, the hypothesis.

A *hypothesis* is a statement that goes beyond the available observations. It postulates a generalization or relationship that is *suggested but not proved* by the facts already known. Its usefulness consists in that it provides an interpretation of available knowledge that can be tested by further observations and experiments. The results of these observations and experiments decide the fate of the hypothesis:

1. It may be found to be untenable, an incorrect summary or assumption.

2. It may be found to be partially tenable, in need of modification and then of further tests.

3. It may prove to be very difficult of direct test and either be gradually substantiated by indirect evidence or be abandoned for other and more fruitful hypotheses; or it may long retain its status as an unproved but useful concept.

4. It may be clearly demonstrated or shown to be so highly probable that it ceases to be regarded as a hypothesis and then becomes one of the accepted *principles* or "laws" of the science.

Any science consists, then, of a mass of "facts" derived from observation and experiment, and of summations, classifications, and interpretations of these facts that are in part regarded as proved (principles, "laws") and in part are hypotheses in various stages of acceptance or rejection.

One of the main requisites of science and the scientific method is the objective viewpoint. This is the ideal and, largely, the practice of making all observations and all proposals and tests of hypotheses without any personal bias. It holds that how gratifying or how abhorrent an observation or a hypothesis may seem has no possible bearing on the scientific truth or falsity of that observation or hypothesis, that *the testimony of checked and repeated observation and experiment is the final authority on which truth or falsity must rest.*

The gathering of precise observations, the free use of hypotheses, and the objective viewpoint are all characteristics of the scientific method; but their fruitful use depends upon the desire to know, a constructive imagination that "sees" relationships between formerly isolated observations, and a degree of critical skepticism that scrutinizes the accuracy of observations and the validity of the conclusions drawn from them.

It is also important to keep in mind that science and the scientific method have limitations. From its very nature science is man-made; it has rejected any thought or expectation of a Mount Sinai, whence absolute truth can be received with final authority. Such authority as it has is due to the consensus of its accepted practitioners and to the fact that it provides the most accurate account of its phenomena that man has yet discovered. Moreover, from a practical standpoint, it is often difficult to know where fact and proved principle leave off and hypothesis begins. Indeed, scientific facts are often partial and incomplete, having been selected and understood because they appeared to answer the question in mind at the time they were chosen and verified. Further, as we have already said, science *assumes* that the phenomena with which it deals are related and that there is a definite orderliness in nature. This assumption lies back of all science, and in a strict sense is probably incapable of proof. Even if this assumption can be accepted as true, science can hope only to answer questions of "how"—not questions of "why" unless we are to define "why" in terms of "how." And finally, as Sir Francis Bacon pointed out centuries ago, we must "ask nature fair questions." Many questions that we propose unwittingly take for granted conditions that do not exist. For example, the old question, "How (or why) does the seeing of a rabbit by a pregnant woman cause a harelip in her child?" is "unfair," because it has assumed an unproved affirmative answer to an unrecognized antecedent question, "Does seeing a rabbit cause harelip in the child?"

The development of the "cell doctrine"—an example of the growth of a hypothesis into a principle.   We shall soon be concerned with cells, and their roles in the structure, functioning, development, and inheritance of the organism. It is therefore pertinent to use the growth of the modern cell doctrine, or cell principle, to illustrate the steps by which accumulation of facts may lead to formulation of a hypothesis, and the hypothesis become established as an accepted principle.

1. *The Accumulation of Observations.*   This step began soon after the invention of the microscope, and was doubtless long retarded by the slow development of satisfactory microscopes. Robert Hooke (1635–1703) first observed cellular structure in cork and other plant tissues; he named the small spaces he saw *cells*, because they looked like little rooms. Malpighi (1628–1694), in Italy, made many microscopic studies of insects, plants, and human tissues. He remarked on the "repeated vesicles" that seemed to make up many of the tissues he examined. Other students of plant and animal structures from time to time saw and mentioned that various parts of their specimens were composed of microscopic units,

which they called by various names and interpreted in various fashions. By the early part of the nineteenth century these observations had become more frequent, and came to include many kinds and parts of plants, and a smaller number of animal tissues. No great interest or importance was, however, attached to these findings.

2. *The Statement of a Hypothesis.* In 1839 two men, the botanist Schleiden and the zoologist Schwann, announced the hypothesis that "all organized bodies are composed of essentially similar parts, namely, of cells. . . . " They came to this conclusion partly from the work of others and partly from their own investigations. They had examined a

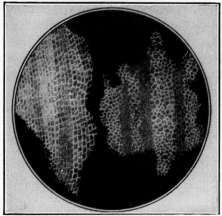

FIG. 1.1. Robert Hooke's illustration of the cells in cork, from his *Micrographia*, published in 1665.

very large number of plant and animal parts in a special search for cellular structure. Their generalization, however, went far beyond any actual observations that they could have made or have gathered from the writings of others. Only a small fraction of the multitude of living things had been examined for cells, and not all parts of even a single organism had been thoroughly explored. Yet wherever Schleiden and Schwann had made a careful microscopic examination they had found cells, and they had also noted that cellular structure is often hard to detect and is demonstrable only by careful technique. They had found cells in many organisms; their hypothesis was that *all* life was cellular in composition. Both these men had many erroneous ideas about cells. They regarded them as vesicles or spaces formed from a noncellular "mother liquor" and thought that they were formed much as crystals are formed in solutions.

3. *Corrections, Modifications, and Extensions of the Original Hypothesis.* The published hypothesis of Schleiden and Schwann stressed the impor-

tance of cells and at once attracted the attention of many other microscopists. New observations were made, many more materials were examined, and the structure of the cell itself was scrutinized. It was discovered that some tissues—bone and cartilage, for instance—are built not of cells but very largely of substances produced by bone-forming and cartilage-forming cells. The cell was found not always to have a wall but to consist more essentially of a peculiar stuff called *protoplasm*. It was also found that cells do not crystallize out of noncellular stuff but instead are invariably formed by the division of a previously existing cell.

4. *Establishment of the Corrected Hypothesis.* By about 1860, as the result of the observations and experiments of many talented workers, the cell theory had been restated somewhat as follows: All living things are composed of cells and cell products; the cell consists of a bit of protoplasm containing a nucleus; and cells are always derived from other previously existing cells. This statement still stands today and is now accepted as entirely substantiated. We no longer speak of the cell hypothesis, but of the *cell doctrine* or *cell principle*.

Part I: THE INDIVIDUAL ORGANISM

CHAPTER II

THE ORGANIZATION OF THE INDIVIDUAL

Our own bodies furnish an excellent example from which to study the structure and functioning of the individual. Although man is one of the more complex organisms, he is built upon the same basic plan as any other familiar animal. Considered as a functioning biological machine, he is little if at all more difficult to comprehend than would be a cat, a frog, a fish, or even a spider or lobster.

When we attempt to understand the structure and functioning of any of these animals, we encounter the high development of organization from which our overworked term *organism* is derived. This organization is roughly comparable to that of some huge modern factory. In an automobile factory, for example, each worker or group of workers specializes on some one detail. The work performed by any individual or group is meaningless in itself, but the cooperation of some groups results in the production of a motor, that of other groups in a chassis, of still others in a body. Finally, when still other specialists have assembled motors, chassis, and bodies into automobiles, we see that the highly organized and coordinated specialization of workers, departments, and divisions forms a complete and efficient whole.

In the human body, or that of any higher animal, division of labor and coordination are far more detailed and intricate than in any factory. Just as in the factory, however, the differentiation of parts and division of labor are so organized and related as to form a functioning whole—in this case an individual organism. Fortunately for our ease of comprehension, the several divisions, departments, and subdivisions of the animal body can be classified into a relatively few types of organizational groups, no matter how much they may differ in detail. The general plan of the organization of the higher animals is illustrated by that of the human body.

SCHEME OF ORGANIZATION OF THE HUMAN BODY

1. *The living body* is a self-maintaining unit or individual, composed of a number of closely integrated systems.

2. *Systems* are major physiological or functioning divisions of the body. Each is concerned with the performance of some closely related group or

11

sequence of body functions. Examples are the digestive, locomotor, circulatory, nervous, and excretory systems. A system can be subdivided into a number of connected and coordinated organs.

3. *Organs* are major subdivisions of a system, which accomplish some essential and more or less complex task or tasks in the total functioning of the entire system. To illustrate, the stomach is one of the organs that make up the digestive system. It performs certain essential but incomplete parts of the whole digestive process. Organs, in turn, are composed of a number of appropriate and coordinated tissues.

4. *Tissues* are groups of similar cells (or of cells and their joint products) united to fulfill a common function. The stomach, for example, is made up of muscular, secreting, connective, and other types of tissues; in combination these make possible the complex functions of the organ. Each tissue consists of a group of similar cells or of such cells and their common products.

5. *Cells.* Here we have reached not the ultimate subdivision of the body but a very real *biological unit* of structure and functioning. This is so because the cell cannot be divided into any smaller *living* units. The human body comprises billions of individual cells, specialized in hundreds of different structural and functional ways. But all are alike in fundamental structure and properties, and all are composed chiefly of the peculiar living stuff which we call *protoplasm*.

SOME STRUCTURES AND PROPERTIES OF PROTOPLASM

When one examines a bit of protoplasm beneath a microscope he is apt to be disappointed by how little he can see. The semitransparent, somewhat viscid material looks not unlike raw egg white, with little discernible detail or evidence of structure. The tremendous actual complexity is invisible, partly because of the lack of optical contrast between its grosser but still minute parts but chiefly because of the submicroscopic dimensions of its finer details.

The earlier microscopists, lacking the concepts and techniques of modern chemistry and physics, had to be content with establishing the fact that protoplasm is the common formative material of all plant and animal life and with discovering such of its structures and properties as they could observe with the microscope and the simple chemical and physical techniques then at hand. These early workers noted certain characteristic phenomena that occur in protoplasm as well as in nonprotoplasmic matter, but they and biologists in general were especially impressed with the capacity of protoplasm for carrying on certain adaptive and apparently purposive activities that did not occur in any nonliving substance. The properties exhibited by protoplasm thus came to be classified into two groups—the so-called "nonvital" and "vital" properties. This classification is still useful, not so much for its distinction between the features of living as opposed to nonliving matter as for the emphasis it places upon the adaptive end results of the innumerable and still incompletely analyzed chemical and physical processes and relationships found in protoplasm.

Vital properties of protoplasm. Vital properties owe their name to the once widely held view that they were controlled by some peculiar life principle inexplicable by ordinary chemical and physical laws. They may still be termed vital in that they are only exhibited by living organisms; our inability to explain them is probably attributable only to their complexity. "Vital" properties are the end results of chemical and physical relationships too complex and involved to be completely analyzed in the present state of scientific knowledge.

1. *Metabolism.* All protoplasm, unless temporarily dormant, is constantly capturing energy and utilizing it for activity or growth. The storage of energy and its subsequent use may add an intermediate step to the process. This ability to capture energy and particularly the ability to change energy (food) into more protoplasm (growth) are capacities peculiar to protoplasm. The term *metabolism* comprises all the chemical processes occurring in living things and includes a great variety of chemical reactions. It is convenient to divide metabolism into two phases —*anabolism*, which includes the synthetic processes by which simple substances are changed into the complex materials of protoplasm (assimilation), and *catabolism*, which includes the breaking-down processes by which complex substances are split into simpler ones, liberating energy and yielding wastes (disintegration). Anabolism results in storage of energy and in growth; catabolism furnishes energy for heat, motion, and chemical syntheses.

2. *Reproduction.* All units of protoplasm have the power to divide and produce new units of the same kind. This is in part dependent upon growth, but it also involves the maintenance of a constant type and size of organization in spite of growth.

3. *Irritability or Reactiveness.* This is the property of being able to respond to stimuli. A large variety of stimuli, both external and internal, may produce adaptive responses on the part of protoplasm. Protoplasm may react to the stimuli of light, temperature change, contact, gravity, electric current, change in degree of acidity or alkalinity, and various chemical substances.

Nonvital properties of protoplasm. Many of the characteristic phenomena shown by protoplasm were found to occur also in nonliving substances and systems. Here they are more susceptible to experiment and measurement, and they were soon recognized as expressions of physical and chemical properties and relationships. Diffusion, osmosis,

Brownian movement, surface tension, adsorption, and an increasing number of chemical reactions came to be included in the growing list of characteristic nonvital properties of protoplasm.

The modern attack upon the problems of the structure and nature of protoplasm is made possible by the great advances that have been made in chemistry and physics. The application of the data and methods of these sciences to the problems of biology has created the new sciences of biophysics and biochemistry, both of which are concerned primarily with what exists and goes on within the cell. Here we can only attempt to summarize briefly some of the more elementary and basic findings which throw light upon the nature and activities of protoplasm.

Chemical Composition. Protoplasm is made up of nearly a score of common elements and contains none that are not also found in nonliving substances. They include carbon, oxygen, hydrogen, nitrogen, calcium, sodium, potassium, sulfur, phosphorus, iron, copper, and chlorine, with traces of boron, bromine and a few other elements. The great bulk of these occur in the form of compounds—water (composing about three-fourths of the total volume of protoplasm), a variety of salts in solution, and the characteristic organic compounds classed as proteins, fats, and carbohydrates. Few if any of these compounds are present in fixed amounts, but vary within certain limits and are ordinarily in a state of change. Protoplasm takes in selected substances and gives off others in a continual interchange with the surrounding medium.

Physical State. Protoplasm exists in what is known as the *colloidal* state. This means that many of its component substances are dispersed as minute separate particles suspended in a fluid or semifluid. This fluid is a watery solution of salts, gases, and soluble organic substances; the particles comprise notably the proteins, fats, and other nonsoluble organic substances. Most of the particles are too small to be seen under the microscope and yet are larger than the dispersed molecules of a true solution.

The colloid state, in which minute discontinuous particles are dispersed throughout a continuous medium, is not peculiar to protoplasm. Familiar examples of nonliving colloids are seen in liquid glue (the name *colloid* comes from the Greek *kollos*, "glue"), jelly, and gelatin. The simplest colloids consist of only two substances—a dispersed phase and a continuous phase. The colloid of gold in water is a beautiful red or blue fluid in which the dispersed phase is a solid; cream is a colloid in which both the dispersed and continuous phases are fluid. Protoplasm contains both solid and fluid particles.

Even the simplest nonliving colloids show many complex and characteristic properties. One of the most conspicuous is the capacity of many colloids to change from semifluid to semisolid and back again with relatively small changes in temperature or other agents; and their liability to become irreversibly solid ("set") or fluid when subjected to greater changes or when acted upon by chemical agents is another striking feature. These changes are the result of complex and delicate relationships between the discontinuous particles and the continuous medium about them. At one temperature, for example, the solid substance may be dispersed and the colloid be a fluid, while at a lower temperature the solid may be the continuous phase, and the colloid be a gel. In protoplasm the situation is enormously more complicated because of the many and changing kinds of discontinuous particles involved.

Many of the other properties of colloids are caused by the tremendous amounts of surface provided by the billions of discontinuous particles, for these surfaces are the site of peculiar properties of adsorption and electric charge. A great deal of the chemical activity within the cell is also concentrated along these boundaries and may occur at rates which would be impossible except for the immense area of contact between the reacting substances which the colloidal state provides.

The modern worker is still unable to analyze, explain, or synthetically duplicate metabolism, reproduction, and irritability, but he finds no evidence that these result from any nonphysical property of protoplasm. The problems of protoplasmic structure and function appear to differ from other problems of matter only in their unique complexity.

THE STRUCTURE OF THE CELL

The simplest description of a cell would be "a small mass of protoplasm differentiated into nucleus and cytoplasm."[1] The actual size of this small mass varies greatly between different kinds of cells. If we disregard such specialized exceptions as yolk-gorged eggs, the maximum size is well below a cubic millimeter (about 1/16,000 cubic inch), and the minimum less than one-thousandth of this. Such a size range extends from cells that are easily seen with the unaided eye to ones that require the higher powers of a microscope to be at all visible.

The shapes of these masses are almost as varied as their sizes. A bit of protoplasm free from stress or pressure tends to take a spherical form, and not a few cells have this shape. The great majority of cells, however, have various nonspherical shapes. The cells in tissues subject to strains, stresses, and pressures of various kinds may be cubical, cylindrical, flattened, keystonelike, or spindle-shaped, as shown in Fig. 2.3. Most nerve cells have long, slender, branched processes that extend far out

---

[1] The lowly bacteria and blue-green algae do not show differentiation into nucleus and cytoplasm; in them the entire cell seems to function somewhat like a nucleus. Various other special exceptions to the conditions here described as typical are to be found in different groups of organisms.

from the main body of the cell. If one turns to unicellular organisms he will find many sorts of regular and irregular shapes imposed by the surrounding cuticles. In contrast to the great variety of size and shape shown by a variety of kinds of cells, those of any one kind tend to be essentially alike in both size and form.

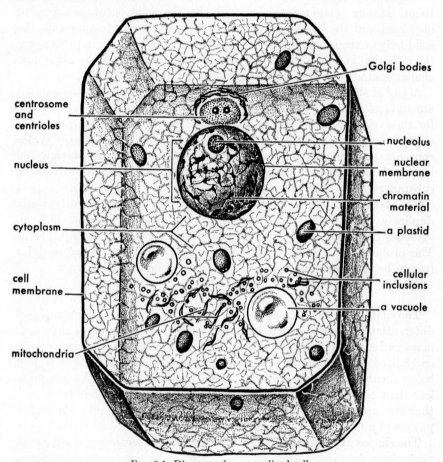

FIG. 2.1. Diagram of a generalized cell.

Figure 2.1 is a somewhat diagrammatic drawing of a fairly typical cell. The *nucleus* is shown as a sphere enclosed in a *nuclear membrane*, turgid with a semifluid *nuclear sap* and containing an irregularly dispersed, somewhat more solid substance called *chromatin*. Chromatin derives its name from the Latin *chroma*, "color," because of its marked affinity for certain stains or dyes. The smaller sphere within the nucleus is a *nucleolus*—another strongly staining body that is absent from some cells and multiple in others. Just outside of the nucleus, and here shown above it, is a small and sometimes optically distinct body called the *centrosome*, containing a pair of very minute *centrioles*.

All of the protoplasm outside of the nuclear membrane constitutes the *cytoplasm*. Its surface is differentiated into a living *cell membrane*, capable of regulating much of the cell's interchange of substances with the surrounding medium or with other cells. Internally the cytoplasm may show various specialized regions, structures, and inclusions. Among these are thread-shaped structures known as *mitochondria*, which appear to be the seat of important metabolic enzymes (organic catalysts), and *Golgi bodies*, which may usually be demonstrated in animal cells but are of unknown function. Other cytoplasmic structures which may or may not be found in a given kind of cell include vacuoles and plastids. A *vacuole* is a usually spherical space that contains fluid or suspended wastes or cell products and that is enclosed in a cytoplasmic membrane. *Plastids* are especially characteristic of plant cells; they are definitely organized bodies of protoplasm surrounded by bounding membranes, and may be spherical, ovoid, or sometimes ribbon-shaped or collarlike. They may be colorless but often contain the characteristic plant pigments which give color to leaves and flowers. In addition, cytoplasm will usually be found to contain a changing variety of inclusions, granules or droplets of secreted substances, and of foods and wastes that are accumulated or produced by the metabolic activities of the cell.

The cell that we have briefly described is one in the so-called "resting" stage, or condition. Actually such a cell is engaged in a host of metabolic activities and is only "resting" in the sense that it is not in the process of division. The discernible structures and activities of the resting stage, however, give but little indication of the complex structure of the nucleus or of the precise organization of the chromatin material into bodies called *chromosomes*, which maintain their identities throughout all the nuclear transformations that occur in cell division.

MITOSIS

The typical and almost invariable method of division of cells is a complex process named *mitosis* (Greek, *mitos,* "thread") in allusion to the conspicuous threadlike structures that appear in its early stages. Once begun, the process is a more or less continuous one that lasts from 2 to 24 hours in different kinds of cells. But it is customary and convenient to recognize four successive stages in the process: *prophase, metaphase, anaphase,* and *telophase.* The events that take place during these stages are somewhat diagrammatically illustrated in Fig. 2.2, which begins with the resting stage of a cell containing six chromosomes. The following account will be more easily understood if frequently compared with the appropriate drawings.

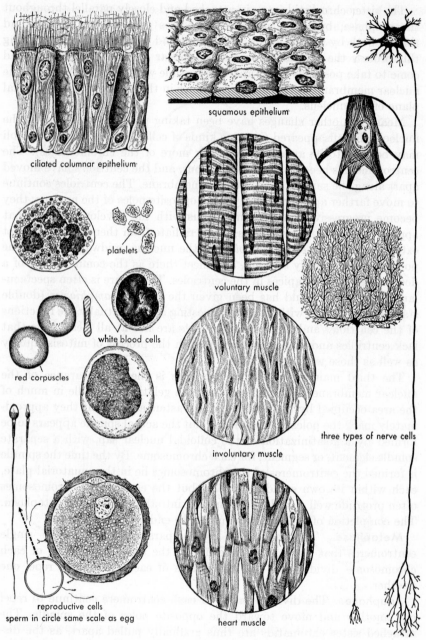

squamous epithelium

ciliated columnar epithelium

platelets

white blood cells

red corpuscles

voluntary muscle

involuntary muscle

three types of nerve cells

reproductive cells
sperm in circle same scale as egg

heart muscle

Fig. 2.3. Some cells from the human body.

partly attributed to a constriction of the spindle in the region of its equatorial plate.

It is during anaphase that individual chromosomes show their characteristic "J" or "V" shapes. The former shape is associated with a centromere near the end of the chromatid; the latter with a centromere near the center. The free ends of the J or V are swept back as the chromatid is drawn through the viscid material of the spindle.

Telophase. The telophase may be thought of as prophase in reverse. The two groups of chromatids (which now constitute the chromosomes of the daughter nuclei) have come to lie near the opposite poles of the spindle. The daughter chromosomes now gradually uncoil and begin to lose the property of taking a clear-cut stain. The spindle disappears, and a nuclear membrane forms about each group of chromosomes. Any nucleolus or nucleoli that disappeared at prophase reappear. The cytoplasm now divides, usually in the plane occupied by the equatorial plate of the spindle, to form two complete and separate daughter cells.

The foregoing account has been kept as brief as possible. Many details of interest to the cytologist have been omitted, and little notice has been given to the variations in other details that would be found if one compared the mitotic processes of a number of different kinds of cells. We have attempted to describe the essential events and consequences of mitosis that are of marked importance in nearly all considerations of biological processes. The following points should be particularly noted:

1. Mitosis results in a precisely equal division of each chromosome, so that the daughter cells receive nuclei that are *qualitatively* and *quantitatively* identical.

2. The chromosomes are seen to be double (paired chromatids) at the beginning of prophase, but single when last discernible in telophase. The doubling process evidently takes place during the resting stage, as should be expected theoretically from the necessity of each chromatid duplicating itself by metabolic synthesis of new chromatin material. Unfortunately, in a great number of cells the chromosomes of the resting cell cannot be made visible by the techniques of the microscopist, probably because they imbibe large quantities of water and so change from the condensed condition which they exhibit during mitosis. There is, however, ample reason to believe that they remain intact throughout the resting stage.

3. Our diagram shows six chromosomes. If they are compared, it will be noted that the six include three different sizes of chromosomes, each size represented twice. The members of each pair are to be thought of as being not only alike in size but in all other respects as well. If we should examine the cellular structure of a wide variety of plants and animals, we would find (with certain exceptions to be noted later) that all the cells

of each kind of plant or animal have a characteristic and fixed number of chromosomes. In each case these chromosomes can be grouped into half that number of identical pairs, regardless of the total number of chromosomes present. The characteristic number of chromosomes may range from 2 to more than 100 in different species.

TISSUES AND GLANDS

A tissue may be either a group of like cells, so connected as to perform a common function, or the common product of a group of similar cells. In any of the higher animals, scores of different kinds of tissues may be recognized, but for our purposes we can group all tissues into four great groups:

1. *Sustentative tissues* are adapted to provide mechanical support and to bind various other tissues together. In addition, certain types of sustentative tissues are modified for such special functions as fat storage or the formation of a circulating medium. Examples of sustentative tissues are bone, cartilage, ligament, tendon, and the cells and fluids of the blood. Many of these tissues are chiefly cell products, their living cells functioning to provide the needed material rather than to perform the necessary tasks directly.

2. *Contractile tissues* include various types of muscle cells; all are adapted to perform work by contracting or shortening.

3. *Nervous tissues* are specialized to receive stimuli and transmit impulses.

4. *Epithelial tissues* are variously specialized to cover the external and internal surfaces of the body. The formation of glands is a characteristic and peculiar property of epithelial tissues.

Glands are cells or groups of cells that have the function of *secreting* some substance needed in the economy of the body or of *excreting* some waste product or surplus substance. In all glands, the actual secreting (or excreting) cells are derived from epithelial tissues, although these may be supplemented by various sustentative and contractile tissues. In some instances, single epithelial cells (gland cells) function as glands, but typically glands are aggregations of a number of secreting (or excreting) cells that are able to produce a comparatively large quantity of their particular product.

Ordinarily, we think of a gland as being connected with some epithelial surface (the skin or the lining of the gut) by a passageway or duct, through which its products may pass. Examples of such glands will be found in the skin and in the digestive glands of the mouth, stomach, and intestine. Another very different kind of gland will be considered when we come to study the endocrine system.

ORGANS AND SYSTEMS

Organs and systems represent successively higher stages in body organization. An *organ*, as the term is used here, is typically composed of a number of diverse kinds of tissues, brought together to perform some definite and limited function that requires the cooperation of several or many kinds of cells. A skeletal muscle, for example, is an organ whose

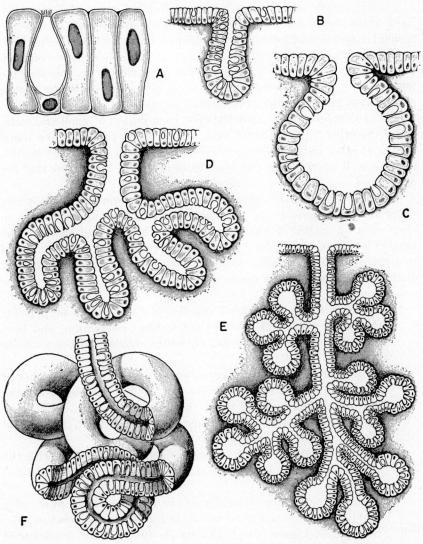

FIG. 2.4. Types of glands. *A*, glandular cells in epithelium. *B*, simple tubular gland. *C*, simple alveolar gland. *D*, compound tubular gland. *E*, compound alveolar gland. *F*, simple coiled tubular (sweat) gland.

function is to produce motion. This requires not only a mass of voluntary muscle tissue but also sustentative tissues to hold the muscle tissues in proper arrangement, to protect them from friction, and to connect the bundles of muscle cells with the skeleton. There must be blood and blood vessels to supply fuel and materials for maintenance, and to remove wastes. Nervous tissues are also required to coordinate and control the activities of these tissues and that of the muscle as a whole.

A single muscle is rarely capable of performing any useful action by itself. Even the simplest voluntary movements involve sets of muscles, skeletal supports, and joints. The mechanical movements of the body are produced by hundreds of different muscles, attached to definite points on a bony framework comprising fixed and movable parts. Together the muscles and bony framework make up a motor or locomotor *system*, composed of many precisely coordinated organs.

Other examples of organs are the eyes, ears, organs of smell and taste, and many other "sense organs" that, together with the brain, the spinal cord, and other parts, make up the nervous system. Again, the mouth, esophagus, stomach, liver, pancreas, intestines, etc., are organs that are united and coordinated into a digestive system.

The integrating physiological systems of the human body.   Just how many and what systems are to be recognized in the human body is to some extent a matter of how we choose to subdivide and classify. The number is perhaps determined in part by whether we are more influenced by structural or by functional considerations. From 8 to 10 are commonly distinguished, and we shall compromise on nine. These are:

1. The *locomotor system*, which supplies protection and support for other body parts and provides for motion, locomotion, and heat production. Often listed separately as the *skeletal* and the *muscular* systems.
2. The *skin* or *integumentary system*, adapted to perform a number of rather diverse functions that are related and correlated by the necessity of their location at the body surface:
   a. Protection of the body against water loss, light, mechanical injury, and the attack of parasitic organisms.
   b. Heat regulation—a function performed in cooperation with the circulatory and nervous systems—a thermostatically controlled radiator.
   c. Sensory perception—the skin is the location and support of a multitude of varied sense receptors for touch, temperature, etc.
3. The *digestive system*, which has for its function the ingestion of foods, their processing into absorbable component parts, and the delivery of these end products to the circulatory system.

4. The *respiratory system*, which has for its function the providing of an adequate gaseous exchange between the blood and the outside air.
5. The *excretory system*, which has as its function the elimination of an important part of the wastes that are invariably produced by the living process. Structurally related to item 9 below and sometimes lumped with it as the *urinogenital system*.

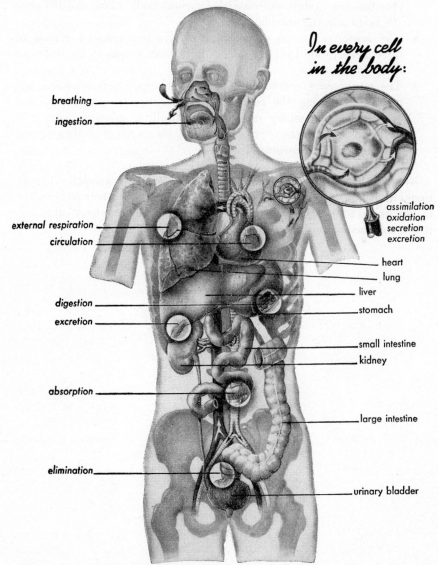

FIG. 2.5. Division of labor as illustrated by some of the structures and processes of the human body. (*Based on a figure in Wolcott, Animal Biology.*)

6. The *circulatory system*, a common carrier system of pumps, pipe lines, and loading platforms that connects and keeps coordinate the other systems of the body and has accessory but very important functions of protection against invasion by parasitic organisms.

7. The *nervous system*, which receives sensory stimuli from the outside world and from other body regions and functions as a special coordinating system between the various body parts and between the body and the outside world.

8. The *endocrine system*, a complex of widely separated glands of internal secretion that provide an important accessory control over body coordination.

9. The *reproductive systems*, male and female in separate bodies, the organs containing the reproductive cells (ovaries or testes) and various supplementary organs, structurally combined (especially in the male) with the excretory system, the two frequently grouped together as the *urinogenital system*.

None of these systems is complete in itself. Each is a specialized functional division of a highly integrated single individual. Their segregation is very useful for analysis, but no system can be wholly understood unless it is recognized as but one dependent part of a whole.

CHAPTER III

THE FRAMEWORK OF THE BODY

The form and symmetry of the human body, as well as the greater part of its bulk and weight, are determined by the skeletal framework and the muscles and skin that cover it. It is the combination of skeleton and muscle that performs all the voluntary movements, makes possible locomotion, and, with the skin, forms a protection and support for nearly all of the more delicate internal organs. Moreover, it is the muscles that utilize most of the energy taken into the body, that provide the greater part of the body heat, and that produce most of the waste that must be continuously eliminated.

THE LOCOMOTOR SYSTEM

Because the skeletal system and the skeletal muscles are so intimately related in their functioning, they are frequently considered together under the heading *locomotor system*. A study of the structures involved in a simple movement of the arm (Fig. 3.10) will illustrate the interdependence between the skeleton and the muscles that surround and cover it.

The Skeleton

Protoplasm, as we have seen, is largely made up of water. It tends to keep a definite volume but cannot keep a definite shape unless it is held in by some membrane or wall. In the instance of single cells and of the smaller and simpler multicellular animals, the presence of cell membranes or cell walls gives sufficient support. The larger and more highly developed many-celled animals, however, especially those that must live upon land, have had to develop a more or less complicated accessory supporting mechanism. In the vertebrates, this mechanism consists of an internal skeleton made up of *bones*, *ligaments*, and *cartilages*. The skeleton not only helps to support the massive protoplasmic elements that constitute the body proper but also provides leverage for the action of the muscles that move the body. It is imperfectly represented by the usual mounted skeleton or by the bones that remain after the rest of the body has disintegrated. In life, the 200 odd bones of the human skeleton are connected

27

into a single framework by a variety of devices. These include dovetailed connections that lock certain bones immovably together, cartilaginous junctures or pads that provide slightly flexible unions between bones, and joints that are more or less freely movable.

Skeletal units. The most conspicuous units of the skeleton are obviously the *bones*. These may be roughly classified according to shape. There

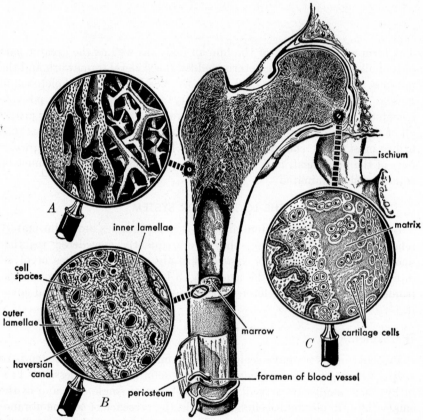

Fig. 3.1. Diagrammatic section through the upper end of the femur, with magnified detail of (*A*) spongy bone, (*B*) cross section of compact bone of the shaft, and (*C*) articular cartilage.

are the *long* bones, including those of the upper and lower arms and legs; *short* bones, such as those of the wrist and ankle; *flat* bones, such as the shoulder blade and some of the cranial bones; and *irregular* bones, exemplified by the vertebrae.

If a long bone is sawed lengthwise and the cut surface is examined, the following parts can easily be identified. There is first a thick, hard outer layer or shell of *compact* bony material. This forms a cylinder surrounding a central cavity except at the ends, where the interior of the bone is filled with a *spongy* open network of bone substance. In life, both the central cavity of the shaft and the meshes of the spongy bone at the ends are filled with a soft tissue called *bone marrow*, and the outer surface of the bone is enclosed in a sheath of dense connective tissue called the *periosteum*.

The disposition of the bone substance in the form of a cylinder with internally reinforced ends, instead of a solid rod, gives the bone the greatest mechanical strength attainable for the quantity of structural material used. The strength of the bone is also materially increased by the arrangement of its finer structural elements. The inner and outer walls of the shaft are formed of circumferential layers, or *lamellae*, and the spongy bone at the ends of the shaft is not haphazardly arranged but has its partitions aligned in definite planes and curves. A study of these details of structure in relation to the work done by the bone shows that they form a pattern giving maximum resistance to the stresses to which the bone is exposed. The same structural efficiency is found in the arrangement of the materials in other bones of the skeleton.

All of the materials that are utilized in bone, cartilage, and ligament belong to the group of tissues called *sustentative*. These tissues are notable for being composed largely of cell products rather than of cells. In the living body the sustentative cell products everywhere contain the living cells that produce them. In *ligaments* the cell products are elongated and very strong fibers, some elastic and others nonelastic. In *cartilage* the cell product is a tough, usually semitransparent material that under the microscope can be seen everywhere to enclose the cartilage-producing cells. In *bone* the matrix consists both of calcium phosphate, which makes the bone hard, and of a strong and tough organic material that pervades the mineral parts. One can take two fresh bones from a recently living animal, burn one to remove the organic parts, and place the other in acid to remove all minerals. The bone treated with fire is dry, hard, and brittle; that treated with acid is a tough, flexible structure of organic material. Both retain the recognizable shapes and dimensions of the original bones. The accompanying illustration (Fig. 3.1) shows more or less diagrammatically the relationship of the *matrix* (the cell product in bone and cartilage) to the cells that produce it. The matrix is penetrated by nerves and blood vessels that supply the living cells; in bone these occupy the channels called the Haversian canals.

The divisions of the skeleton.   The complete human skeleton is shown in Fig. 3.2. Two chief regions or divisions of the skeleton may be recognized, each with minor subdivisions. The *axial skeleton* comprises the head and backbone (skull and vertebral column), together with the ribs, the sternum, and the cartilages that connect the front, or ventral, ends

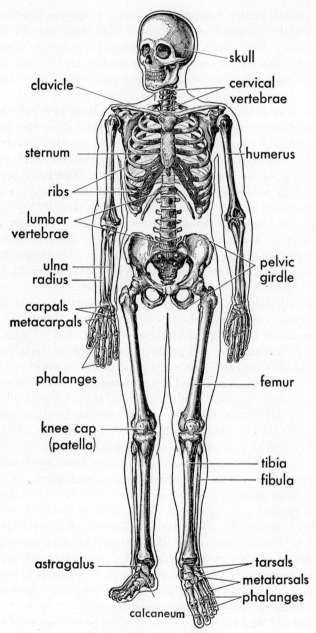

skull

clavicle

cervical
vertebrae

sternum

humerus

ribs

lumbar
vertebrae

ulna
radius

pelvic
girdle

carpals
metacarpals

phalanges

femur

knee cap
(patella)

tibia
fibula

astragalus

tarsals
metatarsals
phalanges

calcaneum

FIG. 3.2. The human skeleton.

of the ribs. In addition, the skeleton includes two so-called "girdles" and their appendages—an upper one, the shoulder or *pectoral girdle*, to which the arms are attached, and a lower one, the hip or *pelvic girdle*, bearing the legs. These two girdles and their appendages make up the *appendicular skeleton*.

The axial skeleton. The axial skeleton forms the longitudinal or vertical axis of the body. The *skull* consists of two main parts, the *cranium* or brain case and the bones of the face. The former is a rigid bony box,

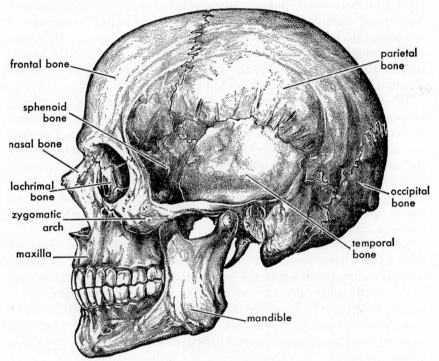

frontal bone

sphenoid
bone

nasal bone

lachrimal
bone

zygomatic
arch

maxilla

parietal
bone

occipital
bone

temporal
bone

mandible

FIG. 3.3. The human skull.

averaging between 1,200 and 1,500 cc. in capacity, which, in life, is completely filled by the brain, its membranes, and the thin layer of fluid that insulates the brain from direct attachment to or contact with the bony walls. The bones of the face surround the mouth and nasal openings, form the lower parts of the eye sockets and the bony partition between the nose and mouth cavities. Except for the strongly hinged lower jaw and three pairs of tiny ear bones, all the bones of the skull are immovable and are fused into a single rigid structure by strong, dovetailed sutures between the various bones.

Altogether, the skull comprises some 22 bones, of which 8 pertain to the cranium and 14 to the facial portion. Sixteen lower teeth are borne by the *mandible,* or lower jaw, and 8 by each of the paired *maxillae* that form the upper jaw.

The vertebral column is joined to the skull by a peculiar hinge joint, in which two rounded projections (*occipital condyles*) on the base of the skull fit into corresponding depressions in the uppermost vertebra and permit a limited rocking motion between the two. This provides the up-and-down nodding motion of our heads. The comparatively restricted rotary motion, used in turning the head to either side, is provided by a pivot joint between the first vertebra and the second. Both motions are limited and restrained by strong ligaments as well as by the muscles of the neck, thus protecting the delicate spinal cord from injury. The spinal cord extends through an opening in the base of the skull into the neural canal of the vertebral column, and would be pinched or twisted by excessive movement of the head upon the backbone.

The whole *vertebral column* consists of some 33 bones, the *vertebrae,* arranged in a linear series from the skull to slightly below the pelvic girdle. All the vertebrae are built upon the same general plan, but they are variously modified in different parts of the column. In each vertebra the large central opening, called the *neural canal,* is bounded ventrally[1] by the dorsal face of a large bony cylinder, the *centrum,* and on all other sides by the *neural arch.* Projecting from the neural arch are a large dorsal *neural spine,* a pair of *transverse processes,* and paired anterior and posterior *articular processes.*

Each vertebra is separated from the one above and the one below by thick cartilaginous pads between the centra and by smooth, cartilage-covered sliding joints where the articular processes are in contact. The movement between any two adjacent vertebrae is very slight, being limited by strong, ligamentous bindings and intricately interlaced muscles. Nevertheless the summation of the slight movements between adjacent vertebrae gives considerable flexibility to the spinal column as a whole.

Notwithstanding the basic similarity between all the vertebrae, the work they have to perform in the several body regions is correlated with differences in proportion and in the details of their structure. Five vertebral regions may be distinguished. The neck region consists of 7 *cervical vertebrae;* then comes the thoracic or chest region, with 12 *thoracic verte-*

---

[1] In describing anatomical features it is convenient to be able to do so regardless of the position of the body. *Venter* means "belly," *dorsum* means "back"; *cephalon* means "head," and *cauda* means "tail." Hence "ventral" or "ventrally" means of or toward the belly, regardless of whether the posture is erect as in man or horizontal as in four-footed animals. "Dorsal" pertains to the back, "cephalic" to the head region, and "caudal" to the tail region, or to directions toward those regions. "Upper" and "lower," "front" and "rear" are unsatisfactory terms for anatomical use, since they depend upon external orienting criteria.

brae, each bearing a pair of movable *ribs;* then the lower trunk or lumbar region with 5 large *lumbar vertebrae;* then the pelvic region with 5 vertebrae tightly fused into a *sacrum,* which is rigidly attached to the pelvic girdle; and finally comes the *coccyx* or bony remnants of the tail, consisting of 3, 4, or 5 small vestigial vertebrae.

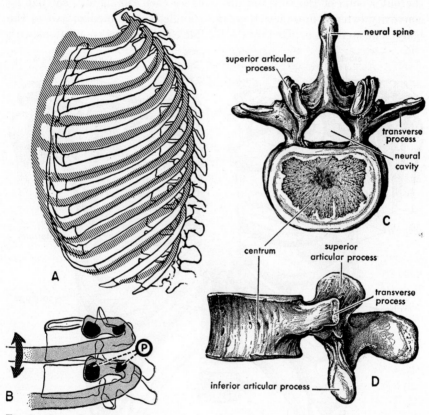

Fig. 3.4. Some details of vertebrae and ribs. *A,* diagram of rib movement in breathing. *B,* articulation of ribs, showing the two pivot points (*p*). *C,* a lumbar vertebra from above. *D,* the same vertebra from the left side.

Seen from the front or rear the vertebral column forms a straight line, but in side view it is curved. Its curvatures give the spine spring and resilience in walking and jumping and enable it to absorb more completely the shocks produced by these and other body movements. The tilt of the sacrum brings the weight of the body directly over the legs and, with the lumbar curvature, makes possible the fully erect posture characteristic of man.

The walls of the *thoracic cavity* (which encloses the heart and lungs) are supported by the ribs, together with the thoracic vertebrae, the *sternum,* and the cartilages that connect the ends of the ribs with the sternum. Each rib at its basal end is attached to a vertebra by means of two movable articulations. The curved ribs not only project forward but also slant downward, and their convexities also tilt somewhat downward. Their attachments are such that contraction of the thoracic muscles lifts the outer ends of the ribs and also rotates each rib slightly so that its convexity extends more nearly at right angles to the median axis of the body. The sternum is lifted by the flexible cartilaginous connections with

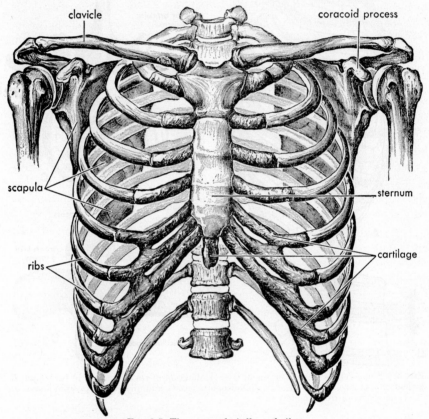

FIG. 3.5. The pectoral girdle and ribs.

the ribs and pushed somewhat outward. The result is that the depth and breadth of the thoracic cavity are increased. At the same time the up-domed muscular diaphragm that forms the floor of the cavity contracts and pulls downward. These movements increase the cubic capacity of the thorax and cause inspiration of air into the lungs.

The appendicular skeleton.   The bony framework of the arms and legs, and the girdles that attach these appendages to the axial skeleton, constitute the appendicular skeleton. Comparison will show that the two girdles and their appendages are built upon the same fundamental plan. There are, however, considerable differences in the sizes and shapes of the corresponding bones. The pelvic girdle is rigidly fused to the sacrum of the axial skeleton, while the pectoral girdle is very loosely and flexibly joined to the thoracic portion of the axial skeleton by means of ligaments, cartilages, and muscles.

The pectoral girdle and the arm. A pair of slender, curved, rodlike *clavicles* (collarbones) extends from the upper end of the sternum to the upper part of the shoulder. There each clavicle forms a movable joint with one of the *scapulae* (shoulder blades). These are broad, flattened plates which extend from the shoulders toward the backbone above the upper thoracic ribs. On the dorsal surface of each scapula there is a flattened, projecting ridge, the *spinous process*. The apex of this process overhangs the shoulder joint, forms the point of the shoulder, and has the clavicle attached to its inner face. Just inside of the shoulder joint there is another projection of the scapula, the *coracoid process*. This is the reduced remnant of another bone, fused to the scapula; it forms the point of attachment for certain arm and shoulder muscles. The *humerus*, or bone of the upper arm, has a rounded head which fits into a shallow socket in the outer end of the shoulder blade; this socket is the *glenoid fossa*. The ball-and-socket joint thus formed permits great freedom of movement of the arm.

The skeleton of the arm consists of the *humerus*, just mentioned, two long bones of the forearm (*radius* and *ulna*), and the bones of the wrist and hand. The humerus forms a hinge joint at the elbow with the radius and ulna. The lower end of the ulna lies on the little finger side of the forearm, and its upper end encloses part of the end of the humerus to form the elbow. The radius, at its lower end, lies on the thumb side of the forearm. Its upper end is somewhat cupped, forming a rotatable junction with a convexity at the end of the humerus. This permits the radius to turn so as to move across and partly around the ulna in the familiar movement of turning the wrist (Fig. 3.6).

The skeleton of the hand comprises eight small wrist, or *carpal, bones*, five long *metacarpal bones* imbedded in the palm of the hand, and the *phalanges*, or finger bones. There are two phalanges in the thumb and three in each of the other fingers. The human hand is essentially generalized in structure. This is another way of saying that it is not highly modified for the performance of a special function (*cf.* whales, horses, moles, bats) but is more like the primitive ancestral condition. Nevertheless, certain features of the hand and arm may be regarded as specializations for variety of movement and versatility of use. Such are the rotatability of the radius, the great flexibility of the fingers, and the opposability of the thumb to the other fingers. The general usefulness of the hand and arm of man, and especially the ability to grasp and manipulate objects, have evidently had much to do with the development of his mentality and attainment of the dominant position that he now holds in the world.

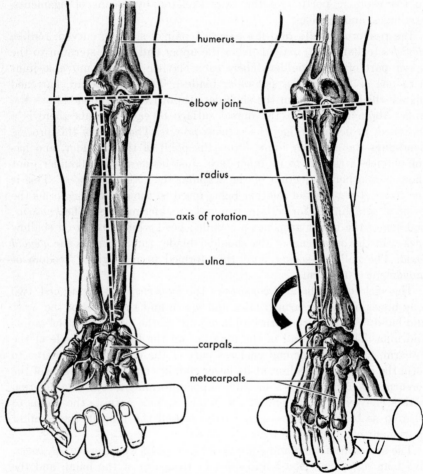

Fig. 3.6. The bones of the arm, showing the joints and movements involved in turning the wrist.

The pelvic girdle and the leg.   The pelvic girdle has the form of a large and irregularly symmetrical bony ring. It is made up of three pairs of strongly fused bones—the *ilium*, or hipbone, the *ischium* (on which we sit), and the *pubis* (in front). On each side of the pelvic girdle there is a deep socket called the *acetabulum*, into which fits the rotatable ball-like head of the femur or thighbone. The shape of the pelvis differs slightly in the two sexes. That of the male is somewhat narrower, deeper, and more funnel-shaped; the female pelvis is wider, shorter, and shallower and is adapted to the requirements of childbirth.

The skeleton of the leg consists of a single thigh bone, the *femur*, and of two lower leg bones, the *tibia* and *fibula*. A small, separate, flattened

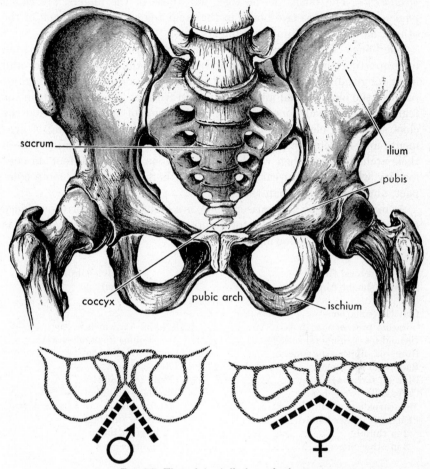

Fig. 3.7. The pelvic girdle from the front.

bone forms the kneecap, or *patella*. The tibia, or shinbone, is larger than the fibula. At the ankle the tibia is on the inside and the fibula on the outside of the leg.

The foot is more highly modified for a specialized function than is the hand. Along with the domed brain case, it is the most characteristically human modification of the skeleton; yet it is clearly built on the same plan as the hand. The heel and ankle are made up of seven smallish bones of various sizes and shapes; collectively these are known as the *tarsal bones.* The largest is the *calcaneum*, which forms the point of the heel; the second largest is the *astragalus*, which lies above the heel bone and articulates with the end of the tibia. In front of the tarsals are five longer bones, forming the anterior part of the arch of the foot; these are the *metatarsals.* The bones of the toes, like those of the fingers, are called *phalanges.* There are two bones in the great toe and three in each of the others, as with the thumb and fingers.

The bones of the foot are so arranged as to form three *arches* that aid in supporting the weight of the body. Two of these are the outer and inner longitudinal arches; the third is the transverse arch. The highest point of the longitudinal arches lies just in front of the ankle joint, in the region of the tarsal bones. Although the bones of the foot provide the chief structural elements of these arches, it is the tight binding of ligaments and muscles that enables them to yield elastically and yet keep their arched shape when weight is placed upon them. The foot, in conformity with its weight-carrying function, is much stronger, more compact, and less flexible than the hand.

As may be seen by comparison, there is a high degree of correspondence between the bones of the pectoral and pelvic girdles and limbs. This is brought out in the following table.

Pectoral Girdle	Pelvic Girdle
Scapula (shoulder blade)......................	Ilium (hipbone)
	Pubis
Clavicle (collarbone)	
Coracoid process of scapula..................	Ischium (on which we sit)
Glenoid fossa (humeral socket)..............	Acetabulum (femoral socket)
Humerus (upper-arm bone)..................	Femur (thigh bone)
Radius (of forearm)........................	Tibia (shinbone)
Ulna (of forearm).........................	Fibula (of shank)
Carpals (8) (wrist bones)....................	Tarsals (7) (anklebones)
Metacarpals (5) (palm bones)...............	Metatarsals (5) (arch bones of foot)
Phalanges (finger bones)....................	Phalanges (toe bones)
2 in thumb............................	2 in great toe
3 in other fingers.......................	3 in other toes

Joints. We have seen that all the bones of the head are immovably fused, except the lower jaw and the three pairs of tiny ear bones. The bones of the hip girdle are also fused, and in the adult so are those of the sacrum to which the hip girdle is attached. Most of these immovable joints or *sutures* are tremendously strong, being reinforced by intricate dovetailing along the lines of juncture. The first 10 pairs of ribs and the collarbone are attached to the sternum by cartilaginous connections which are more or less flexible. All the other joints between bones of the skeleton are to some degree movable. Appropriate movements are provided for by smooth articular surfaces, sheathed in "bearings" of cartilage and held in contact by strong ligamentous bindings.

The variety of movable joints in the skeleton is considerable, and each joint is remarkably adapted for the particular requirements of movement,

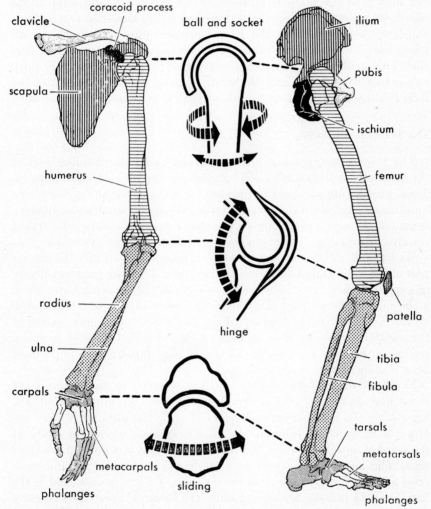

FIG. 3.8. Bones of the leg and arm, showing three types of joints, and the part-for-part correspondence of the two limbs.

limitation of movement, and strength required at that point. Although each joint has its own special features, we can group all the joints into a few main types. There is the *pivot joint*, represented by that between the first two cervical vertebrae; the *ball-and-socket joint*, as at the head of the humerus and of the femur; the *hinge joint*, as between humerus and ulna

and between femur and tibia; and the *sliding joint,* as found between the
articular processes of the vertebrae and between the bones in the arch
of the foot. Other joints may be of one of these types, or may show combinations of hinge and sliding movements. Examining Figs. 3.6 and 3.8,
one may note the peculiar arrangement of the radius and ulna at the
elbow, with a strong hinge joint between ulna and humerus, and a pivot-
and-hinge combination in the joint between radius and humerus. All
joints that involve much motion are particularly adapted to reduce friction. The cartilaginous cap of each bearing surface is comparatively thick
and extremely smooth; and the whole joint is bathed in a lubricating
fluid held by a surrounding capsule of flexible but fluid-tight ligaments.

The Skeletal Muscles

The active, energy-using, heat-producing, and waste-forming part of
the locomotor system is the great complex of *voluntary* or *skeletal* muscles.
These muscles are attached to the skeleton and provide the power for its
movements. (Later we shall encounter other types of contractile tissue—
heart muscle, and involuntary or visceral or smooth muscle—as parts of
the circulatory, digestive, reproductive, and other organ systems.)

We have already noted that the skeletal muscles account for the greater
part of the weight and bulk of the human body. They are made up largely
of a type of contractile tissue known as *voluntary* or *striated muscle,* which
is the most highly adapted of all contractile tissues for rapid and powerful
movement. The familiar "meat" of our diet consists to a great extent of
the skeletal muscles of other animals. A slice of round steak or ham is a
section of the large leg muscles of a cow or pig, together with portions of
bone and connective tissue.

Nearly all skeletal muscles are attached to bones in such a way as to
cause movement of parts of the skeleton when the muscles contract.
Frequently the bone serves as a lever. Thus, in the instance of the forearm, the elbow is the fulcrum, the force is applied beyond the elbow at
the point of muscle insertion, and the action is that of a lever of the third
class. The muscle here works at a mechanical disadvantage and must
exert a force of many pounds to lift a weight of a few pounds held in the
hand, but the muscles are able to move the forearm rapidly and to carry
the hand through a wide arc while they themselves shorten by only a few
inches.

The structure and functioning of the biceps. As an example of a
typical skeletal muscle let us consider the *biceps*—one of the larger muscles
of the upper arm. The biceps is attached at its upper end by two tendons,
one to the shoulder blade and the other to the end of the humerus just
below its joint with the scapula. The two "heads," each with its own

tendon, give the muscle its name *biceps*, which means "two-headed." The lower end of the biceps is attached by another strong tendon to the upper part of the radius. We speak of the relatively immovable anchorage at one end of a muscle as its *origin* and of the attachment to the part that is normally moved as its *insertion*. The origin of the biceps is at the shoulder, and the insertion is on the radius. The movement that results from the shortening of a muscle is known as its *action*. When the biceps alone contracts, its action is to pull the radius upward, bending the arm at the elbow. But in normal arm movements many other muscles cooperate with the biceps, and the elbow may be either bent or lifted, depending upon what other muscles take part in producing the action.

Now let us examine the structure of the biceps in more detail. We find that it is covered with a tough, smooth sheath of connective tissue, which binds its parts firmly together and allows the muscle to slide and move over other muscles without noticeable friction. We note also that the muscle is thickest near the middle and tapers toward the ends. If now we cut the biceps in two across the middle, the cut end will be seen to have a structure similar to that shown in Fig. 3.9. It is evident at once that the muscle is not entirely composed of a single kind of tissue. In fact, as was previously pointed out, a skeletal muscle is an *organ*, in which various tissues contribute toward the performance of a particular function—contraction and the production of movement.

Within the outermost sheath of connective tissue there are a number of smaller compartments, or bundles (*fasciculi*), separated by connective tissue walls. These fasciculi are in turn composed of still smaller bundles, also surrounded by connective tissue. And each of the latter (Fig. 3.9, enlarged detail), when "teased out" beneath the microscope, is found to contain many elongated, closely packed muscle cells (or muscle fibers as they are often called). Blood vessels and nerves ramify in a fine network throughout the whole muscle, so that each muscle cell is in contact with blood capillaries, is bathed in fluid lymph exuded from the capillaries, and receives the endings of one or more motor nerve fibers.

Each of the elongated muscle cells is somewhat spindle-shaped. Unlike most cells it contains numerous nuclei, scattered along its length just under the cell membrane. Microdissection reveals the presence within the cell of many fine threadlike strands, the *fibrils*, which run from end to end of the cell and are immersed in a more fluid portion of the cytoplasm. Each fibril is made up of alternating sections composed of different materials, like repeated beads on a string; under the microscope these appear as a regular succession of light and dark portions of the thread. Since the cell is packed with fibrils and these are all precisely "dressed" upon one another, the entire cell (muscle fiber) has a cross-banded or "striated" appearance (Fig. 2.3).

The finer structure of the muscle cell is so extremely minute, and the sequence of physicochemical events that takes place at each contraction is so complex and so rapid, that the exact mechanism of contraction is still an unsolved problem. Theories are numerous, but none is yet established. Nevertheless a great deal has been learned about what goes on in muscle cells, and the brief account that follows is accurate *so far as it goes*.

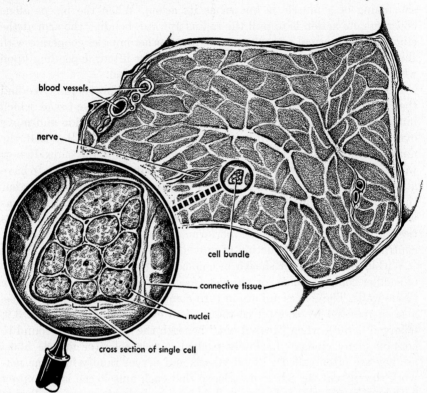

blood vessels

nerve

cell bundle

connective tissue

nuclei

cross section of single cell

Fig. 3.9. Cross section of a fasciculus of a skeletal muscle. A single cell bundle is shown magnified.

Each muscle cell receives the end of a tiny motor nerve that comes from the central nervous system. When a nerve impulse enters the cell, there is a delay of only a few thousandths of a second, and then each of the minute, string-of-beads-like fibrils suddenly contracts, causing the cell as a whole to shorten and thicken, though its volume remains almost the same. This contraction occurs simultaneously with the occurrence of an explosively sudden energy-releasing change of an energy-storing substance in the fibrils. The nature of this change will be discussed a little farther on. If only a single nerve impulse is received by the muscle cell (fiber), relaxation follows immediately, and the fibrils resume their former shape. The whole response is completed in a few hundredths of a second, relaxation taking somewhat longer than contraction. It is only in laboratory experiments that the effects of a single impulse can be studied; in life no voluntary movement is due to a single impulse. Even the quickest and briefest movement is produced by a stream of nerve impulses sent into the muscle at a rate which varies from 40 per second for some of the leg muscles to more than 100 per second for the jaw muscles. The rate at which the impulses come is quite constant for a given muscle. Following one another so rapidly, these impulses do not give the cell time to relax but keep it in a continuous state of contraction known as *tetanus*[1] until the stream of impulses stops.

As we have said, the actual mechanism by which the chemical energy of the contracting muscle is converted into mechanical energy is quite unknown. It seems clear, however, that the transformation must be more or less direct. It is probably a physical process—comparable, let us say, to the release of a coiled spring. All the chemical changes seem to be subsequent to contraction and to restore the energy for the physical process— to rewind the spring, as it were. The nerve impulse is the trigger which releases the spring. The most likely hypothesis as to the nature of the physical change that causes contraction is that it is the sudden alteration of elongate protein molecules into shorter, thicker spirals. This, however, is only a guess, and no chemical mechanism for causing such a change is known.

The source of the energy for contraction and the process by which it is stored have been partially worked out. According to a widely held theory supported by much evidence, the actual energy-storing substance in the fibrils is a compound called *adenosine triphosphate* (or *ATP* for short). When the trigger is pulled by a nerve impulse, an enzyme (organic catalyst)[2] is liberated in the fibrils, causing a part of the stored ATP to unite with water and to split into adenylic acid and pyrophosphoric acid, with explosive release of energy. The exact nature and source of the activating enzyme and the means by which the released energy is transformed into mechanical tension and shortening of the muscle are two of the important gaps in our knowledge.

During the period of relaxation the ATP is resynthesized, thus "rewinding the spring" in the fibrils. This synthesis requires a large amount of energy, which comes from a complex series of chemical transformations of other substances, each reaction being controlled by enzymes and related to those above and below it in the chain. At the base of the series, and ultimately furnishing most of the energy used by muscle, is

---

[1] From the Greek, *tetanos*, "stretched." The disease commonly known by this name is characterized by intense and prolonged tetanus of the voluntary muscles, especially those of the lower jaw, whence the alternative name "lockjaw."

[2] The nature of enzymes is discussed in connection with the digestive system.

the oxidation of the simple sugar *glucose*. This substance and oxygen enter the cell from the blood. Much of the sugar is not burned at once, but is changed within the cell into *glycogen* (animal starch) and stored in this form. This glycogen constitutes an energy reserve which can be drawn upon during periods of muscular activity. When it is used, it is broken down by a series of steps into *lactic acid*. Under conditions of moderate muscular activity and sufficient oxygen supply all of the lactic acid is used within the cell, some being burned for energy and some being resynthesized into glycogen. When muscular action is prolonged or excessively vigorous, insufficient oxygen may reach the muscle cell to maintain this balance and oxidize the required amount of fuel. Under such circumstances the glycogen-to-lactic acid reaction may itself serve as an anaerobic (oxygenless) source of the energy required for continued muscular activity. Excess lactic acid accumulates in the cell, causing fatigue and building up an "oxygen debt" in the form of unoxidized lactic acid. Some of the excess lactic acid is set free into the blood, and is excreted via the kidneys; the remainder is in part oxidized and in part rebuilt into glycogen during a period of rest and recovery from fatigue.

This explanation of the changes known to occur in the muscle cell during and after contraction is very much simplified. Even so it will serve to indicate how complex and how delicately balanced are the reactions and processes involved in such an apparently simple act as "flexing the biceps."

The contraction of a whole muscle is produced by the shortening of its individual cells and is thus many-cell-powered. It is initiated by nerve impulses simultaneously reaching many individual cells, and these contracting cells are held together and mechanically coordinated by connective tissues. The amount of muscular power exerted by a particular muscle varies greatly. Thus the biceps may contract gently or powerfully. The difference is largely a function of how many of the thousands of individual cells are stimulated to contract. A gentle contraction utilizes only a part of the whole number; when all of them contract together, the maximum power of the muscle is exerted. Each muscle cell (muscle fiber) operates on the principle of "all or none"; *i.e.*, it either contracts fully or not at all.

Under the influence of continued exercise the skeletal muscles increase in size and correspondingly in strength. Contrary to what might be supposed, this enlargement is due not to an increase in the number of muscle cells but to an increase in the size of the individual cells. Since it is a response to activity, and since the activity of the muscle cell is determined by the frequency with which nerve impulses are received, it is natural that reduction in the number of nerve impulses should have the opposite effect. If, therefore, the efferent (outgoing) nerve to a muscle is destroyed by accident or by disease, as in poliomyelitis, the muscle shrinks and may ultimately disappear. Exercise brings increased muscular efficiency not merely by strengthening the muscles; the result is due in even greater degree to improvements in circulatory and respiratory adjustments and to better nervous coordination.

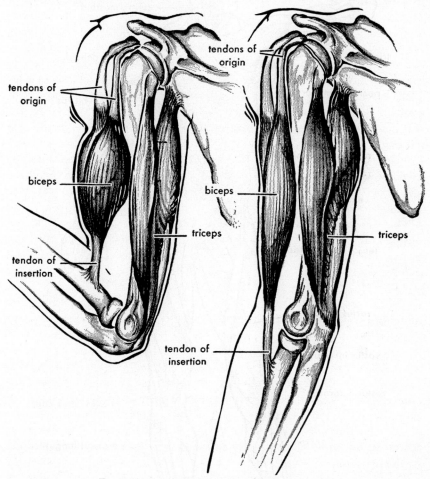

Fig. 3.10. Antagonistic muscles of the upper arm.

It is important to note that muscles in action can only *pull* and never push. The biceps can perform but one useful action—that of pulling its origin and insertion closer together. It cannot push them apart again. Except in rare instances, therefore, skeletal muscles are always arranged in *antagonistic* pairs or sets. The action of each muscle is opposed by the action of one or more other muscles. After one muscle has contracted

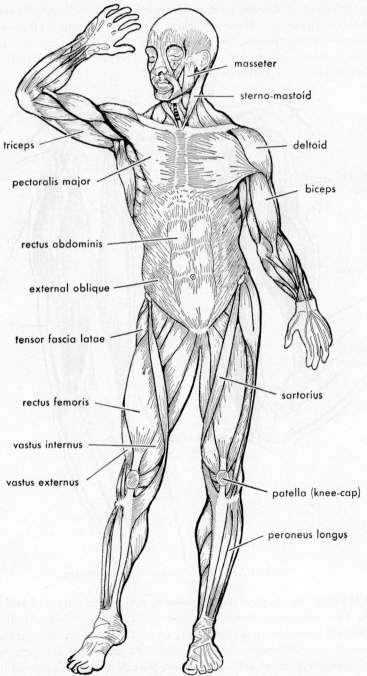

masseter

sterno-mastoid

triceps

deltoid

pectoralis major

biceps

rectus abdominis

external oblique

tensor fascia latae

sartorius

rectus femoris

vastus internus

vastus externus

patella (knee-cap)

peroneus longus

FIG. 3.11. The musculature of the human body, front view. (*Redrawn from Clendening, The Human Body, by permission Alfred A. Knopf, Inc.*)

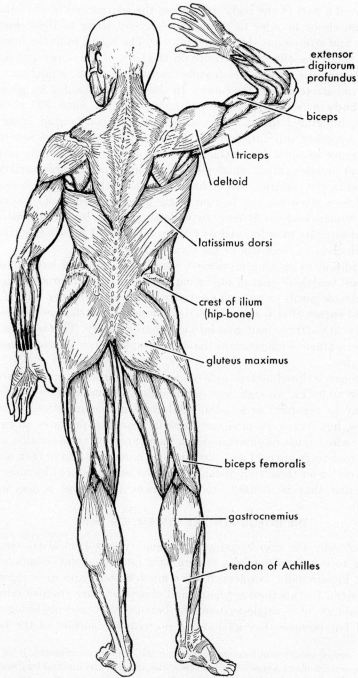

FIG. 3.12. The musculature of the human body, rear view. (*Redrawn from Clendening, The Human Body, by permission Alfred A. Knopf, Inc.*)

and moved a part of the body, it requires the contraction of the antagonistic muscle or muscles to restore the skeletal parts to their original
position and stretch out the relaxed muscle. The biceps pulls the forearm
up and bends the elbow; the triceps on the back of the upper arm is the
chief antagonistic muscle which pulls the forearm down, straightens the
elbow, and stretches out the biceps. In this it may be aided by gravity.

The body muscles. The human body contains some 700 skeletal
muscles, integrated into a muscular system and constructed upon the
plan of opposing and antagonistic sets of muscles. Any movement that
we can make requires the contraction of one or more (and usually several
or many) muscles. Most muscles take part in a considerable variety of
movements, the variations depending upon what other muscles cooperate
to produce a given motion. In view of the great versatility of movement
of the human body it is easy to understand why it contains several
hundred separate muscles, and why the total skeletal muscle tissue comprises much more than half of the total body weight.

In addition to causing movement the skeletal muscles have another
important function—that of producing heat. Indeed, heat production is a
nonavoidable result of muscular activity. Some 70 to 80 per cent of the
chemical energy that is released in the muscles is transformed into heat,
and only 20 to 30 per cent goes into contractile energy. This is about the
same percentage of efficiency as that of a good steam or internal combustion engine.

Since our bodies function at a more or less constant temperature of
about 98 to 99°F.,[1] enough heat to maintain this temperature is utilized
and may be regarded as a useful product of muscular action. In most
climates, however, even moderate muscular exertion produces an excess
of heat, which must be eliminated as a waste product. Occasionally, when
our surroundings are cold and our muscular movements have been slight,
we shiver; under these circumstances it is the heat produced by muscular
contraction that is utilized, and movement (shivering) is the waste
product.

THE INTEGUMENTARY SYSTEM, OR SKIN

Structurally the skin would scarcely qualify as a typical system, according to our definition of a system as a functional unit composed of
organs. Functionally, however, it has a much better claim to be regarded
as a system. Its functions are many and diverse and are grouped into the
responsibility of a single system not because they are physiologically
related but because they all have to do with the surface of the body.

---

[1] The normal mouth temperature, marked on the clinical thermometer, is 98.6°F.,
but temperature shows a regular daily cycle of rise and fall, and internal temperatures
are somewhat higher than those in the mouth.

Everything that must be or can most efficiently be performed by the external body surface is a function of the integumentary system. We may list these things as follows:

1. Protection of the body against: .
   a. Mechanical injury or abrasion.
   b. Loss of water.
   c. Harmful light rays.
   d. Disease-producing organisms (parasites).
2. Heat regulation and heat elimination.
   The skin forms an efficient, thermostatically controlled radiator.
3. Reception of stimuli.
   The skin houses a tremendously numerous and varied set of sense receptors, capable of receiving detailed information about the general and special conditions of the body's environment.
4. Production of skin appendages.
   The skin produces the hair, nails, and teeth that form more or less useful parts of the body.

The structure of the skin. The skin is composed of two closely knit layers—a comparatively thin, bloodless *epidermis* and a much thicker *dermis*, crowded with blood vessels and rich in nerve endings. An examination of Fig. 3.13 will show the general arrangement of parts and make the following description much clearer.

The inner portion of the epidermis is a compact layer of columnar epithelial cells (*malpighian layer*) that is everywhere in close, inseparable contact with the upper surface of the dermis. It receives a rich supply of nourishment from the blood vessels of the dermis. All through the life of the individual, cells of this inner layer of the epidermis are multiplying by cell division, and the excess cells are being pushed outward toward the surface of the skin; the many-cell-thick epidermis is thus composed of cells that are in process of being shoved to the surface, where they are constantly being worn away. As each cell progresses from the inner layer toward the surface, it becomes more and more compressed and changed in composition, until at the surface the formerly columnar cell has now become flat, thin, and lifeless and is ready to be shed from the body.

The *dermis*, which is many times thicker than the epidermis, is composed chiefly of connective tissues, through which ramify numerous small blood and lymph vessels and in which are imbedded a huge number of nerve endings, dermal sense organs, and smooth muscle cells. It is the comparatively thick, tough, outer portion of the dermis that, when tanned, is known as *leather*. The inner, less tightly compacted region of the dermis may contain many globular fat cells and is one of the principal regions for the storage of body fat.

As a receptor system, the dermis contains thousands of nerve endings for the reception of heat, cold, touch, pressure, and pain stimuli. Indi-

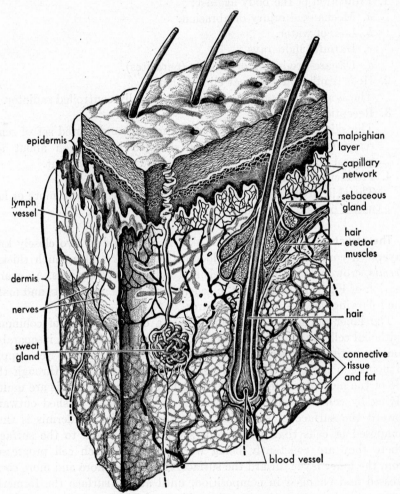

Fig. 3.13. A stereogram of the structure of the skin.

vidual receptors for each of these sensations occur over all of the body surface, although they are much more closely spaced in some regions than in others. Touch receptors, for instance, are many times more numerous per unit of surface on the finger tips than on the back of the hand and much more numerous on the back of the hand than on the small of the back.

Some parts of the body have the skin very firmly attached to the deeper tissues, but in other regions the skin is very loosely and movably attached, permitting free play of the enclosed parts. The skin likewise varies greatly in thickness from one region of the body to another. On the inner surfaces of the hands and the soles of the feet, there are multitudes of tiny ridges that increase friction and reduce the tendency to slip. These form the familiar fingerprint pattern and leave their traces on objects touched because of the alignment of sweat glands along the ridges. The pattern of these ridges is individually characteristic and remains constant throughout life.

Appendages of the skin. The appendages or accessory structures of the skin are the nails, hair, glands, and teeth. An inspection of Fig. 3.13 will show a *hair follicle* and *root*, a *sweat gland* and an *oil gland*. It will be observed that both the hair follicle and the glands are formed by long invaginations of the malpighian layers of the epidermis, extending deep into the dermis. Incidentally, the sweat and oil glands show two rather different devices by which an epithelium may be enormously expanded to form a many-cell-powered secreting structure.

Hairs are formed by the cells that line the bottoms of the deeply pitted hair follicles. The part of the hair contained within the pit is the *root;* the portion extending above the surface of the skin is the *shaft*. With the exception of the palm of the hand, the sole of the foot, and the last phalanges of the fingers and toes, the whole skin is provided with hair follicles. The nature and color of the hair in different individuals are due to details of hair growth and development that are, in part, determined by inherited factors. In general, hair "grows" from the bottom of the follicle, the previously formed portion being pushed out of the follicle to project farther and farther from the surface of the skin. Loss of hair may be due to inherited factors or to disease and functional disorders.

Nails are composed of clear, horny dead cells joined to form a solid continuous plate. Nail growth is rather similar to that of hair, except that in the case of the nails, the nail-producing cells are densely packed along the invaginated furrows from which the nails are developed.

Oil glands occur everywhere over the surface of the skin except on the palms of the hands and the soles of the feet. They are very abundant in the scalp and in the face. Nearly everywhere they are associated with hair follicles. A typical oil gland is shown in Fig. 3.13, opening into the upper part of the hair follicle, through which its oily secretion reaches the surface of the skin to spread as a protecting oily film. This film of oil keeps hair from becoming dry and brittle and serves to prevent undue absorption or evaporation of water from the skin itself.

Sweat glands are abundant over the whole body skin but are largest and most numerous under the arms, on the palms of the hands and the soles of the feet, and on the forehead. These glands have separate openings on the skin surface, the pores, there being as many as 2½ million of these on the entire body. Sweat is, in a sense, a waste product, and sweating plays a part in the elimination of body wastes; but a much more important function of sweating is the control of body heat through the evaporation of water.

We have seen that body heat is largely produced by the muscles. This heat is taken up by the blood and distributed throughout the body, which has a normal temperature of approximately 98 to 99°F. The skin, with its abundant blood supply, is so situated that it acts as an effective heat-eliminating surface. Contraction of the muscle fibers of the dermis and of the walls of its blood vessels reduces the amount of warm blood entering the capillaries and there exposed to loss of heat; relaxation of the muscle fibers and dilation of the blood vessels allow a more rapid loss. In addition to the considerable loss of heat by radiation, the skin is cooled by the evaporation[1] of a watery fluid, sweat, from the body surface; the amount of cooling is varied as required, by changes in the activity of the sweat glands.

Teeth. A conspicuous feature of the skull is the double row of teeth imbedded in the upper and lower jawbones, similar to bones in their hardness and appearance. Structurally, however, teeth are a part of the skin and are more comparable to such skin appendages as nails and hair than to the bones of the skeleton. Their relation to the skull is entirely secondary, their implantation in the jawbones being merely an arrangement for strength and support. Teeth, being used for the breaking up of food materials in the process of chewing, are functionally most closely associated with the digestive system.

Like other mammals, man has two sets of teeth. The temporary first set, the deciduous or "baby" teeth, are 20 in number. They are "cut" (or erupted) between the ages of six months and two and one-half years and are gradually replaced by the teeth of the second or permanent set. The latter are normally 32 in number and comprise, on each side of each jaw, 2 incisors, 1 canine (cuspid or "eyetooth"), 2 premolars (bicuspids), and 3 molars. The incisors are the "front" teeth—flat, edged, used for cutting off morsels of food; the canines are heavier and more pointed and correspond to the tearing and stabbing "tusks" of carnivorous mammals; the premolars are broad-surfaced grinding teeth with two elevated cones on the grinding surface; and the molars are larger grinding teeth with four (sometimes five) elevated cones on the grinding surface. The last pairs of molars are the so-called "wisdom teeth," which in man are

---

[1] It is this large loss of heat by evaporation that permits the human body to maintain its normal temperature, even though the air temperature may be well above 100°F.

sometimes not erupted until late in life, if at all. Since these groups of teeth are common to the mammals in general and vary in number, kind, and use from one animal to another, it is customary to express the dental armature of a given kind of mammal by means of a shorthand formula

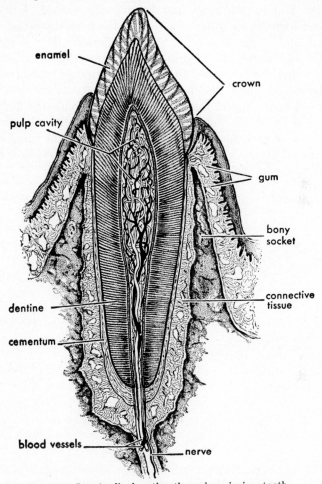

FIG. 3.14. Longitudinal section through an incisor tooth.

that shows the number of upper and lower teeth on one side of the jaw. The dental formula of man and of all his nearest allies is

$$I\frac{2}{2}, \ C\frac{1}{1}, \ P\frac{2}{2}, \ M\frac{3}{3} = 16$$

The structure of a typical tooth is shown in Fig. 3.14. The outer layer of enamel that covers the surface of the exposed parts of the tooth is the hardest tissue in the human body.

The skin and disease.   One of the outstanding functions of the skin is to repel the invasion of disease-producing organisms. In this respect it plays a dual role. The first line of defense of the body is the skin surface, both because the outer part of the epidermis is tough and relatively impervious and impenetrable and because the normal skin secretions have a considerable bactericidal action. If the normally intact epidermis is injured and bacteria penetrate to the dermis, they encounter the second line of defense, provided in part by tremendous numbers of white blood cells that can be carried to the invaded dermis by its rich network of capillaries and lymph vessels, and in part by chemical means. This will be discussed more fully in the treatment of the circulatory system.

In spite of the skin's protective ability, many plant and animal organisms have developed the capacity to live in it (*e.g.*, the fungi that cause ringworm and athlete's foot) or to penetrate it and reach the internal organs (*e.g.*, the larvae of hookworms).

CHAPTER IV

THE INTAKE OF MATERIALS AND ENERGY

As long as the body is alive, it requires a constant supply of materials to provide energy and to take care of growth and repair. All body energy is derived from the slow burning (oxidation) of certain food substances within the cells of the body. The materials needed for growth and repair include these same foods and, in addition, such other component parts of protoplasm and body fluids as water, various inorganic salts, and a group of special substances known as *vitamins*.

All the materials required by the body, except oxygen, are taken into it by way of the *digestive system;* the intake of oxygen is provided for by the *respiratory system.*

WATER

Surprisingly large amounts of water are required for the functioning of the body. Every 24 hours about 1,500 cc. of water is secreted in the saliva, about 1 liter in the pancreatic juice, another liter in the bile, 3 liters in the intestinal juices, and 2 liters in the gastric juice. Besides these amounts, 170 liters is required in the kidneys in 24 hours, of which $\frac{1}{2}$ to 1 or more liters is lost as urine. From $\frac{1}{2}$ to $2\frac{1}{2}$ liters is given off by the skin in perspiration, and $\frac{1}{2}$ liter by the lungs in respiration. The total physiological requirement for these processes is more than 180 liters, or almost 200 quarts per day. Most of this amount is recaptured and re-utilized, but the daily loss of water amounts to several quarts, which must be made good in part by drinking water and in part by water produced by oxidation of the hydrogen contained in food.

FOOD MATERIALS

Food may be so defined as to include all the essential materials taken into the digestive system. In this sense the term includes proteins, carbohydrates, and fats, also water, a considerable list of inorganic salts, and the vitamins. In a narrower sense, we may restrict the term *food* to those substances which not only are required for the building up of protoplasm but which are also capable of being oxidized to provide energy. It is the substances of this last class, comprising the proteins, carbohydrates, and fats, that commonly occur in nature in a condition unsuitable for direct passage through cell membranes. In consequence they require a digestive process before they can be taken into the cells or blood stream and become available for use.

Carbohydrates contain carbon, hydrogen, and oxygen, usually with the hydrogen and oxygen in the same proportion as in water (H_2O). Glucose (dextrose or grape sugar), $C_6H_{12}O_6$, is an example. It is readily soluble in water and will pass through a cell membrane. Carbohydrates with this chemical formula are known as *single sugars,* or monosaccharides. *Disaccharides*—for example, cane sugar—have the formula $C_{12}H_{22}O_{11}$ and may, under suitable conditions, be split into two molecules of a

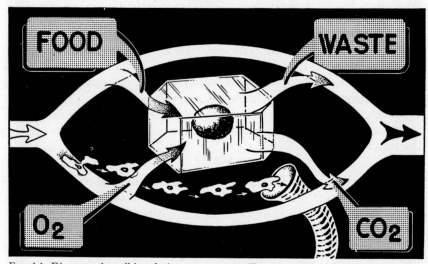

FIG. 4.1. Diagram of a cell in relation to artery, capillary, vein, and lymph vessel, to show intake of oxygen and food, and outgo of carbon dioxide and metabolic wastes, via the tissue fluid (black). A leucocyte is shown leaving a capillary and entering a lymph vessel.

monosaccharide after a molecule of water has been added. Various *polysaccharides* exist, the formulas of which may be expressed by the generalized formula $n(C_6H_{10}O_5)$. Starch, glycogen, and cellulose are examples. Under suitable conditions, polysaccharides may be split into monosaccharides. Carbohydrates are primarily energy foods. When a monosaccharide is oxidized in the body, energy is released, and CO_2 (carbon dioxide) and H_2O (water) are the end products.

$$C_6H_{12}O_6 + 6O_2 \rightarrow 6CO_2 + 6H_2O + \text{energy}$$

Fats, like carbohydrates, are composed of carbon, hydrogen and oxygen, but much less oxygen is present in proportion to the carbon and hydrogen. As in the case of carbohydrates, oxidation of fats results in the release of energy and production of carbon dioxide and water. However, more oxygen is required to oxidize a fat than is necessary to oxidize a carbohydrate, and the energy derived from the oxidation of fat is correspondingly greater. The energy value of fats in human metabolism is about two and one-fourth times that of carbohydrates. Fats are stored as such in many parts of the body, especially in the deeper layer of the skin and around the intestines.

Proteins contain nitrogen and sulphur and sometimes other elements in addition to carbon, hydrogen, and oxygen. Proteins cannot pass through cell membranes; under suitable conditions, however, they can be split into *amino acids* and in this condition become available to the cell. The amino acids are the building stones from which proteins are constructed. They are nitrogenous derivatives of the fatty acids. Glycine, $CH_2.NH_2.$-COOH, is an aminoacetic acid, and the simplest member of the amino-acid group. At least 23 such acids are known, some of which are more important in human physiology than others. The various amino acids are combined in the cells to form the particular proteins required by each cell. There is little storage of excess proteins in the body tissues, and new supplies are therefore constantly needed. Proteins are essential for growth and repair, but they may also be used for fuel. When they are oxidized, the nitrogenous part is split off and excreted as a waste product by the kidneys.

Vitamins. The vitamins are a numerous and varied group of organic substances essential to the maintenance and proper functioning of the body but required in extremely small quantities. They are used in too small amounts to be sources of energy; their importance lies in the fact that they are catalytic agents, without which certain indispensable reactions cannot occur. Their action is quantitative and markedly specific. Substances are classed as vitamins largely as a matter of convenience; vitamin is a functional term and not a chemical classification.

Recognition of the existence of vitamins has come from the study of disease, or malfunctioning, associated with some type of diet and found to be curable by some other type of diet. By chemically fractionating the curative diet and determining which of the fractions has retained the curative properties, the search has been gradually narrowed. Today many vitamins have been isolated and their chemical formulas determined. Much of the experimental work has been done with laboratory animals, and the results have later been applied in medical practice.

The very existence of these essential substances was unknown prior to 1881, and most of our information about them has been gained since 1920. Although knowledge of vitamins is recent, certain human diseases were long ago ascribed to deficiences in diet. Experience had shown that rickets could be cured by liver or liver extract, beriberi by rice polishings or by whole rice, and scurvy by fresh fruit and especially by the juice of limes and lemons. Between 1907 and 1920, it was demonstrated that these three diseases were caused by deficiencies in three specific dietary factors. Since their chemical natures were unknown, these factors were designated respectively A, B, and C. Since 1920, the discovery of additional vitamins has been rapid, and the original vitamins A and B have been found to be mixtures of distinct vitamins with unlike properties. By 1949, vitamin A had been divided into A, D, and E, about 12 individual vitamins had been separated from the original B, and of the three originally known vitamins only C remained undivided.

Today the chemical compositions and structures of many of the vitamins are known, and some of them have been synthesized in the laboratory. Present terminology is a mixture of the old alphabetic designations and of chemical names. The tendency is for the letter names to be dropped, since splitting and synonymy have made for confusion among them. In our account we use the name most frequently encountered.

Most of the important vitamins can now be obtained either as concentrates from natural sources or in synthetic form. About sixteen (some of them complexes) are currently recognized. Eight of these are of proven importance in human metabolism, and five others may be important though proof is lacking. The eight vitamins known to be essential are as follows:

Fat-soluble vitamins:
    Vitamin A⎫
    Vitamin D⎬ from the original A complex
    Vitamin K
Water-soluble vitamins:
    Vitamin B_1 (thiamine)
    Riboflavin (vitamin B_2 or G)⎫
    Niacin (vitamin P-P or nicotinic acid)⎬ from the original B complex
    Folic acids⎭
    Vitamin C (ascorbic acid)

THE FAT-SOLUBLE VITAMINS

Vitamin A is an alcohol ($C_{20}H_{29}OH$) formed in man and other animals from an essential precursor or provitamin called *carotene*. The latter is a yellow or orange pigment common in plants and especially abundant in carrots; it gives the yellowish color to cream, butter, egg yolk, etc. Herbivorous animals are able to secure their entire vitamin A requirements by eating carotene; man has to eat twice as much carotene as vitamin A to obtain equivalent amounts of the latter. Excess vitamin A is stored in the liver of vertebrate animals; cod-liver oil and other fish-liver oils are especially rich in this substance.

Vitamin A is specific for the prevention and cure of night blindness, day blindness, and a disease known as xerophthalmia, which causes a drying of the outer covering of the eyes. It is essential to the normal structure and functioning of all epithelial tissues, and is also a growth factor. The first symptoms of vitamin A deficiency are usually a hardening and roughening of the skin, and night blindness, or inability to see under twilight conditions. Night blindness is directly caused by lack of the vitamin, which is the precursor from which *visual purple* is formed. This pigment in the retinal cells breaks down when exposed to light, forming vitamin A and causing stimulation of the visual receptors. Normally it is quickly rebuilt from vitamin A when light intensity decreases, but is only slowly restored when the vitamin is deficient.

Vitamin D, the antirachitic vitamin, is known to be a mixture of at least two vitamins—*calciferol*, or D_2, and *dehydrocholesterol*, or D_3. Chemically these are solid alcohols (sterols); the chemical formula of calciferol is $C_{28}H_{43}OH$. Both of these D vitamins occur in animal oils but in the form of inactive precursors. Ergosterol is the precursor of calciferol and changes into the active vitamin when irradiated with ultraviolet light; the precursor of D_3 behaves similarly. When the ultraviolet rays of sunlight fall upon human skin, D_2 and especially D_3 are activated in the oil droplets in the dermis and become available for use by the body. Fish-liver oils are rich in the D vitamins, which are also present in eggs, butter, and milk but do not occur in plants. The D vitamins may be stored in the body (chiefly in the liver) during the months of strong sunshine, forming a reserve for winter use.

Unless sufficient amounts of the D vitamins are present in the body, calcium and phosphorus cannot be absorbed properly from foods nor sufficiently retained in the body. These vitamins also maintain the concentration of phosphatase (an enzyme causing phosphate deposition in bone) in the region of the bone-forming cells. Deficiency results in a lack of calcium and phosphate, producing in children the disease known as *rickets*, in which the bones become bent and deformed. Prolonged excessive intake of the D vitamins may cause overdeposition of calcium and phosphate and has even been known to produce death from partial calcification of the kidneys. This is the only vitamin in which overdosage is known to be injurious.

Vitamin K, like vitamin D, is known to occur naturally in two forms—K_1 and K_2 (empirical formulas $C_{31}H_{46}O_2$ and $C_{41}H_{56}O_2$). Two synthetic compounds known as phthiacol and menadione possess similar properties and can substitute for the natural vitamins. K_1 is a light yellow oil, K_2 a yellow crystalline solid at ordinary temperatures. Vitamin K in some way acts upon the liver, causing that organ to produce a supply of *prothrombin*, a substance essential for the clotting of the blood. The basic function of the K vitamins is, therefore, to prevent hemorrhage, by maintaining the normal clotting power of blood. Human beings normally get their supply of these substances either from the diet or by synthesis in their own intestines by the intestinal bacteria. The latter source is probably the most important. Both on this account and because K_1 is abundant in many foods (especially leafy green vegetables), vitamin K deficiency is rare.

The above three vitamins are the only ones of the fat-soluble group known to be essential for human nutrition. **Vitamin E** (tocopherol) may eventually be added to this list. This is the so-called "antisterility" vitamin (actually a complex of at least 4 related substances), which occurs in the oils of plant seeds and in some green, leafy vegetables. In rats a deficiency of this vitamin causes sterility due to degeneration of the sperm-producing tissues of the male and to abnormal development and intra-uterine death of embryos in the female. Most of the effects seem to be traceable to the action of vitamin E as an antioxidant; in its absence carotene and vitamin A are rapidly destroyed both in the digestive tract and in tissues. There is no reliable evidence that vitamin E is indispensable in man, but it seems likely that it is required by all mammals. Attempts to use it therapeutically have thus far been disappointing.

THE WATER-SOLUBLE VITAMINS

The original vitamin B is now known to have been a complex of at least 12 distinct vitamins. Three of these are known to be essential in human nutrition, and some of the others may prove to be so.

Vitamin B₁ (the antineuritic vitamin, thiamine, $C_{12}H_{17}N_4OSCl$) is perhaps the most important member of the B complex. It is abundant in the germ and outer layers of seeds and also occurs in nuts, legumes, most vegetables, eggs, pork, liver, and the tissues of many animals. In the form of thiamine chloride it is now made synthetically. Thiamine deficiency is the most prevalent vitamin lack among human beings. Though required in only small amounts, it must be continually taken into the body, since little of it is stored; any excess is excreted via the skin and the kidneys.

The importance of thiamine lies in its relation to carbohydrate metabolism. In the form of diphosphothiamine it acts as a coenzyme with a carboxylase enzyme to release energy from glucose. By their combined action these two enzymes convert glucose to pyruvic acid and the latter to water and carbon dioxide, with liberation of energy. When thiamine is lacking or inadequate in amount, the reaction is not completed, pyruvic acid accumulates, and the full energy value of the glucose is not obtained. This relationship explains the fact that the thiamine requirement of the human body is not fixed but increases with the consumption of carbohydrate foods. It has been found that the daily human need of thiamine in micrograms may be expressed as equal to $0.00213 \times$ weight in pounds $\times$ Calorie intake. For a 150- pound man eating 2400 Calories of food a day this totals 767 micrograms, and for such an individual 1,200 micrograms per day would allow a reasonable margin of safety.

Pronounced thiamine deficiency results in the disease called *beriberi;* lesser deficiencies are manifested in a variety of symptoms, mostly involving the nervous system. Prominent among such symptoms are neuritis, resulting from nerve lesions and damage to the finer structure of nerves, loss of appetite, circulatory disturbances and malfunctioning of the heart, and neurasthenic symptoms such as easy tiring, weakness, head pressures, poor sleep, tenseness, irritability, undefined aches and pains, and inability to concentrate. In so far as these symptoms are the result of thiamine deficiency, they disappear promptly under administration of sufficient (often large) amounts of this vitamin. One of the earliest symptoms of lack of thiamine is the tendency of arms and legs to "go to sleep" from poor circulation, especially during the night. Thiamine deficiency is one of the easiest to recognize and correct.

Riboflavin (vitamin B_2 or G, $C_{17}H_{20}N_4O_6$) is a yellow pigment found in many animal and plant tissues, and especially in yeast, milk, liver, wheat germ, eggs, cheese, green vegetables, and the muscles of animals. On account of its wide distribution riboflavin deficiencies are not common, but when they do occur, normal nutritional and growth processes are upset. The symptoms are varied and none is wholly characteristic. Riboflavin plays an essential role in the oxidation reactions associated with cell respiration and is therefore necessary for the maintenance of health, efficiency, vigor, and resistance.

Niacin (vitamin P-P, nicotinic acid, the antipellagra vitamin, $C_6H_5O_2N$) is a white crystalline substance chemically related to nicotine but with none of the toxicity of the latter. It occurs in association with riboflavin, and is furnished by the same foods. As in the case of other vitamins, niacin is a constituent of respiratory coenzymes, and probably plays a role in the maintenance of normal tissue metabolism.

The most important therapeutic use of niacin is in the prevention and cure of the serious nutritional disease known as *pellagra*, which involves the digestive tract, the skin, and the nervous system, with severe mental symptoms in the later stages and often death as the result. This disease is commonly associated with diets rich in corn (maize), and this has led to the discovery that it is deficiency of the amino acid tryptophan in corn that is responsible. Tryptophan seems to be the immediate precursor from which niacin is manufactured in the tissues; a corn diet therefore produces niacin deficiency. Administration of the vitamin causes immediate improvement and ultimate complete recovery unless degenerative changes have occurred.

The folic acids. These are a large and still imperfectly understood group of B-complex vitamins, some of which have already been shown to be necessary in human nutrition. The folic acids are present in many foods, some of the best sources being kidney, liver, mushrooms, yeast, and green leafy vegetables. In rats synthesis of these vitamins by intestinal bacteria is so effective that deficiencies can be produced only by reducing the bacterial population of the intestines by means of sulpha drugs. In monkeys and man there seems to be less intestinal synthesis. The blood condition in man called macrocytic anemia is prevented and cured by the folic acids known as PGA, P3GA, and P7GA. This condition is found in sprue and some other diseases and consists of a marked reduction in number and increase in size and hemoglobin content of the red blood cells. Pernicious anemia patients are benefited but not cured by these folic acids. The curative property of liver extract in pernicious anemia is now thought to be due to another member of the B complex, B_{12} (animal protein factor), mentioned below.

Ascorbic acid (vitamin C, the antiscorbutic vitamin, $C_6H_8O_6$) is one of the longest known vitamins and the only one of the three originally recognized that has not been subdivided. It occurs in fresh fruit and fresh meat and can be synthesized by many animals but not by man, monkey, and guinea pig. Since it is very largely destroyed or lost by cooking, raw fruits or vegetables are required as a part of human diet.

Vitamin C affects the health of all the tissues of the body, but the details of its functioning are not understood. It seems to be necessary for the formation of the normal intercellular substances that form the bulk of cartilage and bone and bind the cells of other tissues together. Capillary bleeding is one of the characteristic symptoms of ascorbic acid deficiency and is explained by failure of the intercellular binding material, with resultant rupture of the capillary walls and leakage of blood. This vitamin is necessary for normal tooth and bone formation and for the maintenance of healthy gums in man. Pronounced deficiency results in the disease called *scurvy*, the symptoms of which include redness, swelling, and bleeding of the gums, which eventually become thickened and retracted, and in severe cases the loosening and shedding of the teeth. Capillary fragility is marked, with hemorrhages occurring in the skin; the flesh bruises easily, and wounds are slow to heal. Scurvy has a long record in medical history as one of the to-be-expected horrors of sieges and prolonged voyages. The English, long before vitamins were heard of, found that fresh fruit and especially lime or lemon juice added to the navy rations would prevent or minimize scurvy.

This completes the list of vitamins known to be essential in human nutrition. However, there remain many others, some of which may prove to have this status. Besides the fat-soluble vitamin E, already mentioned, the following water-soluble vitamins are being investigated from this standpoint: *pyridoxine* (vitamin B_6), required in the diet of all laboratory animals studied but not proven essential for man, and concerned in the maintenance of normal skin function, hemoglobin synthesis, and muscular coordination; *pantothenic acid*, required for the growth of many bacteria, and deficiency of which in laboratory animals causes changes in hair color, adrenal and digestive malfunctioning, and many other disorders; *inositol*, a necessary growth factor for some yeasts, which has a wide variety of effects in laboratory animals; *paba* (para-aminobenzoic acid), which reverses the bactericidal action of sulfanilamide and appears to affect hair color and milk production in rats and growth in chicks; *biotin*, lack of which produces a characteristic group of effects in rats, usually ending in death, and which is present in unusually high proportion in embryonic cells and in skin tumors; *choline*, especially concerned in fat metabolism, and considered by some students a food rather than a vitamin because, like inositol, it is used in amounts much larger than the minute quantities required of most vitamins; the *vitamins P* (citrin, rutin), which seem to affect capillary fragility in some way different from the action of ascorbic acid; and *vitamin B_{12}* (animal protein factor), unusual in that its molecule contains cobalt, and strongly suspected of being involved in the prevention of pernicious anemia. Still others might be mentioned.

Inorganic materials. Besides proteins, fats, carbohydrates, and vitamins, the body requires a number of inorganic substances. Chief among these is *water*, which is an essential part of protoplasm and all body fluids, and makes up over 70 per cent of the weight of protoplasm and about 57 per cent of the body weight.[1] It is also the solvent and carrier of excreted wastes and is evaporated in the maintenance of proper

[1] Of all the water in the body, about 5.5 per cent is in the blood, some 25 per cent in the extracellular tissue fluids, and the rest in the protoplasm.

body temperatures. The other inorganic materials essential to the body include chlorides, sulphates, and phosphates of calcium, sodium, potassium, iron, magnesium, and zinc. Iodine is a constituent of thyroxin, one of the hormones to be discussed later; minute amounts of copper, manganese, cobalt, and bromine are also needed.

Diet

The sum of the food materials taken in by an animal over a specified period of time makes up its diet. As we have already seen, the diet must include materials to be burned as fuel for the release of energy; materials for building and repairing cells; inorganic materials to be used as structural elements, as solvents, as cooling agents, or for other purposes; and certain special substances (the vitamins) required for the proper functioning of the organism.

For an animal simply to eat until its hunger is satisfied is no guarantee that all these dietary requirements will be met. Cattle in southern Florida, eating their fill of the lush pasturage, fell victims by the thousands to a disease called "salt-sick." They were actually starved for certain minerals lacking in the soil, and hence in the plants which formed their food. By supplying these minerals in salt blocks or by other means the cattle were restored to health. Man, omnivorous in his food habits, would seem much less likely to suffer from dietary deficiencies, but actually, from ignorance or necessity, he very often does so. It will be of interest to consider briefly the kinds and amounts of food that are required adequately to maintain the human body under various circumstances.

An ordinarily active man weighing 150 pounds needs enough food to yield approximately 3900 Calories[1] of heat per day. If he is engaged in hard physical work the Calorie requirements may be as great as 5000 or even 6000 per day. Obviously the age, sex, weight, and activity of an individual, as well as the climate in which he lives, enter into a determination of his Calorie requirements. A two-year-old child may need only 900 Calories per day; the average woman needs about 2100.

In addition to the fats and carbohydrates that are the chief energy-furnishing foods, the diet must include proteins, essential minerals, and vitamins. The proteins, as previously mentioned, yield amino acids for building the new proteins needed by the cells for growth and repair. Of the 23 amino acids known, 10 are believed indispensable for human metabolism, and the diet must include protein foods from which these particular amino acids may be derived. At least 8 of the approximately

---

[1] "Calorie," spelled with a capital letter, is the great calorie—the amount of heat required to raise the temperature of 1,000 grams (1 liter) of water 1°C. The small calorie, written without a capital letter, is $\frac{1}{1000}$ of the great calorie.

20 known vitamins are important in the functioning of the human body; and no fewer than 12 mineral elements are essential, either as building materials or as chemical tools. A balanced diet is one that contains all these important substances in the required proportions. It has been estimated that for a person whose total Calorie requirements run about 2700 per day, the ideal distribution of food materials would be as follows:

Food materials	Grams	Calories per gram	Total Calories	Uses
Carbohydrates.....	333	4	1332	Energy release
Fats.............	100	9	900	Energy release
Proteins..........	120	4	480	Growth, repair (energy release)
Minerals.........	Small amount	0	0	Various
Vitamins.........	Trace	0	0	Proper functioning

Since 1940, a United States governmental agency, the Food and Nutrition Board, has published periodically revised tables of human nutritional requirements, and has at the same time been assembling data on food composition. From these studies it has become evident that the nutritional values of many foods are changed by processing and cooking. Vitamins and minerals are generally reduced in amount; but processing may increase the availability of other nutrients. Furthermore, natural foods can be improved by combining two incomplete food products or by adding minerals and synthetic vitamins or even amino acids. Iodized salt, milk fortified with vitamin D, and bread with added minerals and thiamine are now in general use.

In all research dealing with the food supply, the economic aspects cannot be neglected. Malnutrition is most common among low-income groups; cheaper as well as more nutritious foods are therefore needed. Potatoes and corn (maize), the staple foods of millions of people, can supply much more of the essential vitamins and minerals than they actually do, if means are found to reduce storage and cooking losses of these substances. In spite of the great advances that have been made in the science of nutrition and in food technology, the world food problem today is still one of total Calories; but in regions such as the United States, where Calorie undernutrition has been rare for many years, the chief problem is to assure a proper balance of nutrients in the diet.

DIGESTION AND THE DIGESTIVE SYSTEM

Except oxygen, all the essential supplies needed for maintenance and growth enter the body by way of the digestive system. Water, salts, and most of the vitamins require no special process to prepare them to pass through the walls of the intestine. For them the digestive system merely provides a sufficient area of permeable surface through which they may pass into the blood and lymph of the circulatory system. The carbohydrates, proteins, and fats, on the other hand, are taken into the digestive tract in a form in which they cannot pass through the intestinal walls and must be first digested (broken down) into simpler substances— monosaccharides, amino acids, and fatty acids and glycerol.

Digestive enzymes. Digestion involves both mechanical and chemical processes, the latter chiefly of a type known as *enzyme action*. Enzymes, sometimes termed *organic catalysts*, have the power to hasten enormously certain chemical reactions that otherwise would take place very slowly. The digestive enzymes act upon the carbohydrates, proteins, fats, and certain of their derivatives and break them down into simpler chemical compounds until the final products are able to permeate the walls of the intestine. This process is greatly facilitated and quickened by the mechanical maceration that is also a part of the digestive process. The complete process and the structures that accomplish it can be best described by following the sequence of events when a meal is taken into the digestive system.

The mouth and esophagus. Digestion and the digestive system begin with the mouth. As the food is chewed, it is mixed with *saliva*, the watery product of three pairs of mouth glands. Saliva is nearly neutral in reaction and contains two enzymes, *ptyalin* and *maltase*, which act upon certain of the carbohydrates. Chewing not only permits carbohydrate digestion to begin but prepares the food for swallowing by breaking it into smaller pieces and forming it into an easily swallowed paste. The voluntary muscles of the tongue and pharynx perform the action of swallowing, *i.e.*, passing the food through the pharynx into the esophagus. (Since the pharynx is a common part of both the digestive and pulmonary systems and a passageway for both food and air, the air passages that connect with the pharynx are closed in the act of swallowing. The posterior ends of the nasal passages are closed by the soft palate, and the opening of the upper end of the windpipe by a lid known as the *epiglottis*.)

The wall of the esophagus, like those of the stomach and intestine that follow it, is composed of five layers of tissue. There is first an inner epithelial layer, called the *mucosa;* this is surrounded by a layer of connective tissue, the *submucosa;* then come two layers of *smooth (involuntary) muscle tissue,*[1] and finally, on the outside, there is a smooth, thin, moist

---

[1] The muscles of the walls of the digestive tract are typical of *visceral muscle* in general. The cells making up this type of contractile tissue are flattened and spindle-shaped. Unlike skeletal muscle cells, they possess only a single nucleus and are not striated—*i.e.*, they do not possess the cross-bandings so typical of skeletal or voluntary

epithelium, known as the *peritoneal layer*.[1] Like the stomach and the small and large intestines, the esophagus is a tube; but unlike the stomach and intestines it is a relatively flabby, thin-walled tube, producing no enzymes and serving merely to connect the mouth with the stomach.

Digestion in the stomach. The swallowed food is not retained in the esophagus but passes immediately into the stomach, which is closed at its lower end by the *pyloric valve*, a sphincter muscle at the juncture of the stomach and small intestine. The food is retained in the stomach for some time—usually from 3 to $4\frac{1}{2}$ hours in the case of an ordinary mixed meal. Fluids and semifluids commence to leave the stomach almost immediately after being swallowed. On account of the rates at which they are liquefied, carbohydrate leaves more rapidly than protein and protein more rapidly than fat. While the food is in the stomach, a number of important digestive processes take place.

The mucosa of the stomach contains a multitude of glands that, when stimulated, pour their secretion, the *gastric juice*, into the cavity of the stomach. This gastric juice contains *hydrochloric acid* and three enzymes. The most important enzyme is *pepsin*, which aids in the digestion of proteins. The others are *rennin*, which coagulates milk, and small amounts of *lipase*, which aids in the digestion of fats. The walls of the stomach also secrete *mucin*, a slimy and viscous substance that coats the wall of the stomach and helps to protect it against the action of the gastric juice.

The muscle layer of the stomach is thick and powerful and forms the greater part of the thickness of the stomach wall. During digestion, waves of muscular contraction begin in the region of the broad upper or cardiac end of the stomach and sweep toward the narrow lower or pyloric end, becoming increasingly powerful as they proceed. There may be several of these waves in progress at one time. Thus the contents of the

---

muscle. For this reason, visceral muscle is often called *smooth muscle*, as opposed to striated.

Most of the internal organs of the body are essentially tubular in construction, and the walls of these tubes usually possess an outer layer of longitudinal smooth muscle, surrounding an inner and heavier circular layer. Contraction of the longitudinal layer shortens and thickens or expands the tube; contraction of the circular layer thins and elongates it. These muscles, therefore, are arranged in opposing sets like the skeletal muscles, though they are not attached to bony levers.

Compared to the action of skeletal muscles, the contraction of smooth muscles is slow and prolonged, that caused by a single stimulus lasting some 20 seconds. The action of the visceral muscles is controlled by the autonomic division of the nervous system and is not conscious; these muscles are therefore often called *involuntary muscles*.

[1] In the neck region, before the esophagus enters the body cavity, the outer layer is formed of connective tissue rather than of peritoneum. In general, the peritoneum not only forms the outer covering of the portions of the alimentary canal lying within the body cavity but lines the entire wall of the body cavity as well.

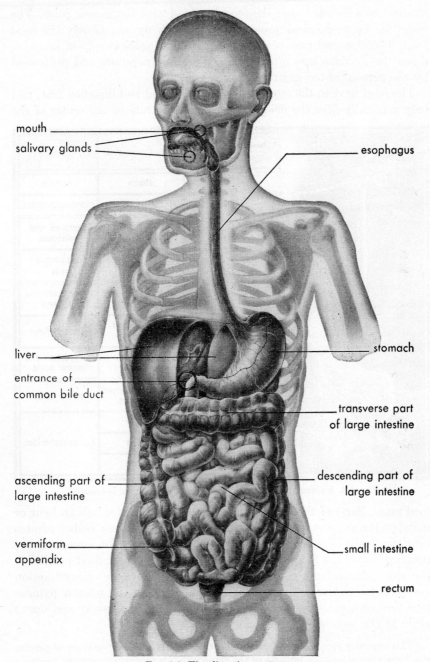

FIG. 4.2. The digestive system.

stomach are kneaded, and the food is mixed with the gastric juice. The effect of the mechanical processes is to break up and liquefy the solid food. The chemical part of gastric digestion consists chiefly of breaking down the proteins into intermediate products (peptones and proteoses) by the pepsin[1] of the gastric juice.

The food next to the stomach walls is digested and liquefied first, and only gradually does the acid gastric juice penetrate to the center of the

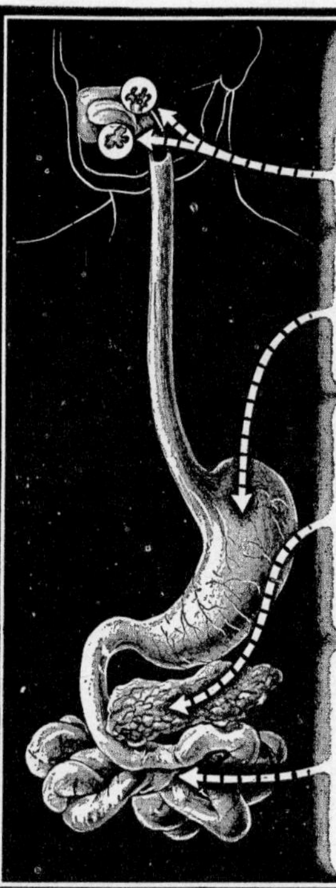

Gland source	Enzyme	Food affected	Product
SALIVARY	ptyalin	starch	maltose
	maltase	maltose	monosaccharides
GASTRIC	pepsin	protein	peptones and proteoses
	rennin	milk protein	coagulated milk
PANCREATIC	steapsin	fats	fatty acids and glycerol
	amylopsin	starches and glycogen	disaccharides
	trypsin	protein	polypeptids and amino acids
INTESTINAL	erepsin	peptones, proteoses, polypeptids	amino acids
	maltase	maltose	
	lactase	lactose	monosaccharides
	invertase	sucrose	

FIG. 4.3. A summary of digestion in man. Gastric lipase is omitted.

food mass. Parts of the mass remain slightly alkaline for half an hour or more, on the average, and so long as this condition persists, carbohydrates continue to be digested by ptyalin. As gastric digestion proceeds, the contractions of the stomach squeeze the outer and more fluid portion of the stomach contents toward the pylorus. Each wave of contraction sweeps a jet of the liquefied food (*chyme*) through the relaxed pylorus into the small intestine; the pyloric valve then closes briefly and opens again at the approach of the next wave.

[1] This digestive enzyme is secreted as *pepsinogen* (an inactive precursor of pepsin, which does not attack the proteins of the gland cells); pepsinogen is changed to active pepsin by the hydrochloric acid in the cavity of the stomach. The stomach walls, as noted above, are protected by their coating of mucin.

Digestion in the small intestine.   The chyme is highly acid. Upon its entry into the normally alkaline intestine, it prod⸻ ⸻two immediate effects. The first is the production of pancreati⸻ ⸻ second the entry into the intestine of a quantity of bile⸻ ⸻tions occur in response to stimuli that are partly c⸻ ⸻ous. The acid chyme, coming into contact with t⸻ ⸻mucosa, causes a substance called *secretin*[1] to be h⸻ ⸻ream.

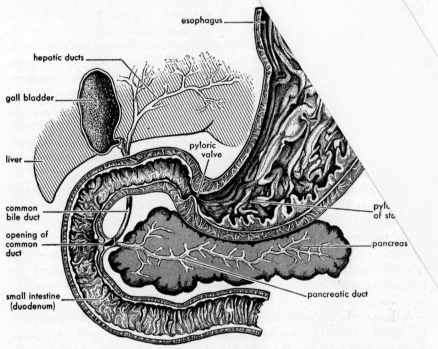

esophagus

hepatic ducts

gall bladder

liver

pyloric valve

common bile duct

opening of common duct

small intestine (duodenum)

pyl⸻ of st⸻

pancreas

pancreatic duct

FIG. 4.4. Sectional diagram to show the functional relationships of liver and pancreas to small intestine.

Secretin is a *hormone*,[2] or chemical messenger. Carried rapidly to all parts of the body by the blood, it reaches the pancreas and liver and stimulates both these organs to secrete.

[1] The discoverers of secretin thought that it was represented in the mucosa cells by an inactive precursor, *prosecretin*, and that the latter was changed into secretin by the hydrochloric acid of the chyme. More recent studies, however, show that secretin exists preformed in the mucosa cells, from which it can be extracted by water, alcohol, and other solvents, as well as by acid. Secretin has been obtained in pure crystalline form and proves to be a proteinlike substance.

[2] A *hormone*, or chemical messenger, is a substance which, secreted in one part of the body, is capable of regulating the functions of other parts when carried to them by the blood stream.

The principal substances secreted by the pancreas upon stimulation by secretin are water and the inorganic constituents of the pancreatic juice. The pancreas is also under control of the *vagus nerve*, which plays a large part in many visceral reflexes, particularly in glandular control. Stimulation of the vagus nerve by the entry of chyme into the duodenum reflexly stimulates the cells of the pancreas, and this nervous stimulus is chiefly responsible for the secretion of the enzymes in the pancreatic juice.

The secretion from the pancreas (pancreatic juice) contains three important enzymes: *trypsin*,[1] which digests proteins into polypeptids or even into amino acids; *steapsin* (also called *pancreatic lipase*), which digests fats into fatty acids and glycerol; and *amylopsin*, which changes starches (and glycogen) into disaccharides. Steapsin has only a weak reaction until it has been activated by the bile salts in the intestine. Other enzymes are present in the intestinal juice that is secreted by the mucosa of the intestine itself. These include *erepsin*, which acts upon the peptones, proteoses, and polypeptids to form amino acids; and the inverting enzymes—*maltase, lactase,* and *invertase*—which split the disaccharides maltose, lactose, and cane sugar, respectively, into monosaccharides.

Bile is secreted continuously by the liver and stored in the gall bladder; secretin merely increases the rate of its production. Discharge of bile into the intestine is caused by contraction of the walls of the gall bladder in response to stimuli produced by entry of chyme into the intestine. As in the pancreas, these stimuli are in part nervous, in part chemical. The contact of fat or of acid with the walls of the duodenum apparently liberates another hormone, related to but not the same as secretin; this hormone causes contraction of the gall bladder, forcing bile into the intestine.

Although the bile contains no enzymes, it plays an important part both in digestion[2] and in the absorption of digested fats. In both these processes the bile salts are the effective agents. Besides activating steapsin, they emulsify the fats in the intestine, breaking them up into minute particles and enormously increasing the surface exposed to enzyme action. Indirectly they aid also in the digestion of proteins and carbohydrates, by removing the fat from the surface of particles of these substances and thus exposing them to more efficient enzyme action. The role of bile in absorption is mentioned below.

The enzymes of the intestine all work best in a slightly alkaline to neutral medium; but chyme, as we have seen, is quite strongly acid.

[1] This is secreted by the pancreas in the form of an inactive precursor, *trypsinogen*, which is changed to active trypsin by an activator, *enterokinase*, that is secreted by the intestine.

[2] Bile is also in part an excretion, the bile pigments representing waste products from the breakdown of hemoglobin.

Pancreatic juice is mildly to rather strongly alkaline; bile, though quite alkaline in the liver, becomes neutral or weakly alkaline during a process of concentration that it undergoes in the gall bladder. The intestinal juice is definitely alkaline through the presence of sodium carbonate and bicarbonate. The mixing of these juices with the chyme tends to neutralize the acid of the latter and establishes a circumneutral or slightly alkaline condition that persists, with some variation, throughout the intestine.

The work of the intestinal and pancreatic enzymes is greatly facilitated by the muscular activity of the intestinal wall. The mass of food

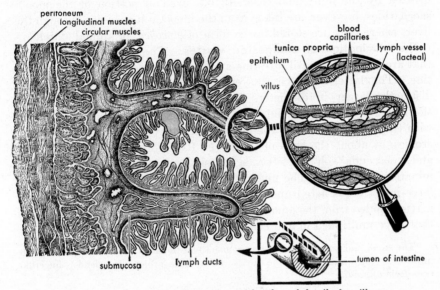

FIG. 4.5. A section of small intestine, with enlarged detail of a villus.

received from the stomach is pinched into numerous separate portions by local constriction of the intestinal wall, and these semifluid separate portions are shunted backward and forward, reunited and again separated by alternate contraction of the circular (constricting) and longitudinal (dilating) muscle layers. In this way, the food is much more effectively exposed to the action of the digestive fluids, and new portions are continually brought in contact with the absorptive walls of the intestine. Peristaltic waves of contraction passing along the intestine keep the food moving gradually toward the posterior end.

Digestion is completed when the proteins, carbohydrates, and fats have been broken down into amino acids, monosaccharides, and fatty acids and glycerol. As soon as these end products of digestion are formed, they, like water and the salts and vitamins, tend to be absorbed through the walls of the intestine. The presence of the bile salts is necessary for the absorption of the fatty acids, with which they apparently unite; the bile salts are thus reabsorbed into the body and are eventually returned to the liver. These salts are necessary also for the absorption of carotene and vitamin D and aid in the absorption of vitamins K and E. The end products of digestion, together with the other substances mentioned above, pass through the walls of the intestinal mucosa and into the capillaries and lymph vessels of the submucosa. Once they enter the blood system, either directly or by way of the lymphatic vessels, the absorbed substances are carried throughout the body, to be taken in and utilized by the individual cells. All but a small portion of the monosaccharides, however, are taken from the blood in its passage through the liver, where they are stored in the form of *glycogen*, or animal starch.

The elimination of undigested wastes. The undigested materials that are left in the small intestine are finally passed into the large intestine.[1] The latter is much shorter than the small intestine, although distinctly larger in diameter. The undigested materials pass rather slowly through the large intestine, which "ascends" from its juncture with the small intestine in the lower right side of the abdominal cavity; crosses, at about the level of the navel, from the right to the left side; and "descends" on the left side, passing into the rectum, which terminates in the anus. The undigested waste, in its passage through the large intestine, is acted upon by a multitude of bacteria, and the fecal matter voided from the anus consists in considerable part of the bacteria that have multiplied in and considerably modified this undigested mass.

---

[1] The small and large intestines do not meet end to end; the inner end of the large intestine forms a blind pouch, the *caecum*, from which projects the slender, fingerlike *vermiform appendix*.

CHAPTER V

RESPIRATION AND EXCRETION

Food taken into the body represents merely stored or potential energy. To release this energy and make it available for work, the food must be burned—*i.e.*, combined with oxygen; and this must occur within the cells that do the work. Large amounts of oxygen must therefore be taken into the body and distributed to all the cells. The supply must be continuous, for even the energy necessary for merely keeping alive comes from the burning of food, and the cells soon die if deprived of oxygen.

The oxidation of food materials not only releases energy in the form of heat and work but also gives rise to new chemical substances. Carbon dioxide and water are always produced; they are the only products of the oxidation of carbohydrates, almost the only ones from the burning of fats, and a part of the results of protein oxidation. Water is useful in the metabolism of the body; but carbon dioxide is a substance that, although necessary in minute amounts, becomes harmful if allowed to accumulate. In addition to water and carbon dioxide, the burning of proteins results in the production of nitrogenous compounds and inorganic salts that are toxic in any except low concentrations. Certain substances, notably salts, may be ingested with the food in amounts greater than can be utilized. There is also to be considered the residue of undigestible material left in the intestine after absorption of the usable parts of the food. All these useless or harmful substances must in some manner be removed from the body.

The intake of oxygen and the removal of carbon dioxide—both gases—are provided for by a single mechanism, the *respiratory system*. The food residues are eliminated by the action of the digestive canal itself. All the remaining metabolic wastes—nitrogenous compounds, excess salts, and other waste substances—are soluble solids and are disposed of in aqueous solution by the operation of the *excretory system*.

THE RESPIRATORY SYSTEM

Oxygen and Carbon Dioxide Exchange

The taking in of the oxygen needed by the body and the expulsion of the waste carbon dioxide are accomplished by a special *respiratory sys-*

tem. This system consists essentially of (1) a large expanse of moist, thin epithelium, permeable to oxygen and carbon dioxide; (2) air passages through which the outside air reaches this epithelium; and (3) a breathing mechanism to provide continual renewal of the air in contact with the epithelial surface.

Air enters the respiratory system through the mouth or nose and, crossing the food passage in the pharynx, enters the upper end of the *trachea,* or windpipe, where the *larynx,* or voice box, a strong cartilaginous cylinder, contains the *vocal cords.* The lower end of the trachea extends into the thoracic cavity to a point somewhat below the level of the first pair of ribs and there branches into the right and left *bronchial tubes.* Each bronchial tube leads into a *lung,* in which it branches repeatedly into smaller and smaller tubes (the *bronchioles*) until the minute terminal branchlets end in expanded air sacs (*alveoli*) of thin epithelial tissue. Each lung may be roughly compared to a huge bunch of grapes; the stem and its branches correspond to the bronchial tubes; the grapes, to the air sacs. In the lung, of course, all these structures are hollow, and the bronchial tubes show a much more intricate and compounded branching. In addition to the structures just described, each lung contains an abundant supply of blood vessels, and is closely covered externally by a thin, moist, elastic membrane, the *pleurum.* Each lung is suspended by its root—the point where the main bronchial tube enters its medial surface—in a cavity lined by a second (outer) layer of pleural membrane.

The *thoracic cavity* is enclosed above and on the sides by the body wall. Its floor is formed by the *diaphragm,* a dome-shaped muscular partition that separates the thoracic and abdominal cavities. The cavity is divided into right and left sides by (1) a central, connective tissue framework that supports the esophagus, the trachea, and a number of blood vessels and (2) the *pericardium,* which contains the heart.

In *breathing,* the capacity of the thoracic cavity is markedly changed by the movements of its walls. When its muscles contract, the diaphragm becomes much less dome-shaped, and the floor of the thorax is considerably lowered. At the same time, contraction of the intercostal muscles lifts the anterior ends of the downward sloping ribs, increasing the depth of the thorax from front to back, and rotates them slightly outward, increasing the breadth of the thorax from side to side. The space between the inner and outer pleural membranes is airtight, and when the outer pleural membrane is pulled outward and downward by its tight connection to the diaphragm and body walls, the elastic inner pleural membrane must likewise expand. Since the inner pleural membrane is closely attached to the air sacs of the lungs, they too must enlarge and so draw in[1]

---

[1] To be more accurate, air is forced by atmospheric pressure into a space wherein the air pressure has been lowered.

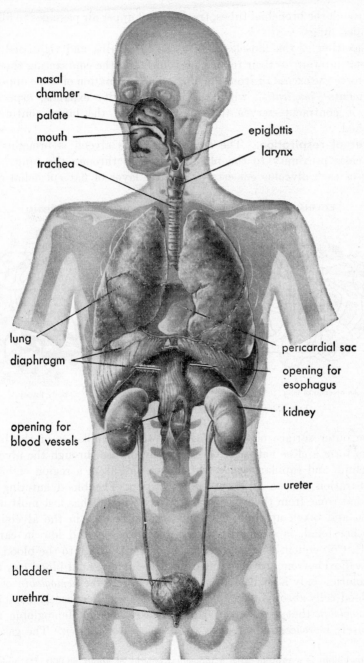

nasal chamber

palate

mouth

trachea

epiglottis

larynx

lung

diaphragm

pericardial sac

opening for esophagus

kidney

opening for blood vessels

ureter

bladder

urethra

Fig. 5.1. The respiratory and excretory systems.

air through the bronchial tubes, trachea, and upper air passages to fill the expanded lungs.

Relaxation of the muscles allows the lifted ribs and tightened diaphragm to return to their resting positions, and the contracting thoracic walls force the excess air from the lungs. The alternation of these opposing movements—*inspiration* when the thoracic cavity expands, *expiration* when it contracts—serves to keep the air in the lungs continually refreshed.

External respiration.   The air entering the alveoli is brought into very close proximity to the blood that flows through the lungs. The lining of each alveolus consists of a single layer of flat epithelial cells,

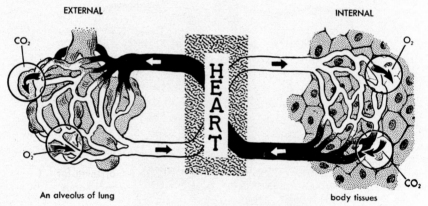

EXTERNAL   INTERNAL

CO_2 O_2

O_2

CO_2

An alveolus of lung   body tissues

FIG. 5.2. Scheme of internal and external respiration.

on the outer surface of which the thin-walled capillaries of the blood system form a close network. Gases readily diffuse through the alveolar epithelium and capillary walls and so can pass from a region of higher concentration to one of lower concentration. The blood entering the lungs has come from the other body tissues, where it has lost most of its oxygen and taken up much carbon dioxide. The air in the alveoli, on the other hand, is comparatively high in oxygen and low in carbon dioxide. Consequently oxygen passes from the alveoli into the blood and carbon dioxide from the blood into the alveoli. The fluid blood can take into solution only a small amount of oxygen, but the *hemoglobin* of the red blood cells absorbs oxygen molecules to form the loosely combined *oxyhemoglobin* that gives arterial blood its red color. Hemoglobin thus immensely increases the capacity of the blood for oxygen.[1] The gaseous

[1] Hemoglobin is a protein with a molecular weight of about 68,000. Its molecule contains four smaller units of structure, each having a weight of about 17,000 and containing globin and hemin, the latter including a single atom of ferrous iron. Each

interchange between the blood and the air in the lungs constitutes external respiration, as a result of which the blood that leaves the lungs is rich in oxygen and low in carbon dioxide.

Internal respiration. When the blood from the lungs reaches the other body tissues, it again enters capillary vessels that permit a gaseous exchange. The tissues are poor in oxygen and have a high carbon dioxide concentration. Oxygen therefore diffuses from the capillaries into the fluid bathing the tissues and thence into the cells, while carbon dioxide diffuses in the reverse direction. This interchange constitutes internal respiration, in which O_2 is delivered to the ultimate consumer, the tissues, and CO_2 is taken from its source in the body. Since most of the oxygen of the bright red oxyhemoglobin is released, the venous blood assumes the dark red color of hemoglobin.

EXCRETION AND THE EXCRETORY SYSTEM

We have seen that the materials taken into the body through the digestive and respiratory systems are used for growth, repair, and the liberation of energy. These processes, in turn, produce waste substances that become poisonous if allowed to accumulate.

As was pointed out in the beginning of this chapter, the wastes resulting from cell metabolism (chiefly oxidation) are water, carbon dioxide, nitrogenous salts (urea), and inorganic salts. One of these, carbon dioxide, is a gas; this substance is eliminated principally through the lungs, together with water in the form of water vapor. The other products of cell metabolism are nongaseous and require a different means of elimination; it is with this group of wastes that the organs of excretion are mainly concerned. In addition to the metabolic wastes, there are other waste products of the body, such as feces and dead skin, hair, and nails. *Feces* consist of the indigestible or undigested portions of the food eaten, together with bile pigments and other products of digestive glands, and bacteria and other organisms that multiply in the intestines. This material is eliminated by the action of the large intestine. Dead portions of the skin and its appendages are mechanically shed from the body surface.

The portions of the body that function as excretory organs are not all included in the excretory system proper. They are tabulated below, together with the products that they eliminate.

---

iron atom is able to unite loosely with an oxygen molecule (O_2), so that in changing to oxyhemoglobin each hemoglobin molecule takes on four oxygen molecules. The reaction is freely reversible: Hemoglobin $+ 4O_2 \rightleftarrows$ oxyhemoglobin. Since it has been calculated that a single red corpuscle contains about 240 million hemoglobin molecules, its oxygen capacity is approximately 960 million oxygen molecules.

Organs	Excretory function	Substances eliminated
Kidneys...............	Primary	Water and soluble salts resulting from protein metabolism—chiefly nitrogenous wastes
Lungs.................	Secondary	Carbon dioxide and water vapor in exhaled air
Skin..................	Secondary	Water, carbon dioxide, and salts, as sweat
Alimentary canal.......	Secondary	Feces, bile pigments, water, and salts (chiefly nonnitrogenous)

The Excretion of Nitrogenous Wastes

Nitrogenous wastes are formed by the continual wearing out of proto-plasm and from the nitrogenous portions of such amino acids as are oxidized for energy. Together with certain salts and a part of the excess body water, they are eliminated by a special excretory system.

The *excretory system* consists of a pair of kidneys, a urinary bladder, a pair of tubes called the ureters that lead from the kidneys to the bladder, and another tube called the urethra extending from the bladder to the exterior of the body. Each *kidney* is a compact, glandular organ somewhat larger than the fist. One lies on each side of the middorsal line of the abdominal cavity in the region of the small of the back. The medial (inner) margin of each kidney is concave, and on this concave side the kidney contains a funnel-shaped space that leads into the ureter. In this same region the kidney also receives a large artery and gives off a vein. Internally the kidney is closely packed with a multitude of microscopic tubules. Each tubule begins in an expanded and invaginated blind end (*Bowman's capsule*) situated near the outer surface of the kidney. Beyond this expanded portion the tubule becomes truly tubular and, after several loops and turnings, runs into a larger *collecting duct*. This, in turn, leads to the funnel-shaped cavity that ends in the ureter.

Each minute Bowman's capsule encloses a dense capillary network known as a *glomerulus;* a capsule and glomerulus together form the struc-ture known as a *malpighian corpuscle*. Each glomerulus is supplied by a tiny artery and is drained by an even smaller one,[1] so that the blood pres-sure within the capillaries of the capsule is unusually high. A some-what more diffuse network of capillaries is also in close contact with the walls of the long tubular portion of each tubule.

Blood, entering the glomerulus under pressure, is filtered in large quantities through the thin walls of the capillaries and the thin inner wall of the capsule into the expanded upper end of the tubule. Blood cor-

[1] The outgoing vessel, like the incoming one, is an arteriole, not a vein as might naturally be supposed; it carries concentrated arterial blood to the capillaries around the uriniferous tubules.

puscles and colloidal particles do not pass through the walls of the capillaries, but the filtrate is little different from the plasma of the blood. This fluid, in the course of its long tortuous passage through the tubule, returns the greater portion of its water and nearly all its nonwaste materials to the blood stream by way of the walls of the tubule and their surrounding network of capillaries. The reduced amount of fluid that

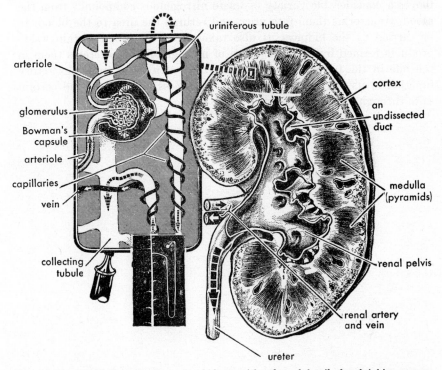

Fig. 5.3. Longitudinal section through a kidney, with enlarged detail of malpighian corpuscle and uriniferous tubule, and (in silhouette) the relation of the corpuscle and uriniferous tubule to a collecting tubule.

reaches the lower portion of the tubule contains the dissolved nitrogenous (and other) wastes and is known as *urine*.

The minute quantity of urine formed in each tubule passes into a larger collecting duct (each duct receives the discharge of many tubules); and the thousands of ducts empty into the pelvis of the kidney and thence into the *ureter*, through which the urine is propelled by muscular contractions into the *bladder*. The latter is a hollow muscular organ located in the lower, ventral part of the abdominal cavity. A tube, the *urethra*, leads from the lower, funnel-like end of the bladder to an opening on the outside of the body. The juncture of the bladder and urethra is closed by a muscular valve, so that the urine that continuously flows into the bladder from the kidneys is stored in the bladder (which may become markedly distended), until a voluntary impulse causes the muscular valve to relax. Contraction of the muscular wall of the bladder then expels the urine from the body.

Although not ordinarily considered a part of the excretory system, the *liver* also plays a role in the excretion of nitrogenous wastes. It removes a considerable variety of waste nitrogenous compounds from the blood, transforms them into urea, and returns the urea to the blood, to be carried to the kidneys. It also takes from the blood certain waste products formed by the breakdown of hemoglobin and excretes them in the bile in the form of bile pigments. The *skin* has a minor excretory function in its elimination of part of the excess body water and certain salts through the sweat glands.

CHAPTER VI

THE CIRCULATORY SYSTEM: THE COMMON CARRIER FOR THE BODY

Although the circulatory system might logically be classed, along with the nervous and endocrine systems, among the coordinating systems of the body, its role as a coordinator is the result of the fact that it acts as the common carrier for all of the other body parts. As a transport system it is intimately involved in the functioning of all the other systems, providing for a rapid collection from and delivery to all the tissues of the body. Its chief functions may be listed as follows:

1. It carries digested food from the intestine (and liver) to all tissues.
2. It carries oxygen from the lungs to the tissues and carbon dioxide from the tissues to the lungs.
3. It carries nitrogenous wastes from the tissues to the kidneys.
4. It connects the heat-producing tissues (chiefly muscles) and the heat-eliminating skin (and lungs) with the rest of the body and so maintains a fairly uniform temperature throughout the body.
5. It carries hormones (chemical messengers) from the glands where they are produced to the regions of the body where they regulate activity.
6. It acts as a defense mechanism against disease-producing organisms by
   a. Producing antibodies.
   b. Producing white blood cells and transporting them to the invaded region, where they attack and engulf certain types of disease-producing organisms.
   c. Filtering out bacteria and cell debris from the blood and lymph.
7. It protects its own system from loss of blood by forming clots in cut or broken vessels.

Essentially the circulatory system comprises a circulating fluid (the *blood*), a muscular pump (the *heart*), an intricate system of pipe lines (*arteries*, *veins*, and *capillaries*) that carry the blood from the heart to all parts of the body and back to the heart, and accessory drainage tubes (the *lymphatics*) that collect the leakage from the blood conduits and return this fluid (*lymph*) to the main circulation.

Blood. Although fluid, blood is a *tissue*, in which the cells are separated by large amounts of a fluid intercellular substance, instead of by a solid substance as in bone. Blood makes up about 8 per cent of the entire body weight, and there are about 6 to 8 quarts of blood in the body of a 150-pound man. Somewhat more than half of this volume is made up of the noncellular fluid portion, or *plasma*. About 90 per cent of plasma is water; the remaining 10 per cent is a complex and somewhat variable mixture of dissolved and suspended substances. These include proteins and amino acids, carbohydrates (chiefly glucose), various salts, nitrogenous wastes, vitamins, internal secretions (hormones), and immunity-producing substances (antibodies).

The cellular portion of blood comprises three kinds of cells—red corpuscles (*erythrocytes*), white blood cells (*leucocytes*), and blood platelets. Examples of these are shown in Fig. 2.3.

Red Corpuscles. These are incomplete cells that lack nuclei, for reasons that will be clear when we see how they are formed. They constitute the bulk of the blood cells and give blood its characteristic red color. Each is a biconcave disk, about $8/1000$ mm. in diameter. The number of corpuscles varies from person to person and from time to time in the same individual but averages between 4.5 and 5 million per cubic millimeter in a healthy adult. The red color is due to the contained *hemoglobin*, a respiratory pigment the functions of which have already been considered in our discussion of the respiratory system.

White Blood Cells. These are of several types, all of which fall into one or the other of two general classes—granular and nongranular. These cells are all nucleated, and none contains hemoglobin. Leucocytes are much less numerous than the red corpuscles, averaging perhaps 6,000 to 8,000 per cubic millimeter of blood in a normally healthy adult. Under certain conditions of bacterial infection (appendicitis, for instance) they multiply until as many as 30,000 may be present per cubic millimeter. The functions of the white cells are varied. A great many of them serve as *phagocytes*, or "eating cells" (Greek, *phago*, "to eat," and *kytos*, "cell"), which destroy invading bacteria, dead cells, and organic particles by ingesting them. Some phagocytes are important in defense against disease; others aid in the healing of wounds and other injuries by removing the dead cells and damaged portions of tissues.

Platelets. These are colorless like the white cells but are very small, only about half the diameter of a red corpuscle. In shape they are typically biconvex disks. The platelets have an important role in the process of blood clotting, as is described below.

Blood cell formation. Red blood cells live only a short time; there are indications that in man their average life is about 8 weeks. The life span of the white cells is even shorter, estimated at about 4 days, and this does not include the many which die prematurely. Both types of cells must therefore be continually replenished, and this is accomplished by the so-called "blood-forming organs."

The primary source of the nongranular white cells is lymphoid tissue, which occurs in the lymph nodes, tonsils, and spleen. The granular white cells and the red corpuscles are formed in the red marrow of the bones. Red cell formation is most active within the vertebrae, ribs, sternum, upper ends of the humerus and femur, and in some of the cranial bones. After extensive blood loss or destruction of red corpuscles, the red marrow increases in extent, and in the long bones it may invade the greater part of the shaft, taking the place of the normal yellow marrow.

In the very young embryo all the red cells are nucleated and are formed by mitosis from parent cells in the epithelial lining (*endothelium*) of the blood vessels. Later they are produced in several organs, especially the liver. But after birth the formation of red cells is taken over exclusively by the red bone marrow, and all those produced are nonnucleated. Until very recently the nucleated cells were regarded as immature forms of the nonnucleated ones, which were thought to lose the nucleus by degeneration as they matured. But in 1947, August Krogh called attention to the work of a young Danish investigator, Claus Plum, who has radically changed our concepts of erythrocyte formation. By simple and ingenious experiments Plum was able to follow the entire process, and our account is based on his discoveries.

The blood vessels of bone marrow, like others, are lined with an endothelial layer and consist of arteries, veins, and a rich plexus of interconnected spaces, the *sinusoids*. At any given time many of the sinusoids are collapsed and closed to the passage of blood. Some of the endothelial cells lining the sinusoids are modified into *erythroblasts*, or erythrocyte-producing cells. Direct observation of living bone marrow tissue in a small culture chamber showed that the spherical erythroblast becomes oval, with the nucleus toward the basal end; protoplasm flows toward the opposite (free) end, where suddenly a drop of it is detached to form a small nonnucleate cell. No mitosis is involved in the process. In the rat embryo the maximum rate of erythrocyte formation is just before birth, at which time each erythroblast produces about 260 erythrocytes per day. In the adult rat 35 to 100 are produced from each erythroblast per day, and the total daily production of red cells is about 9×10^9, a truly enormous figure.

The young erythrocytes are flushed from the sinusoids into the blood stream. They are called *reticulocytes*, because after special staining they show a network of threads inside the cell. Blood contains a substance which causes the reticulocytes to "ripen" into mature red corpuscles—a change involving loss of the internal network. Various tissues produce this ripening substance, but the chief source in the pig was found to be the pyloric mucosa and in man the mucosa of the lower part of the stomach. The ripening substance was also discovered to have a marked accelerating effect upon the rate of production of new red cells. The increase in rate of production following injury and loss of blood may be a result of increased concentration of the ripening substance in the blood.

The spleen. This is an organ closely associated with and important for the proper functioning of the vascular system. It is an ovoid body about 5 inches in length and 6 ounces in weight, located in the upper left portion of the abdominal cavity. The functions of the spleen are still not fully understood but are known to include the following:

1. Destruction of old red corpuscles by two kinds of phagocytic cells that abound in the splenic tissues. Most of the iron-containing substances thus liberated are carried by the white cells to the liver for storage.

2. The filtering out from the blood of solid particles, including cell debris, foreign protein masses, and disease-producing organisms. These particles are "eaten" by the phagocytes. The spleen serves as the great blood filter, and this may be its most important function.

3. Production of nongranular white cells in the lymphoid tissue. In embryonic life and in certain types of anemia the spleen also produces granular white cells and red corpuscles.

4. Serving as a reservoir of red blood corpuscles. When there is a deficiency of hemoglobin or of oxygen in the blood, the spleen contracts, driving some of the corpuscles it contains into the general circulation. This contraction is at least in part a response to the hormone *adrenalin*, which is discussed in the chapter dealing with the endocrine glands.

The heart. This is the powerful double pump that forces the blood to circulate through the blood vessels. It is a muscular organ situated nearly in the center of the lower part of the thoracic cavity. It is enclosed in a tough membranous sac, the *pericardium*, which contains the pericardial fluid that bathes the heart and protects it from friction with the surrounding organs.

The heart has four chambers. The upper two are the relatively thin-walled *auricles* or *atria*, which receive blood from the veins. The two lower chambers, the *ventricles*, have heavy muscular walls that, by contracting, propel the blood throughout the body. The auricle (atrium) and ventricle on the same side of the heart are connected by a valve that permits blood to pass from auricle to ventricle; but the chambers of the right side are completely separated from those of the left by strong, impervious partitions. The heart may therefore be thought of as composed of two separate pumps, often designated the *right heart* and the *left heart*.

The walls of the heart, except for thin outer and inner epithelial linings (the inner lining called *endothelium*) and some connective tissue, are composed of a special type of contractile tissue known as *cardiac* or *heart muscle*. The heart is a modified blood vessel, and its muscle tissue has the same origin as the smooth muscle of artery and vein walls; but its fibers are nevertheless cross-striated, though imperfectly so, and in this respect suggest the structure of skeletal muscle. Cardiac muscle also resembles skeletal muscle in the strength and rapidity of its contractions, but with one very important difference. A skeletal muscle is capable of graded contractions, the strength of which is dependent upon the intensity of the nerve stimulus and the resultant variation in the *number of individual*

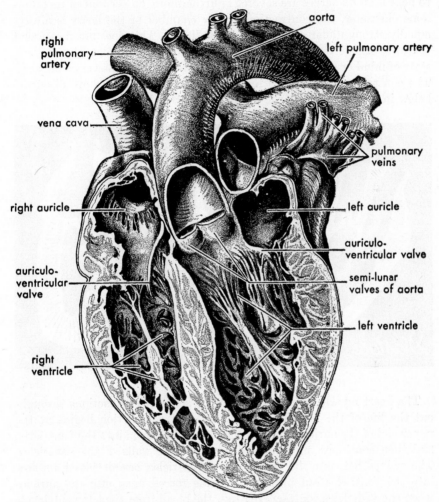

right pulmonary artery

aorta

left pulmonary artery

vena cava

pulmonary veins

right auricle

left auricle

auriculo-ventricular valve

auriculo-ventricular valve

semi-lunar valves of aorta

left ventricle

right ventricle

Fig. 6.1. A section through the heart, from the front.

muscle fibers stimulated to contract. In the heart, on the other hand, any stimulus strong enough to cause the heart muscle to react at all will cause complete contraction of an entire auricle or ventricle. The heart chambers, *as units*, follow the *all-or-none rule*, whereas in skeletal muscle it is only the individual muscle fibers that behave in this way. The reason for the difference is that in skeletal muscle the fibers are separate, whereas in cardiac muscle they branch and join together in such a way that a stimulus spreads from fiber to fiber throughout the whole auricle or ventricle.

In a sense, the beating of the heart is automatic—*i.e.*, it is not dependent upon stimuli from the central nervous system. The heart will continue to beat if all its nerves are severed. Furthermore, on account of its all-or-none character, the contraction of any chamber of the heart is always equally strong under a given set of conditions. This does not mean that the strength of the heartbeat does not vary; as everyone knows, the state of mind or body can modify both the rate and the power of the beat. The controlling mechanisms responsible for these changes are discussed below in connection with the mechanics of circulation.

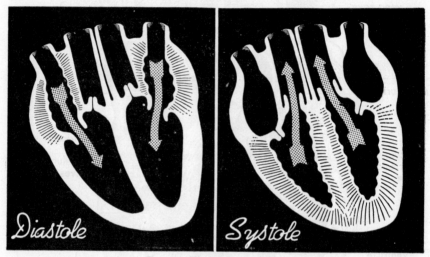

Fig. 6.2. The pumping heart.

The heart muscle keeps up a rhythmic series of contractions throughout the life of the individual. Each wave of contraction begins at the upper end of the auricles, forcing the blood from them into the ventricles, and then continues, more powerfully, into the walls of the ventricles. The valves between the auricles and ventricles permit blood to flow into the ventricles but prevent its being forced back into the auricles when the ventricles contract. Instead, the blood from the left ventricle is forced into the main systemic artery, the *aorta*, and that from the right ventricle into the *pulmonary artery* leading to the lungs.

Blood vessels are of three main types: *arteries*, which carry blood from the heart to the tissues; *veins*, which carry blood from the tissues to the heart; and *capillaries*, the minute blood vessels in the tissues that connect the arteries with the veins. The walls of the arteries and veins have much the same structure, but the walls of the arteries are markedly heavier and more muscular than the walls of the veins. In both, a smooth, thin lining of epithelial cells (endothelium) is surrounded by several layers of smooth muscle cells and connective tissue. The walls of the capillaries lack the smooth muscle and connective tissue layers and consist of a single layer of thin endothelial cells.

The great arteries that leave the heart, the *aorta* and *pulmonary artery*, branch into successively smaller ones, so that all parts of the body are supplied with an abundance of small arteries. These continue to branch until they pass into the enormous network of capillaries. The latter, after a short course through the tissues, unite to form small veinlets. These, in turn, unite to form larger and larger veins and finally pour their blood into the great veins that lead back to the heart—the *pulmonary veins* from the lungs, entering the left auricle, and the two *venae cavae*, entering the right auricle. The veins of the lower part of the body empty into the *inferior vena cava;* those of the head, neck, and arms into the *superior vena cava.*

The capillaries have the task of bringing the blood into the immediate vicinity of the cells, and it is essential that no cell be far removed from a capillary. For this condition to exist it is necessary that the capillaries be exceedingly numerous. It has been calculated that the capillaries in the human body, if placed end to end, would form a tube 62,000 miles long. Since each capillary is only about a millimeter in length, the number of capillaries is beyond comprehension. To illustrate the closeness of the spacing of cells and capillaries, it may be noted that there are about 2,500 capillaries in a cross section of 1 sq. mm. of skeletal muscle, or about 1,562,500 per square inch. The total surface of the 62,000-mile capillary tube mentioned above is about 67,000 square feet, or $1\frac{1}{2}$ acres; and it has been calculated that 1 cc. of blood is exposed to a capillary surface of 7,300 sq. mm., or 8 square feet. The cross-sectional area of the total capillary network is estimated as 400 to 1,000 times that of the aorta, and considering the relatively small amount of blood in the entire vascular system, it is evident that all these capillaries cannot be filled at the same time. As is mentioned below in connection with the lymphatic system, only a part of the capillaries of a resting organ contain blood at any one time, but the entire capillary system of the organ may become filled during periods of activity.

FUNCTIONAL DIVISIONS OF THE CIRCULATORY SYSTEM

The Pulmonary Circulation.   In man, as in all the higher vertebrates, the circulatory system is double. The *right* auricle and ventricle receive only the dark venous blood that has returned to the heart from all the tissues of the body except the lungs. When the heart contracts, the blood from the right ventricle is forced into the pulmonary artery, which leads to the lungs. In the lungs the blood enters the capillaries that are in contact with the alveoli, loses its load of carbon dioxide, and becomes oxygenated. The capillaries of the lungs lead to veins that unite to form the large pulmonary veins. These lead back to the heart and empty into the *left* auricle.

The Systemic Circulation. The blood that returns to the *left* side of the heart from the pulmonary circulation is the bright-red oxygenated blood, that is often termed *arterial blood*. Contractions of the left ventricle force it out into the *aorta*, the largest artery of the body, which sends branches to all parts of the body except the lungs. The capillaries supplied from the systemic arteries bring arterial blood into intimate contact with the tissues. Blood leaving the capillaries passes into the veins, and the two venae cavae finally return the now deoxygenated dark-red venous blood to the *right* auricle, from which it will be taken into the pulmonary circulation.

The routes that the blood may traverse in the systemic circulation are varied, but except for a considerable portion carried to the digestive system, the blood from each region returns directly to the heart after traversing a single set of capillaries.

The Portal System. Certain of the large abdominal arteries that lead from the aorta carry blood to the stomach, intestines, liver, pancreas, and spleen. Here the blood supplies the needed oxygen and takes up the excess carbon dioxide and nitrogenous wastes and also the digested foods that have passed through the walls of the intestine. From the capillaries of these organs, this blood passes finally into a large vein, the *hepatic portal*, which carries the blood to the liver, where it enters a second set of capillaries that form a network in the tissues of the liver. In the liver the surplus monosaccharides are taken from the blood and stored in the liver cells. From the capillaries of the liver the blood again passes into a venous system, which leads to the heart.

The Lymphatic System. Although all the materials used by the cells of the body are obtained from the blood and all the waste products of cell metabolism find their way into it, blood as such does not come into direct contact with the cells. It remains within the capillaries, and these capillaries in most instances are not even in immediate contact with the cells. Between the capillaries and the cells, and between the cells, there exists a multitude of *tissue, or lymph, spaces*, mostly microscopically small but varying much in size and shape. Filling these spaces and bathing the cells is a tissue fluid, the *lymph*.[1] Lymph is formed by a "leakage" of water, salts, glucose, amino acids, etc., from the blood capillaries into the surrounding tissue spaces. The red blood cells do not pass through

---

[1] A distinction is sometimes made between tissue fluid and lymph, the latter term being then restricted to the fluid contained within the lymph vessels.

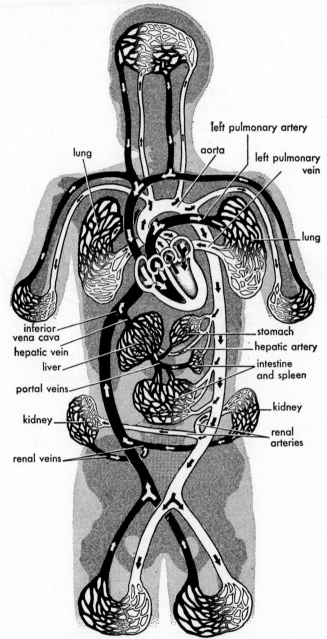

FIG. 6.3. The circulation of the blood.

the capillary walls; but many of the white blood cells force their way, amoebalike, between the endothelial cells composing these walls and enter the lymph spaces. Although the tissue fluid at first probably differs little from blood plasma, it is soon modified by the activities of the cells with which it is in contact; they take from the lymph the food substances that they need, and discharge into it their waste products. Being constantly bathed by the tissue fluid, the cells of the body may truthfully be said to be aquatic, the tissue fluid constituting their environment, or internal medium.

It is evident that there must be some means of preventing stagnation of the lymph in the tissue spaces—of draining off the "used" lymph, waste-charged and low in food, and of replacing it with fresh lymph.

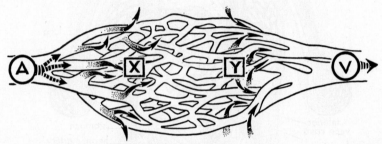

Fig. 6.4. Diagram of the pressure relations concerned in loss and recovery of fluid by the capillaries. A is a small artery, V, a small vein. At X the hydrostatic blood pressure in the capillaries exceeds the combined opposing effects of the osmotic blood pressure and the outside lymph pressure, and fluid leaves the capillaries. At Y the pressure relations are reversed, and fluid reenters the capillaries.

There are two mechanisms by which this is accomplished—the lymphatic system, discussed below, and the blood capillaries themselves. It may seem paradoxical that the same capillaries that lose fluid to the tissue spaces to form lymph should also absorb "used" lymph back into the blood stream, but this can be understood in the light of the following considerations (see Fig. 6.4).

The chief factor in forcing the fluid of the blood into the tissue spaces is the hydrostatic blood pressure in the capillaries, produced by the beating of the heart. Were this not opposed by the pressure of the lymph already in the tissue spaces and by the osmotic pressure of the blood caused by its contained colloidal proteins, most or all of the blood fluid would be forced out through the walls of the capillaries. As it is, wherever the hydrostatic blood pressure exceeds the combined effects of the osmotic and lymph pressures, fluid does escape from the capillaries; where the forces are balanced, there is no loss or gain of fluid; and where the osmotic pressure plus the lymph pressure exceeds the hydrostatic blood pressure, fluid enters the capillaries. Hydrostatic blood pressure is high near the arterial ends of the capillaries (at X in Fig. 6.4), and here fluid is lost. However, the hydrostatic pressure falls rapidly along the course of each capillary, because of friction and loss of fluid, and the colloidal proteins become more concentrated, causing an increase in osmotic pressure within the capillary. As a consequence, the pressure relations are reversed toward the venous ends of the capillaries (at Y in Fig. 6.4), and here lymph tends to flow back through the capillary wall into the blood stream.

Diffusion also plays an important part in the blood-lymph relations. Blood entering the capillaries is rich in oxygen and dissolved foods and low in metabolic wastes. Lymph is low in food and oxygen, which are continually removed from it by the cells, and is high in wastes received from the cells. It results that oxygen and food substances continually diffuse through the capillary walls into the lymph, and wastes diffuse in the opposite direction into the blood. Of all the food substances, the colloidal proteins pass through the capillary walls with the greatest difficulty, their concentration being therefore always much greater in the blood than in the lymph.

During the inactive state of an organ, nearly all the lymph is drained directly into the blood capillaries; but increased activity of the organ brings greater blood supply and increases the formation of lymph. This is partly the result of increased blood pressure but is more largely caused by a great increase in the capillary surface. As was mentioned above, only a fraction of the capillaries of a resting organ contain blood, the remainder being collapsed and empty. In a resting muscle, for example, a cross section of 1 sq. mm. of muscle tissue shows only about 200 open capillaries. When the muscle becomes active, however, a combination of nervous and chemical stimuli causes the small arteries and capillaries to dilate, enormously increasing the blood flow through the organ. In a cross section of 1 sq. mm. of active muscle, there are about 2,500 open capillaries—more than 12 times as many as in the resting muscle. Each capillary is furthermore dilated, offering more surface for filtration of lymph into the tissue spaces. With the increase in leakage, the capillaries can no longer absorb the lymph as rapidly as it forms, and the lymphatic system comes into operation.

The lymphatic system is an accessory circulatory or drainage system. Like the blood circulatory system, it is made up of tubes, in this case called *lymph vessels;* but unlike that system, it does not form a continuous closed circuit but is a many-branched one-way drainage system comparable to a river with its affluents and head waters. It contains no pumping organ and has nothing analogous to the arteries, but it may be likened to the capillary and vein portions of the blood circulatory system. In all the tissue spaces there are very delicate tubes, the *lymph capillaries*

(Fig. 6.6), closed at the ends but communicating freely with each other and fusing to form larger and larger vessels. The latter resemble veins and, like them, are provided with valves that permit the movement of lymph only in one direction, toward the heart. The large lymph vessels finally converge to the region of the left shoulder, where the main *thoracic duct* empties the lymph into a large vein of the blood circulatory system. This duct carries the lymph from all parts of the body except the right side of the head, neck, and thorax and the right arm; the lymph from

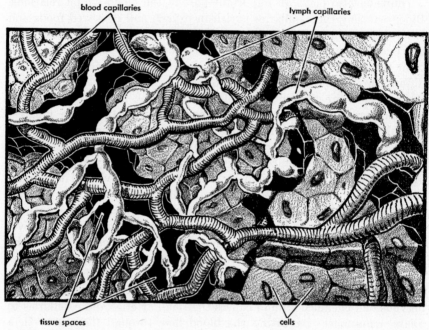

Fig. 6.5. Diagram of the relationships between blood capillaries, tissue spaces, cells, and lymph capillaries in a tissue.

those regions enters the corresponding vein on the right side of the body. Movement of the lymph in the vessels is brought about by muscular movements of the body that incidentally compress the lymph vessels and squeeze the lymph in the direction determined by the valves.

The intimate contact between the lymph and the tissue cells supplements and completes the functioning of the circulatory system proper by permitting a much more complete interchange between the circulating medium and the body tissues. The lymphatic system also provides an important means of defense against the invasion of the body by disease-producing organisms. Most of the lymph vessels have, at intervals, small filterlike enlargements, the *lymph nodes*, where numerous phagocytes are concentrated. Here invading bacteria, as well as worn-out cell fragments, are ordinarily destroyed by the phagocytes before they can be carried into the blood stream.

THE MECHANICS OF CIRCULATION

We have seen that it is the powerful contraction of the ventricles that pumps the blood out along the arteries. When the ventricles contract, 50 to 100 cc. of blood is forced into the aorta and an equal amount into the pulmonary artery. The passage of the blood through the smaller arteries, especially through the fine capillaries, encounters marked frictional resistance, so that the blood in the arteries is always under pressure, which somewhat distends the elastic walls of these vessels. The elasticity of the arteries continues to force the blood into the capillaries, even in the intervals between heartbeats. Each beat of the heart suddenly pumps another 50 to 100 cc. of blood into the aorta and pulmonary artery, and the increased pressure causes a short section of the elastic artery walls to expand. The wave of pressure travels rapidly out over the arteries and their branches at a rate 10 to 15 times as fast as the flow of the blood itself and is gradually extinguished in the smaller arteries. It is the succession of such impulses, or pressure waves, produced by the rhythmic contractions of the ventricles and accompanied by a bulging of the arterial wall, that constitutes the *pulse*, by means of which the rate of heartbeat can be determined. It is also this series of repeated impulses from the heart that produces an alternating maximal (*systolic*) and minimal (*diastolic*) pressure in the arteries.

The average normal blood pressure increases slowly with age. This is often attributed to the loss of elasticity and tone of the arteries, but the cause is somewhat obscure. According to studies published in 1950, the range of normal variation is much greater than is commonly assumed. The following table gives this range for different ages, in terms of millimeters of mercury:

Age	Men		Women	
	Systolic	Diastolic	Systolic	Diastolic
20	105–140	62–88	100–130	60–85
30	110–145	68–92	102–135	60–88
40	110–150	70–94	105–150	65–92
50	115–160	70–98	110–165	70–100
60	115–170	70–100	115–175	70–100

Owing to the damping out of the pulse by friction and the elasticity of the arterial walls, blood enters the capillaries in an almost steady stream. The capillary resistance to flow is so great that nearly all the pressure created by the beating of the heart is utilized in overcoming it; only a small residue of this pressure remains when the blood flows from the capillaries into the veins. The return of the blood to the heart is caused in part by this residual pressure but is greatly aided by other factors. We have already noted that the veins, like the lymphatics, are well provided with valves opening in the direction of the heart. Muscular

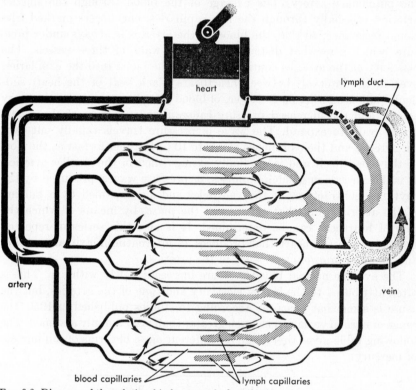

FIG. 6.6. Diagram of the relationship between the lymphatic and blood circulatory systems. (*Adapted from Carlson and Johnson, The Machinery of the Body, by permission University of Chicago Press.*)

movements of the body, including movements of the viscera and those of breathing, aid in the return flow by squeezing the veins and forcing the blood in the direction determined by the valves. The breathing movements also assist the process in another manner. The same movements of the diaphragm and ribs that reduce the pressure within the thoracic cavity, causing air to flow into the lungs, also reduce the pressure in the auricles and the veins that lie within this cavity and tend to "pull" blood into the auricles and adjacent portions of the venae cavae.

In response to variations in the circulatory needs of the body, the normal heart is capable of making great adjustments in rate and *power* of beat and in the volume of blood discharged at each stroke. While the body is at rest, the amount of blood discharged from each ventricle averages about 50 cc. per stroke; at maximum capacity, the heart can increase this amount to about 150 or 200 cc. per stroke. This is not, as might be thought, a contradiction of the all-or-none principle already described as governing the contraction of the heart. Under a given set of conditions, it remains true that each beat of the heart is as strong as every other beat and that the strength of the beat is independent of the strength of the stimulus. But in heart muscle, as in skeletal muscle, the muscle fibers (within limits) contract the more powerfully the more they are stretched when contraction begins. If for any cause the volume of blood entering the auricles is increased, this stretches the heart muscles, and the resulting contraction is more powerful and expels a greater volume of blood. Increased muscular activity, accompanied by more rapid and powerful respiratory movements, is one of the more common conditions that will cause an increased flow of venous blood into the heart, automatically bringing about an increase in the strength of the heart contraction.

The mechanism controlling the *rate* of heartbeat is quite complex, involving physical, chemical, and nervous stimuli.[1] We shall be able only briefly to consider some of the factors involved. First of all, we may recall our earlier statement that the beating of the heart is "automatic," produced by an "inner stimulus," and that it goes on even in the absence of outside stimulation. The heart is, however, subject to influences that modify its independent activity. It is connected with the central nervous system by two nerves[2]—the *vagus* and the *cervical sympathetic*. Cutting these nerves does not stop the action of the heart; their function is merely regulatory. Impulses from the vagus slow the heartbeat or, if sufficiently intense, may cause it temporarily to cease.[3] Impulses from the cervical sympathetic nerve accelerate its rate. Both these nerves possess "tone"; *i.e.*, they both transmit impulses more or less continuously, and the rate of the heartbeat is in large part a resultant of the balance between the stimuli received from the two nerves. The vagus may be thought of as the "brake" upon heart action; the cervical sympathetic nerve, as the "accelerator." Increase in the inhibitory impulses from the vagus may be brought about reflexly by stimulation of certain sensory nerves, including those of the viscera, skin, and sense organs. In this connection, the sensory nerves of the aorta, the venae cavae, and right auricle are of particular importance. For instance, sensory stimuli caused by increase of blood pressure in the aorta affect the vagus, slowing the heartbeat and thus automatically lowering the pressure and safeguarding the heart and arteries against excessive strain.

[1] The pulse rate is generally more rapid (1) in the female than in the male; (2) during and immediately after muscular activity; (3) during digestion or mental excitement; and (4) after sudden changes in position. The rate also changes with age; at birth it may be 130 to 150 beats per minute; in adult life it averages about 72 per minute; and in old age it falls to about 67 per minute.

[2] Actually, a right and left vagus nerve and a right and left set of cervical sympathetic nerves.

[3] Under exceptional circumstances, vagal stimulation may cause death from cessation of circulation; but normally, after a certain period of inhibition, the heart escapes from the control of the vagus and resumes its beat.

Heartbeat rate commonly varies inversely as the blood pressure, although since the controlling factors are numerous and are not the same for the two phenomena, the relation is naturally not a fixed one. As an illustration of a case in which this relationship does hold, the heartbeat is rapid immediately following a severe hemorrhage, when blood pressure is very low. In this condition, no great force of heartbeat is possible or necessary, the heart chambers not being much distended; but the small amount of blood left in the vessels must be distributed as quickly and used as often as possible.

The emotions also have a pronounced effect upon the heart. Strong emotion, by stimulating the vagus, may slow the heart sufficiently to cause fainting. Another factor influencing the rate and power of the heartbeat is the presence of varying amounts of chemical substances in the blood. Thus increase in carbon dioxide and lactic acid concentration in the blood, as a result of muscular activity, tends to dilate the arteries and capillaries and by thus causing an increased flow of blood back to the heart affects the rate and power of its beat. One of the most important chemical effects is that produced by the hormone *adrenalin*, a substance produced by the adrenal glands and discussed more fully in the later section on the endocrine glands. This substance causes a rise in blood pressure, accompanied by strengthening of the heartbeat. In the absence of nervous control, it also increases the rate of heartbeat, but when the nerves are intact, a reflex inhibition slows the heartbeat rate and thus prevents the blood pressure from rising too high. Adrenalin also has numerous other effects on the circulatory system, including constriction of the arteries and capillaries of the skin and viscera and dilation of those of the heart and skeletal muscles.

The efficiency of the heart as a pumping organ is strikingly shown by the rapidity with which the blood is circulated. According to Best and Taylor, the time required for a given blood corpuscle to make the pulmonary circuit (heart to lungs and back to heart) averages about 11 seconds in man. The length of the different systemic circuits varies so much that the time spent in traversing this part of the system cannot be accurately stated. It takes about 4 seconds for the blood to go from the heart to the capillaries of the forearm and about 6.6 seconds to return to the heart. It is calculated that the time required for the complete double circuit, from the right side of the heart to the lungs, back to the left side of the heart, out to the systemic capillaries, and back once more to the heart, probably averages 25 or 30 seconds. Blood going to the foot would, of course, take much longer than this to complete its circuit.

The amount of blood pumped by the heart is also of interest. For a heart with a stroke volume of 75 cc., a rate of 70 beats per minute, and a total volume of blood in the body of 5,000 cc., a volume of blood equal to all that contained in the body will pass through a single chamber of the heart in a little less than 1 minute.[1] This does not mean, of course,

----

[1] 70×75 cc. = 5,250 cc.

that all the blood will have traversed this chamber of the heart in this time; part of the blood, on the shorter circuits, will have been through more than once, and part will not yet have passed through. The time required to handle this quantity of blood is much reduced when, as a result of exercise or other factors, the heartbeat rate and the volume discharged at each beat are increased.

THE CLOTTING OF THE BLOOD

As long as the circulatory system is uninjured and blood pressures remain normal, the blood is a fluid that flows through even the smallest capillaries. If pressure is reduced below a certain point the corpuscles tend to settle out—a condition known as "sludged blood"—and clotting may follow. If a blood vessel is cut or ruptured, the escaping blood quickly clots, thus plugging the opened vessel and preventing continued bleeding. Clotting may also occur at the sites of bacterial or mechanical injury to the smooth inner wall of a blood vessel.

In spite of our familiarity with the phenomenon of clotting and the fact that it is a constant property of all normal blood, the mechanism responsible for its occurrence is only partly understood. Nevertheless some of the important steps in the process have been discovered. Consideration of these will emphasize two important points: (1) what a large number of delicately and precisely adjusted chemical reactions may be involved in an apparently simple physiological process; and (2) how far we still are from a complete understanding of the way in which the individual organism works.

When we watch under the microscope a thin film of blood as it coagulates, delicate threadlike strands can be seen to form within it. In larger quantities of blood a dense, fine meshwork of such strands, or fibrils, develops, entangling the blood cells, enclosing the liquid part of the blood, and transforming the whole mass into a sticky, jellylike substance. Contraction of the network soon follows, squeezing out of the clot a clear yellowish fluid called *serum*. (The main difference between serum and blood plasma is that the former is no longer capable of clotting). The fibrils of the network are made up of needlelike crystals of an insoluble protein called *fibrin*. This substance is found to come from *fibrinogen*, one of the characteristic soluble blood proteins always present in normal blood plasma. Clotting, then, results from the change of fibrinogen to fibrin. What causes this to happen when blood is shed, when blood vessels are injured, or when sludging occurs?

The full answer to this question cannot yet be given, but the known steps in the process are approximately as follows: The reaction begins by the liberation into the blood plasma of a substance called *prothrombokinase*, which is present in most cells but has its chief source in the blood platelets, which break down and free it under conditions presently to be described. In the presence of calcium ions, which are of normal occurrence in blood plasma, prothrombokinase is changed to the active enzyme *thrombokinase*. Plasma contains another enzyme precursor, *prothrombin*. In the presence of thrombokinase and calcium ions prothrombin is changed to the active enzyme *thrombin*. This enzyme changes the soluble protein *fibrinogen* to the insoluble protein *fibrin*, and clotting results.

Small amounts of prothrombokinase must continually be liberated into the plasma by the normal destruction of cells and platelets, but there is no resultant clotting within the blood vessels. This is prevented by the presence in plasma of minute amounts of at least two protective substances called *antithrombins*. These, in the presence of neutral salts, inactivate the small amounts of thrombin produced and thus prevent the formation of fibrin.

When sludging occurs, or when blood is shed or comes into contact with masses of bacteria or with roughened surfaces in the blood vessels, the platelets first

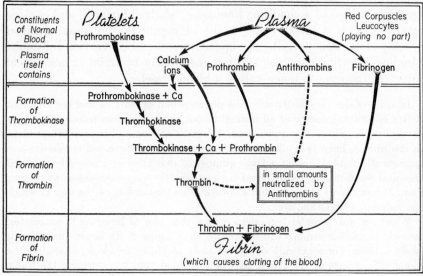

Fig. 6.7. Diagram of the physiological mechanism of blood clotting.

clump together and then disintegrate in great numbers. This releases large amounts of prothrombokinase, which is activated to thrombokinase by calcium ions. The thrombokinase changes prothrombin to thrombin in amounts exceeding those inactivated by the antithrombins, and the excess changes fibrinogen to fibrin. The entire process is shown in the accompanying diagram (Fig. 6.7).

Even this is by no means the whole story. *Vitamin K* in some unknown manner enables the tissues of the liver to produce the prothrombin of the blood. Deficiency of this vitamin diminishes or destroys the ability of the blood to clot. Fortunately in man and various other animals vitamin K is synthesized by the intestinal bacteria, so that deficiencies are rare. In persons showing the congenital "disease" *hemophilia* the blood clots with extreme slowness if at all. This is thought to be caused by failure of the platelets to yield prothrombokinase in sufficient quantity, either because of their small numbers or because they do not disintegrate so easily as in normal individuals. Local application of snake venom to a wound destroys the platelets and thus sets in motion the clotting process. Hemophilia is transmitted through the female (who is not affected) to the male descendants by a mechanism which is discussed in our account of genetics.

DEFENSE AGAINST DISEASE-PRODUCING ORGANISMS

Although the circulatory system plays a major role in defense against disease, it is by no means the sole agency. Blood, skin, and the tissues in general all play a part, and we shall need to consider the defensive mechanisms of the body as a coordinated whole.

The microorganisms capable of producing disease are myriad and ever-present, ready to invade the body at any opportunity. They include bacteria, fungi, protozoa, and the quasi-living viruses. Many of them normally live in the outer environment, and are only casual or accidental invaders. Others can multiply only in the human body or in the bodies of man and other animals, and some of these have insect or other hosts that aid in their transmission. These microorganisms produce their injurious effects in two ways: Some of them, like the diptheria and tetanus organisms, liberate poisonous substances called *toxins*. Others, including many kinds of streptococci and staphylococci, the typhoid bacilli, and the bacillus of tuberculosis, produce their effects by growing in the tissues and thereby interfering with normal cell life.

The body has multiple defenses against invasion by microorganisms. The first of these is a sort of general chemical defense called *immunity*. The newborn baby has no immunity save that which it gained passively from the mother's circulatory system. But as soon as it enters the world it comes into contact with a multitude of microorganisms and begins to fight off their attacks. In repelling each invasion the tissues develop substances (or the capacity to produce substances) that are specific antagonists of the invading cells, and these substances become available for fighting later invasions by the same type of organism.

Many or all of the cells and tissues of the body show these *immunity reactions*—and not merely to viruses and living microorganisms. The same type of response is elicited by suspensions of dead bacteria, or by any kind of foreign protein such as egg albumin or a protein mixture such as horse serum. Evidently the production of immunity is a chemical phenomenon. Any type of substance capable of calling forth this response is called an *antigen*, and the substance produced by the cells which reacts with the antigen and renders it harmless is called an *antibody*. When the antigen is a toxin, the antibody is called an *antitoxin*. The relation between antigen and antibody is highly specific; a given antibody is fully effective only against the antigen that produced it. An animal that has developed antibodies against particular antigens is said to be *immunized* against those antigens.

Now let us consider the various stages and events in the history of an infection—an invasion by microorganisms. We have already noted the importance of the skin as a protective layer. Not only does the unbroken surface of the skin interpose a mechanical barrier to entry, but its secretions have a bactericidal effect. Let us say that a group of microorganisms enters the skin tissues through an abrasion. If the body has no natural immunity to them, they may rapidly gain access to the circulatory system and be carried through the body, to multiply undisturbed; this is what happens with the syphilis organism. Ordinarily, however, if they are at all common, the body possesses some immunity to them from previous contacts. In this event the first of the protective mechanisms comes into play—*localization* of the infection. The invading organisms are held within the area of attack until reinforcements are brought by the circulation in sufficient quantity to destroy them. All of the tissues of the body have this power of localization to some extent, but the skin is pre-eminent in this ability, as would be expected.

Immunization enormously increases the capacity of tissues to localize antigens or antigen-containing microorganisms, as Kahn has shown by an ingenious experiment. Diphtheria toxin injected into the blood stream of a rabbit soon kills the animal, but death can be prevented by a simultaneous injection of sufficient antitoxin in horse serum. However, rabbits which have been immunized to horse serum localize it in the tissue into which it is injected, and since this incidentally prevents the diphtheria antitoxin from reaching the blood these rabbits die. The amount of horse serum antitoxin which they can thus localize is a function of the degree of their immunization. Nonimmunized rabbits could localize in the skin only 15 to 20 units of horse serum antitoxin. By contrast, rabbits which had received two previous injections of horse serum could localize 1,000 to 1,500 units, while four or five previous injections would give a localizing capacity of 3,500 units. Tissues other than skin had smaller localizing capacities, which were similarly increased by immunization.

Just how tissues are able thus to block the spread of antigens and of antigen-containing microorganisms is not known, but there is reason to believe that immunized cells unite with the antigens by some sort of colloid chemical bond and thus hold them fixed. If a person with natural immunity to streptococci develops a streptococcic sore throat, it probably means that the surface cells of the throat, upon contact with the microorganisms, have bound them chemically and thus kept them from entering the blood stream. These cells undergo injury and perhaps death to protect the body as a whole.

The moment tissue injury occurs in a given area of the body, a chain of events takes place aimed at destroying the substance responsible for the injury and healing the injured tissue. *Inflammation* occurs. This includes the dilation of the capillaries in the area to increase blood supply, the accumulation of fluids and phagocyte cells from the blood, and the formation of a fibrous wall around the area of infection. If the invading microorganisms or the antigens are destroyed and the injured cells repaired, the inflammation subsides; but if the cells in the area are killed, a boil or abscess is formed—a boil if the infection is in the skin, an abscess if it is in deeper tissues. Sometimes it happens that the invaders overcome the localizing action of the tissues and spread until they reach the blood stream.

The defensive mechanisms of the circulatory system comprise mechanical readjustments of blood and lymph flow, fixed and mobile phagocytic cells, and chemical responses. We have just noted that the capillaries of infected areas dilate, bringing more blood to aid the local tissue cells and causing the characteristic reddening implied by the word "inflammation." The lymph vessels also dilate, and tissue fluid accumulates in the inflamed area.

The *phagocytes* include the motile white blood cells, or leucocytes, and the fixed phagocytes of spleen, liver, and lymph nodes. The leucocytes are "shock troops" that seek out the invading cells. As they are brought into the vicinity of the infection by the blood stream, they squeeze their way out between the cells that form the thin capillary walls, and move amoebalike to the infected area. There they ingest the foreign cells, and in so doing generally pay with their lives. Their dead bodies, along with dead tissue cells and lymph, form the pus that develops in an infected wound. If the infection is small the dead cells are removed by other leucocytes, but if the destruction of phagocytes and tissues is extensive the pus may drain to the surface. Prolonged or extensive infection stimulates the body to rapid production of leucocytes. The resultant high "white count" of the blood may be used by the physician to diagnose the existence of infection and to gain some notion of its severity.

The *fixed phagocytes* that line the blood and lymph channels in the spleen, liver, and lymph nodes remove foreign cells and antigen particles from blood and lymph and thus filter the blood. They constitute a part of the inner defense line that comes into operation when infection fails to be localized and reaches the circulatory system.

The *chemical defenses* of the blood are a part of the general immunity reactions common to all tissues. The blood plasma becomes charged with antibodies produced by cells. These antibodies include many and varied substances: *antitoxins* that neutralize toxins; *precipitins* that unite with antigens to form insoluble and therefore harmless precipitates; *agglutinins* that cause the cells upon which they act to become clumped or glued together, immobilizing and weakening or destroying them; and *cytolisins*, which dissolve the cells against which they are specific. One of the most characteristic properties of antibodies is their specificity. As we have previously mentioned, each is produced in response to a particular antigen, and is fully effective only against that antigen, though it may react to some extent with chemically related substances. The causative agents of diphtheria, smallpox, measles, typhus, yellow fever, and other diseases stimulate the production of antibodies which are highly specific and in most cases give partial or complete immunity against subsequent attacks. The action of the blood antibodies supplements that of the antibodies present in the invaded tissues and becomes of utmost importance in those instances where microorganisms or antigens gain access to the blood itself.

In present-day medical practice two main types of immunity are recognized—*active immunity*, developed by the body in response to entry of antigens or antigen-containing microorganisms, and *passive immunity*, produced by injecting into the body a serum containing antibodies or antitoxins actively produced by some laboratory animal. Active immunity is comparatively lasting and in many instances permanent; passive immunity endures only so long as the foreign antibodies or antitoxins persist in the person receiving them.

The common phenomenon of *allergy* is an aspect of tissue immunity that deserves brief mention. Many persons become "sensitized" to specific antigens to such a degree that exposure to minute amounts of these substances produces disproportionately large reactions. The symptoms are varied and may include hives, skin rash or inflammation, eczema, and asthma. If the antigen is injected into the blood stream, death from immunologic shock may follow. The causes of allergy are still obscure, but we may quote Kahn on this point. He says: "Neither immunity nor allergy can be fully understood without realizing the tremendous burden of defense carried on by the exposed tissues of the body. Through evolutionary ages these tissues had the task of warding off microorganisms, and preventing their entrance into the blood stream and into the deeper tissues. Is it not significant then that these surface tissues should be largely involved in allergic disturbances of man? . . . Like over-vigilant guards, the surface cells begin to treat harmless substances as though they were harmful microorganisms, and react with great intensity on slight provocation. . . . It would appear that the allergic person suffers from hyperactivity of the immunologic function."

CHAPTER VII

COORDINATION AND CONTROL:
(1) THE NERVOUS SYSTEM

Thus far we have been concerned chiefly with the parts of the body that account for most of its bulk and form and that carry on the greater part of its metabolic activities. We have seen that one of these functional units, the circulatory system, provides an important measure of coordination by serving all parts of the body with rapid and continuous transportation of supplies and products. In this and in the following chapter we now turn to a consideration of two more specialized coordinating agencies—the nervous system and the endocrine glands. These unite the body into a single working entity, the individual; they control the pattern of its development and regulate the functioning of its parts; and they enable the individual to make the adjustments required by changes in its internal state and external environment.

The two coordinating systems are to a degree independent of one another, and each has its own particular functions and responsibilities. The *nervous system* is especially concerned with immediate adjustments to external and internal conditions, with causing appropriate responses to specific stimulations, and with the regulation of various precise vital activities. It is also the seat of sensation, consciousness, memory, and intelligence. The other system is made up of the interconnected and interacting *endocrine glands*. It is more particularly concerned with general body states and adjustments to internal changes and especially with the maintenance of balance between various phases of metabolic processes. In spite of these differences and the very unlike structure and mode of functioning of the two systems, they are closely integrated, and most of the activities of the body are, in consequence, subjected to a dual nervous and endocrine control.

It is common knowledge that the brain and spinal cord, encased in and protected by the skull and backbone, exercise a high degree of control over the various parts of the body. Together with the nerves, they constitute the nervous system, which is probably the most complex part of the entire body. Although much of the more intricate and finer detail of the functioning of this system is beyond our present knowledge, the elements of nervous structure and processes are relatively simple and clear-cut.

MAJOR FEATURES OF THE NERVOUS SYSTEM

Two main divisions of the nervous system are generally recognized: the *central nervous system*, consisting of the brain and spinal cord; and the *peripheral nervous system*, which includes all the nervous tissue outside the brain and spinal cord and is made up largely of the nerves that extend from the central nervous system to all parts of the body.

The brain is a large organ contained within the cranium. It weighs approximately 49 ounces, on the average, and has a volume of between 1,200 and 1,500 cc. By far the largest and most conspicuous portion of the brain is the greatly convoluted *cerebrum*. As seen from above, the cerebrum is rounded oval in outline and is divided by a deep median fissure into two lateral hemispheres. Issuing from the undersurface of the cerebrum is the lower part of the *brain stem*. This part of the brain is rather complex in structure, but we may recognize within it four regions. Named from above downward, these are the *thalamus*, the *midbrain*, the *pons*, and the *medulla*. Another convoluted structure, the *cerebellum*, is attached to the posterior (dorsal) face of the brain stem.

The **spinal cord** is a long, relatively slender cylinder that lies in, but only partially fills, the canal formed by the vertebrae. At the upper end, it merges with the brain stem by way of the medulla; in the opposite direction, it terminates at the level of the first lumbar vertebra.

Nerves arise from both the brain and the spinal cord. Those issuing from the brain are called *cranial nerves;* they arise from the lower or ventral surface of the brain, and in man there are 12 pairs of them. These nerves chiefly supply the head and neck. Some of them, like the olfactory, optic, and auditory nerves, carry sensations from specialized sense-receiving organs (nose, eyes, ears, etc.) to the brain; others carry impulses out from the brain or combine both functions. The tenth pair of cranial nerves, known as the *vagus nerves* (Latin, *vago*, "to wander") arise from the medulla and carry impulses to and from many of the visceral organs and the blood vessels. They play an important part in the unconscious reflex control of visceral and circulatory functioning, as has already been noted in connection with the heart.

The *spinal nerves* arise from the lateral aspects of the spinal cord and supply the rest of the body. There are 31 pairs of spinal nerves, leaving the cord at regular intervals. With some minor exceptions, there is one pair of spinal nerves for each vertebra in the spinal column; the nerves alternate with the vertebrae, each pair leaving the spinal column through an intervertebral opening. These nerves differ considerably among themselves in size, those supplying the arms and legs, for example, being much

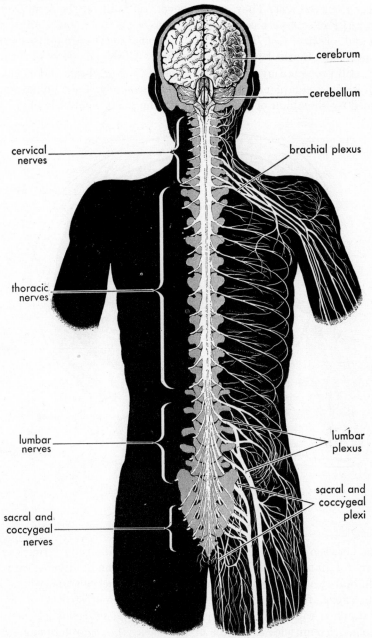

FIG. 7.1. The nervous system from the rear.

longer than the rest. They are, however, all built on the same common
pattern. Each nerve has two connections with the spinal cord, a *dorsal
root* and a *ventral root*. The roots of the spinal nerves are quite short and
are protected by the bone of the vertebrae. Along the course of the dorsal
root, still protected by the bony tissues of the vertebrae, there occurs on
each a slight enlargement, the *dorsal-root ganglion*. Each spinal nerve is
formed by the union of its two roots at the point where the nerve issues

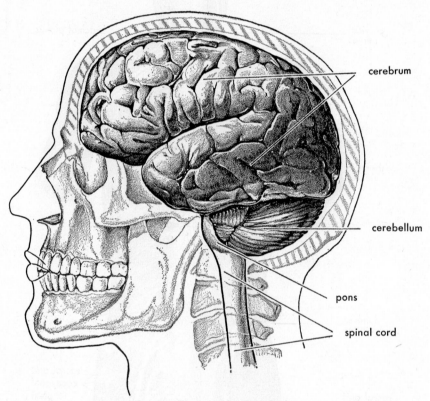

cerebrum

cerebellum

pons

spinal cord

Fig. 7.2. The left side of the brain.

from between the vertebrae. The common trunk thus formed is very
short, for immediately beyond the spinal column it divides into three
main branches, the *rami*. Each ramus is a great nerve trunk which, like a
main artery, divides again and again until the remotest parts of the body
are supplied with minute nerve endings. The *dorsal ramus* of each nerve
supplies the muscles and skin of the back; the *ventral ramus* (usually
much the largest of the three) supplies the muscles and skin of the
lateral and ventral parts of the body wall and the arms and legs. The
third branch, the *ramus communicans*, supplies the smooth muscles,

glands, blood vessels, visceral organs, etc. The motor nerves of the smooth muscles, blood vessels, and viscera constitute the so-called *autonomic nervous system*.

Each nerve is composed of an enormous number of *nerve fibers* lying side by side like the separate wires in a telephone cable. The fibers in a nerve are collected into bundles and are joined together by a little connective tissue. As the nerve extends away from its roots and begins to branch, the fiber bundles and eventually the individual fibers part company and disperse to their various destinations. Some of them are connected to sense organs and carry information to the spinal cord and brain; some go to voluntary muscles causing them to contract; and still others go to, or come from, the smooth muscles and internal organs. Each nerve fiber is a living thread of astonishing delicacy and variable length, attaining in some instances a length of several feet.

STRUCTURAL AND FUNCTIONAL ELEMENTS

The nerve cell or neuron.   The fundamental unit of all nervous structure and function is the nerve cell, which, because of its unique nature, has been given the special name *neuron*. These cells differ from other cells in that they project into long, slender fibers of living substance. Each neuron is composed of a cell body containing a nucleus and of one or more filamentous processes. In the typical motor neuron, usually cited as an example, the processes are of two sorts—at one side an elongated *axon*, which is usually unbranched except near its tip, and at the other side several shorter, branched *dendrites*. Axons and dendrites may be exceedingly long (several feet in the case of numerous spinal nerves), and many of them are encased in a sheath of whitish, fatty material (*myelin*) that distinguishes the myelinated white matter of the nervous system from the nonmyelinated gray matter. The cell bodies themselves and the extreme tips of the axons and dendrites are never covered with this white sheath, and many parts of the central nervous system and of the autonomic portion of the peripheral system appear to lack it altogether.

The nerve impulse.   When a neuron is stimulated at any point on its surface, a nerve impulse results and spreads to all parts of the cell. Two different processes seem to be at work in the production of such an impulse. One involves a small amount of physiological activity on the part of the cell and is capable of causing gradual fatigue of the neuron. The other, which requires the presence of oxygen, is apparently a purely physical, reversible change that can be indefinitely repeated without fatigue. Theory and experiment strongly suggest that it depends upon the formation of a thin colloidal membrane over the surface of the neuron. Destruction of this membrane at any point (stimulation) results in a difference in electrical potential between the exposed (excited) and filmed portions. An electric current flows from the passive to the active region, and this causes breakdown of the film in the adjacent region, which thereupon itself becomes active. A wave of excitation is thus propagated throughout the cell. In its wake the nerve fiber is left briefly insensitive, but as soon as oxidation has restored the film, the neuron is ready to respond in the same way to the next stimulus. The restoration is very swift, so that impulses can follow one another with great rapidity. The rate at which an impulse progresses along an axon or dendrite varies markedly in different types of nerves. It has usually been measured at between 20 and 100 meters per second, the slower rates being more

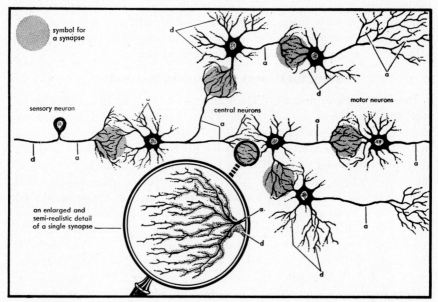

Fig. 7.3. Diagram of seven neurons, showing the cell bodies (containing nuclei), the axons (a), dendrites (d), and synapses between neurons (shaded). (*Redrawn from Gates, Elementary Psychology, by permission The Macmillan Company.*)

characteristic of nerve fibers that run to the internal organs. The nature of the nerve impulse is apparently the same in all nerves, regardless of the kind of stimulus that provokes it.

The synapse.   A nerve impulse runs along a chain of neurons like a series of explosions, each neuron "touching off" the next. Transmission occurs at the *synapse* or place where the axon of one neuron touches the cell body or dendrites of another. Upon excitation the axon produces a tiny amount of a substance, acetylcholine, that sets off an impulse in the second neuron. An impulse can therefore be transmitted across a synapse *in only one direction—from axon to cell body or dendrite.* The action of the synapse as a one-way valve for impulses is fundamental to the operation of the nervous system.

Ganglia. A ganglion is a group of nerve-cell bodies held together with a small amount of connective tissue. Ganglia are found in connection with the autonomic nervous system and are present as part of the dorsal root of each spinal nerve. Ganglia are outside the spinal cord and brain.

Nerve centers or "nuclei." These are groups of nerve-cell bodies *within* the spinal cord or brain.

SENSATION AND THE SENSES

The central nervous system is constantly receiving impulses from a large variety of sources. In addition to the sensory impressions received from the organs of sense—*smell, taste, hearing, sight,* and *balance*—there are a number of general *sense receptors* distributed to all surfaces of the body, where they are located in the dermis of the skin. This latter group includes receptors for *touch, pressure, heat, cold,* and *pain.* Another group of receptors ending in the muscles, joints, and tendons bring in *kinesthetic* information that has to do with the *stress, position,* and *tension* of the various body parts. Still other receptors in the visceral system give rise to impulses that do not ordinarily affect consciousness.

Each of these numerous kinds of receptors, however it be stimulated, can convey only its own particular type of information. Stimulation of a touch receptor can produce only a sensation of touch; stimulation of the retina or optic nerve can produce only a sensation of light, even though it is an electric needle or a knife that has produced the stimulation. Since all nerve impulses appear to be identical, we are forced to conclude that the impulses received over any given receptor neuron can be interpreted in only one specific way; that, however this neuron is stimulated, the nerve impulse that results can produce only the type of sensation normally received by its receptor. If the point of a rather blunt needle is brought gently against the skin, only a touch receptor will be stimulated; if it is pressed harder, pressure receptors will also be stimulated, and a sense of pressure is combined with or supersedes the sensation of touch; if the needle is still more strongly pressed against the finger, the somewhat less sensitive pain receptors are stimulated, and a sensation of pain[1] results. We know, of course, from everyday experience that various objects may stimulate two or more types of sense receptors at one time, as when the handling of a small piece of ice gives rise to sensations of both cold and touch.

---

[1] The nerve endings, which, when stimulated, produce a sensation of pain, are numerous and widely distributed over the surface of the body but end nakedly. Touch, pressure, cold and heat receptors, on the other hand, end in capsules (or, in the case of some touch receptors, at the bases of the hairs) that appear to make them much more sensitive to their specific sources of stimulation.

Smell. The cell bodies of the olfactory nerves are located in the mucous membrane that lines the upper parts of the nasal chambers; their axons extend thence to the lower part of the cerebrum. Stimulation of these neurons by volatile substances causes them to produce and transmit impulses that are perceived as the sensation of smell.

Taste. Unlike those of the olfactory nerves, the cell bodies of the taste nerves are situated far from the point of stimulation, in the ganglia of three cranial nerves. Fibers from these neurons extend to the tongue, where they make contact with receptor cells located in taste buds. Stimulation of the receptors by various dissolved substances gives rise to impulses that are perceived as the four sensations *sweet, sour, salty,* and *bitter.* The receptors are so localized that the tip of the tongue is most sensitive to sweet; the sides, to sour; the sides and tip, to salty; and the back, to bitter. The senses of smell and taste are intimately associated; both respond to chemical stimulation, and a large part of what we think of as the taste of substances is in reality their smell.

Sight. The cell bodies of the optic nerves are located in the *retina,* which forms the innermost layer of the eyeball and extends from the point where the optic nerve enters the eye to the region of the lens. Outside the retina is a black layer, the *choroid coat,* containing many blood vessels and continuous with the *iris* that surrounds the pupil. The iris is furnished with muscles that regulate the size of the pupil and thus govern the amount of light that reaches the retina. The outermost layer of the eyeball is the hard and semirigid *sclerotic coat.* Anteriorly, the sclerotic coat is continuous with the transparent *cornea.* The *lens* is located just back of the iris and is held in place by ligaments. These ligaments divide the interior cavity of the eyeball into two compartments —a smaller outer space between the lens and the cornea, filled with a watery fluid (the *aqueous humor*), and a larger chamber between the lens and the retina, filled with a more viscid substance (the *vitreous humor*). Light entering the eye is refracted by the spherically curved cornea and also by the lens, so that images are sharply focused on the retina. The position and degree of convexity of the lens are regulated by the involuntary *ciliary muscles,* which extend forward from the region of the ligaments of the lens. The ligaments are normally under tension and hold the lens in a flattened shape adapted to distant vision. When the ciliary muscles contract, they relieve the tension on the lens ligaments, and the elastic lens takes on a more rounded shape adapted to close vision. With increasing age the lens stiffens, resulting in loss of accommodation.

The light receptor cells of the eye are the *rods* and *cones.* Peculiarly enough they are not situated on the side of the retina exposed to the light, but next to the choroid coat under layers of nerve fibers, blood vessels, and connective tissue, and their sensitive ends are turned *away* from the light. Each receptor is composed of an inner segment much like an ordinary nerve cell and a rod- or cone-shaped light-sensitive tip. The *cones* are the organs of vision in bright light and also of color vision. The *rods* provide a special apparatus for vision in dim light, and their excitation yields only neutral gray sensations.

The change from cone to rod vision, like that from "slow" to "fast" photographic film, involves a change from a fine- to a coarse-grained mosaic. The cones are not smaller than the rods, but they act individually, while the rods act in large clumps. Each cone connects with an individual nerve fiber leading to the

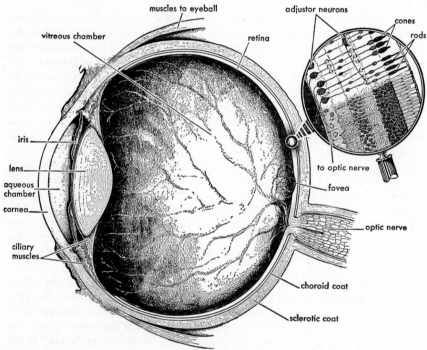

Fig. 7.4. A section through the eye, with enlarged detail of the retina (the upper portion diagrammatic).

brain, while large clusters of rods have but a single nerve fiber. The capacity of rods for image formation is correspondingly coarse. In very dim light only the rods function, the relatively insensitive cones remaining unstimulated. At moderately low intensities of light, about 1,000 times the minimum intensity to which the eye responds, the cones begin to function, bringing a dilute sensation of color. Over an intermediate range of intensities rods and cones operate together, but with increasing brightness the cones come to dominate vision. Whether the rods cease to function in bright light is not known, but they make no perceptible contribution to vision.

The tips of the rods contain a light-sensitive pigment called visual purple, or *rhodopsin,* which bleaches upon exposure to light. As we have already seen, it is formed from vitamin A, deficiency in which causes night blindness. The chemical change caused by light in this pigment is apparently the origin of the nerve impulse responsible for the sensation of light. How color vision is caused is unknown. Normal human color vision seems to be compounded of three kinds of responses, and is therefore called trichromatic or three-color vision. The three kinds of response call for at least three kinds of cones differing in their sensitivity to the various parts of the spectrum. Presumably they contain three different light-sensitive pigments, but this is still a matter of surmise. We do know that a cone or rod is excited by light to yield either its maximal response or none at all; like a muscle fiber it follows the "all-or-none" rule. We also know that to produce this effect in a rod—and perhaps in a cone—only a single quantum of light need be absorbed.

The lens of the eye is well corrected for spherical aberration but contains no correction for chromatic or color aberration. This is in part compensated for by three devices. The first is the yellow lens, which filters out all the ultraviolet and near ultraviolet part of the spectrum in which the color error is greatest. The second is the fact that as rod vision decreases and cone vision increases with brighter light, there is a shift in sensitivity toward the red, with the maximum sensitivity passing from the blue-green (rods) to the yellow-green (cones). Color aberration is less toward the red end of the spectrum. And finally, man (along with apes and monkeys) is peculiar in having a yellow patch on the retina opposite the center of the lens—the *macula lutea*. Its pigmentation lies as a yellow screen over the light receptors of the central retina, subtending a visual angle of some 5 to 10 degrees. The yellow pigment is *xanthophyll*, common in many plant tissues. This pigment takes up the absorption of light in the violet and blue regions of the spectrum just where absorption by the lens falls off. Thus the macula lutea removes for the central retina the remaining regions of the spectrum for which the color error is high. In effect, the human eye, unable to correct for color aberration, throws away those portions of the spectrum that would cause most difficulty.

One final feature of the retina requires mention. At the center of the yellow spot is a depression, the *fovea*, the function of which is to spread apart the light rays by allowing them to fall upon its inclined sides. This permits the rays to be distributed over more cone cells (the only ones present in the whole area of the macula lutea) and thus has the effect of increasing the fineness of "grain" of the retina. The fovea lies at the central point of the visual field, and accounts for the great acuity of vision in this tiny region. Without its aid we would be unable to distinguish such fine detail as is required for reading small print or observing the structure of a cell beneath the microscope.

The rod and cone neurons make synapses with chains of adjustor neurons within the retina. The last member of each chain gives off an axon that leaves the eyeball by way of the optic (second cranial) nerve and so connects with the midbrain and, through thalamic synapses, with the cerebral cortex.

Hearing. The ear is a double sense organ. Part of it has to do with hearing, the other part with static sensations. Sounds (air vibrations) cause the *tympanic membrane*, or eardrum, to vibrate in resonance with

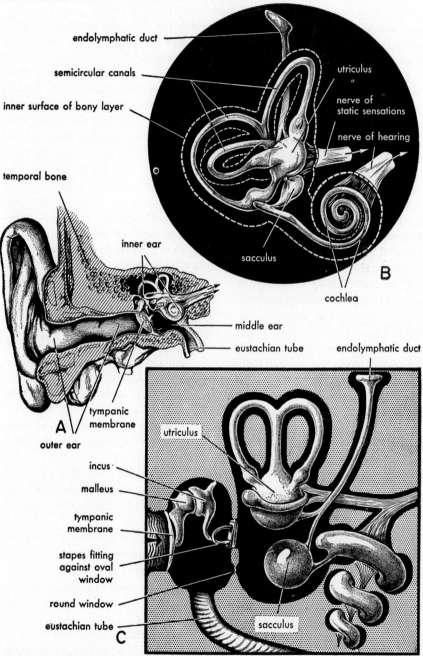

FIG. 7.5. The human ear. *A*, section through the ear. *B*, enlarged detail of the inner ear. *C*, a diagram to show the functional relations of the middle and inner ear.

the pulsations of the air. This membrane separates the canal of the external ear from the cavity of the *middle ear*. The air pressure in the latter is kept in equilibrium with that of the outer air by the *eustachian tube*, which connects the middle ear with the pharynx.

Vibrations of the tympanic membrane are transmitted across the middle ear to the *inner ear* by three small bones—the *malleus, incus,* and *stapes*. The last of these fits against a membrane-filled opening, the *oval window*, through which it sets into vibratory motion the fluid *perilymph* that surrounds and in part fills the structures of the inner ear. A second membrane-filled opening, the *round window*, makes the motion of the perilymph possible by bulging out when the stapes presses the oval window in and springing back when the pressure is relaxed.

The pulsations in the perilymph stimulate auditory receptor neurons located within a coiled structure called the *cochlea*, from its resemblance to a snail shell. Essentially the cochlea consists of three closely applied tubes. The central one of these contains the elongated *organ of Corti* in which lie the auditory receptors. It ends blindly at the tip of the cochlea but at the base is narrowly connected to a fluid-filled reservoir, the *sacculus;* the fluid *endolymph* which fills the sacculus and tube is entirely separated from the surrounding perilymph. The two outer tubes of the cochlea are really the two arms of a perilymph-filled loop that starts at the oval window and ends at the round window. The organ of Corti is separated from the second half of this loop only by a thin membrane. Vibrations in any part of this membrane stimulate the receptors at that point, and since the width of the membrane diminishes gradually from the base to the tip of the cochlea, sounds of different wave lengths (pitch) cause different parts of the membrane to vibrate. The nerve impulses sent to the brain from receptors located along the organ of Corti thus correspond to different frequencies of vibration.

The impulses from the auditory receptors travel over the auditory (8th cranial) nerves to the medulla. Thence they pass to the auditory center of the midbrain and on by way of the thalamus to the cerebral cortex, where they result in sound perception.

Static sensations. The part of the ear that gives rise to static sensations consists of three *semicircular canals* in the inner ear. One is horizontal, the other two are vertical, and each is situated in a plane approximately at right angles to the planes of the other two. The two vertical canals stand at an angle of about 45 degrees with the median plane of the body.

The ends of all three canals open into a sac called the *utriculus*, which is narrowly connected with the sacculus mentioned above. The endolymph, that fills the middle tube of the cochlea and the sacculus, also fills the utriculus and the semicircular canals.

The static sensation receptors fall into two functional groups. Those of the first group are stimulated by rotational movements of the head, and are located in enlargements at one end of each of the semicircular canals. The receptor cells have hairlike projections that extend into the cavity of the canal. When the head is turned in any direction, the semicircular canals move with it, but inertia causes the endolymph within the canals to tend to remain at rest. Any rotation having a component parallel to the plane of one or more of the canals will therefore cause a movement of the endolymph *relative to the canal* and thus stimulate the projecting ends of the receptor hair cells.

Information concerning fixed positions of the head comes from the other group of receptors. Patches of hair cells are located in the walls of the sacculus and utriculus. They are stimulated by the position of a gelatinous mass which rests upon them—the *otolithic membrane*. This shifts its position as a result of gravity when the head is moved, and remains displaced as long as the head keeps its new position.

These two sets of receptors (as well as the sound receptors located in the cochlea) stimulate afferent[1] neurons whose axons go to the medulla by way of the eighth pair of nerves. Unlike the auditory stimuli, those from the static receptors are routed primarily to the cerebellum. Here they are correlated with stimuli from *kinesthetic receptors* located in muscles, tendons, and joints, thus providing information about the position and movements of the rest of the body relative to the head, and making possible such actions as balancing the body. These two sets of afferent neurons make synapses in the cerebellum with neuron chains ending in muscles, so that this part of the brain is largely responsible for motor coordination, much of which is accomplished without the necessity of conscious control. Only occasionally do static and kinesthetic sensations rise to the level of consciousness.

THE NERVOUS MECHANISM AND THE BRAIN

Our knowledge and inferences as to the functioning of the human nervous system come largely from three sources: (1) its *structure*, as determined by both gross and microscopic dissection; (2) *experiment* on living animals, including many types of experiments with human subjects as well as those that must be confined to laboratory animals; and (3) *subjective observation* of one's own mental and nervous functioning. Each of these has inherent advantages and limitations, and much of our considerable, although still highly incomplete, knowledge of how the nervous system works is due to pooling the information derived from each type of observation.

Any detailed summary of what is known of the functioning of the nerv-

---

[1] Afferent—carrying impulses *to* the central nervous system; see p. 116.

ous system would entail a preliminary study of the tremendously intricate details of neural anatomy. This would lie far beyond the scope of our treatment. Moreover, all our present-day knowledge falls far short of describing, to say nothing of explaining, such higher neural functions as those we call memory, consciousness, volition or "willing," and the whole complex that we vaguely describe as "intelligence." What follows can be no more than a summary of some of the simpler aspects of the functioning of the nervous system.

First-level response—the spinal cord. An animal that has been deprived of its head may be capable for a short time of showing response to stimuli. The physiologist often prepares an experimental animal by removing the part of the brain that has to do with consciousness and "willing." One of the simplest (and most limited) preparations is made by snipping off the head and brain of a frog and leaving the rest of the body intact. In half an hour or so, when the severed nerves in the cord have had time to recover from the "shock," the animal will still show a considerable variety of actions. If one of the toes is pinched, the leg will be lifted and the toe pulled away from the pinch. If a drop of some irritant, a weak acid, for instance, is placed on the animal's chest, it will brush the spot with its hand, and if its arms are now held immovable, it will bring up one of its feet to brush across the spot; if that foot is held, it will often then use the other foot. Such action is carried out without aid from the brain, but it does involve both the nerves and the spinal cord. The term *reflex action* is applied to responses of this order, and they are carried out by means of the reflex arc.

The reflex arc. A simple spinal reflex arc is diagramed in Fig. 7.6. Here an outline of a cross section of the spinal cord shows three diagrammatic neurons. The neuron with its cell body located in the dorsal-root ganglion is a *sensory, afferent* (Latin, "carrying to") neuron, with its exceptionally long dendrite[1] extending to a sense receptor (let us say a pain receptor in this case) in the skin; the axon of this sensory neuron extends into the cord, where it makes a synapse with one of the dendrites of an *adjustor* neuron, which lies wholly within the cord. The axon of this adjustor neuron makes a synapse with one of the dendrites of the third neuron, a *motor, efferent* (Latin, "carrying from") neuron in one of the "ventral horns" of the gray matter of the cord. The axon from this neuron extends out from the cord to end in skeletal muscle fibers. Here is one of the simplest nerve sequences that can provide for the reception, transmission, and "delivery" of a nerve impulse.

---

[1] Unfortunately there is considerable divergence in the definition of many terms that apply to the nervous system (and other body parts); this afferent process of the spinal sensory nerve is physiologically and embryologically a true dendrite, although very different in appearance from the dendrites of a motor neuron.

Suppose that the pain receptor is in the skin of the right forefinger and that the axon of the motor neuron ends in a muscle that retracts this finger. Any stimulus, a pinprick, for instance, that stimulates the pain receptor will initiate a nervous impulse at that point. This sweeps up the dendrite of the sensory nerve, passes on into its axon, and makes a synapse with the dendrite of the adjustor neuron. The nerve impulse now moves across this neuron and into its axon and makes a second synapse with the dendrite of the motor neuron; it passes into the axon of this neuron and thus reaches the muscle fibers, which immediately contract to jerk the finger away from the pin. The whole process, from pinprick to jerk, requires but a small fraction of a second, but it has involved all the events enumerated above.

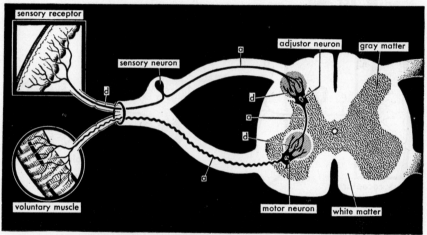

Fig. 7.6. Diagram of a simple reflex arc. (a) Axon; (d) dendrite.

Any chain of neurons leading from a receptor to an effector (in a muscle or gland) is a *reflex arc;* and the action that results from a stimulus received through such an arc is a *reflex action.* Many reflex arcs—hence much reflex action—are far more complicated than the one described above. They may involve many neurons and traverse long distances through the brain and spinal cord. Figure 7.6 includes only three neurons (actually many thousands would be shown in any thin slice from the cord), but it will be noted that the tips of all the axons are finely branched and that both the adjustor and efferent neurons have a number of dendrites. This branching provides for many possible synapses, other than the two that are shown. It is also obvious that the greater the number of connecting or adjustor neurons involved the greater will be the possible variety of synapses among different neurons.

If we exclude the autonomic system and the connections with sensory receptor cells, all synapses occur within the central nervous system—*i.e.*

within the spinal cord or brain. In these organs we find a large variety of "levels" at which synapses may take place. We have already seen that a number (really a rather large number) of reflex arcs can occur within a "spinal reflex" frog. Synapses may connect a receptor and an effector through the dorsal and ventral roots of the same nerve, or they may connect the left dorsal root of a given nerve with the right ventral root of its mate, thus involving the crossing of the spinal cord. Other synapses may unite the afferent nerve of one dorsal root with one or more efferent neurons in spinal nerves above or below the one that received the stimulus. The spinal cord thus provides for a great number and variety of neural

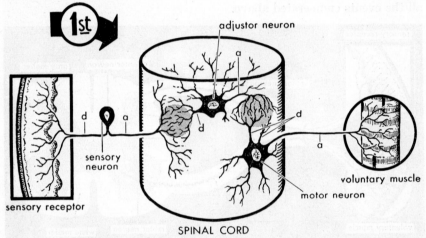

Fig. 7.7. The mechanism of first-level response. (a) Axon; (d) dendrite. (*Modified from Gates, Elementary Psychology, by permission The Macmillan Company.*)

connections, and some of the white matter of the cord is formed by fibers of neurons that connect the various levels of the cord with one another.

Most of the fibers of the white matter of the cord, however, connect with the brain and here provide for still further synapses.

The autonomic nervous system. There is another division of the nervous system that we have as yet scarcely mentioned. As was stated above, the *ramus communicans*, leading out from a spinal nerve, contains the nerve fibers that supply the visceral organs, including smooth muscle, blood vessels, and glandular tissue. The fibers of this ramus *do not go directly* to the visceral organs, but make synapses in the autonomic ganglia, especially those of the *autonomic trunks*. The latter are of a pair of large nerve tracts that lie along the dorsal wall of the body cavity, parallel to and on either side of the aorta. There are 24 ganglia along the course of each autonomic trunk, and the two trunks join in a common ganglion in the lower abdomen.

These autonomic trunks and ganglia provide pathways and connections for reflexes that are semi-independent of the central nervous system. Nerve fibers from the ramus communicans enter the autonomic ganglia and either make synapses with neurons that lie wholly in the autonomic division or pass along the autonomic tracts to various visceral receptors. Apparently all efferent impulses that reach the viscera from the central

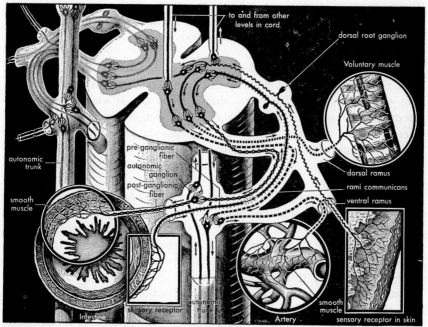

FIG. 7.8. A stereogram to show some of the relations between the central and autonomic nervous systems. The rectangular insets show details of receptors, the circular insets show effector endings. The cord is sectioned at the level of a pair of spinal nerves. Note that each autonomic trunk bears a ganglion at this level.

nervous system must traverse at least two efferent neurons, a *preganglionic* neuron, the body of which lies in the central nervous system, and a *postganglionic* neuron, which lies wholly within the autonomic system and relays the impulse to the effector. In addition, many purely autonomic neurons make direct connections between the various ganglia of the paired autonomic trunks; other autonomic fibers connect the trunk ganglia with other and special autonomic ganglia that lie deep within the viscera.

In spite of its name, the autonomic system is not independent but is closely tied to and acts in intimate relation with the central nervous system. Two distinct functional divisions of the autonomic system are

generally recognized. The first, or *sympathetic* division, comprises those
autonomic fibers that arise in the thoracic and lumbar regions of the
spinal cord. The second, or *parasympathetic* division, includes those fibers
that come from the brain and those arising in the sacral region of the
cord. In general, the actions of the sympathetic and parasympathetic
nerves are different, and commonly antagonistic, and the visceral organs
for the most part receive a double (sympathetic and parasympathetic)
autonomic innervation. Thus in the instance of the heart, the vagus nerves
(parasympathetic) slow or inhibit its action, while the cervical sympathetic nerves accelerate the heartbeat. Glands, smooth muscles of the
viscera, and smooth muscles in the blood vessels are under similar dual
nervous control.

Second-level response—the lower brain centers. We have seen
that the simplest known activity of the nervous system is the conduction of the nerve impulse over a simple reflex arc. If we turn once more
to our experimental animal, the frog, we can demonstrate other and
more complex actions. If another specimen is prepared in which the
brain stem and cerebellum are left intact but in which the cerebrum is
removed, more, but not all, of the normal responses of the animal to
external stimuli are possible.

A frog thus deprived of its cerebrum can jump and swim; it can breathe
and swallow. If food is placed in the mouth, it not only will be swallowed
but also will be digested. However, no attempt is made to capture food,
even if the animal is starving; food is not recognized as such. In general,
"decerebrated" animals make no response at all unless the stimulus can
be carried directly to the spinal cord.

Such experiments as these are, of course, out of the question with man;
but the accumulated observations from accidents, operations, and dis-
eased nervous systems and from a considerable variety of noninjurious
and nonpainful experiments on volunteer subjects show the same results
in man.

We have seen that the brain is composed of the large cerebral hemispheres and the less conspicuous cerebellum and brain stem—this latter
portion being divided into the medulla, pons, midbrain, and thalamus.
We can get a better idea of the relationships of these parts by examining
the median surface of a brain that has been divided longitudinally into
right and left halves. Such a section is shown in Fig. 7.10. Here it was
necessary to pull the cerebral hemispheres gently apart and then to
divide the rest of the brain longitudinally with a sharp knife.

The nervous mechanisms of the second level directly involve the spinal
cord and all the portions of the brain shown in Fig. 7.10 except the cerebrum. The medulla, pons, midbrain, and thalamus act, like the spinal
cord, partly in the capacity of conductors. The white matter of these

parts contains a number of nerve tracts of different function, which serve as communicating lines to and from various portions of the central nervous system. The *medulla* contains the centers for the regulation of many autonomic activities, such as the heartbeat, respiration, swallowing, visceral movements, the dilation and constriction of the blood vessels, glandular secretion, and perspiration. It is from this part of the brain that the *vagus nerves* extend to the heart and viscera.

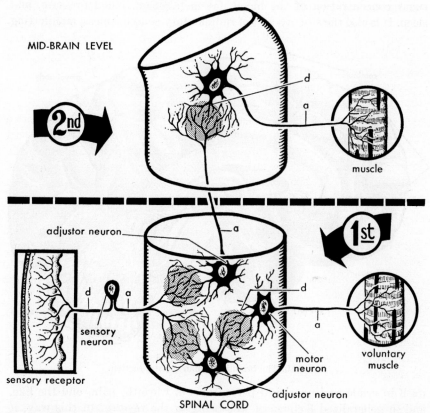

FIG. 7.9. The mechanism of second-level response. (*a*) Axon; (*d*) dendrite. (*Modified from Gates, Elementary Psychology, by permission The Macmillan Company.*)

The gray cortex of the *cerebellum* is a center for the correlation of a host of afferent impulses (from the muscles, joints, and tendons and from the static balance, touch, and pressure receptors, etc.) with the complex of efferent impulses that are required to maintain the body's posture and unconscious adjustments to its environment. It is not certain how independent some of these synapses may be from cerebral control; but it is clear that in normal functioning, even voluntary movements that are initiated in the cerebral cortex involve a host of relays and connections

in the cerebellum that correlate the multitude of separate details necessary for the performance of such a complex action as (for example) hit-
ting a tennis ball with a racket. The *midbrain* is a center for certain visual
and auditory reflexes, and both it and the *pons* serve as highways for
nerve impulses.

The *thalamus* is of particular interest. It contains the body-temperature
regulating center, as well as others apparently affecting water balance,
sugar concentration of the blood, fat metabolism, blood pressure, and
sleep. It is also the site of a sort of rudimentary consciousness, manifesting

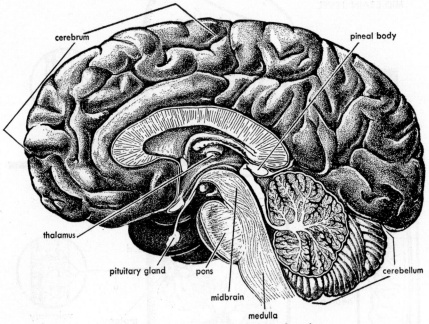

FIG. 7.10. The brain in median sagittal section.

itself in crude and uncritical perceptions of warmth, pain, and the like,
and in generalized feelings of well-being or the reverse. In this way, it
helps to color the background of consciousness and thus to create moods
or feelings. The most important function of the thalamus is, however,
that it serves as the gateway to the cerebral cortex. There are no direct
connections between the cortex and the receptors and effectors. The
influence upon the cortex by the receptors and the control by the cortex
of the effectors are usually mediated by the thalamus. It is the portal to
the third-level of response, which we shall now consider.

Third-level response—the cerebrum. The cerebrum is the organ
of the mind. Its actions are superposed upon the system of automatic
machinelike responses described for the first- and second-level responses.

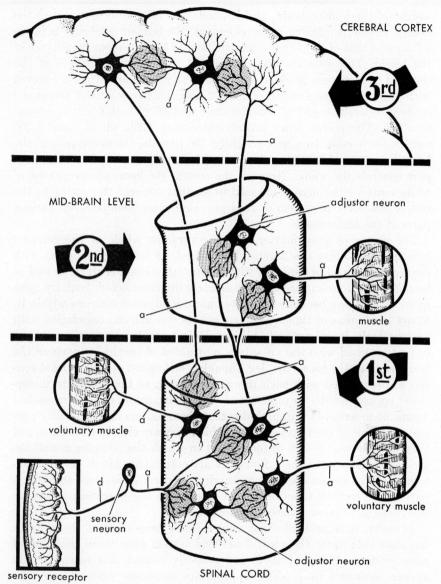

CEREBRAL CORTEX

MID-BRAIN LEVEL

adjustor neuron

muscle

voluntary muscle

sensory neuron

voluntary muscle

sensory receptor

SPINAL CORD

adjustor neuron

FIG. 7.11. The mechanism of third-level response, superimposed on those of the first and second levels. (*a*) Axon; (*d*) dendrite. (*Modified from Gates, Elementary Psychology, by permission The Macmillan Company.*)

It is the supreme governing agency of the nervous system and is capable of interfering with and modifying the activities of the lower centers.

The cerebrum, or forebrain, is a fissured and convoluted mass, composed of two hemispheres. Its weight is more than four-fifths of the total weight of the human brain, and it practically fills the larger part of the cranial cavity. In degree of development, the human cerebrum is far in advance of that of any other organism, and to it we owe our dominance in the world. The intricate convolutions of the external surfaces of the cerebral hemispheres produce a comparatively huge area that is covered with gray matter to a depth of some 2 mm. This gray matter forms the *cerebral cortex*, the seat of consciousness and all of man's higher mental faculties. The cortex is an intricate structure made up of some 9,200 million nerve cells. In a man weighing 150 pounds, the nerve cells of the brain cortex would weigh only about $\frac{1}{5000}$ of the total, but this small part controls the whole. Beneath the cortex, the hemispheres consist of white matter—the myelin-encased fibers that connect the cortex to the rest of the nervous system or that provide connections between various parts of the cortex itself.

The cortex of gray matter, which covers the whole of the cerebral hemispheres, forms the highest brain level. It is richly supplied with connections with the cord and with all the other brain centers, as well as having its various surface areas intimately interconnected, both by communicating fibers beneath the cortex and by adjustor neurons within it. Many local areas of the cortical surface show a marked correlation with various body functions and abilities. Definite motor centers are known to be concerned with the voluntary movement of particular parts of the body, such as the toes, foot, leg, shoulder, or fingers; other localized centers are concerned with such things as hearing, or the ability to understand spoken words, to understand written language, or to form spoken words, or to write. It is improbable that these centers independently control the whole of the functions with which they are clearly correlated, but they do represent a sort of focal point in which the complex neural activities necessary for these functions are correlated. Much of the functioning of the cortex does not ordinarily affect consciousness, and only a part of the cortical functioning has to do with the phenomena that we designate as volition, reason, and intelligence.

Actually, it is probable that only a small proportion of the nervous impulses that enter the central nervous system ever reach the level of consciousness. Many of them are properly routed and connected by various synapses to produce appropriate responses without our ever becoming aware of them. Some of these "routings" are permanently below the level of consciousness and cannot produce a sensory impression; others we may "by taking thought" become aware of, although we do not ordinarily sense them—as, for example, the position of a hand or foot that is quietly at rest. Any impulse that we can sense must have reached the cortex, but probably only a small proportion of even these impulses are ordinarily "conscious."

CHAPTER VIII

COORDINATION AND CONTROL:
(2) THE ENDOCRINE GLANDS

We have just examined one of the two chief coordinating mechanisms of the human body—the nervous system. The other is a system of *chemical* coordination that depends for its functioning upon the circulation of the blood. The agents are the *hormones,* or chemical messengers. These are special substances, many of them proteins, which are carried in the blood stream to all parts of the body and produce appropriate responses in the proper tissues and organs. Numerous different hormones have already been discovered. They are all produced in ductless glands that pour their secretions directly into the blood that flows through them. Such glands, lacking ducts, are called *endocrine* glands (Greek, *endon,* "within," and *krino,* "to separate"), or *glands of internal secretion.*

A good illustration of hormone action is furnished by *secretin.* As we learned in Chap. IV, this is a substance produced by the mucosa cells of the duodenum. Under the stimulus of the acid chyme from the stomach, secretin is liberated into the capillaries of the intestinal wall and is carried by the blood throughout the body. It has no effect upon most of the body tissues and organs, but when it reaches the capillary network of the pancreas, the liver, and the gall bladder, secretin[1] stimulates these organs to immediate activity. The pancreas begins to pour its secretion into the intestine, the liver and gall bladder to discharge bile, and the enzyme-producing cells in the intestinal wall to liberate their products.

Bayliss and Starling discovered the existence and function of secretin in 1902. They had found that the intestine, liver, and pancreas continued to liberate their secretions whenever food entered the intestine from the stomach, even after every conceivable nervous connection had been severed. They considered the possibility that the hydrochloric acid of chyme, absorbed into the blood stream, might act as the stimulus responsible, but they found that injecting dilute hydrochloric acid into the blood produced no effect. When, however, they scraped mucosa from the duodenal wall of an experimental animal, ground it up with sand and

---

[1] Here used in the wide sense, to include the substances that cause the gall bladder to contract and the intestinal mucosa to secrete.

dilute hydrochloric acid in a mortar to break up the cells, neutralized and filtered the product, and injected some of the resulting fluid into the veins of another experimental animal, a copious flow of pancreatic juice ensued. The substance responsible was named *secretin*.

In the period since secretin was thus discovered a great amount of information has been gained about hormones, and a field of science called *endocrinology* has come into being. Various glandular structures that had long been known to be in some way essential to life, though not part of any recognized physiological system, now were recognized as endocrine glands producing important hormones. Other organs such as the pancreas, the functions of which had seemed simple and well understood, were found to have additional endocrine functions.

There still remain a number of glandular tissues of uncertain function; investigation of these and the search for additional hormones that may be produced by better known glands is still in progress. In spite of all that has been learned, we are still very far from a complete understanding of hormones and their mode of action.

The deciphering of the body's endocrine control is beset with special difficulties. For one thing, the amount of hormone secreted by a gland (although sufficient to produce stimulation or inhibition of bodily function) is very small, and it is difficult to obtain a sufficient quantity for study. Moreover, many of the endocrine glands are located deep within other vital tissues and are difficult to reach surgically without killing the experimental animal. Much of our present information has had to be obtained by removing some gland suspected of producing a hormone from an experimental animal and then comparing the functioning of this animal with one that remains intact. If the animal that has had a gland removed shows specific symptoms, and if these symptoms can be alleviated by feeding or injecting the animal with extracts taken from the same glands of other individuals, the existence of an endocrine function is indicated. The next step is to obtain a sufficient quantity of the secretion and to isolate the essential substance. If possible, this substance is purified, and its chemical composition and structure are determined. In the case of adrenalin, thyroxin, testosterone, and other important hormones, such knowledge is now sufficient to permit synthetic manufacture. These and other hormones that must at present be obtained from the glands of fish or sheep or other animals are already an important part of the "medicines" available to the modern physician.

Another difficulty in determining the role of any given hormone is that the endocrine glands appear to be particularly susceptible to the influence of other hormones. Removal or disease of one endocrine gland may markedly affect the functioning of another that has no evident connection with it. Investigation of the pituitary gland, for example, is

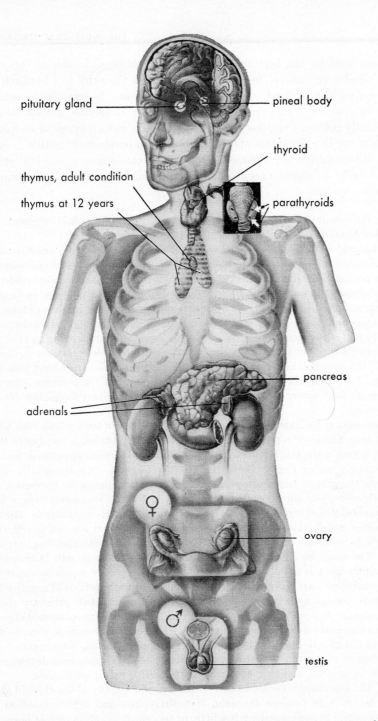

pituitary gland — — pineal body

thyroid

thymus, adult condition

thymus at 12 years — parathyroids

pancreas

adrenals

ovary

testis

FIG. 8.1. The principal endocrine glands. Note that both male and female gonads and both juvenile (twelve year) and adult thymus are included in the same manikin. The inset shows the glottis and edges of the thyroid from the back, with the right parathyroids indicated by the small arrows.

127

complicated by the fact that not only is it situated in one of the most inaccessible regions in the whole body (within the skull and beneath the brain stem) but it produces several hormones that, in large part, regulate the output and functional rhythms of other endocrine glands located in totally different regions of the body. Again, not all types of endocrine control are in continuous operation. Some are particularly active in early life, others show a rhythm associated with sexual changes, and still others are largely quiescent except when stimulated by way of the autonomic nervous system.

In the account that follows, some of the more important endocrine glands and the hormones that they produce are listed and briefly discussed.

Pituitary. This gland (sometimes called the hypophysis) is a small mass of tissue about the size of a pea, located at the base of the brain and enclosed in a bony pocket in the floor of the skull. It has four main parts—the *anterior lobe*, the *pars nervosa*, the *pars intermedia*, closely applied to the pars nervosa, and a *stalk*, which attaches it to the brain. The parts are closely fused but are different in structure and origin. The anterior lobe is entirely glandular, derived from a pouch on the roof of the mouth of the developing embryo. The pars nervosa and the pars intermedia together form the posterior lobe; the first is derived from the brain, while the second arises in the same way as the anterior lobe. At least nine hormones have been obtained from the anterior lobe, while the posterior lobe produces at least three. The more important of the pituitary hormones are the following:

Hormones of the Anterior Lobe. All of the hormones of the anterior lobe which have been prepared in pure or nearly pure form are proteins. A number of them exert effects upon the morphological development of other structures, and are accordingly called *trophic* hormones (Greek, *trophein*, "to nourish"). These include the growth (somatotrophic) hormone, two gonadotrophic hormones, and the thyrotrophic, adrenocorticotrophic, and lactogenic hormones; others have been postulated. There is also good evidence for the existence of anterior pituitary hormones which have direct effects upon metabolism and are not trophic hormones; these include the diabetogenic hormone and the fat-metabolizing hormone.

1. *The somatotrophic or growth hormone* stimulates body growth. A deficiency of this hormone in childhood results in the development of a *pituitary dwarf*. If such individuals are recognized early enough and given injections of anterior lobe extracts, normal growth may be produced or approximated. Pituitary dwarfs are mentally normal, become sexually mature, and are well-proportioned of body, unlike the cretin dwarfs that result from lack of thyroid secretion. Overproduction of the growth hormone in childhood results in *gigantism*. When overproduction begins after adult stature is reached, it causes disproportionate development of the jaws, arms, and legs, producing the condition called *acromegaly*.

2. The *thyrotrophic hormone* controls the size and activity of the thyroid gland and causes it to produce thyroxin. Hypothyroidism and hyperthyroidism are physiological states caused by too little or too much secretion of this hormone.

3. The *adrenocorticotrophic hormone* (commonly abbreviated to ACTH) con-

trols certain functions of the adrenal cortex, notably the production of the hormone cortisone, with which it is in reciprocal balance. ACTH stimulates cortisone formation, while cortisone inhibits production of ACTH.

4. *The gonadotrophic hormones* affect reproductive processes and sexual characteristics. The *follicle-stimulating hormone* (FSH) causes sexual maturation in both male and female; removal of the anterior pituitary in youth therefore has effects much like those of castration. The *interstitial-cell-stimulating hormone*[1] (ICSH) stimulates testis and ovary to produce hormones that control the development of secondary sex characters. In the female, FSH and ICSH act reciprocally with the ovarian hormones to cause the phenomena of the menstrual and pregnancy cycles. *Luteotrophin* (which may be the same as *prolactin*) plays a part in the pregnancy cycle. The interaction of the gonadotrophic hormones with those of the gonads is discussed more fully in our account of human reproduction (Chap. XVI).

5. *The lactogenic hormone, prolactin,* stimulates milk secretion in the mammary glands after birth of the child; it is also apparently responsible for maternal behavior toward the young.

6. *The blood-sugar-raising hormone* increases the concentration of sugar in the blood; under ordinary conditions its influence is balanced and counteracted by the effects of insulin from the pancreas. Insulin and BSRH form an antagonistic chemical pair, and together control the level of blood sugar. The mechanism is unknown, but it seems likely that the two hormones in some way control the rate at which the liver liberates sugar into the blood.

7. *The fat-metabolizing hormone* controls by its amount the rate at which fats are broken down into fatty acids in body metabolism.

Hormones of the Posterior Lobe.   The posterior lobe of the pituitary produces no trophic hormones, but three metabolic hormones have been obtained from it.

8. *The water-balance (antidiuretic) hormone* controls the rate at which water is excreted from the body by the kidneys. Removal of the posterior lobe is followed by excretion of abnormally large amounts of urine accompanied by extreme thirst. This may be the same hormone as (9).

9. *Oxytocin* (also called *pitocin*) throws the muscular wall of the uterus into strong contractions and appears to have importance in relation to childbirth. It has no known function in the male.

10. *Vasopressin* (also called *pitressin*) causes a rise in blood pressure by constricting the walls of arteries and may act also on the smooth muscles of the gut, causing them to contract.

Thyroid.   This gland is situated in the neck, and consists of two lobes connected by a thin band of thyroid tissue; it partly encloses the trachea. It produces the hormone *thyroxin*, which is well known chemically and has a large iodine content. This substance controls the general level of metabolism and has marked effects upon growth. If the thyroid glands are removed from young tadpoles, they never change into frogs, but if they are fed large amounts of thyroid tissue, they metamorphose much earlier than is normal and become fully-formed but minute frogs. Thyroid deficiency in human beings is manifested by various effects. If it occurs in infancy and childhood, it produces *cretin dwarfs*—stunted individuals characterized by obesity, softness and flabbiness of all tissues, feeble-mindedness,

---

[1] Formerly called *luteinizing hormone* (LH).

and failure to develop sexually. Cures that can only be described as amazing are obtained by feeding thyroids to cretins. Deficiency in the adult causes *myxedema*, a condition of lowered metabolism accompanied by puffy swelling of parts of the body, especially the hands and face, and by sluggish physical and mental functioning. Excessive activity of the thyroid, on the other hand, results in a marked increase in oxidative metabolism, with loss of weight. Both figuratively and literally the individual is burning himself up.[1] Such hyperthyroidism is accompanied by nervous disorders, restlessness and great excitability, high heart rate, derangement of reproductive functions in women, and protruding eyeballs. It can be alleviated or cured by removal of part of the thyroid or by tying off some of the arteries supplying it. Some forms of *goiter* are caused by deficiency of iodine in the diet, but exophthalmic goiter results from enlargement and hyperactivity of the thyroid, resulting from overproduction of thyrotrophic hormone.

Parathyroids. The parathyroid glands comprise four small bodies, two on each side, attached to or imbedded in the dorsal surface of the thyroid. Functionally they are entirely independent of the latter. They secrete *parathormone*, which regulates calcium metabolism of the body. Removal of these glands quickly causes death. In excess parathormone leads to removal of calcium from the bones and its addition to the blood and may result in the formation of calcium deposits in the kidneys, ureters, or various body tissues.

Adrenals. The adrenal (or suprarenal) glands rest atop the kidneys like two miniature cocked hats. They are about 2 inches long and $\frac{1}{10}$ to $\frac{1}{8}$ inch thick. Each consists of two distinct parts, an outer *cortex* and an inner *medulla*. Embryologically the cortex is derived from the same body layer as the kidney, but the medulla comes from the same embryonic structures as the autonomic nervous system and is largely composed of nervelike tissue.

Cortisone (cortin) is the hormone or group of hormones produced by the adrenal cortex. It seems to be the most versatile and perhaps the most essential of all the hormones. Chemically it belongs to the steroid group, but it has not yet been fully analyzed. There is reason to suppose that it is actually a hormone complex, in view of the diverse actions it controls. Removal of the adrenals causes death in a matter of weeks, with the symptoms long known in *Addison's disease*. There is first a bronzing of the skin; this is followed by profound weakness and languor; gastric acid disappears from the stomach, and glucose is not absorbed by the intestine; the body temperature drops several degrees; the blood loses water and salt through the kidneys and rapidly diminishes in volume; toxic nitrogenous and potassium wastes are retained and reach high concentration in the blood. Finally the glucose level of the blood falls to zero, as in insulin shock, and death results. All these effects can be counteracted by injection of cortisone.

The prime function of this hormone seems to be to act as a *regulator of functional balance* in the body. To any disturbing factor it sets up a counter action which, while it may not restore the original condition, results in a new working balance. It is to this property that it owes its palliative effects in a great variety of diseases and other such disturbances as shock, burns, and wounds. It does not cure the

---

[1] One milligram of thyroxin produces an increase in heat equivalent to the oxidation of 267 grams of glucose, with liberation of 400 grams of carbon dioxide and 160 grams of water.

condition, but it enables the body to live with it and perhaps in the end to over-come it through other body defenses. In addition to this major function cortisone performs many lesser ones. It is involved in maintaining the supply of carbohydrate fuel to the muscles, in the balancing of important components of the blood, in control of the rate of glucose combustion in the muscles, in making the circulatory system leakproof, and in keeping down the concentration of potassium and nitrogenous wastes in the blood. Perhaps its major regulatory role is merely the sum of all these and other minor ones. As already noted, cortisone has a reciprocal relation to ACTH; it inhibits production of that hormone, while ACTH stimulates formation of cortisone. The two work as a balanced system.

Adrenalin (also called adrenine or epinephrin) is the hormone produced by the adrenal medulla. In contrast to cortisone, its chemical structure and mode of action are well known. It was the first hormone to be isolated in pure form and chemically identified.

Amberson and Smith describe the action of adrenalin as follows. "When we inject an extract of the adrenal medulla into the arm of a human being, its effects are felt almost immediately. The skin and face become pale, the heart beats more strongly but slowly, and blood pressure rises, sometimes doubling itself in a few seconds. The subject experiences a feeling of anxiety or apprehension sometimes accompanied by marked muscular tremors, an empty feeling in the pit of the stomach, and shortness of breath. All activity ceases in the stomach and intestines.

"These more obvious effects of adrenalin result chiefly from its actions upon smooth muscle. The effect of the hormone upon the stomach and intestine is to inhibit their action, a change of which we become vaguely aware in consciousness. The slowing of the heart and shortness of breath are the result of carotid sinus reflexes inaugurated by the high blood pressure. If the cardiac nerves are cut in an experimental animal the effect of adrenalin injections is to speed the heart as well as to strengthen its beat, by direct chemical action. But when the nerves are intact a reflex inhibition overcomes the direct chemical effect, in the interest of preventing too high a rise in blood pressure. Adrenalin also causes a transformation of muscle and liver glycogen into glucose which appears in the blood stream. The hormone is a very efficient agent for increasing the level of the blood sugar in time of crisis. It also shortens the coagulation time of the blood."

Here is a description of a body all ready to fight or run; the function of adrenalin is obviously the preparation of the body to meet an emergency. Transportation by the circulatory system is speeded up, and the blood is shunted from the viscera to the skeletal muscles. Fuel (glucose) for muscle use is poured into the blood, and more oxygen is made available so that this fuel can be rapidly used by the muscles. The body is thus prepared for a maximal physical effort. Even the clotting time of the blood is shortened, as if in anticipation of possible injury. The sensation of pain, or the emotions of anxiety, fear, or anger bring this hormone mechanism into play. The adrenal medulla is controlled by the sympathetic division of the autonomic nervous system. Impulses set off by the above-mentioned responses to environmental stimuli travel from the brain to the adrenals and cause immediate liberation of adrenalin into the blood stream.

Pancreas.   Although the pancreas produces an external digestive secretion, it functions also as an endocrine gland. Certain of its tissues, known as the *islands* *of Langerhans,* produce the hormone *insulin.* This substance (in cooperation with one of the pituitary hormones) regulates the sugar metabolism of the body. Insufficient production of insulin causes *diabetes,* in which the sugar content of the blood rises and sugar is excreted in the urine, the power of the body to oxidize sugar is reduced, and many of the amino acids derived from protein foods are transformed into glucose. An excess of insulin causes a fall in the level of blood sugar, which if sufficiently pronounced may cause insulin shock. Insulin must be liberated into the blood stream continuously to maintain proper sugar balance, and it is required in amounts nearly proportional to the carbohydrate intake of the body.

Pineal body. This is a small mass of tissue near the base of the brain, which embryologically corresponds with the third median eye of some of the lower vertebrates. In man it develops as a glandular organ until about the seventh year, after which it gradually transforms into a non-glandular fibrous structure; the change is completed some time after puberty. There is reason to believe that some hormone affecting rate of development and time of attainment of sexual maturity is produced by the pineal body, but the hormone has not been isolated and its effects are still obscure.

Thymus. In infancy and childhood this is a large gland that surrounds the trachea at its lower end. It nearly or completely disappears after puberty. Its chemical composition is unique in that it contains a larger proportion of nucleoprotein than does any other animal structure. Although it may be one of the endocrine glands, this has not been established, and there is some evidence that it may be a storage place for certain food materials useful in growth processes and especially required while sexual maturity is being attained. Experimental animals from which the thymus has been removed in infancy can sometimes be reared to full and apparently normal development if an adequate growth-promoting diet is furnished. Daily injection of thymus extract into rats through nine generations of inbreeding was followed, after the third generation, by precocity in growth and development, which became more marked in each succeeding generation. Compared with the first generation and with controls, the following changes occurred from the first to the ninth generation: increase in birth weight from 5.1 to 6 grams; teeth present at birth instead of erupting at 8 to 9 days; eyes open at 1½ instead of 12 to 14 days after birth; testes descending at 2 to 3 instead of at 15 to 29 days after birth; females pregnant at 22 instead of at 70 days after birth, and producing young in 11 instead of in 12 days. These results, though amply confirmed, are not easily interpreted.

Digestive system. In addition to *secretin,* already discussed, the digestive system produces a number of other hormones. The stomach mucosa produces a hormonal substance which is liberated into the blood under the stimulus of meat extracts and peptones and causes the gastric glands to secrete. The name *gastrin* has been proposed for this substance, but it may prove to be histamine, a well-known product of protein oxidation which, produced by the dying tissues of wounds, is at least partly responsible for the phenomenon of surgical shock and is also thought to play a role in allergic reactions.

The intestine produces four imperfectly known hormones besides the well-understood secretin. One stimulates the gall bladder to contract and discharge bile into the intestine; another increases the production of pancreatic enzymes without increasing the amount of pancreatic juice; a third inhibits gastric secretion; and the fourth excites secretion in the intestinal glands.

Gonads.   The soma cells of the testis and ovary produce hormones that regulate various sexual phenomena and body characteristics. Since their primary roles are concerned with reproduction, they will be discussed in the chapter dealing with reproduction in man.

We have now dealt at least briefly with all aspects of the human body that are related to its successful existence *as an individual organism*. We are nearly through with man, considered solely as an illustration of how the individual animal is built and how it works. There remains, however, one important feature of the human body—the reproductive system— which has scarcely been mentioned. The reason it has not yet been mentioned is that this system is not essential for the existence of the individual but has to do with the perpetuation of the race to which the individual belongs. It will be discussed in the following section of the book, which is concerned with our second viewpoint, the continuity of the race. Nevertheless the reproductive system is not segregated from the remainder of the body; it has important influences upon the individual considered as an individual. Therefore our survey of the structure and function of the individual human organism cannot be considered complete until the topic of reproduction has been covered.

CHAPTER IX

THE ORGANIZATION OF THE INDIVIDUAL PLANT

In our study of the problems presented by the individual organism we have thus far been concerned with the animal type of organization, as exemplified by man. We have looked at the structure and functioning of the human body in some detail, seeking to learn what its problems of maintenance are and how they are met. Animals, however, are only one of the two great divisions of life; it is now time for us to examine the very different scheme of individual organization that has been developed among plants.

All the higher forms of life, including those organisms most familiar to us, are either animals or plants. This fundamental dichotomy among living things extends far down the scale of organization. Not until we reach certain of the lowly unicellular forms of life does the distinction between plant and animal become obscure—and this in spite of the tremendous diversity in size, form, and mode of life exhibited by the members of the two groups. In what, then, does the difference consist? What fundamental characteristic makes one organism an animal, another a plant? In final analysis, if we ignore for the moment all superficial differences and all exceptional cases, it comes down to this—that animals *capture* their food ready made, whereas plants *manufacture* their food from simple chemical substances. The most important structural and functional differences between plants and animals are attributable to the unlike requirements of their methods of nutrition.

We shall best be able to comprehend the way in which the individual plant is built and functions by analyzing some representative plant type in detail, just as we did the human body. For this purpose, we shall choose not some single species of plant but a group of the flowering plants called the *dicotyledons*. We are interested in all the details of the human body because they are a part of ourselves. We are not so concerned with the minor features of individual plant species; by treating plants as a group we can select the best examples or generalize for all plants and thus obtain a comprehensive picture of plant structure and functioning.

The dicotyledons are those flowering plants that have two cotyledons (seed leaves) in the seed, net-veined leaves, and flower parts usually in fours or fives. They include a great many familiar plants. As examples, we may cite such trees as oak, maple, sweet gum, apple, and orange; such shrubs as oleander, lilac, wax myrtle, blackberry, blueberry, and gallberry; such vines as woodbine, grape, and poison ivy; and such herbs as tomato, tobacco, carrot, bean, cabbage, clover, poppy, dog fennel, dandelion, thistle, and goldenrod.[1] Even this small number of examples is sufficient to show how great a range in size, form, and growth habit exists among the dicotyledons. Yet in spite of their superficial diversity, the members of this group all share a basic structural and functional pattern that we shall soon proceed to examine.

COMPARISON OF PLANT AND ANIMAL ORGANIZATION

Before entering upon our detailed study of the individual plant, it will be well for us to look more closely at the principal similarities and differences between animals and plants. This will help our understanding of the plant type of organization and some of its basic requirements, limitations, and peculiar features. We shall see how the requirements of food manufacture account for all the most important features of plant structure except those relating to reproduction.

Features common to plants and animals. Like animals, plants are made up of cells and cell products. The protoplasm of plant cells resembles that of animal cells in appearance and properties and in nearly all plants is similarly differentiated into nucleus (or nuclear material) and cytoplasm. Each cell of the plant, like that of the animal, is bounded externally by a living *cell membrane*. Unlike most animal cells, the cells of plants are also usually enclosed in a more or less rigid, nonliving *cell wall* secreted by the cell; this is not an essential difference, since some plant cells are naked, whereas some animal cells, such as those of bone and cartilage, are similarly enclosed by a nonliving cell product. The cell wall of most plant cells is composed of *cellulose*, a substance chemically

---

[1] The flowering plants, or *angiosperms*, have two great subdivisions—the *dicotyledons*, defined above, and the *monocotyledons*, the members of which have only one seed leaf, parallel leaf veins, and flower parts usually in threes or multiples of three. The grasses, palms, lilies, orchids, and many other familiar plants are monocotyledons. The angiosperms are placed with the *gymnosperms* (pines, cycads, etc.) to form the division Spermatophyta, or seed plants—the highest of the four plant divisions. None of the remaining types of plant produces seeds; they form the three lower plant divisions (Pteridophyta, or ferns and fern allies; Bryophyta, or liverworts and mosses; and Thallophyta, or algae, fungi, lichens, bacteria, etc.). The members of these three lower divisions are simpler in structure than the seed plants and differ more or less markedly from the structural and functional pattern here described. Their features of organization are briefly discussed in Chap. XIII, and a more detailed treatment of plant classification will be found in Appendix A.

related to starch. The cell membrane is normally held in close contact with the inner surface of the cell wall by osmotic pressure within the cell, but the cell can be made to shrink away from the cell wall by immersion in a concentrated salt or sugar solution. Many animal cells contain liquid-filled vacuoles; in plant cells, the *vacuoles* are often so large as to occupy most of the space within the cell, the living protoplasm lining the cell walls or sometimes extending through the vacuoles as protoplasmic strands. Plant cells divide by mitosis just as animal cells do, except that

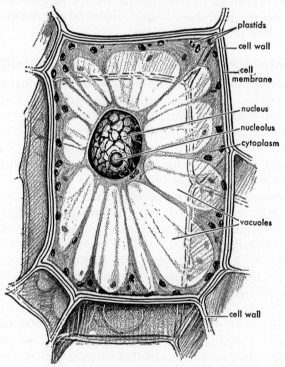

plastids

cell wall

cell membrane

nucleus

nucleolus

cytoplasm

vacuoles

cell wall

Fig. 9.1. Diagram of a typical plant cell.

in most plant cells there are *no centrosomes*, and the division of the cytoplasm in the telophase is usually accompanied by the formation of a *cell-wall plate* between the daughter cells.

Cell differentiation and division of labor are as marked among plants as among animals. The cells of the higher plants are of many types, each specialized for the performance of a particular function. As in animals, similar cells are grouped into tissues, and the tissues are, in turn, built into organs and systems of organs adapted for carrying out major functions. The organization of the plant body is less complex than that of the higher animals, in conformity with the greater simplicity of its tasks, but it rests upon the same basis—the orderly cooperation of a multitude of living units, the cells, each of which has some small part to play that is related to the functioning of the whole organism.

The plant is confronted by the same fundamental problems as the animal. These are: (1) The *maintenance of the individual*, in the first place, by the capture, transformation, storage and utilization of energy and materials; in the second place, through devices for protection against unfavorable factors in the environment, both physical and biotic. (2) The *maintenance of the race*, through reproduction. The second of these problems constitutes the theme of the next section of this book.

Some important differences between plants and animals. The most obvious and characteristic features of the higher plants, including the division of the plant body into root, stem, and leaf, its relative immobility and rigidity, and the prevailingly green color of the foliage, are all directly related to the method of food getting. All green plants[1] owe their color to the presence in their cells of the complex substance called *chlorophyll*, which functions as a catalyst.[2] In the presence of chlorophyll the energy of sunlight causes carbon dioxide and water to combine into the simple sugar, *glucose*, which is the basic plant food (not the carbon dioxide, water, and minerals taken in by the plant, as is sometimes stated). The process of glucose manufacture is called *photosynthesis* (Greek, *phos*, *photo*, "light," and *synthesis*, "putting together").

Organisms may be divided into two great functional groups according to whether they do or do not possess chlorophyll and in consequence can or cannot manufacture their food. Only the green plants belong to the first group, having chlorophyll. Practically all other organisms, including multicellular animals, Protozoa, and certain plants that have lost the ability to produce chlorophyll, must obtain their food directly or indirectly from green plants.

A typical animal, in order to obtain food, must be able to move about, to recognize and secure the food, and to rework it into a form suitable for its own use. Furthermore, the existence of other food-seeking organisms necessitates means of protection or escape. Related to these needs is the general development among animals of locomotor and sensory devices,

---

[1] Some "green" plants appear to be of colors other than green, because of the presence of masking pigments in addition to chlorophyll. The true antithesis of the "green" plants is found in certain plants that lack chlorophyll.

[2] A *catalyst* is a substance in the presence of which a specific chemical reaction takes place that would otherwise occur slowly or not at all. The catalytic agent takes part in the reaction but does not itself enter into permanent combination with the reacting substances. An *enzyme* is a catalyst produced as a result of cellular activity but independent of the presence of living cells in its operation. According to this definition, chlorophyll is not an enzyme, since photosynthesis is not produced by chlorophyll extracts nor by isolated chloroplasts but occurs only in intact cells.

complex coordinative mechanisms, and digestive apparatus, all of which are largely without counterparts among plants.

The requirements of the green plant are fundamentally different. Typically, it must have an extensive absorptive (root) surface for taking in water and dissolved inorganic substances. It must also have a large chlorophyll-bearing (leaf) surface exposed to light for the capture of energy for photosynthesis, and to air (or water), for obtaining the neces-

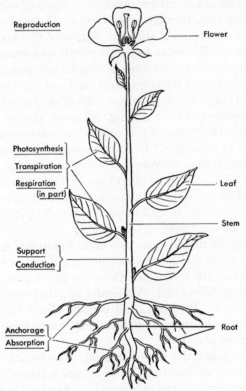

Reproduction

Flower

Photosynthesis
Transpiration
Respiration
(in part)

Leaf

Stem

Support
Conduction

Anchorage
Absorption

Root

FIG. 9.2. Diagram of the important structures and functions of a seed plant. (*Modified from Turtox chart, courtesy General Biological Supply House, Inc.*)

sary carbon dioxide. The relatively great expanse of surface that these requirements necessitate simplifies the problem of respiration and eliminates need for an elaborate breathing mechanism but introduces other problems in the use and control of evaporation of water. Since the light, water, carbon dioxide, and minerals that the plant requires are almost everywhere available, locomotion is nonessential and is largely precluded by the necessity of a root system. Unable to escape their enemies by flight or active resistance, plants avoid or minimize damage by rapid repair of injury and by such protective adaptations as armoring bark, defensive spines, or repelling taste. Rigidity and strength are called for in order to support the requisite leaf spread. A digestive system is unnecessary, since the food is manufactured within the cells and is either used at once or stored in simple, easily altered forms. A transporting system is, however, essential for carrying water, food and inorganic salts, and products of metabolism to different parts of the plant body. The chief by-products of plant metabolism, oxygen from photosynthesis and carbon dioxide and water from food oxidation, are themselves substances necessary to the plant and are more or less completely reutilized. Oxygen and carbon dioxide are gases that can diffuse through the leaf surfaces, and since few liquid or solid wastes are produced the plant needs no special excretory system. Coordination of the activities of the various parts of the plant is simple and largely under direct chemicophysical control; the plant has developed no complex nervous system or highly specialized sense organs.

The Indeterminate Scheme of Plant Growth. A second major difference between the higher plants and the metazoan animals is the method of growth. In the dicotyledons, zones of active growth lie everywhere beneath the surface—at the ends of the branches, at the root tips, and forming a sheath, the *cambium,* around the branches, stem, and roots. The cells of these zones remain always young, unspecialized, and similar in characteristics and potentialities to those of the embryonic plant. Together these growth zones constitute the *meristem.* Throughout the active life of the plant, the cells of the meristem continue to reproduce, giving rise to new tissues and causing the plant to increase in size. The cell layers thus produced are added to those previously present, and the individual cells cut off from the meristem become specialized for particular functions according to their location in the plant.

Many tropical plants grow throughout the year; in these, the meristem is active until the death of the plant. More often, especially in temperate regions, growth takes place chiefly during the spring and summer; the meristem actively produces new tissues at this time but goes into a resting condition during the remainder of the year.

As a result of the indeterminate scheme of growth the structure of the tip of a branch or root is not the same as that of an older part of the same branch or root. The growing point is actually in an embryonic state, and the degree of maturity of structure increases proportionately with the distance from that point. This situation makes it advisable to give a unified treatment of the development, structure, and functioning of the plant.

GENERAL ORGANIZATION OF THE PLANT

The seed and the embryo. All the highest plants produce special reproductive bodies called *seeds* and form a group which derives its scientific name from this characteristic—*Spermatophyta* (Greek, *sperma,* "seed," and *phyton*, "plant"). Seeds are not eggs; they are embryonic plants enclosed in tough *seed coats*. By the time the seed is ripe, the embryo has developed far enough so that the principal parts of the body of the plant can be distinguished. In the dicotyledons, of which the bean may be taken as an example, the greater part of the seed generally is made up of two greatly swollen leaves (*cotyledons*), filled with a store of

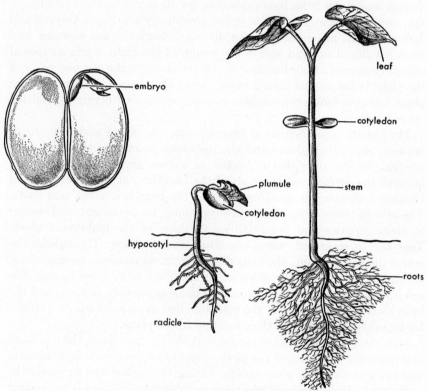

FIG. 9.3. Germination of a seed plant, the bean.

starchy food that carries the developing plant through the period of germination and establishment. The cotyledons enclose and partly conceal the rudiments of the rest of the plant; these rudiments are the *radicle* or embryonic root, the *hypocotyl* or embryonic stem, and the *plumule* or embryonic leaf shoot. The entire embryo is in a resting state, with all metabolic activities reduced to a very low point.

Germination. Under proper conditions of moisture and temperature the embryonic plant becomes active and begins to grow. The seed coat splits, and the radicle and plumule emerge. The elongating radicle is *positively geotropic* and *negatively phototropic—i.e.*, it turns toward the center of the earth under the influence of gravity and away from light.

Thus, regardless of the position in which the seed may happen to lie, the developing root will always tend to penetrate the soil instead of growing upward or sideways. As the radicle pushes downward, the elongating hypocotyl, bearing the cotyledons and plumule, grows upward,[1] its reactions being just opposite to those of the radicle. Upon emerging into the light, the cotyledons, together with the rest of the free parts of the plant, become green. This enables them to assist the plumule and stem in manufacturing food, besides yielding the store that they already possess.[*] As the developing leaves take over food manufacture, the cotyledons waste away and are ultimately shed.

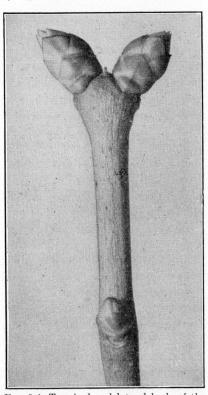

FIG. 9.4. Terminal and lateral buds of the lilac, showing bud scales. (*Photo by Prof. E. B. Mains.*)

The **principal parts of the plant body** are already differentiated in the seed—*root* and *stem* (which together form the *axis*) and *leaves*. These parts are analogous to the organs of a higher animal, since each consists of many types of specialized cells grouped into tissues, and since the arrangement of the tissues is such as to fit the entire structure for the performance of specific tasks. The roots anchor the plant, take in soil water and its dissolved substances, and store manufactured food. The stem supports the leaf spread and transports water and other raw materials to, and manufactured food away from, the leaves; it is often also a storage place for food. The leaves capture the energy of sunlight and use it to manufacture food, act as the chief organs of respiration, and largely control the evaporation of water. The *flower* and the *fruit* are organs adapted to the purposes of reproduction. *Buds* are embryonic leaf and flower shoots in a state of arrested development, awaiting the advent of favorable conditions; in this respect, they resemble the resting embryo in the seed. Like the seed, they are enclosed in a resistant coat, in this instance composed of overlapping scales.

[1] In many plants, however, only the plumule emerges from the ground, the hypocotyl and cotyledons remaining buried.

CHAPTER X

ROOTS AND THEIR FUNCTIONS

We ordinarily think of a *root* as being any part of a plant that is buried in the soil. Actually many subterranean plant structures are not really roots, and not all roots are buried. A true root has a number of identifying characteristics. It does not possess nodes bearing leaves or leaf buds; its tip is covered by a special root cap; the internal arrangement of its tissues differs from that in a stem; and it generally possesses root hairs in a zone just back of its tip. Furthermore, the branches of roots do not develop from buds, as do those of stems. Instead they originate from a layer of cells within the root, and push their way out through the overlying tissues to the surface.

A *typical root* is almost cylindrical, tapering gently from the base to the free end. The root cap at its tip protects the delicate tissues of the growing point from abrasion as the root pushes through the soil. The zone of root hairs a short distance behind the root tip is the region where absorption of soil solutions occurs. Back of this zone, the root does not increase in length but only in thickness; the primary functions of this older part of the root are the conduction of absorbed materials, anchorage of the plant, and the production of branch roots.

The radicle of the seed develops into the *primary root*, which tends to grow straight downward. In many plants, this primary root gives rise to the entire root system, by sending off *secondary lateral roots*. These develop in regular succession from above downward; since they originate in a definite position within the primary root (generally opposite the xylem masses, described below), they tend to be arranged in longitudinal rows. True forking of roots is unknown in the higher plants, though subsequent enlargement of some of the branch roots may simulate forking. In plants where the primary root continues to elongate, producing lateral branch roots in regular succession (an inverted counterpart of the conical trunk-and-branch pattern often seen in the aerial parts of plants), the arrangement is called a *taproot system*, exemplified in pine, dandelion, clover, and carrot. In plants in which the primary root soon ceases to grow, the major part of the root system is formed from many thin, nearly equal branch roots developed from the short axis, producing what is known as a *fibrous root system,* as in many grasses. Other types of root systems also exist. In many plants, the primary root system is supplemented or superseded by the development of numerous *adventitious* or accessory roots, which may develop from any part of a plant. They are especially numerous on underground stems, but they may also arise from the leaf nodes of aerial stems or even from leaves themselves.

The root tip. The apical portion of the root as far back as the base of the zone of root hairs (generally 1½ to 2 inches in length) constitutes the root tip. This is the part of the root that grows in length, produces new tissues, and carries on absorption of soil moisture and dissolved substances. Beginning at the apex, four regions may be recognized in the root tip: the *root cap,* the *growing point,* the *region of elongation,* and the *region of maturation, or zone of root hairs.*

The *growing point* is a part of the meristem. It is composed of embryonic tissue—undifferentiated cells that grow and divide very rapidly. The divisions occur mostly at right angles to the axis of the root, so that cells are cut off from the meristematic zone alternately on the side toward the tip of the root and on the side toward the base. Those produced on the side toward the tip are added to the root cap and make good the constant loss of its outer layers caused by abrasion. Those

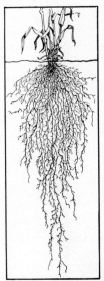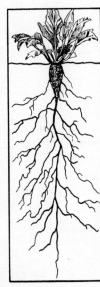

FIG. 10.1. Comparison of fibrous and taproot systems. In the grass (left) the roots are slender, much branched, and mostly shallow. In the beet (right) there is a single large, deep taproot from which lateral roots arise. The enlarged base of the root serves for food storage.

cut off on the side toward the base of the root are destined to form the various tissues of the mature root. Between these two regions of differentiating daughter cells, the parent meristematic zone remains as the persistent growing point, continuously shifted forward by its own active cell division.

As the growing point advances away from the cells cut off behind it, those cells first elongate and later begin to broaden out and to differentiate into the various sorts of tissue cells characteristic of the fully formed root. This sequence of changes is responsible for the zonal arrangement of the cells of the root tip. The surface layer of cells forms the *epidermis,* one cell in thickness. These cells are roughly cuboidal in shape and are thin-walled. By the time the *zone of elongation* has progressed beyond any given group of epidermal cells, they have produced delicate tubular outgrowths, the *root hairs*, from a fraction of a millimeter to a centimeter in length, closed at the free ends. Thus the surface of the *zone of maturation* that follows the region of elongation becomes clothed with a dense growth of root hairs which penetrate the soil crevices and absorb water and dissolved substances through their thin walls. The region from the root

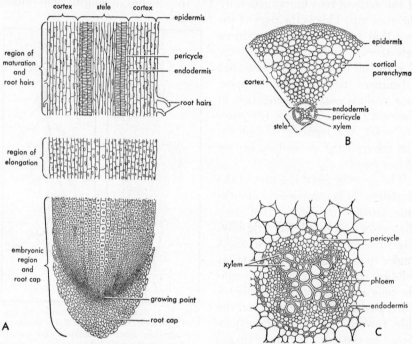

FIG. 10.2. The structure of a dicot root. *A*, longitudinal section of root tip. *B*, part of a cross section in the region of maturation. *C*, part of last, more highly magnified, showing stele and surrounding tissues. (*Modified from Turtox chart, courtesy General Biological Supply House, Inc.*)

cap to the beginning of the root-hair zone is also absorptive, but its surface is so small compared to that of the mass of root hairs that the latter are many hundredfold as effective. As the root grows forward, new root hairs are continually produced at the *distal*[1] border of the root-hair zone, and those at the *proximal*[1] border die. Behind the region of root hairs the surface of the root becomes nonabsorptive because of the deposi-

---

[1] These terms are useful in describing position and direction in relation to projecting structures, such as an arm or a plant root. The tip is the *distal end*, the attached base, the *proximal end;* but with reference to any point along the structure, *distal* means the direction away from the base; *proximal,* the direction away from the free end.

tion in the walls of the epidermal cells of a corky substance called *suberin* (from *Quercus suber*, the "cork oak")—the same material that makes cork so impenetrable to water.

The structure of a young root. The arrangement of tissues in the root is best seen in a cross section through the region of root hairs, where the cells produced by the growing point have become differentiated into tissue cells but where complications due to secondary thickening have not yet entered. At the surface is the *epidermis*, with its root hairs. Beneath the epidermis is a zone called the *cortex*. Most of the cortex is composed of a spongy tissue called *parenchyma*, made up of rounded cells with thin walls and large vacuoles; the cells of the innermost layer of cortex have thickened walls, and this layer, which surrounds the stele, is called the *endodermis*.

The inner core of the root, including everything inside the cortex, comprises the *stele*.[1] Its outermost layer is a cylinder of parenchyma cells called the *pericycle*, which gives rise to branch roots and which in perennial plants plays a part in the radial growth of the root. Beneath the pericycle, the stele contains the vascular system, the cambium layer, when one is present, and sometimes a central pith and groups of fibers that add to the strength of the root.

The *vascular system* consists of two specialized types of tissue which together form the transporting or conductive system of the plant. One of these, the *xylem*, is essentially a structure of thick-walled dead cells, so arranged and connected as to function as water conduits. The other tissue, the *phloem*, is composed of living cells connected through openings in the cell walls. In the phloem, substances in solution pass through the protoplasm from cell to cell. The structure and functions of these vascular tissues are more fully treated in dealing with the stem. In a cross section of a young dicotyledonous root the *primary xylem* forms a star-shaped figure with three, four, or five rays; it generally extends to the center of the root. The strands of *primary phloem* lie between the rays of the xylem star, separated from the xylem by parenchyma; in cross section, they appear as small, isolated cell groups.

The structure of older roots. In many plants, including most annuals, the roots do not increase in thickness. In such plants the structure of the older parts of the root does not differ in any essential respect from that just described, and such roots lack a cambium layer. In perennial plants, on the other hand, the year-by-year growth of the whole plant makes necessary additional support by the roots and an increase in the capacity of the vascular system. The roots of such plants grow in diameter with age.

This is made possible by the presence of the meristematic layer called

---

[1] Pronounced *sté'lé*.

the *cambium*. The cells that lie between the arms of the xylem star and the phloem strands (and which become parenchyma in the roots of annual plants) in perennials retain their meristematic properties and constitute a *cambium layer*. The cambium forms a fluted cylinder (a wavy circle in cross section), extending out around the ends of the xylem star and separating the xylem from the phloem strands, so that the xylem is inside the cambium and the phloem is outside. Like the cells of the growing point, those of the cambium layer are undifferentiated and are capable of rapid growth and division. In the region between the xylem arms and the phloem the cells cut off on the side toward the xylem become xylem; those cut off on the side toward the phloem become phloem. Where the cambium layer bends around the arms of the xylem star, it produces neither xylem nor phloem but only parenchyma cells.

As this growth process goes on, the cambium ring (or cylinder) smooths out. Between the arms of the original xylem star there grow out masses of *secondary xylem*, separated by rays of parenchyma opposite the arms of the star. The original phloem is pushed out toward the periphery of the growing root and may be crumpled up and destroyed by the pressure of the developing secondary phloem and xylem. The *secondary phloem* lies just outside the masses of secondary xylem, separated from them by the cambium ring.

While this thickening has been going on, the pericycle (also composed of parenchyma) has again taken on the functions of meristem and has formed a second cambium layer (the *cork cambium*) outside the first. This cambium produces a layer of cork cells, the walls of which are impervious to water because they contain suberin. The cork layer cuts off the cortex from access to food and water, causing it to die and disappear. Thus the older parts of the root come to consist solely of the greatly modified stele, with a covering of corky bark instead of the original epidermis.

THE FUNCTIONING OF THE ROOT

The soil as the environment of roots. The soil consists of a porous mass of large and small mineral grains, together with a variable proportion of organic material derived from the decay of plant and animal bodies and animal excreta. Its deeper parts are more or less saturated with water, but in the upper layers, the spaces between the grains are filled with air. In the minute passages and cavities of this aerated zone live innumerable bacteria and simple plants, engaged in decomposing the organic debris. Here also live minute animals of extraordinary diversity, so numerous that their excrement and their dead bodies form important constituents of the soil materials. In this zone, each mineral grain is coated with a colloidal film of organic or inorganic material and enclosed in a thin layer of water that contains from 0.1 to 1.0 per cent of various dissolved substances, including those essential to plants.

Substances taken in by the roots. Aside from carbon dioxide and oxygen, which are discussed later, the various inorganic substances upon which plant metabolism is dependent are obtained from the soil. Water enters largely into the composition of all protoplasm and cell products. It is one of the two substances from which the basic plant food glucose is manufactured. It carries in solution the other materials used by plants. Lastly, it maintains the internal pressure (*turgor*) within the cells of the plant, which is responsible for much of the stiffness and strength of the plant body and furnishes a mechanism for the movement of various parts of the plant. The very large amounts of water used by plants are almost wholly obtained from the soil, with some minor exceptions (aquatic plants, epiphytes, or "air plants," parasites, and plants living in other unusual situations).

Besides the elements contained in carbon dioxide and water, plants require relatively large amounts of certain others for the synthesis of fats and proteins from glucose and its derivatives and for the building of protoplasm and cell products. These *essential elements* include phosphorus, potassium, calcium, sulfur, magnesium, and nitrogen. All of these are absorbed from the soil in the form of dissolved salts—nitrates, phosphates, sulfates, and ammonium salts. *Phosphorus* is a constituent of certain fats and of nucleoproteins and is concerned in carbohydrate transformations and in respiration. *Potassium* is in some way necessary for the formation of sugar and starch, though how is not clear. *Sulfur* is a component of many plant compounds, including proteins, and has something to do with the formation of chlorophyll. *Calcium* is essential for the formation of the initial plate of new cell walls, and plays other physiological roles. *Magnesium* is a constituent of chlorophyll and is therefore indispensable to green plants; it also has other functions. *Nitrogen* is essential for the synthesis of proteins and fats.

Besides the above, plants require certain other *trace elements* in minute amounts. Those known to be essential are iron, manganese, boron, copper, zinc, and molybdenum. Although several thousand times as much potassium as manganese may be utilized in the growth of a given plant, the manganese is just as important to the normal existence of the plant as the potassium. The significance of these trace elements has been realized only in the last half century, and especially since 1923, when boron was found to be essential to development of the broad bean, and 1927, when a group of Florida investigators found that addition of copper to unproductive Everglades' soils rendered them valuable for truck growing.

Many formerly obscure plant diseases have been traced to deficiency of one or more of these trace elements in particular soils, and the ailments so caused have come to be known as *mineral deficiency diseases*. They bear a certain analogy to vitamin deficiencies in animals. Mineral deficiencies are much more prevalent in some regions than in others, and are determined largely by the mode of origin and parent rock materials of the soils. In the Atlantic coastal plain the soils have been largely derived from materials carried to ancient seas by ancient streams. The sorting of the sediments by rivers and waves, and the leaching to which the derived soils have been subjected have left many soils in this region deficient in certain elements—especially manganese, zinc, and copper. The deficiencies are especially marked in Florida, which lies farthest from the Piedmont and Appalachian sources of these materials, and which has unusually heavy rainfall to cause leaching. The various roles played by the trace elements in plant physiology are still poorly understood.

Other elements, such as sodium, chlorine, silicon, aluminium, nickel and perhaps others, are often beneficial to the growth of plants, and some of these may be found necessary to particular species of plants.

Intake and transportation by roots. The root hairs penetrate into the crevices of the soil, pressing close against the surfaces of the soil particles. These particles are wet with soil moisture—a dilute solution of salts. Water and solutes pass through the permeable walls and the semipermeable cell membranes into the epidermal cells of the root tip, thence across the cortex into the stele, and along the conductive tissues to the rest of the plant. Some of the factors involved in this movement are well known, but others cannot yet be explained. Our lack of knowledge concerning so familiar a phenomenon as absorption by roots is another reminder of how close the frontiers of science lie, and how much remains to be learned about even the simpler life processes.

Absorption of Water. We may regard the epidermal cells and root hairs as being immersed in the dilute soil water solution, and separated from it only by the living cell membrane (the cell wall being freely permeable). The cell membrane is said to be *semipermeable*, for while it is permeable to water and such solutes as are ionized or have small molecules, it is increasingly impermeable to solutes with increase in the size of their molecules. It is also differentially permeable, as we shall see. Proteins, fats, and large carbohydrate molecules pass through the cell membrane with great difficulty, if at all.

It is a well-known fact that water moves through a semipermeable membrane from the region of lesser to that of greater concentration of a solute or solutes. This phenomenon is called *osmosis*. The concentration of solutes in the epidermal cells of the root tip is normally greater than in the soil solution, and water therefore enters the cells. Osmosis accounts for much of the absorption of water by roots, but it is not the whole story. Protoplasm is a colloid and, like many colloids, has the property of soaking up (imbibing) water. Much of the water taken in by *imbibition* is closely held to the colloidal particles by adsorption, but the remainder is more loosely held, and can be withdrawn from the cell by osmosis or by suction.

Besides osmosis and imbibition, there is a third factor concerned in water absorption. This is *suction force*, concerning which a few words of explanation are required. The plant cell is contained within more or less rigid walls against which the cell membrane is pressed. These walls can resist varying amounts of pressure, depending upon their strength and the amount of counterpressure exerted against them by adjoining cells. The cell as a whole tends to maintain an unchanging volume. When water enters the cell by osmosis, an internal pressure is created. The actual pressure exerted by the cell contents against the cell wall is called *turgor pressure*. It results from but is not the same as *osmotic pressure*, which is the maximum pressure that can be developed in a given solution separated from pure water by a rigid semipermeable membrane. Turgor pressure is determined in part by the osmotic pressure of the cell contents and in part by the available water supply outside the cell membrane.

Let us consider a hypothetical cell in which the sum of the molar concentrations[1] of all the solutes present amounts to 0.3 M. This cell, immersed in pure water, should attain a turgor pressure equal to the osmotic pressure and equivalent to 0.3 M at 0°C., or 6.7 atmospheres. When the cell is immersed in a 0.1 M solution, its turgor pressure should be equivalent only to 0.2 M, and in a 0.3 M solution its turgor pressure must be zero. The cell would lose water to any solution with a molar concentration greater than 0.3 M.

A cell which has a capacity to reach a 0.3 M turgor pressure but actually has a pressure of only 0.2 M has a *turgor deficit* of 0.1 M. This

---

[1] A *mole* (gram-molecular weight) of any substance is the number of grams of that substance that corresponds to its molecular weight. A mole of any substance therefore contains the same number of molecules as a mole of any other substance. A *molar solution* is one that contains one mole of solute per liter of solution; such a solution is said to have a *molar concentration* of 1.0 M, where M stands for *molar*. The osmotic pressure is a function of the number of solute particles relative to the number of solvent particles, regardless of what the solute particles are. Any dilute solution of a nonelectrolytic substance contains as many solute particles as there are molecules of solute; therefore a solution containing 0.1 M glucose, 0.1 M maltose, and 0.1 M lactose has the same molar concentration (0.3 M) as one containing 0.3 M glucose. The osmotic pressure of a 1.0 M solution is 22.4 atmospheres at 0°C.; that of a 0.3 M solution is 6.7 atmospheres. Electrolytes such as sodium chloride ($NaCl$) have higher osmotic pressures than nonelectrolytes, since in solution some of their molecules are dissociated into ions which act as independent solute particles.

deficit is the *suction force* which measures the power of the cell to take up more water (always assuming that no change in volume of the cell takes place). A cell with a suction force of 0.1 M will take water from any soil solution having a molar concentration less than 0.1 M, and from any adjoining cell that has a suction force of less than 0.1 M. These facts find application not only in explaining the entry of water into roots but in accounting for its movements within the plant. Osmotic pressure is probably the chief agency in the entry of water. The walls of the delicate epidermal cells and root hairs cannot withstand much pressure; the cells would doubtless be ruptured were not water continually withdrawn from them by the deeper tissues.

The mechanism for such withdrawal and for producing a continuous flow across the cortex to the stele is found in the gradient of increasing osmotic concentrations and amounts of suction force that exists from epidermis to stele, together with the mechanical suction exerted by the transpiration pull—a matter which will be discussed in a later chapter. In some plants the cells of the innermost layer of the cortical parenchyma have about four times the osmotic concentration of the epidermal cells. This means that each layer of cells exerts suction force on the cells toward the outside of the root, while at the same time it loses water to the next inner layer of cells. Along with the transpiration pull, this causes the soil water entering the epidermal cells to move across the cortex toward the vascular tissues of the stele. Here the water is pulled into the xylem and is carried along the roots and up the stem to the leaves. The force that causes the water to enter the xylem tubes seems chiefly that of the *transpiration pull* exerted along the water columns in the tubes, as later described. The transpiration pull is in turn the product of the suction force of the cells in the leaf tissues, created in those cells by loss of water in transpiration.

Intake of Solutes.   Much of the intake of dissolved substances by roots seems to be a matter of simple diffusion. When the concentration of a solute is higher in the soil solution than in the epidermal cells, its molecules or ions diffuse into the cell faster than they diffuse out, raising the concentration in the cell. If they are also diffusing into the deeper tissues, the net result will be a flow into the plant.

Diffusion, however, does not account for all the facts of absorption of solutes. There is abundant evidence that molecules and ions of many substances continue to enter the epidermal cells even when the concentration within the cells is higher than that in the soil water. This may go on until the concentration in the cell reaches 25, 40, or even (in some fresh-water plants) 1,900 times that outside. This *active absorption*, as it may be called to distinguish it from simple diffusion, takes place *against* the diffusion gradient, and must require the expenditure of energy. Proof that it is caused by protoplasmic activity of some sort is afforded by the fact that it occurs only in cells supplied with oxygen and sugar (fuel) and that it varies with the rate of oxidation in the cell. The physical mechanism responsible for active absorption is not understood, but obviously it involves the activities of the cell membrane, which, as one authority says, "must be of a very peculiar nature."

CHAPTER XI

STEMS AND THEIR FUNCTIONS

Stems vary more than roots, both in form and in details of structure. They may be thick, strong, and relatively rigid, like those of trees; delicate and succulent, like those of many herbs; long, slender, flexible, and tough, as in vines; rootlike and subterranean, as in dewberry and Solomon's-seal; or they may be modified in a variety of other ways. Although they somewhat resemble roots in the arrangement of their tissues and share with them the functions of support and transportation, they show numerous striking differences from roots. They normally have no absorptive function and lack epidermal structures corresponding to the root hairs; the apical growing point is not protected by a cap of cells; their outgrowths (leaves and branches) are restricted to definite parts of the stem separated by leafless and branchless intervals, and these outgrowths develop from surface buds instead of pushing out from the pericycle. The arrangement of the vascular tissues in the stele is also somewhat different from that of roots.

Certain important characteristics of stems may be most easily comprehended by study of deciduous trees or shrubs, *i.e.*, those which shed their leaves at the end of the growing season. While the leaves are still on the tree, it may be noted that they are all attached to the short terminal portions of the branches; such leaf-bearing shoots are called *twigs*. All parts back of the twigs constitute the trunk and its branches. When the leaves are shed in the fall, a *leaf scar* marks the former position of each, and it can then easily be seen that just above each leaf scar there is a bud. The buds situated along the sides of the twig occur singly or in pairs or whorls, according to the particular habit of the tree; they are called *axillary buds*, because each arises in an *axil*, or angle between a leaf petiole and the twig (cf. Latin, *axilla*, "armpit"). At the tip of the twig is a *terminal bud*. Each bud contains a rudimentary twig, already bearing rudimentary leaves. This delicate embryonic structure is enclosed and protected by overlapping, waxy *bud scales*, which are regarded as modified leaves.

With resumption of activity by the tree in the spring, the terminal bud and one or more of the axillary buds (generally those nearest the tip) begin to swell with the rapid growth of the enclosed structures. The bud scales then open, and the young shoot pushes out. It elongates rapidly, chiefly by lengthening of the *internodes*, or intervals between the regions where leaves and axillary buds develop, which are called the *nodes*. Soon the shoot appears as a replica of last year's twig; the latter no longer bears leaves and has become a part of the branch. The bud scales at the base of the new twig drop off after a time, leaving a group of *bud-scale scars*. The space between two such groups of scars marks the amount of growth accomplished in one season, and each section of the branch between two groups of bud-scale scars was originally an embryonic shoot inside a bud.

The structure of a bud. From the facts described above, it is evident that each bud contains a growing point. In fact, the bud, or stem tip, resembles the root tip in fundamental respects. Its growing point is apical, instead of being covered by a cap of cells, as in the root; but in both stem and root the meristematic zone is followed first by a region of elongating cells and then by a region of cell differentiation in which the tissue groups are formed. On the other hand, roots possess nothing corresponding to the nodes and internodes of stems, nor does the internal structure of roots and stems correspond in all details.

The structure of the young woody stem. There are three principal types of stem structure among the spermatophytes: (1) the *woody stem of the dicotyledonous trees and shrubs* (to which the stem of pines and their relatives is essentially similar), (2) the *succulent stem of the herbaceous dicotyledons,* and (3) the *very differently organized stem of the monocotyledons* (the palms, grasses, lilies, etc.). The following account applies especially to the first of these, the woody dicotyledonous-gymnosperm type; the features of the other two can be mentioned only briefly.

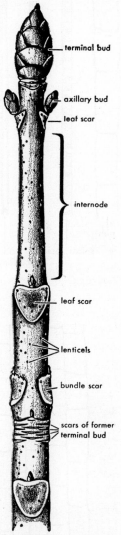

FIG. 11.1. A woody twig (horse chestnut) in winter condition, to show the principal external features of the stem. (*Redrawn from Sinnott, Botany: Principles and Problems.*)

A cross section of a one-year-old branch (stem) of such a tree as an oak shows the following arrangement of tissues. The surface is covered with a layer of *epidermis*, one cell thick. The outer surfaces of the epi-

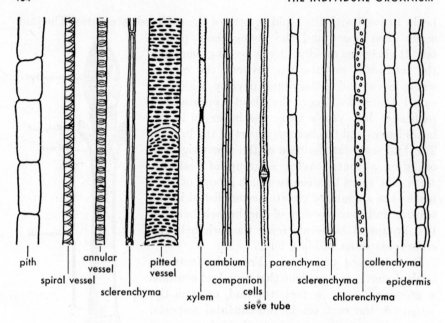

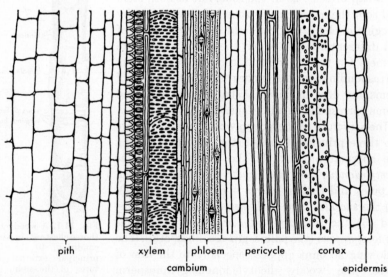

FIG. 11.2. Longitudinal section of a part of a dicot stem. The lower drawing shows the tissues in place; in the upper figure they are separated to show the kinds of cells that compose them. (*Modified from Brown, The Plant Kingdom, courtesy Mrs. Mary A. Brown.*)

dermal cells are protected by a thin layer of *cutin* (a waxy substance related to suberin and, like the latter, impervious to water). Beneath the epidermis lies the *cortex*, extending inward as far as the stele. The outer layers of the cortex are usually composed of elongated cells with thickened corners, forming a type of mechanical or supporting tissue called *collenchyma*. Within this zone the cortex is made up of parenchyma, sometimes with the innermost cell layer differentiated into an *endodermis* composed of mechanical tissue.

Inside the cortex is the central cylinder, or *stele*. The stele of the stem differs from that of the root in having a central *pith* of large or small

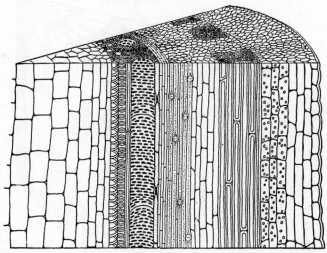

Fig. 11.3. A stereogram to show the relations of the parts of the dicot stem illustrated in Fig. 11.2. (*Modified from Brown, The Plant Kingdom, courtesy Mrs. Mary A. Brown.*)

diameter, enclosed in a cylinder of *vascular tissue*,[1] the outer surface of which is bounded by the pericycle. The inner portion of the vascular cylinder is composed of xylem; the outer part, of phloem, with a thin cambium layer between.

The structure and growth of older stems. Lengthening of the stem and its branches is entirely the result of the growth of the twigs. As soon as a twig is fully developed, it ceases to elongate and henceforth increases only in diameter. Its radial growth is accomplished primarily by the activities of the *cambium* lying between the xylem and phloem. The cells of the cambium layer are mostly tall and slender, and the layer itself is normally only one cell thick. Except for the occasional radial divisions that enable the cambium cylinder to enlarge with the growth of the stem, the cambium cells always divide parallel to the surface

[1] The *vascular cylinder* may be complete or may be interrupted by *pith rays* extending from the central pith to the cortex; the former condition is that described here.

of the stem. One of the two cells produced at the division remains a part of the cambium; the other, if on the inside, becomes a xylem cell; if on the outside, a phloem cell. Usually several layers of xylem cells are produced for each layer of phloem.

Besides the ordinary tall cambium cells that produce the vertically elongated cells of the vascular tissues, the cambium contains other cells that are radially elongated. These generally occur in groups, forming vertical bands or streaks in the cambium cylinder one to several cells wide and sometimes as much as several inches high. These groups of

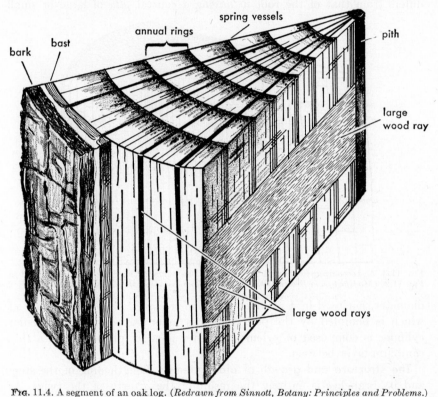

Fig. 11.4. A segment of an oak log. (*Redrawn from Sinnott, Botany: Principles and Problems.*)

special cells constitute the *ray cambium* and give rise to radial rays of parenchyma cells called the *vascular rays*.

The *wood* of the stem is the xylem. In most trees of the temperate zone the cambium is most active in the spring and then produces numerous large xylem cells; such spring wood is porous and light and usually contains many vessels large enough to be seen with the unaided eye as minute pores on a cross section of the wood. Later in the season the cambium becomes less active, and the summer wood then formed is made up of much smaller cells with relatively thick walls; it is denser and usually darker in color than the spring wood. Because of the regular alternation of seasons the wood comes to be made up of concentric cylinders (rings, in cross section) of spring and summer wood. A pair of such layers constitutes an *annual ring*,[1] and the age in years of any particular part of the tree may be determined by counting them. In tropical regions with uniform temperature and rainfall throughout the year, most trees do not produce annual rings; but any regular alternation of favorable and unfavorable conditions, such as wet and dry seasons, results in their formation. Another well-known feature of the xylem is its differentiation into heartwood and sapwood in many trees. The *heartwood* is the older, central portion of the xylem. It no longer functions as part of the vascular system, for its cells have become impregnated and darkened with resins and tannin, increasing its density and strength but blocking the water channels. It is thus transformed into an exclusively mechanical tissue. The *sapwood* is the younger outer portion of the xylem: its main function is water transport.

The "bark" of the stem is made up of all the tissues that lie outside of the xylem—the phloem, the cortex, and (in younger stems) the epidermis. It can readily be stripped from the wood, since the layer of delicate, thin-walled cambium cells is easily ruptured; "peeling" a stem destroys the cambium.

During periods of growth the cambium adds to the *phloem* from the inside. As the diameter of the xylem cylinder increases, the original continuous enclosing cylinder of phloem becomes too small to encircle the stem and breaks apart. Since the cambium, by radial cell division, keeps pace with the growth of the xylem cylinder and always forms a continuous layer outside it, the new phloem which the cambium produces at any given growth stage is always just large enough to enclose the cambium and xylem at that stage. The broken remnants of the earlier phloem layers, crumpled and discontinuous, are forced outward by the enlargement of the xylem and phloem cylinders beneath them. The spaces left between these remnants become filled with cortical parenchyma.

Beneath the original epidermis there develops a *cork cambium*, as in the root. The impermeable layer of cork cells produced by this cambium causes the death of the epidermis, and becomes itself the outer protective sheath of the stem. In *smooth-barked trees* the original cork cambium persists, increasing in diameter as the trunk enlarges. It continuously replaces from within the thin cork layer that forms the outer bark, as fast as the older parts of this layer crumble off from the surface. In *rough-barked trees* deeper layers of cork cambium form one after another beneath

---

[1] The figure or pattern seen on the cut surfaces of wood is caused by the annual rings—narrow parallel stripes if the log was sawed radially, broad bands or parabolas or ellipses if the log was cut tangentially.

the first. Each successively deeper layer causes the death of all cells outside it by cutting off their supply of water and food. This process converts more and more of the original cortex into dead outer bark, and results in the formation of a thick protective covering, the surface of which scales off or is fissured into ridges or plates as the trunk increases in diameter from within. When the zones of cork formation finally invade the outer and older layers of the phloem, the trunk comes to consist solely of the stele. New layers of phloem, continually formed by the cambium, replace those lost to the outer bark.

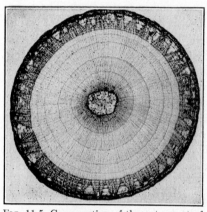

Fig. 11.5. Cross section of the outer part of a young stem of basswood (Tilia), showing annual layers of xylem and the broken phloem segments outside the cambium layer. The spaces between the phloem columns are occupied by parenchyma. (*Photo courtesy of General Biological Supply House, Inc.*)

Other types of stem structure. The kind of stem just described is that characteristic of the woody dicotyledons, typified by the hardwood trees. The *pines* and their allies (gymnosperms) have a very similar type of stem. It differs from the hardwood type chiefly in that the conducting tissue of the xylem is composed almost entirely of tracheids, without vessels but generally with resin ducts, and that the sieve tubes of the phloem have no companion cells. (Tracheids, vessels, sieve tubes, and companion cells are described on pages 160–161.)

Herbaceous dicotyledons, such as bean and thistle, have stems built on the same general plan as those of the woody dicotyledons. The amount of vascular tissue is relatively less and the pith and cortex are relatively greater in amount, and the vascular ring is generally broken by pith rays into a number of separate *vascular bundles* arranged in a ring around the pith. Each of the vascular bundles is like a segment of the vascular ring of the typical woody dicot stem; it contains a cambium layer, separating an outer group of phloem cells from an inner group of xylem cells. Because of the presence of the cambium these bundles are capable of growth and are hence called *open bundles*, in contrast to the closed bundles of the monocotyledons.

Monocotyledons (for example the grasses, maize or corn, lilies, and palms) have a type of stem (Fig. 11.6) very different from the other two sorts. The meristematic zone in the growing point is almost as great in diameter as the mature stem. It gives rise to an outer epidermal layer, which encloses a narrow zone that corresponds to the cortex and pericycle of the dicot stem; this zone is often strengthened with mechanical tissue to form a supporting cylinder, the position of which gives maximum strength for amount of structural material used. The rest of the interior of the stem tip is made up chiefly of parenchyma cells, among which are scattered strands of cambium, most numerous toward the out-side. These cambium strands produce phloem without and xylem within, as in the dicotyledonous stem; but the *whole of the cambium is eventually transformed into phloem and xylem.* In the mature stem the completed bundles are without cambium and are incapable of further growth; they are therefore called *closed bundles.* The xylem and phloem produced by the original cambium must function throughout the life of the plant, and the total quantity of vascular tissue cannot be increased. Growth in diameter of the stem is usually slight, and is caused almost

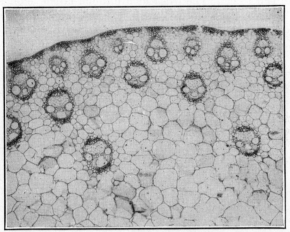

FIG. 11.6. Cross section of outer part of stem of corn (maize), a monocot, showing scattered vascular bundles. (*Courtesy General Biological Supply House, Inc.*)

entirely by increase in the breadth of the individual cells left behind by the advancing meristem of the growing point.

THE FUNCTIONING OF THE STEM

The functions of the stem are primarily (1) *support* of the leaf spread, and (2) *transport* of inorganic materials, food, and metabolic products from one part of the plant to another. Support is accomplished largely by the various mechanical tissues, aided by the turgor pressure within the cells. In young dicot stems the outer cylinder of collenchyma adds stiffness to the structure, but the mechanical strength of older stems resides almost wholly in the xylem, or wood. Transport is accomplished by the xylem and phloem, which together make up the vascular system.

The xylem, or wood.   Mature xylem consists chiefly of mechanical and conductive tissues but contains a certain amount of parenchyma that serves as a storage tissue.

The mechanical tissue is made up of *fibers*—elongated cells with very thick walls strengthened by deposits of an impermeable substance called *lignin.* The walls of these cells become so thick and impenetrable that the enclosed cell finally dies, and the space that it occupied is nearly obliterated. Masses of these lifeless fibers, packed side by side, form the tissue called *sclerenchyma*—the strongest mechanical tissue developed by the plant. The strands of sclerenchyma lie longitudinally in the xylem and so do not hinder the transport of water.

The conductive tissue is made up of two principal types of cells. The *tracheids* are spindle-shaped and relatively short. They are arranged in long strands of overlapping cells, and have pitted walls that permit water to pass from cell to cell. The *tracheae* are much larger, elongate, tubular cells. They are arranged end to end in vertical alignment, with the end walls of the cells perforated or dissolved away so that a row of tracheae forms a continuous tube. Such many-celled tubes are called *vessels*. The

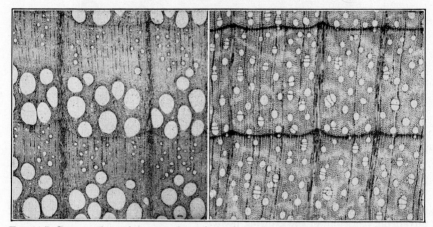

Fig. 11.7. Cross sections of ring-pored wood of red oak (left) and diffuse-pored wood of hard maple (right). (*Courtesy General Biological Supply House, Inc.*)

length of vessels varies; in diffuse-pored woods such as apple and maple, individual vessels range from a fraction of an inch to perhaps 6 feet in length, while in ring-pored woods like oak and ash some vessels run unbroken the full length of the trunk and main branches.[1] Each mature tracheid or trachea consists merely of the wall of a dead cell or cells, the protoplasm having died and disintegrated. It is only after the death of the cell that the lifeless cell walls can become functional conduits for water transport.

The phloem. Unlike xylem, the phloem is composed mainly of living cells. The principal conducting elements are the *sieve tubes*—vertical rows of large, elongate cells with perforated end walls through which protoplasmic strands connect one cell with the next. It is these perforated partitions that give the sieve tubes their name. Commonly the mature

[1] There are probably never any open tubes connecting the leaves with the vessels of the stem.

sieve tube cell lacks a nucleus; this is the rule in angiosperms, in which each sieve tube cell is accompanied by a *companion cell* of the same length but smaller diameter, containing a nucleus and connected protoplasmically to the sieve tube cell through openings in the cell wall. A sieve tube generally functions during only one season and ends by forming an impervious callus plate over the end walls, closing the transport channel.

With an increase in the thickness of the stem, the cambium produces an ever increasing number of *vascular rays* composed of radially elongated parenchyma cells. The rays are in the form of thin, vertical, radially arranged bands or sheets of cells from a fraction of an inch to a few inches in vertical extent and only a few cells thick. The same ray extends both inward into the xylem and outward into the phloem, since it is produced by the formation of new cells alternately on the two sides of the same group of ray cambium cells. The vascular rays come into contact with both phloem and xylem conducting tissues and provide a path for radial transfer of water and solutes between these parts of the stem. In addition to the ray parenchyma, phloem (and to a lesser extent xylem) contains strands of parenchyma that serve for storage of food and metabolic products.

Water transport. The great volume of water needed to make good the constant loss by transpiration from the leaves is carried almost wholly by the tracheids and vessels of the xylem. The pith, cambium, phloem, and cortex are scarcely involved. This can easily be demonstrated by experiment. If the stem is "girdled" by removing the tissues outside the cambium, including the phloem, the leaves do not wilt until the plant begins to die from interference with food and mineral transport in the phloem. But if the outer tissues are split on each side of the stem, the phloem carefully separated from the xylem with as little injury as possible, and the xylem then cut across leaving the phloem intact, wilting follows at once.

Any explanation of the rise of water (sap) in the xylem must account for the large volume and rapid rate of movement, and for the height to which it is lifted. A single maize plant loses over 50 gallons (more than 400 pounds) of water from its leaves during its 100-day life span, while a large apple tree loses about 10 gallons every day during the growing season. Such losses require rapid upward flow of water in the xylem. In the trunks of ring-pored trees such as oak, ash, and black locust a rate of upward flow of 13 inches per minute has been observed, with a maximum of 30 inches per minute in some vessels. In diffuse-pored trees such as apple, beech, maple, and basswood the rate in the trunk is about 3 to 4 inches per minute, while in conifers (which lack vessels) it is much slower, only about 0.5 inch per minute. As regards the height to which water may be raised, consider the American sequoia or the Australian blue gum—trees which attain heights of about 300 feet and carry water to their topmost twigs.

We have, then, to seek a mechanism capable not only of holding up a column of water to a maximum height of about 300 feet but also of driving or pulling many gallons per day to this height. The water flows through ducts of extremely small diameter, the walls of which are wettable; *capillary attraction* could therefore account for the rise of water to a height of perhaps 5 feet in the smaller tracheids, and about 2 to 3 inches in the largest vessels. *Atmospheric pressure* could cause a rise of only 33 feet, even supposing the pressure in the ducts were reduced to zero by transpiration from the cells of the leaf. The *osmotic root pressures* developed by some plants are considerable, but such pressures would have to be enormously greater than they are to drive water to the top of a tall tree, even with the aid of capillarity and atmospheric pressure. Furthermore, root pressures are highest in spring, when rise of water is slow, and fall to low or even negative levels when the leaves are developed and rise of water is rapid. Doubtless all of the factors mentioned aid in the process, though they cannot themselves account for its entirety.

The principal cause of the upward movement of water in the plant seems to be *transpiration pull*. This is an actual pulling force exerted from above and transmitted along the water columns in the tracheids and vessels—not in the way that air is "pulled" into the lungs, rushing into a region of lowered pressure, but in the way that a wire transmits a pull through its tensile strength.

It has been found that water enclosed in a rigid tube of small diameter will transmit a considerable tension through cohesion of the water molecules, provided the material of the tube wall is wettable and there are no air bubbles present to break the column. Confined by the walls of the tube, the fluid is unable to change its shape and behaves in some respects like a solid. Under these circumstances a force in excess of 200 times atmospheric pressure is required to rupture the water column. The water occupying the xylem channels seems to fulfill these conditions, adhering to the rigid walls of the vessels and tracheids; it is, therefore, able to transmit any pull exerted on the water threads from above. The cross walls present in the xylem channels do not interfere with the practical continuity of the water columns, since they are perforated as well as saturated with water. Experiments have shown that (1) the osmotic concentrations in the upper part of a plant are more than adequate to pull the water to the top, being equivalent to 10 to 20 times atmospheric pressure; (2) water can be pulled up through the xylem as a cohesive column; and (3) air bubbles that occasionally enter tracheids and vessels are kept from spreading into other units by the wet cell walls.

As is explained in the next chapter, water is being continually lost by transpiration (evaporation) from the cells surrounding the air spaces of the leaf. The suction force of these cells consequently rises, and they take water from the adjoining cells, which in turn take water from the tracheids in the fine vascular bundles (veins) of the leaf. The water columns in these tracheids are continuous with those in the rest of the xylem, so that withdrawal of water from the leaf tracheids creates a tension that is transmitted throughout the plant and thus to the roots. In the roots the transpiration pull is felt by the cells adjoining the xylem strands, and water is drawn from them into the xylem tubes. This increases the suction force of the inner cortical cells and, combined with the osmotic gradient already mentioned, leads to movement of water across the cortex and intake of soil water by the epidermal cells and root hairs.

There are certain difficulties involved in accepting this as the whole story of water intake and upward transport in the plant. The development of air bubbles in any great number of the xylem conduits would render those channels useless, seriously diminish the flow of water, and cause wilting or death of the plant. How this is prevented or overcome is not understood. Again, water filaments under tension in glass tubes are broken by a slight jar, while a tree can thresh wildly in the wind without breaking them. Perhaps the greater resiliency of cellulose tubes as compared with glass accounts for this. In spite of such difficulties transpiration pull is the most satisfactory explanation yet found for the rise of water in plants. The water columns, established by capillarity or root pressure while the plant is small, are continuously maintained and pulled upward during the growth of the plant, like so many slender wires hanging suspended from the leaf surfaces. In this way they can be lifted hundreds of feet into the air. The reality of transpiration pull becomes evident when one cuts into the base of a tree; air enters the cut ends of the tubes and follows the unsupported water columns as they are drawn upward.

Transport of solutes. Prior to 1920, botanists were generally agreed that upward transport of solutes, both organic and inorganic, occurs in the water-conducting conduits of the xylem and that downward transport takes place chiefly in the phloem. In that year two papers appeared, one by Curtis, giving the results of experiments that seemed to prove that both upward and downward transport of sugars takes place in the phloem, and one by Birch-Hirschfeld, indicating that, on the contrary, both upward and downward transport takes place through the xylem. The resulting controversy led to much further experimentation, and while the results are not altogether consistent, the problem has been somewhat clarified though not simplified.

It now appears that while the prime function of the *xylem* is to act as a one-way transport system for water, it may under some conditions and in some plants also carry inorganic salts taken in by roots and also perhaps sugars released from storage in stem and roots. Mineral transport in the xylem seems to occur (1) more in herbaceous than in woody plants, (2) more in plants showing active root pressures than in those without, (3) more near the base of the plant than near the top, and (4) more under certain special conditions of mineral abundance, root nourishment, etc. than under others. The situation with regard to sugars is less clear. The classical example of supposed upward movement of sugar in the xylem is that of the sugar maple in spring. Experiments by Curtis showed that even when sugar concentration was at a maximum in the xylem sap, and when upward movement of stored sugar was probably at its peak, upward transport would not take place if the phloem were completely cut. Curtis thinks that although much carbohydrate is stored in the xylem, it is carried there from the phloem for storage and carried out into the phloem for transport up or down the stem.

The *phloem* has been proved to be a two-way transport system for minerals and organic substances. It carries sugars and other organic materials in both directions—downward from the leaves to the stem and roots where these substances are used or stored and upward from storage in roots and stem. Experimental evidence is now clear that minerals are also carried in the phloem in both directions; but whether the xylem or the phloem is more important in mineral transport is still a matter of opinion. It seems to be established that the movement of minerals into leafless twigs and unexpanded leaves in spring occurs wholly through the phloem and that the phloem can supply the amounts required for rapid growth. This does not prove, however, that the phloem is the chief path of upward transport of minerals from roots to leaves; in fact, when the required amounts are small, it seems probable that either xylem or phloem alone can supply them. Proteins and the simpler nitrogenous compounds are abundant in the sieve tubes, and transport of these substances seems to be one of the chief functions of the phloem. Since movement of materials in the sieve tubes is by transfer through the protoplasm and not by a current of water, one substance may be moving toward the roots simultaneously with the leafward movement of another.

We may pause here to contrast the vascular system of the plant with the circulatory system of a higher animal. Both animal and plant possess main channels for the transport of liquids to all parts of the body. There the analogy ceases. In such a vertebrate as man a pumping mechanism, the heart, propels through a closed circuit a fluid medium carrying oxygen, food, and wastes. A circulatory system of this type may be compared with an endless belt, upon which various needed materials and waste products are continually deposited at different points and from which these substances are continually removed for use or disposal at various other points.

The transporting system of the plant, on the other hand, is composed of two independent units, each doing a different job and operating on a different principle and neither of them at all like the circulatory system of the animal. The *xylem* conduits form a unidirectional system of water transport, operating largely through transpiration pull—a mechanical process. The *phloem* channels are made up of the linked protoplasm of the phloem cells and through them, in either direction, move food and inorganic salts by diffusion or cell activity. Neither part of the vascular system is vitally concerned with respiration or excretion; oxygen and carbon dioxide are carried in solution in both, but the supply and elimination of these gases is accomplished for the most part by direct interchange with the atmosphere.

In addition to the primary functions of support and transportation, parts of the stem (particularly the phloem and parenchyma) may serve for temporary storage of manufactured food, water, or other substances. In many plants, also, the stem may play an important part in vegetative reproduction.

CHAPTER XII

THE LEAF AND ITS FUNCTIONS

The leaf is the food-manufacturing organ of the plant. Typically, it is a flattened structure, attached to a node of a stem, supported in such a way as to receive an optimum amount of sunlight, and green in color because of the presence of great numbers of chlorophyll-containing cells.[1]

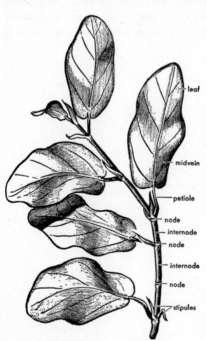

FIG. 12.1. Stem and leaves of the climbing fig, a dicot.

Leaves are extremely varied in form and size, and their differences are among the conspicuous features that aid in recognizing the various kinds of plants. Nevertheless, most leaves are built on a common plan, which includes the following parts. There is a broad, flat, expanded portion, the *blade*, supported by a stalk, the *petiole*. Where the petiole is attached to the node, its base may be flanked by a pair of small leaflike appendages, the *stipules*. On both surfaces of the blade there may be seen numerous *veins*, which are vascular bundles formed by repeated division of the large bundles that enter the blade from the petiole. The *venation*, or arrangement of the veins, forms a branching network in most dicotyledons, whereas in most monocotyledons the veins run parallel, or approximately so.

The structure of the leaf.   In cross section the blade of a leaf is seen to consist of several layers. The upper and under surfaces are covered

[1] All functional leaves contain chlorophyll. If they do not appear green to the eye, it is either because of the presence of additional pigments that mask the green of the chlorophyll or because the surface is covered with light-reflecting hairs or is otherwise modified.

with a very thin *cuticle*—a noncellular layer composed of cutin, which is a waxlike, impermeable material secreted by the epidermal cells.[1] The presence of this coating greatly diminishes loss of water by evaporation. Just beneath the cuticle lies the *epidermis*, a single layer of cells that is continuous over the entire surface of the leaf. The upper surface is usually smoother than the lower, and one or both may be more or less densely covered with microscopic hairs. Small openings, the *stomata*, penetrate the cuticle and epidermis and communicate with air spaces within the leaf.

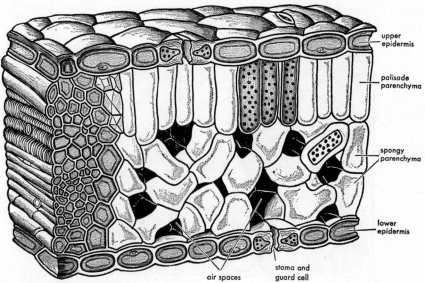

upper epidermis

palisade parenchyma

spongy parenchyma

lower epidermis

stoma and guard cell

air spaces

Fig. 12.2. Cross section of a leaf, including a vein. (*Modified from Turtox chart, courtesy General Biological Supply House, Inc.*)

The space between the two epidermal layers is filled, except where the veins occur, with parenchymous tissue, which is differentiated into two layers. The upper layer, one or two cells deep, is composed of tall, finger-shaped cells standing vertically beneath the epidermis. This is the *palisade parenchyma*. Its cells are closely packed together but with air spaces so arranged that each cell has at least one face in contact with the air. The palisade cells have a large central vacuole filled with cell sap, surrounded by a thin layer of protoplasm containing numerous small green plastids (*chloroplasts*), which contain chlorophyll. The lower and thicker layer of the parenchyma consists of a mass of thin-walled, loosely arranged cells, the *spongy parenchyma*, enclosing abundant air spaces that communicate with those of the palisade parenchyma. The cells of the spongy paren-

[1] A cutin layer covers all exposed surfaces of seedlings, herbaceous plants, and the young twigs of woody plants, as well as leaf surfaces.

chyma also contain chloroplasts, though not nearly so many as the palisade cells.

The *stomata* are openings enclosed by a pair of specialized epidermal cells called *guard cells*. There are about 40 stomata per square millimeter on the upper surface of the bean leaf, compared to about 250 per square millimeter on the lower surface; this ratio is quite typical of leaves in general. Under ordinary circumstances the stomata open when light falls upon the leaf and close when the light is withdrawn. This is caused by increase in turgor of the guard cells during the day and decrease at night. Since light is associated with photosynthesis, it was formerly believed that sugar manufacture within the guard cells was responsible

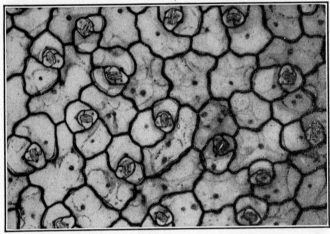

Fig. 12.3. Leaf epidermis of a rock-garden plant, Sedum, showing stomata. (*Courtesy General Biological Supply House, Inc.*)

for the daytime increase in turgor; but this appears not to be the explanation. Little photosynthesis goes on in these cells; most of their carbohydrate comes from outside, and the total amount remains fairly constant. At night, however, most of the carbohydrate in the guard cells is in the form of starch, which is changed to sugar during the day, probably as a result of acidity changes in the protoplasm. Whatever the explanation for the turgor changes, their result is to open the leaf for free gaseous interchange with the atmosphere during those periods when active photosynthesis requires it.

Because of this relation to sunlight, however, the stomata are relatively ineffective in controlling evaporation. Concentration of stomata upon the lower surfaces of the leaves helps to reduce water loss, and devices to reduce air movement past the stomatal openings and thus lessen evaporation are common. Thus the stomata may open at the bottoms of deep pits or in a dense forest of minute hairs; or the leaf may be curled so that it will partly protect the lower surface from air currents.

THE FUNCTIONING OF THE LEAF

The food of plants. The inorganic materials used by plants are commonly called *plant foods;* in popular usage this term has become associated with fertilizers. It is, of course, a matter of definition as to what shall be regarded as a food. According to one commonly accepted definition, *a food, whether used by animals or plants, is a substance which, either immediately or after a digestive process, may be oxidized to furnish energy or may be used in the building of protoplasm.* By this definition, carbon dioxide, water, and the mineral constituents of the soil and of fertilizers can scarcely be classed as foods. The true foodstuffs are *carbohydrates, fats,* and *proteins* and possibly, by stretching a point, the *vitamins.* This definition of food has the advantage of emphasizing the fact that nutrition in plants and animals is an identical process. The two kinds of organism differ, not in the nature of the food that they use but in the *method of obtaining it.* We have already stressed the fact that the plant manufactures its food from inorganic substances, whereas the animal cannot do this and therefore must obtain its food directly or indirectly from the plant.

The manufacture of food by photosynthesis. The basic food of the green plant is the simple sugar called *glucose,* which has the chemical formula $C_6H_{12}O_6$. From glucose the plant can manufacture other carbohydrates, and from carbohydrates and minerals it can make the fats, proteins, enzymes, vitamins, and plant hormones that it requires.

Glucose is synthesized in the green plants and only in them. It is formed by the chemical combination of water and carbon dioxide through the agency of *chlorophyll* and by means of the energy of sunlight. If we consider only the end products of the reaction, it appears quite simple, as is shown by the following equation:

6 molecules of water	+	6 molecules of carbon dioxide	+	Light energy (through agency of chlorophyll)	(yields)	1 molecule of glucose	+	6 molecules of oxygen

$$6H_2O + 6CO_2 + \text{Energy} \rightarrow C_6H_{12}O_6 + 6O_2$$

It is well established that in the process of photosynthesis carbon dioxide and water are the raw materials, chlorophyll and light are necessary, sugar and oxygen are formed, and for each volume of carbon dioxide used an equal volume of oxygen is liberated. For an elementary understanding of plant functioning no more than this is needed; but the actual photosynthetic process is not this simple. In fact it is so complex that no one has succeeded in duplicating it in the laboratory. Nevertheless great progress has been made in its study in recent years, especially since radioactive tracer isotopes of carbon, hydrogen, and oxygen have become available as tools of investigation.[1]

It is now known that chlorophyll is not a single substance but a group of related substances, just as are many of the vitamins and hormones. At least 10 different chlorophylls have been differentiated. Two of these, chlorophyll a and chlorophyll b ($C_{55}H_{72}O_5N_4Mg$ and $C_{55}H_{70}O_6N_4Mg$ respectively) are present in all the higher plants and the green algae. Furthermore, it has been found that chlorophyll is not solely responsible for photosynthesis but is a part of a system involving at least two additional catalysts; that the reaction occurs in steps, one requiring light and the other(s) not; and that 12 molecules of water instead of 6 take part in the reaction

$$6CO_2 + 12H_2O + Energy \rightarrow C_6H_{12}O_6 + 6H_2O + 6O_2$$

Water does not combine directly with carbon dioxide to form sugar but is decomposed to liberate the free oxygen of the right-hand side of the equation and to furnish hydrogen that reduces the CO_2 to sugar and water. Beyond this point we need not go, but enough has been said to indicate the nature of the problems encountered when we try to discover how photosynthesis works.

Any cell containing chlorophyll is capable of manufacturing glucose; but the greater part of the work of photosynthesis is carried on by the parenchyma of the leaves. A leaf is an organ especially adapted for efficient utilization of the energy of light in the synthesis of glucose. The required water is brought from the roots through the xylem conduits. The carbon dioxide is almost wholly taken from the air through the stomata, though small amounts may be derived from the soil, and a part is released within the plant by oxidation of previously elaborated food. As the carbon dioxide is used up in the cells, that in the intercellular spaces diffuses into the cells, and additional quantities diffuse through the stomata into the air spaces.

The absorption area of the plant is so great that, although air contains only about 3 parts in 10,000 of carbon dioxide, relatively great quantities of this gas can be obtained from the atmosphere. Thus a moderately large oak tree may weigh, when dry, as much as 14,000 pounds. About 4 per cent of this dry weight consists of nitrogen and other materials derived from the soil, and about 60 per cent is hydrogen and oxygen. The remaining 36 per cent, or about 5,200 pounds, consists of carbon, originally taken in as carbon dioxide. This amount does not represent

[1] Results of experiments with radioactive isotopes, published in 1949, indicate that in certain simple plants the first *free* carbohydrate to appear following photosynthesis is sucrose, not glucose or fructose. The significance of this observation is still uncertain.

all the carbon dioxide that has entered the tree during its life, for oxidation of food and loss of the resulting carbon dioxide during the night must also be taken into account. But the remaining 5,200 pounds of carbon corresponds to the amount present in the carbon dioxide of 74 million cubic yards of air, which would fill a cube measuring about $\frac{1}{4}$ mile on a side. Proof that the great bulk of the carbon dioxide comes from the atmosphere and not from the soil is afforded by experiments in which plants are found to grow luxuriantly under conditions such that no dissolved carbon dioxide can be obtained by the roots.

In photosynthesis two stable compounds are broken up, and an unstable one is formed. This involves the performance of work, in which the radiant *kinetic energy* of sunlight is transformed into *potential energy* stored in the form of glucose. Oxygen readily unites with glucose to restore the two original stable substances, water and carbon dioxide, and when this occurs, the energy that went into the making of the glucose is released. In the form of kinetic (now *chemical*) energy it becomes available for the synthesis of glucose into other carbohydrates, fats, and proteins and for other forms of work.

All life is made possible by the temporary storage and controlled release of energy, and the overwhelmingly predominant (though not the only) device for energy capture is the sunlight-chlorophyll-glucose mechanism. Most living things are either directly or indirectly dependent upon photosynthesis for their existence. The importance of the mechanism is not merely that it stores energy in the form of organic substances; it also provides the means for the release of this energy through oxidation.

Maintenance of the oxygen content of the air at something like its present level is essential to animal life. Man and all other animals would soon cease to exist if oxygen were not continually being returned to the air through photosynthesis. Oxidation is the spontaneous process, and the freeing of oxygen from combination requires expenditure of energy. With almost negligible exceptions, the green plants are the only present source of free oxygen. The atmospheres of the other planets contain no detectable amounts of this gas, and it is reasonable to conclude that until green plants became established, the earth's atmosphere was also without free oxygen.

SOME FURTHER ASPECTS OF PLANT PHYSIOLOGY

The relation between photosynthesis and respiration.   Respiration in plants and animals is identical; in both the process includes the intake of oxygen and the liberation of carbon dioxide. Each cell of an animal or plant body uses oxygen and produces carbon dioxide (and water) continuously, at a rate that varies with the activity of the cell. In the animal, the nature of respiration is plainly evident, since there is no other process requiring gaseous interchange with the environment. In the plant, on the other hand, there are two distinct processes that must be separately considered if confusion is to be avoided.

Respiration goes on continuously in the cells of the plant, using oxygen and producing carbon dioxide and water. At night, when photosynthesis is inoperative, respiration is the only factor in the situation, and at this time the leaf takes in oxygen and gives off carbon dioxide like an animal body. With the coming of day, the photosynthetic manufacture of glucose is resumed; but respiration also continues, if anything, at a faster rate than during the night. Since, however, photosynthesis requires such great quantities of carbon dioxide, the amount produced by respiration of the cells, although utilized, is altogether insufficient, and carbon dioxide from the outside begins to flow into the leaf. The cells continue to require oxygen for their respiratory needs; but photosynthesis is producing it in such great quantities as a waste product that there is an oversupply within the leaf, and the excess that cannot be used in respiration diffuses out through the stomata.

It is often thought that because leaves take in carbon dioxide and give off oxygen during the day, respiration in plants is exactly the reverse of respiration in animals. In reality, it is identical in principle, and the day-night reversal of intake and outgo of the two gases results from over-balancing of respiration by photosynthesis during the day. The relations may be seen in the following tabular comparison of the two processes:

	Photosynthesis	Respiration
Place of occurrence......	Only in chlorophyll-containing cells of green plants	In every living cell of both plants and animals
Time of occurrence......	Only when the cells are illuminated	At all times during the life of the cell
Materials used..........	Water and carbon dioxide	Oxygen (and fuel)
By-products............	Oxygen	Water and carbon dioxide
Energy relations........	Uses and stores energy	Releases energy
Effect on weight........	Body weight is increased	Body weight is decreased

Synthesis of other materials from glucose. A part of the glucose produced by photosynthesis is directly used by the leaves and other parts of the plant, being oxidized with release of energy. A much larger portion is chemically transformed into a variety of other substances useful to the plant—food in forms suitable for storage; materials needed for building protoplasm and for forming the cell walls; enzymes; and other products. The majority of these syntheses are highly complex, and many of them are not or are but poorly understood; but we can gain some insight into the general nature of the changes that occur by considering a few of the simpler and more important cases.

As we have already seen, *glucose* (dextrose, grape sugar) is one of the simple sugars, or monosaccharides, with the chemical formula $C_6H_{12}O_6$. Plants also make another simple sugar, *fructose* (levulose, fruit sugar), which has the same chemical formula as glucose but somewhat different properties. Fructose, which is perhaps formed directly by photosynthesis like glucose, is still sweeter than the latter and is especially abundant in sweet fruits. It appears to be important for tissue formation, whereas glucose is primarily an energy food.

Most of the sugar stored in plants is in the form of *disaccharides*, or double sugars, which are made by the union of two monosaccharide molecules with the loss of one molecule of water, as shown by the following equation:

$$\underset{\text{fructose}}{\text{Glucose or}} + \underset{\text{fructose}}{\text{Glucose or}} + \text{Energy (yields) A disaccharide} + \text{Water}$$

$$C_6H_{12}O_6 + C_6H_{12}O_6 + \text{Energy} \rightarrow C_{12}H_{22}O_{11} + H_2O$$

The two commonest disaccharides in plants are *sucrose* (cane sugar), composed of one molecule of glucose and one of fructose, and *maltose* (malt sugar), composed of two molecules of glucose. Sucrose is much the sweeter of the two and is the ordinary sugar that we use on the table. It is one of the commoner substances used by plants for food storage, and in plants like sugar cane and sugar beet, it almost wholly replaces starch in this role. Maltose is of interest, since it appears to be an intermediate step in the formation of the important material starch.

Starch is one of the chief food-storage materials; it is especially abundant in tubers, grains, and certain fruits and constitutes 30 to 70 per cent of the dry weight of our own food. Chemically, starch is a *polysaccharide*, i.e., a carbohydrate built up of many monosaccharide units. It is related to maltose in somewhat the same way that maltose is related to glucose, since for each molecule of maltose that enters into the starch, one molecule of water is lost. The chemical formula of starch is $n(C_6H_{10}O_5)$, which, translated, means that the starch molecule is of no fixed size but contains an indefinite number (n) of the $C_6H_{10}O_5$ units; its structure is thought to be that of an indefinitely long chain of linked molecules, and the molecular weight is usually very high. Starch occurs in the form of granules; it is an excellent storage material, both because it is relatively insoluble, yet easily reconverted into soluble sugar for transportation, and because it contains more energy per unit of weight than do the sugars. During the day granules of starch form in the chloroplasts where glucose is being made, the excess sugar being thus removed as fast as it is made and the sugar concentration prevented from becoming injuriously high. At night these starch granules in the chloroplasts disappear, because of the reconversion of the starch into soluble sugars that are carried to other parts of the plant.

Cellulose is another polysaccharide formed from glucose. Although related chemically to starch, it is very much more insoluble and is highly resistant to chemical change. It is not affected by the ordinary digestive enzymes; animals such as ruminant mammals and termites, which use cellulose as food, are able to do so only through the presence in their digestive tracts of microorganisms capable of breaking down this substance. *Fats, oils, and waxes* are synthesized from sugars without the addition of any other elements; but the proportions of carbon, hydrogen, and oxygen in the molecule are changed, and the latter element is so greatly diminished in relative amount that the quantity of stored energy is very considerably increased. Fats and oils are extensively used by plants for food storage on account of this high energy content. In the synthesis of *amino acids and proteins*, carbohydrates are combined with nitrogen from the soil and sometimes also with sulfur, phosphorus, or other elements. The proteins thus formed constitute, with water, the bulk of the protoplasm of the cells; some of them are also stored as food (especially in the seeds of legumes) or are used in the making of enzymes and other cell products.

Enzyme action in plants.   The chemical transformations that occur within the plant are nearly all brought about through the agency of various enzymes. We have already seen something of the nature and functioning of these organic catalysts in our study of the human body, and it will be recalled that one of their characteristics is a high degree of specificity in the substances upon which they act. Each enzyme affects only a single chemical reaction. In view of the multiplicity of the chemical reactions that occur within the plant cell, it would therefore seem that each cell must either be equipped with a battery of enzymes or else be able to produce any given enzyme at need. Some of the enzyme-controlled reactions are reversible, the direction of the reaction being controlled by the relative concentrations of the substances taking part; thus, under experimental conditions, *lipase*, found in plants as well as in animals, in the presence of excess fat splits the fat into glycerol and fatty acids, but in the presence of excess glycerol and fatty acids causes these to combine into fat. The plant cells are apparently able to control the direction of this process by the expenditure of energy. Most enzyme-controlled reactions, however, are in practice unidirectional; thus some enzymes build up a complex substance from simpler ones with the expenditure of energy (synthesis), whereas others break down a complex substance into simpler ones with liberation of energy.

As a concrete example of enzyme activity in plants, we may consider the process by which starch is split up into monosaccharide molecules. Starch being so nearly insoluble, its conversion into soluble form may be regarded as a kind of intracellular digestion comparable to the digestive process in animals. The splitting is accomplished by two specific enzymes. The first of these, *diastase*, changes starch back to the sugar, maltose, by the addition of $n/2$ molecules of water to each starch molecule $n(C_6H_{10}O_5)$, as shown by the following equation, in which we may take n as equal to 200:

Starch molecule	+	Water molecules	(yields)	Maltose molecules	+	Energy
$200(C_6H_{10}O_5)$	+	$100H_2O$	$\rightarrow$	$100C_{12}H_{22}O_{11}$	+	Energy
		(in the presence of diastase)				

As soon as this reaction has taken place, the maltose is generally converted into glucose by the action of the second enzyme, *maltase*, as shown by the equation

Maltose molecule	+	Water molecule	(yields)	Glucose molecules	+	Energy
$C_{12}H_{22}O_{11}$	+	H_2O	$\rightarrow$	$2C_6H_{12}O_6$	+	Energy
		(in the presence of maltase)				

This particular kind of molecule splitting is called *hydrolysis*—the union of a complex compound with water, accompanied by its breaking up into less complex compounds. The process outlined above is just the reverse of that by which the glucose was synthesized into starch.

The enzyme diastase is similar to and perhaps identical with the ptyalin of human saliva. Maltase of plants is the same enzyme as that found in the small intestine of man, where it breaks down maltose sugar just as it does in the plant cell. Some of the other enzymes present in plants are *invertase*, splitting cane sugar into glucose and fructose, and found also in the small intestine of man; *cellulase*, changing cellulose to glucose, and not present in vertebrates; *lipase*, mentioned above as an example of enzymes with reversible action, changing fats to fatty acids and glycerin or vice versa, and found also in the human stomach. Various *proteinases* that convert proteins to amino acids by a series of steps, much as pepsin and trypsin work together in man, are also present.

We closed our account of the human body, considered as an illustration of the structure and functioning of the individual animal, without consideration of the reproductive organs. So we shall also do with the plant. Flowers and fruits and all the processes associated with their formation and functioning have to do with the perpetuation of the race, and will be discussed in that connection; but just as sex in animals affects many aspects of their functioning as individuals, so do the reproductive adaptations of plants affect them. The roles of *individual* and of *member-of-a-race* are played simultaneously by every organism, and interact upon one another in many ways. Our account of the plant, even considered merely as an individual organism, will therefore not be complete until the reproductive processes and structures have been treated in Chap. XVII.

CHAPTER XIII

SOME OTHER TYPES OF INDIVIDUAL ORGANIZATION: VARIETY OF STRUCTURE VERSUS UNIFORMITY OF FUNCTION

One needs only to look about him to see something of the extraordinary variety of size, form, and structure that exists among organisms. When the world revealed by the microscope is also considered, the diversity of living things proves to be very great indeed. Considerably more than a million kinds of animals and plants are known today, and additional ones are constantly being discovered. Out of this vast assemblage, we have examined two types in some detail—man, to illustrate the problems of individual structure and functioning among animals, and a flowering plant, to show how these problems are met by a member of the plant kingdom. Our survey of these has now been almost completed; but a question that still confronts us is to what extent these selected examples are representative of other organisms. In briefly considering this question, we shall also, in a sense, be summarizing the essential features of individual organization and functioning, freed from much specific detail that has necessarily been included in our treatment of man and the higher plants.

The thesis of this chapter is that, no matter what their size, form, or structure, *all individual organisms encounter the same basic problems of living but solve these problems in unlike ways.* The number of different ways of doing the necessary tasks and of types of organization associated with these methods is not, however, so great as might be supposed. We have already seen that the most basic divergence among organisms lies in the means by which the problem of nutrition has been met. The plant has adopted one method, the animal another, and the consequences are so far-reaching that we shall have to examine the chief patterns of animal and of plant life separately and by somewhat different treatments.

THE VARIED PATTERNS OF ANIMAL LIFE

If we ignore all except the most striking and fundamental differences among animals, we can group the more than three-quarter million known kinds into a few major assemblages, based on different degrees of complexity in organization and the extent of "division of labor" among the parts of the individual. We shall first briefly examine four different levels of construction found among animals and then see how the common tasks of life are performed at each of these levels.

Structural Levels

Protoplasmic level. In one large group of animals, the Protozoa,[1] each individual consists of a single cell. (Some are colonial, the individuals being held together mechanically in a group). This one cell must perform all the functions essential for animal life. It must capture its own food

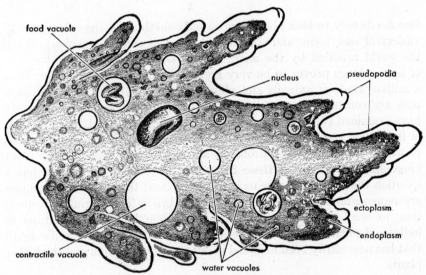

FIG. 13.1. Amoeba, a single-celled protozoan animal.

and digest it, carry on respiration, excrete metabolic wastes, respond appropriately to environmental stimuli, and reproduce its kind. Such a single-celled animal lives on what may be called the *protoplasmic level* of construction. Performance of its various functions is provided for by the organization of its protoplasm, and such organization as it shows is all intracellular. There are no tissues and organs, and the Protozoa do not have any very complex structures correlated with particular functions. Nevertheless they should not be thought of as simple. No cell is simple, and these separate-living cells have to do many more things than the specialized cells of the human body and are correspondingly complicated. *Amoeba* (Fig. 13.1) is an excellent example of these unspecialized,

[1] The animal groups mentioned in this chapter are defined and illustrated in Appendix B.

single-celled animals; *Monosiga* (Fig. 13.2) is a more specialized type of protozoan, fixed by a stalk, and having a sticky protoplasmic collar and a whip that brings food particles to the collar by means of a current.

Some of the Protozoa show an approach to the next level of organization by living together in groups or colonies of cells. Aside from certain mechanical advantages gained by increased size and better protection of the immature cells, they are scarcely different from other protozoans. The cells still function as individual units, and all are alike or potentially alike. In *Proterospongia* (Fig. 13.3), a form closely allied to Monosiga, a group of cells is enclosed in a gelatinous mass. Those at the surface have collars and whips like Monosiga; those within can move about by amoeboid movements, and upon reaching the surface can rapidly produce similar collars and whips. There is no organization of the cells.

In more than 90 per cent of all known kinds of animals the individual is made up of at least many hundreds and often of billions of cells, and these cells exhibit a greater or less amount of differentiation and specialization for particular tasks. In all but the simplest of these *many-celled animals* (*Metazoa*) the cells are organized into tissues, into tissues and organs, or into tissues, organs, and systems.

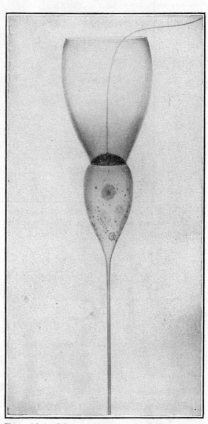

Fig. 13.2. Monosiga, a stalked protozoan with flagellum and sticky food-gathering collar. (*Courtesy American Museum of Natural History.*)

Cellular level. The *sponges* (Porifera) are the simplest and least highly organized of the Metazoa. Essentially they consist of two layers of cells arranged to form hollow tubes or chambers (Fig. 13.4); the layers are separated by a thicker or thinner layer of nonliving cell products, which include gelatinous materials and supporting fibers or rodlike structures. In general the cells on the outside are different in form from those on the inside layer; but a cell from either layer can withdraw into the interior of the mass and later take up a position on the opposite face,

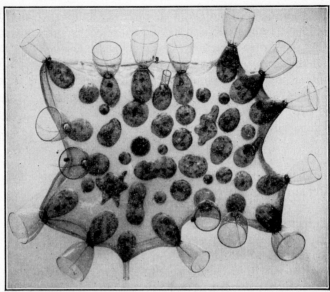

Fig. 13.3. *Proterospongia*, a protozoan colony. Any cell in the gelatinous mass can migrate to the surface and develop a flagellum and collar. (*Courtesy American Museum of Natural History.*)

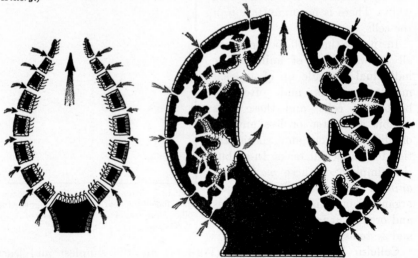

Fig. 13.4. Diagrammatic vertical sections through simple sponge (left) and more complex sponge (right). (*Modified from Berry, Paleontology.*)

changing its characteristics while so doing. The inner cells are much like those of Proterospongia, with food-gathering collars and whips that create a water current through the sponge. These feeding cells can pass on a part of their digested food to wandering cells in the interior, and these in turn supply the cells of the outer layer. If the substance of a living sponge is forced through a fine sieve, the uninjured separated cells will crawl together like amoebae and build many small new sponge bodies, each cell taking on the form appropriate to its position in the developing sponge.

In a sponge, then, the cells have become slightly (and not irreversibly) differentiated and show some division of labor and degree of cooperation. However, they are not organized into definite tissues, and the sponge

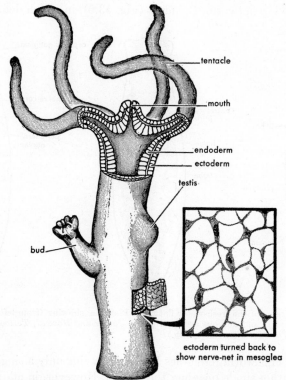

FIG. 13.5. Hydra, a simple metazoan animal. The inset shows a part of the nerve net at the base of the ectodermal layer. (*Inset based on Wolcott, Animal Biology.*)

has no organs nor any means of coordination other than a simple mechanical relationship between the cells. The body functions are carried on by the cells acting as units, and the whole sponge functions at what may be called the *cellular level of construction*.

Tissue level. The simplest animals in which specialized cells are organized into definite tissues are the *coelenterates* (Coelenterata), a group to which belong Hydra, jellyfishes, corals, and sea anemones. In them the grouping of cells into tissues brings increased efficiency. The cells are enabled to act in a more coordinated fashion and with massed effect. The animals of this group may be said to have reached the *tissue level of construction.*

The small, contractile, many-armed animal known as *Hydra* (Fig. 13.5) is a good example of the group. It is saclike in construction, the body wall being made up of two layers of cells surrounding a digestive cavity; this cavity is the only one in the body and has but one opening, the mouth.

A step in advance of the coelenterate type of structure is shown by the small, free-living flatworm, *Planaria* (Fig. 13.6), in which definite organs

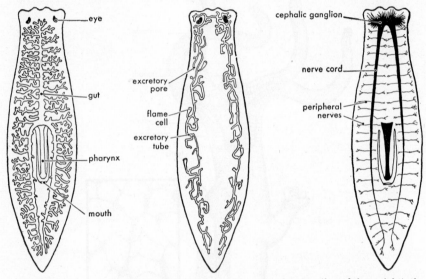

FIG. 13.6. Diagrams of the fresh-water flatworm Planaria, showing (from left to right) the digestive, excretory, and nervous systems. (*From Parker and Haswell, Textbook of Zoology, by permission The Macmillan Company.*)

are present. This worm resembles Hydra in having only a single cavity in the body, with a single opening, the mouth. However, in addition to the two cell layers corresponding to those that form the body wall in Hydra, there is present in Planaria a third layer between them, which makes up most of the bulk of the body and takes part in the formation of various organs. Among the simple organs of Planaria are a muscular pharynx for ingesting food, nerve cords and light-sensitive eyespots, excretory apparatus, and reproductive organs. Even in this lowly worm there is a suggestion of organ systems in the arrangement of the digestive, excretory, and nervous structures.

Organ-system level.   Above the plane of the flatworms nearly all the Metazoa have attained the *organ-system level of construction.* In these higher Metazoa we not only find cells functioning individually, cell groups working together as tissues, and tissues cooperating in the formation of organs—the organs themselves are, for the most part, grouped into systems, each system being adapted for the performance of one or a few functions. The human body is constructed on this plan, and in Chap. II its hierarchy of cells, tissues, organs, and systems was described.

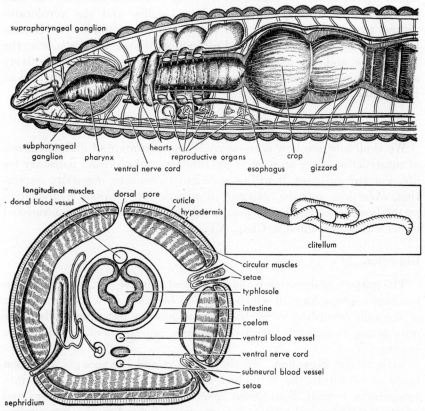

FIG. 13.7. An earthworm (Lumbricus) in diagrammatic longitudinal and cross section, to illustrate a simple organ-system construction. The small inset shows the part of the body longitudinally sectioned; the cross section is made farther back.

Animals whose organization has attained this level share certain fundamental characteristics in spite of their many differences. In all of them the bulk of the body is formed from the third cell layer (*mesoderm*), which we first noted in the flatworms. They all have a body space surrounding the digestive tract, so that the plan of the body is essentially that of a tube within a tube. Further than this it becomes difficult to generalize, because the structural patterns of the higher Metazoa have diverged along a number of quite distinct lines, related to different modes of development, habitat, and ways of life. All, however, have attained more or less high degrees of organization and integration. Most of the higher Metazoa are comparatively bulky; nearly all have some type of circulatory system; and the nervous system and sense organs are much more complex and highly developed than in the lower types, permitting adaptation to more varied and complicated environments. Many of these higher Metazoa are specialized for a wholly terrestrial existence. Insects, spiders, crabs, worms, starfishes, clams, snails, and the vertebrates (fishes, frogs, reptiles, birds, and mammals) are examples of Metazoa built on the organ-system plan. From among these, the *earthworm*, the *grasshopper*, and *man* may be selected as examples to illustrate relatively simple, moderately complex, and highly complex types of structure at this organizational level.

DIFFERENT WAYS OF DOING THE SAME THINGS

We shall now see how some animals representative of different levels of construction carry on some of the fundamental processes necessary for life. For our purposes, it will be sufficient to consider digestion, respiration, excretion, and the response to stimuli. The various reproductive methods and breeding habits associated with the different organizational levels will be presented in Chap. XV.

Digestion

The purpose of digestion is the same in all animals—*i.e.*, to break down foodstuffs into a form in which they can be taken into the protoplasm of the cell. According to whether this is done by individual cells or by cells acting in concert, digestive methods can be classified under two heads.

Intracellular digestion. In the Protozoa and the sponges, digestion takes place within the individual cells. Food particles are taken into temporarily formed, liquid-filled spaces surrounded by protoplasm and known as *food vacuoles*. Digestive enzymes, formed in the surrounding protoplasm, diffuse into the vacuoles and digest the food particles; the products of digestion then diffuse into the protoplasm. Indigestible residues are eliminated from the cell through the cell membrane by a "bursting" of the vacuoles to the outside.

Extracellular digestion. In all the more complex animals digestion takes place in a *body cavity surrounded by digestive cells*. Both intra- and extracellular digestion occur in some of the simple metazoa, such as Hydra. All extracellular digestion requires a digestive organ or organ system. The chief types of digestive structures are:

1. *The Coelenteron.* A digestive sac, found in very simple metazoa; it has but one opening, the mouth. In the flatworms, the coelenteron is

highly branched and ramifies throughout the body so that all other tissues are within absorbing distance of the digested food.

2. *The Enteron.*   In all groups more complex than the flatworms, the coelenteron, as a digestive cavity, is supplanted by a structure known

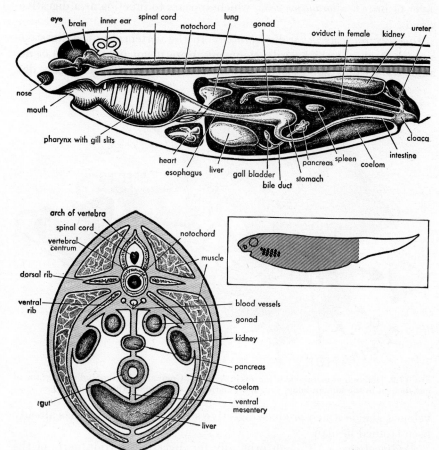

Fig. 13.8. A vertebrate in diagrammatic longitudinal and cross section, to illustrate a highly specialized organ-system construction. The small inset shows the portion of the body represented in longitudinal and cross section. (*Modified from Romer, The Vertebrate Body, by permission W. B. Saunders Company.*)

as the *enteron,* a digestive tube open at both ends, *i.e.,* having both a mouth and an anus.

Digestion in the Earthworm.   The enteron of the earthworm may be used as an example of a digestive tube that has been differentiated to form a system of organs. It consists of a *mouth,* opening into a *buccal cavity,* a *pharynx* with strong muscular walls, an *esophagus,* a *crop* in which food accumulates, a *gizzard* with thick muscular walls and a hard lining by means of which food may be finely ground, an *intestine* with secreting and absorptive cells, and an *anus.* An internal ridge, the *typhlosole,* formed by an infolding of the dorsal wall of the intestine, gives increased surface. The exterior surface of the intestine is covered by a layer of brown *chloragogen cells,* which appears to function as a digestive gland.

Digestive Systems in the Vertebrates. In the vertebrates, the digestive system reaches its highest development. Here it not only consists of an alimentary canal, subdivided into regions, but also possesses highly de-

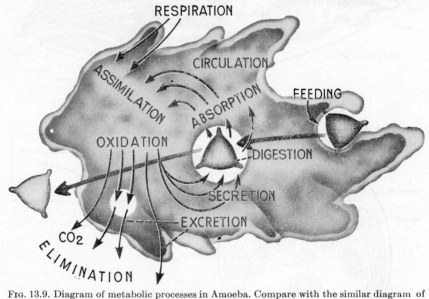

FIG. 13.9. Diagram of metabolic processes in Amoeba. Compare with the similar diagram of metabolism in the human body, Fig. 2.5. (*Adapted from Wolcott, Animal Biology.*)

veloped glands which produce digestive secretions. This type has already been studied in man.

Modifications. Although primarily for digestion, certain parts of the enteron may be used for other purposes in some groups of animals. Thus, in the sea cucumbers and in certain groups of aquatic insects, the rectum is secondarily used as a respiratory organ; and in all insects, excretion is carried on by numerous fine tubules opening into the posterior part of the enteron.

Respiration

All animals are dependent upon the oxidation of foodstuffs for energy and so have a continual need for oxygen and for the elimination of carbon dioxide. The quantities of oxygen required and of carbon dioxide that must be eliminated are proportional to the amount of protoplasm and the rate of metabolism. When the animal is very small, the ratio of its body surface to the volume of its protoplasm is comparatively great, and if the surface is permeable to oxygen and carbon dioxide, it may be sufficient to meet all respiratory needs. Several factors, however, set a limit to the utilization of the body surface as a respiratory membrane. As the size of the body increases, two distinct types of respiratory complications result: (1) the *ratio of body surface to volume* decreases and becomes inadequate for a sufficient respiratory exchange; (2) a high proportion of body tissues are now *internal*, with no direct access to the external medium. Any increase in the metabolic rate will, of course, increase the minimum ratio of surface to volume necessary for an adequate respiratory exchange; and the various adaptations of body surfaces for protection against loss of water or mechanical injury decrease or wholly destroy their properties as respiratory membranes. All but the simplest and smallest metazoans have consequently had to develop special respiratory processes and structures.

Types of respiratory processes. Four more or less distinct types of respiratory processes can be distinguished. *Simple respiration* involves a direct exchange through the cell membrane between the protoplasm of the cell and the gases of the external medium. When a circulating medium (blood) is utilized to provide for the respiratory needs of internal tissues, respiration involves two distinct processes: *external respiration*, in which the blood makes a gaseous exchange with the external medium; and *internal respiration*, in which a gaseous interchange takes place between the aerated blood and the protoplasm of the cells. Finally, in many organisms the necessity of providing special respiratory surfaces (which in most instances must be protected against loss of water, mechanical injury, or both) is associated with *breathing*, a process that results in the continual aeration of the respiratory surface.

Simple direct respiration. The simplest of all respiratory processes is found in the Protozoa, the lowest Metazoa, and in certain minute representatives of the intermediate and higher Metazoa. Here, since the ratio of surface to volume is large, since all protoplasm is within a very short distance of the body surface, and since the latter is freely permeable to oxygen and carbon dioxide, an adequate gaseous exchange is provided by a direct diffusion between the protoplasm and the external medium.

The direct respiration of insects. A far more complicated type of direct respiration has been developed by the insects and certain of their relatives. Here the tough exoskeleton and the comparatively huge proportion of internal tissues preclude gaseous interchange through the body surface, and there has been developed a complex network of ramifying air tubes (*tracheae*), that lead from external openings to all of the tissues. At their ultimate branches the tracheae communicate with numerous very fine, thin-walled, liquid-filled tubules, the *tracheoles*, in which by diffusion oxygen is carried to and carbon dioxide from the immediate vicinity of the cells. Since these tubes and tubules are internal and comprise a tremendous total linear extent, regular muscular breathing movements are required to bring about the necessary renewal of fresh air.

FIG. 13.10. The tracheal respiratory system of an insect. Branches from the main trunks and connectives extend to all parts of the body; their finer ramifications penetrate all tissues and are too small and too numerous to be shown. (*From Shull, Principles of Animal Biology.*)

Various devices for external respiration. Except for the insects and their allies, all metazoan adaptations to provide respiratory exchange for internal tissues involve the utilization of some type of circulatory system and the consequent development of external and internal respiration. The chief variations that occur among these organisms concern the type of respiratory devices that are utilized to accomplish external respiration.

1. *The Skin as an Organ for External Respiration.* In the earthworm and numerous other small metazoans, the body surface is thin and moist and has an area sufficient to provide for an adequate gaseous interchange between the blood and the external medium. Here no breathing is required, since the whole body surface is adapted for respiratory exchange. It is worth noting in this connection that the very properties that make the earthworm's body covering a good respiratory membrane make it impossible for the animal to exist in any except moist, protected situations.

2. *Gills as Organs for External Respiration.* Gills are special respiratory membranes adapted for a gaseous exchange between the blood[1] and an external aquatic medium. The gills of fishes are broad plates of delicate respiratory tissue richly supplied with blood vessels, attached in the region of the pharynx to bony arches; between these are slits through which water taken into the mouth is passed out. Many aquatic animals have gills which, though differing in position and complexity, function on the same general principle as do those of the fish. Examples are to be found among the worms, clams, a few aquatic insect larvae, and tadpoles.

[1] In most aquatic insect larvae, the air of the tracheal system is brought into close proximity to the water in thin delicate outgrowths from the body wall, which are termed *tracheal gills.*

3. *Lungs as Organs for External Respiration.* True lungs are found only in the air-breathing vertebrates. We have seen something of their structure and functioning in man, and, although the lungs of certain of the lower vertebrates are much simpler, they show a comparable structure and have the same function. Some other land animals, such as the spiders and terrestrial snails, also have respiratory organs that function as lungs, although these differ markedly in origin and structure from the lungs of vertebrates.

Excretion

Besides excess water and carbon dioxide, there must be removed certain solids in solution, particularly nitrogenous wastes such as urea and uric acid. The methods found in various animals for the excretion of this type of waste are discussed below.

Excretion in the protozoa. In the Protozoa, excretion doubtless occurs to a greater or less extent through the surface of the body, but usually one or more small *contractile vacuoles* (Fig. 13.1) concerned with this function are also present. Such a vacuole fills with a watery fluid drained from the surrounding protoplasm and periodically discharges it to the outside, thus washing the protoplasm free from soluble waste materials. In fresh-water Protozoa an equally important function of these cell organs is to "bail out" the water which continually enters the cell as a result of osmosis, and which otherwise would soon cause rupture and death of the organism.

Excretion in the metazoa. In very simple multicellular animals, the surfaces of the body suffice for excretion; hence they have no special excretory organs. All except these simplest Metazoa, however, have developed special systems and organs for the removal of wastes. Some of the more important types of these systems are as follows:

Protonephridial System. This type of excretory system is characteristic of the flatworms (Fig. 13.6) and does not require a circulatory system for its operation. The metabolic wastes are carried from the tissues to the outside by means of a system of tubes. This drainage system may be simple or greatly branched, but each tubule originates from a large, cup-shaped cell, the inner wall of which bears a tuft of long cilia. The beating of these cilia suggests the flickering of a flame; hence the cell is called a *flame cell.* Besides withdrawing fluid from the surrounding tissues, the vibrations of the flame-cell cilia create a current that carries the collected wastes to the outside.

Nephridia. In the metameric worms (for example, the earthworm, Fig. 13.7) nearly every segment of the body is provided with a pair of coiled tubes, the nephridia, each of which has a funnel-shaped, ciliated opening, the *nephrostome,* which projects through the septum into the cavity of the segment ahead, and there opens directly into the body cavity or coelom. The other end of the coiled tube opens to the exterior through the body wall. The nephrostome sweeps in liquid and small particles by the action of its cilia, and cilia within the tube assist in propelling liquids to the exterior. Portions of the nephridium are composed of cells that take up water and certain dissolved materials from the fluid in the tube and return them to the blood, thus concentrating the wastes and conserving useful substances. The nephridia are richly supplied with blood vessels.

Kidneys. The excretory organs of the vertebrates are the kidneys, which operate in the manner already described for man.

Coordination and Irritability

We have seen that the various structures employed to accomplish digestion, respiration, and excretion show a wide range in complexity and efficiency. In even the simplest animals it is essential that all these functions (and others) be coordinated to supply the needs of a complete organism. This need for coordination involves the animal's response to the environment; for the rates of digestion, respiration, etc., are largely determined by stimuli that originate in the environment and (because of the irritability of protoplasm) produce appropriate responses on the part of the animal. In the lower animals, the problem of coordination, although very complex, is *relatively* simple; but as digestion and other processes come to involve more and more complicated structures, the magnitude of the problem of coordination increases proportionately. In general, the greater the degree of coordination the more varied the environment in which the animal can maintain itself.

Responsiveness in the Protozoa. The single-celled animals show a surprising degree of adjustment to external factors and have at times a rather complicated behavior. Temperature exerts a general effect on protoplasmic activities, controlling rate of reproduction, locomotion, and physiological processes. Chemical stimuli are important, though there are no special receptors. Mechanical stimuli affect the general irritability of the protoplasm or are received by cilia and flagella (locomotor organelles found in certain groups of the Protozoa). Protoplasm is often directly responsive to light. The stimuli received by the cell may be conducted from the stimulated point to other parts of the cell without the intervention of any specialized structure. However, in some of the more complex protozoa (Ciliata) a "neuromotor" apparatus is present, which consists of protoplasmic fibrils leading from ciliated regions to zones of specially contractile protoplasm. Characteristic movements are produced in response to all the stimuli mentioned above.

Nerve net. In the lower Metazoa special cells have been differentiated for the reception and conduction of stimuli. In Hydra these sensory cells are located in the body wall, and in the inner layer of cells surrounding the coelenteron branches extend between the sensory cells and from them to the contractile processes of the body-wall cells. Thus a network of sensory cells and cell processes is formed between the two layers of the body. (See enlarged detail in Fig. 13.5.) Because of the lack of concentration of sensory cells, the nerve net conducts diffusely; chemical, mechanical, and light stimuli affect it most strongly.

Simple nerve cords and formation of a head end. In the intermediate Metazoa there first appears a concentration of nervous tissue and sense organs in the anterior end of the body—the formation of a *head* end (cephalization). This is first seen in the flatworms, elongated ribbonlike animals, in which the anterior end of the body is specialized. The head end of the flatworm is the part of the body most richly supplied with sense organs (Fig. 13.6, C), and sensitivity decreases toward the posterior end. There is a massing of nerve cells at the anterior end to form a *cephalic ganglion*, which dominates the nerve system of the animal and which receives nerve impulses from the sensory organs of the head. The head end thus comes largely to control behavior, and impulses from the cephalic ganglion are transmitted through the two lateral *nerve trunks* to all other parts of the body.

The ventral nerve cord and its cephalic ganglion. In the segmented worms (for example, the earthworm, Fig. 13.7) and the arthropods (for example, an insect), there has been a marked advance in the degree of cephalization of nerve tissue and sense organs, which reaches a maximum in flies, wasps, and spiders. The enlarged and complicated cephalic nerve mass may be termed a *brain*. Leading from the brain, which is located above the esophagus or pharynx, two nerve strands encircle the digestive tube and unite below into a secondary ganglion. From this *subesophageal ganglion* a double nerve cord runs down the ventral surface of the animal, swelling into small ganglia and giving off lateral nerves in each of the body segments; it is thus somewhat chainlike or ladderlike in appearance. As one proceeds from lower to higher groups within the insect series, there is a tendency for this system to become more and more highly concentrated in the anterior portions of the body. The ganglia and nerve cords at the same time become larger and more compact. Many of the insects with the largest and most concentrated nervous systems (for example, ants, wasps, bees) also show the most complex and highly adaptive behavior, even extending to social and psychic phenomena. These facts suggest that efficient control of a complicated organism requires a concentrated rather than a diffuse nervous system.

Concentrated nervous system of the vertebrates.   Concentration of nervous tissue has gone much farther in the vertebrates (Fig. 13.8) than in any other group of animals. Within this group we note an increasing degree of complexity in the structure and function of the nervous system, in general running parallel to complexity of body organization and culminating in the very highly concentrated and strongly cephalized nervous system of man.

Summing up our survey of form and function in the animal kingdom, we see that no matter what animal we choose to examine, it proves to have the same essential needs and presents the same problems. Every individual animal has to obtain organic food (proteins, carbohydrates, and fats), to prepare this food for assimilation, to utilize part of it for maintaining its own protoplasm and part as fuel for the production of energy. Every animal requires oxygen for internal combustion and must eliminate the products of protein, fat, and carbohydrate catabolism. Every animal shows irritability and appropriate responsiveness to external and internal stimuli. And finally, every animal must have the ability to produce other animals like itself.

In no fundamental respect, therefore, do the other patterns of animal life differ from that typified by man so far as the basic problems of maintenance are concerned. The marked differences in the types of structural organization that are capable of carrying on the functions listed above are due almost wholly to different patterns and degrees of cell, tissue, and organ differentiation and the resulting degrees of "division of labor." Generally speaking, the higher the degree of such differentiation the greater the efficiency of the organism and the greater its freedom from narrow limitations as to where it can maintain itself in nature.

THE MAJOR PATTERNS OF PLANT LIFE

We have just seen that among animals the tasks of individual maintenance may be accomplished by a variety of types of organization, and the same is true of plants. However, all typical plants possess chlorophyll, and manufacture food by photosynthesis. This fact accounts not only for all the major features of their organization but also for the absence of many of the features characteristic of the animal. As we have previously pointed out, the plant has no need of nervous system, special sense organs, or locomotor organs, for it does not have to seek its food and is forced by its method of nutrition to remain fixed in one spot. It requires neither digestive system nor excretory system, for its food is made within its cells, and its wastes are for the most part either reutilized, stored in tissues, or diffused into the atmosphere from the leaves. Its problems are, in fact, far simpler than those of the animal. This not only explains why even the highest plants are far less complex than the higher animals, but also enables us to see that the same problems are common to all plants, more easily than was the case with animals.

Although plants typically possess chlorophyll, there are a few that do not produce this substance and must, therefore, obtain their food in some other way than by photosynthesis. The distinction between the "green plants" and those that lack chlorophyll is functionally a very important one, and we shall use it as the basis for considering the major plant patterns under these two heads.

Types of Organization among the Green Plants

As we have already noted, the plant kingdom can be separated into four major groups, or divisions, which are, in order of increasing complexity of organization, (1) the *Thallophyta* (algae and fungi), (2) the *Bryophyta* (liverworts and mosses), (3) the *Pteridophyta* (ferns and fern allies), and (4) the *Spermatophyta* (seed plants). In part, these divisions are distinguished by the type and degree of individual organization shown by their members, in part by differences in their life cycles and methods of reproduction. Their characteristics and subdivisions are discussed and illustrated in Appendix A.

In a broad sense we may compare the thallophytes with the Protozoa and the simplest Metazoa among animals, since this division contains the unicellular and the simplest multicellular plants. Some of these may be thought of as being on the protoplasmic level and others on the cellular level of construction. All the remaining plants have their cells arranged into definite tissues. The bryophytes are roughly analogous to the flatworms among animals—*i.e.*, they possess definite tissues, plus the beginnings of organs. Beyond this point it is not profitable to carry the comparison. It is true that the two highest groups of plants (the pteridophytes and spermatophytes) possess definite plant organs and even a suggestion of organ systems in some instances, but they all function largely on the tissue level. Nowhere in the plant kingdom do we encounter anything so highly organized and functionally specialized as the organ system as it exists among the higher animals.

Unicellular green plants. Among the great numbers of minute organisms that inhabit the sea and bodies of fresh water, there are many whose bodies consist of a single cell. Some of these are clearly animallike, in that they contain no chlorophyll and feed upon previously synthesized organic material, which they take into the cell for digestion; they are for the most part motile, and they lack cellulose cell walls. These are the Protozoa, or unicellular animals, which constitute the lowest phylum of the animal kingdom. Many of the other unicellular organisms are just as clearly plantlike, making their own food from carbon dioxide and water by means of chlorophyll, and possessing morphological features in common with the cells of higher plants, such as a cellulose cell wall. These organisms, sometimes called the *Protophyta*, are classified as algae, along with certain multicellular forms, and are placed in the lowest plant group, the Thallophyta. As in the Protozoa, these unicellular plants have, as single cells, to perform all the functions necessary for life—to manufacture food, carry on respiration, excrete metabolic wastes, respond appropriately to the stimuli from the environment, and reproduce their kind. Again, as with the Protozoa, these unicellular plant cells must, in general, be more complex in structure than the cells of higher plants, in which there is cell specialization with corresponding division of labor.

FIG. 13.11. Euglena, an example of the Protista. (*Courtesy General Biological Supply House, Inc.*)

For two reasons, the Protophyta do not constitute a clear-cut and easily definable group of organisms. On the one hand, they are closely tied in to the simple multicellular plants through numerous transitional types, starting with simple colonies made up of cells that are all alike and almost indistinguishable from others that are free-living, and progressing through colonies showing incipient cell differentiation and division of labor to the lowest multicellular algae. So numerous are the intermediate types and so close the evident relationships among many unicellular and simple multicellular forms that it is not possible to separate the Protophyta as a distinct plant phylum, as we do the Protozoa among animals.

On the other hand, the Protophyta are hard to differentiate sharply from the Protozoa, and this is the place, which we mentioned in introducing the study of plants, at which the distinction between plant and animal tends to become obscure. Some of the green unicellular organisms, except for the presence of chlorophyll, are almost indistinguishable from other free-living cells that lack chlorophyll and are clearly to be placed in the Protozoa. But this is not the cause of the greatest difficulty. There exist numerous transitional types, which combine plant and animal features in a single cell. This is true, for instance, of *Euglena*— a common fresh-water organism with a body composed of a long, flexible, spindle-shaped cell, to one end of which is attached a lashing flagellum that pulls the organism through the water. Near the end bearing the flagellum there are a reddish, light-sensitive eyespot, and a small, sometimes rudimentary "cell mouth" through which food particles can be taken in. Under ordinary circumstances, Euglena seldom feeds; its body is filled with chloroplasts containing an abundance of chlorophyll, by means of which it carries on photosynthesis.

It is evident, then, that among these lowest organisms, we can no longer distinguish clearly between animals and plants. Because of this difficulty, all the unicellular organisms are sometimes grouped under the name *Protista*, thus avoiding the dilemma by not attempting to differentiate between animal and plant. Since there are equally strong reasons for associating the Protophyta with the multicellular algae, it will usually be a matter of convenience as to which method of treatment is followed. The important thing is not what the organisms shall be called but the

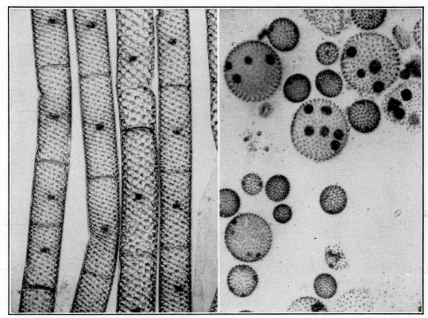

Fig. 13.12. Simple multicellular plants (green algae). At left Spirogyra, a filamentous form; at right Volvox, a spherical colony of cells. (*Courtesy General Biological Supply House, Inc.*)

fact that at the base of the divergent animal and plant series the gap between these two types of life is at least partially bridged.

Simple multicellular green plants. At the next higher level of organization above the single-celled and cell-colony types of plants, we find the *multicellular algae*, represented by the seaweeds, pond scums, and their like. These are aggregates of few or many more or less similar and semi-independent cells, forming a plant body of the type called a *thallus*, without roots, stems, or leaves and with little evidence of cell specialization and division of labor. The beginnings of the latter are found in some of the higher forms, such as the brown and red algae, in which certain cells form a rootlike *holdfast* for attaching the plant to some support, and the body is divided into a stemlike portion and leaflike blades. The resemblance of these structures to roots, stems, and leaves is, however,

purely superficial; the holdfast and "stem" are merely supporting structures, and the "blades" are not comparable to the blades of leaves, since
they consist of semi-independent cells, as in other algae.

In all the algae maintenance is accomplished principally through the
independent functioning of the individual cells. The ability of the algae
to get along without a high degree of organization is the result of their
mode of life. They do not need an epidermis specialized to resist evaporation, for they live in water or in very moist situations; strong mechanical
tissues are not required because of the prevailingly small size of the body
and the fact that the larger algae are all aquatic and are buoyed up by

Fig. 13.13. *Ricciocarpus natans*, a floating liverwort, showing the dichotomous branching of
the thallus. The small oval plants between the liverworts are Lemna, one of the smallest of
flowering plants. (*Photo by Prof. W. C. Steere, courtesy Cranbrook Institute of Science.*)

water; a transporting system would be superfluous, since each cell has
access, immediately or at a few removes, to the surrounding water with
its contained gases and minerals.

Intermediate multicellular green plants. The *liverworts* and *mosses*
(Bryophyta) are the simplest land plants. They are doubtless derived
from some group of algae, but they differ from all the thallophytes in
their higher degree of structural organization, related to the requirements
of life upon land. The most important of these requirements is protection against excessive loss of water by evaporation. In most bryophytes,
the body has become several cell layers thick, so that relatively less
surface is exposed. The outermost layer has become specialized into
an epidermis, composed of cells that secrete a thin layer of cutin, the
cuticle—a structure also present in the higher plants, as we have seen.
The cuticle forms a relatively impervious coating over the exposed parts
of the plant and prevents excessive water loss, but at the same time

it hinders free interchange of oxygen and carbon dioxide between the plant tissues and the air. This difficulty is met by the development of stomata, of a very simple type but functioning as do those of the higher plants already described. The development of a cuticle and stomata, structures first found in the bryophytes and characteristic of all the higher plants, has made it possible for plants to live in air instead of water.

Another feature of the land environment that requires adaptation by the plant is the fact that only a part of the body is in contact with a medium (the soil) from which water and essential salts can be obtained. This makes necessary the existence of special absorptive structures. No such structures are needed or found among the thallophytes, the rootlike holdfasts found in some of the algae playing no part in absorption. Here the bryophytes show another advance in organization; the parts of the plant that touch the soil develop numerous hairlike processes called *rhizoids*, which in part act as holdfasts but also absorb soil water. They are not true roots and compared with roots are relatively inefficient as absorbing organs.

Although the bryophytes are true land plants, they are in some respects quite imperfectly adapted to land life.[1] They are most numerous and successful in moist or wet environments, and although some of them live in situations that at times become very dry, they do so only by suspending all activity during the period of drought. At such times they wither and apparently die, and begin to function again only with the return of adequate moisture. None of the bryophytes attains large size, and most are quite small. Among the factors responsible for this are the following: their mechanism for absorbing soil water is not very efficient and could not supply the needs of a large plant with extensive evaporating surface; they have no well-developed mechanical tissues to support increased weight; and, lastly, they have no vascular system to distribute water and food to the parts of a large body.

The most highly organized green plants. At the highest level of individual organization, we find the members of the last two plant divisions, the Pteridophyta (ferns and fern allies) and Spermatophyta (seed plants). These two groups of plants are fully adapted to life upon land. In spite of a great amount of diversity in form and details of structure, they are, in general, built on the same basic pattern as the dicotyledons, that we have already studied in detail. The body is divided into root, stem, and leaf; it is covered with a protecting epidermis and cuticle or has other evaporation-resisting coverings that replace the cuticle; it contains mechanical tissues that support the body and permit the development of

[1] One important factor that prevents the bryophytes from colonizing the drier parts of the land is their dependence upon water for the accomplishment of fertilization, as will be explained in the section dealing with reproduction.

large size; and it contains a vascular system for transporting water and other substances from one part of the plant to another. On account of the latter characteristic, which is shared by the pteridophytes and the spermatophytes, these two groups are often together called the *vascular plants*.

The *pteridophytes* include the ferns, club mosses, horsetails, and a few other sorts of plants. Although, like the bryophytes, they are dependent upon the presence of water for reproduction, in all other respects they are far more advanced and are closer to the seed plants in type of individual organization. The *roots* of the fern have root hairs, an apical growing point and a root cap; within there is a single central vascular bundle of radial type. In most ferns the *stem* is a horizontal, subterranean *rhizome* which gives off leaves from its upper surface and roots from the underside.[1] Beneath the epidermis of the rhizome there is commonly a cylinder of mechanical tissue, enclosing a mass of parenchyma cells and from two to many vascular bundles separated by a central pith. Each vascular bundle is composed of xylem more or less completely surrounded by phloem, the latter tissue sometimes forming a continuous sheath outside the xylem bundles. There is no cambium layer; growth of the stem is accomplished entirely by the meristematic zone at its apex.

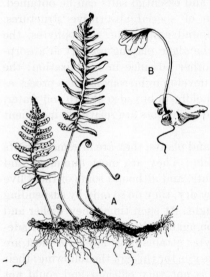

Fig. 13.14. A fern, *Polypodium virginianum*, to show growth habit. *A*, sporophyte, showing rhizome, leaves with "fruit dots" (sori), and roots. *B*, young sporophyte growing from place where zygote was formed on the mature gametophyte plant. (*From Hill, Overholts and Popp, Botany.*)

True leaves are organs that appear for the first time in the pteridophytes. The leaves of ferns have a stalk and a more or less divided blade, the latter often of large size. Unlike those of seed plants, the fern leaf continues to grow for some time after it is formed; when it emerges from the ground, it is coiled like a watch spring, and it continues to elongate at the tip while its older parts broaden and unroll. Another peculiarity of the fern leaf is that each leaf vein, when it forks, divides into two ap-

---

[1] In the tree ferns the stem forms an erect trunk which attains a height of 50 feet in a number of species and 80 feet in the tallest species known. The leaves of large tree ferns may be as much as 20 feet long.

proximately equal branches. The leaves of the fern, unlike those of flowering plants, bear reproductive bodies on their lower surfaces in the form of minute "fruit dots," or *sori*. There are no flowers in the pteridophytes.

The *spermatophytes*, or seed plants, not only are the most highly organized of plants but also are the dominant plants of the modern world. Since we have already examined the structure and functioning of the members of this group in detail, it will be unnecessary to review these matters here.

Plants That Lack Chlorophyll

Although plants typically possess chlorophyll and manufacture food by photosynthesis, certain of them—clearly plants, as judged by structure and life history—lack this substance and must obtain their food in other ways. Such plants are encountered only among the members of the lowest and the highest of the plant divisions—the thallophytes and the spermatophytes. Physiologically they fall into two groups—those which (like the green plants) manufacture their own food, but by means of chemical instead of solar energy; and those which must like animals obtain their food ready-made.

FIG. 13.15. A tree fern in the northern Philippines. (*Photo by Charles Martin (c) NGS. Courtesy National Geographic Society.*)

The plants which depend upon *chemosynthesis* instead of photosynthesis for food manufacture are few. They include the kinds of bacteria called *hydrogen, iron, nitrifying, and sulfur bacteria*, which respectively oxidize hydrogen, certain iron compounds, ammonia, and hydrogen sulphide. These oxidative reactions release energy that is used for the synthesis of carbohydrate from carbon dioxide and water. The nitrifying bacteria, aided by the prior activities of other bacteria yet to be discussed which release ammonia in the soil, play an important role in the cycle of nitrogen utilization by plants. They are of two sorts—*nitrite bacteria*, which convert ammonia into nitrites, and *nitrate bacteria*, which oxidize the nitrites into nitrates, the nitrogen compounds most readily utilized by green plants.

Except for these few chemosynthetic bacteria, all other colorless plants fall into the second group—those which must obtain ready-made organic food. They comprise a large subdivision of the thallophytes (the fungi) and scattered examples among the seed plants.

The *fungi* are defined as those thallophytes that lack chlorophyll. They are of many sorts, the best known being the bacteria, molds, rusts, yeasts, smuts, mildews, cup fungi, bracket fungi, coral fungi, mushrooms, and puffballs. The various groups of fungi are not all closely related. They probably originated at different times and from different kinds of algae, so that they do not form a "natural" group in the sense of having had a common ancestry. Functionally, however, they do form a natural grouping sharply distinguished from other thallophytes by the absence of chlorophyll and the modified nutritional methods that this lack entails. Some fungi are *saprophytes* (Greek, *sapros*, "putrid," and *phyton*, "plant"), which obtain their food from the dead bodies of plants or animals, or from plant and animal products. Others are *parasites*, which get food from the living bodies of plants or animals. Many bacteria and some other fungi make little distinction between these two modes of life and may exist saprophytically at one time, parasitically at another. Still others, although these are relatively few, have developed *symbiotic* (Greek, *symbiosis*, "a living together") relations with green plants, in which both members of the association profit. Let us briefly examine a few instances of these various modes of existence.

Saprophytic bacteria and other fungi are largely responsible for the destruction of the dead bodies of organisms and the liberation of their compounds, which thus are made available for reutilization by the living. Among the important saprophytic soil bacteria are the *ammonifying*, the *denitrifying*, and the free-living kinds of *nitrogen-fixing* bacteria. The ammonifying and denitrifying bacteria break down protein-containing substances. Those of the first class liberate ammonia, which is oxidized into nitrites and nitrates by the nitrifying bacteria already mentioned, while the denitrifying bacteria liberate free nitrogen gas into the air. The former increase soil fertility, the latter diminish it. The nitrogen-fixing bacteria live upon organic materials but have the property of taking nitrogen gas (which green plants cannot utilize) from the air and converting it into organic compounds, which may subsequently be broken down and made into nitrates by other bacteria. Most of the common molds (for example bread mold, Fig. A.5), yeasts, mushrooms, puffballs (Fig. A.8), bracket fungi (Fig. A.9) and coral fungi are saprophytes.

There are thousands of parasitic species of fungi, and few of the higher animals and plants do not at least occasionally serve as *hosts*[1] to some of them. These fungus parasites include the bacteria (Fig. A.4) that cause disease in animals and plants, the fungi that kill fish, the mildly parasitic mildews that grow upon leaves, the molds that cause ringworm and

[1] The organism that supplies sustenance to any parasite is termed its *host*.

athlete's foot in man, the smuts and rusts that attack higher plants (some of which alternate between two different hosts, Fig. 33.2), and certain mushrooms and bracket fungi which are parasitic upon living trees.

A few kinds of fungi have become adapted to symbiotic existence with green plants. The best known examples are furnished by the *lichens*

FIG. 13.16. The Indian pipe, a colorless saprophytic flowering plant. (*Courtesy Ward's Natural Science Establishment, Inc.*)

(Fig. 33.3), which are made up of intermingled cells of a fungus and a green alga. The alga can live alone, while the fungus cannot; but the association is not one of parasitism. The fungus absorbs soil moisture and mineral substances; the alga shares these, and by photosynthesis produces food of which a part is used by the fungus. Another symbiotic relation which has great importance for soil fertility is that which exists between certain of the *nitrogen-fixing bacteria* and plants of the bean family. The bacteria inhabit special *root nodules* formed by the plant (Fig. 33.4) and live at its expense; but the plant also benefits, since through the agency of the bacteria it is able to obtain nitrogen from the air. One more instance of symbiosis may be cited. In many common forest trees root hairs are replaced by fungal filaments; the fungus obtains its food from the tree, while the entry of water into the tree is largely accomplished by the agency of the fungus.

No large group of the seed plants has lost the ability to produce chlorophyll, but here and there among the families we encounter colorless species that have adopted a saprophytic or parasitic mode of life. There

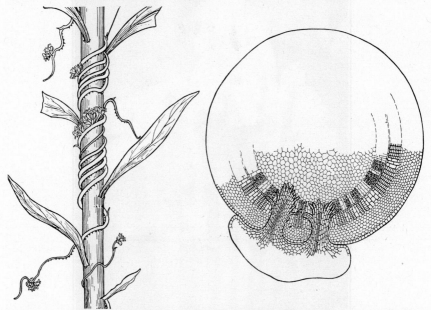

FIG. 13.17. Dodder, a parasitic vine that lacks chlorophyll. At left, the leafless yellow vine and its flowers; at right, a section of the host stem showing the absorptive organs (haustoria) of the parasite penetrating the host tissues. (*Courtesy General Biological Supply House, Inc.*)

are very few saprophytic angiosperms. Well-known examples include the Indian pipe (Fig. 13.16) and the sierran snow plant, both members of the heath family. Parasites are more numerous. Examples are beech drops parasitic on beech roots, broomrape on clover and other roots, squawroot or cancerroot on roots of oaks and other trees, and the dodders (Fig. 13.17), yellowish or whitish vines parasitic on herbs and shrubs. All these lack chlorophyll. Such plants as mistletoe combine the parasitic habit with ability to carry on photosynthesis and illustrate the way in which transition to completely parasitic existence was accomplished.

Finally, we should briefly consider some plants that have developed the ability to capture insects and other small animals as food. These *insectivorous plants* have leaves which are highly modified into various sorts of traps. In the pitcher plants (Fig. 13.18) the vaselike leaves contain water in which insects drown; in the sundew the leaf is covered with sticky hairs that bend and enclose the victim; in the famous Venus'-

FIG. 13.18. The pitcher plant *Sarracenia flava*, an insectivorous plant of wet flatwoods in the southeastern coastal plain. (*Photo by Prof. A. M. Laessle.*)

flytrap the hinged, bristle-fringed leaf closes on the prey much as does a steel trap when the trigger is touched; and in the aquatic bladderworts (Fig. 32.8) the leaves are hollow bladders with in-pointing bristles that hold captive any small creature that enters. In all instances the animal prey is digested by special enzymes and furnishes nitrogenous substances to the plant.

Our survey of the chief patterns of plant life has shown that, including those plants that lack chlorophyll, all plants, from the simplest to the most complex, are faced with the same basic problems. They solve these problems in various ways, as do animals, depending upon their degree of organizational complexity and the particular circumstances in which they live. We can go even further than this; in spite of the superficial dissimilarity between plants and animals, we are now in a position to realize that the fundamental requirements for living are the same for all organisms. Plant or animal, the organism must have access to water, it must obtain food, it must have means of releasing energy from that food (in the enormous majority of organisms, by means of oxidation), it must be able to rid itself of wastes, it must be able to respond appropriately to changes in its environment, and it must be able to reproduce. The types of organization characteristic of plant and animal are adapted to accomplish these things in different ways.

Part II: THE CONTINUITY OF THE RACE

REPRODUCTION, INHERITANCE, AND VARIATION

CHAPTER XIV

THE INDIVIDUAL AS A MEMBER OF A RACE

We have thus far been primarily concerned with the processes that enable the organism to maintain itself as an individual. Much of any organism's structure and behavior are understandable, however, only when we examine its relationships to other individuals. One of the most essential of such relationships is that any individual organism is only a temporary unit in a sequence of generations. Each individual has a definitely limited period of existence. This may be as brief as several days or weeks for the individuals of some species, as much as "three score and ten" years or more for man, or even several centuries for a few kinds of long-lived trees. But in time the individual will cease to exist. The race to which the individual belongs, however, continues through countless generations, so that closely similar individuals successively appear, maintain themselves for a period, and then die—to be replaced by new individuals of the same kind. Here we encounter a new set of questions about organisms: How are these successive generations produced? Why and to what extent are the individuals of each new generation like those of the generation that preceded them? How is the organism's existence as an individual related to its membership in a race?

THE DISCARDED THEORY OF SPONTANEOUS GENERATION

Our modern concept of the origin and development of individual organisms is much more recent than our knowledge of their structure. At a time when a fairly accurate account of gross mammalian structure was being written (by Galen in A.D. 200), nearly all educated men were still willing to believe that most or many forms of life could arise spontaneously from nonliving matter. Frogs and insects were thought to come from mud, bees from the decaying bodies of oxen, such household vermin as mice and cockroaches from refuse. Even the wild geese (which breed in the then unknown arctic regions) were thought to be formed from a certain type of barnacle (still called the goose barnacle) that has a shape suggesting the form of a goose. Ovid, who lived during the reign of the

Roman emperor Augustus, expressed the accepted belief of his time when he wrote:

> By this sure experiment we know
> That living creatures from corruption grow:
> Hide in a hollow pit a slaughtered steer,
> Bees from his putrid bowels will appear,
> Who like their parent haunt the fields, and
> Bring their honey harvest home, and hope another spring.
> The warlike steed is multiplied, we find,
> To wasps and hornets of the warrior kind.
> Cut from a crab his crooked claws and hide
> The rest in earth, a scorpion thence will glide
> And shoot his sting; his tail in circles tossed
> Refers the limbs his backward father lost;
> And worms that stretch on leaves their filmy loom
> Crawl from their bags and butterflies become.
> The slime begets the frogs loquacious race;
> Short of their feet at first, in little space
> With arms and legs endued, long leaps they take,
> Raised on their hinder parts, and swim the lake,
> And waves repel; for nature gives their kind.
> To that intent, a length of legs behind.

Such beliefs appear again and again in the literature of the Middle Ages and seem to have been almost unquestioned until well into the seventeenth century. It was recognized, of course, that men and domestic animals were born from parents, but even here there was much mysticism and sometimes willingness to credit occasional instances to spontaneous origin.

The first clear case of doubt of the actuality of the spontaneous origin of common small animals was that which led an Italian naturalist, Francesco Redi, to perform some simple experiments about 1680. (At this time, Vesalius' great treatise on human anatomy, based upon actual dissection, was already more than a hundred years old.) Redi tested the spontaneous origin of maggots from decaying meat by placing bits of meat in three glasses. The first was left uncovered, the second was covered with fine netting, and the third was covered with parchment. He soon discovered maggots on the meat in the first glass, a few maggots on the fine netting over the second glass, and no maggots at all in the third glass, although in all the glasses the meat appeared equally spoiled. Further observations proved to him that the maggots originated not in the meat but from flesh flies which, attracted by the odor of the decaying meat, came to deposit eggs or living maggots; that the eggs hatched into maggots, the maggots fed and grew and transformed into flies, and that these flies, in turn, produced more eggs.

Although Redi's experiments marked the beginning of a growing disbelief in spontaneous generation, they by no means settled the question. About the time he was making his experiments, another naturalist (Leeuwenhoek) was beginning to make the powerful, simple lenses with which he was to discover the existence of the minute living organisms that we know today as the protozoa and bacteria. The first studies on these minute forms of life strongly suggested that they could arise by spontaneous generation, even though flies, worms, and frogs did not. It was found that one could always obtain such microscopic life simply by placing some clean, dry hay in a glass of clean, clear water. Soon after the water became more or less discolored by soluble substances from the hay, it would be found to be swarming with bacteria and later with protozoa, and even if the infusion were boiled, living organisms would appear a few days after it cooled. Such observations did much to offset the results of Redi's experiments on flies, for they at least seemed to support in principle the possibility of spontaneous generation.

Gradually, however, as compound microscopes became practical instruments and provided detailed images at high magnification, and as appropriate techniques were devised for the study of microscopic life, observations to test the spontaneous generation of even protozoa and bacteria became possible. About 1780, Spallanzani was able to isolate a single bacterium and watch it divide to form first two and then four "daughter" bacteria. He also made numerous experiments on sterilized (boiled) infusions that convinced him that even protozoa and bacteria could not arise spontaneously. Such experiments, however, call for a much more elaborate and precise technique than those that served Redi in his experiments with flies, and it was not until after the work of Pasteur, Cohn, Koch, and Tyndall,[1] in the latter half of the nineteenth century, that all biologists were convinced that *spontaneous generation was definitely disproved for all forms of living organisms.*

Today it is fully established that every living organism comes into existence through the reproductive functioning of parent organisms (or a single parent organism) quite like itself. It follows that each and every kind of organism that exists on the earth today is but a recent link in an unbroken sequence of once living, reproducing individuals. We do not know how life originally came into existence; but whether it was produced by a special creation by some supernatural power, or through spontaneous generation in some earlier and different stage of the earth's history, or whether the first living organisms were somehow transported to the earth from another planet, we are certain that under the conditions that now prevail "all life comes from life."

[1] The application of their work to surgery was first made in the 1860s by Lister, in the introduction of "antiseptic surgery."

It is also clear that once the chain of continuing generations is broken, the race will cease to exist. Actually this has happened for many thousands of kinds of organisms in the past and will continue to happen to many races in the future. The organisms that exist today are members of biologically successful races: some of the individuals of each generation of each race were able to maintain their own normal span of existence and to reproduce still another generation to carry on in turn.

In our study of the individual as a member of a race, it will be more profitable to look at organisms in general than to confine our attention to one or a few, as we did in the preceding section. We shall see that the reproductive processes of one organism will often help in the interpretation and understanding of similar but outwardly different processes of other forms. In the more than a million different kinds of individuals and races of organisms, with their great differences in size, complexity, and type of organization, we should expect to and do find great differences in the details of reproductive methods and adaptations. If we confine our attention to the common and essential processes, however, we find that all reproductive methods may be classified into a relatively small number of different types. These various types and processes of reproduction form the subject matter of the following three chapters.

CHAPTER XV

THE REPRODUCTION OF ANIMALS

Although there are many essential similarities between the reproductive processes of the Protozoa and the Metazoa, the differences between a unicellular and a multicellular scheme of organization are nowhere more marked than in the different problems that they entail for the reproduction of new individuals.[1] As a consequence, it will be simpler and more accurate to consider the reproductive processes of the two groups sepa-

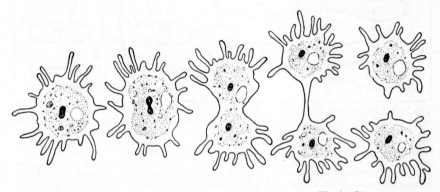

Fig. 15.1. Binary fission in Amoeba. (*Redrawn after Woodruff.*)

rately. Even if, following common usage, we employ the terms *sexual* and *asexual* in both Protozoa and Metazoa, it will be necessary to define them quite differently in the two groups.

REPRODUCTION IN THE PROTOZOA

Asexual reproduction. Perhaps the simplest of all types of reproduction is the *fission* exhibited by many of the unicellular organisms. When an amoeba reaches its maximum size, it divides into two "daughter" amoebae of approximately equal size, and these, when grown to full size, will each, in turn, divide into daughter cells. In *Amoeba* and most protozoa, this division appears to be essentially mitotic, the outwardly visible cytoplasmic division preceded by a more or less precise nuclear

[1] The fundamental difference involved is discussed under Germ and soma on p. 213.

division. Fission is a typical method of reproduction in most protozoa, in the bacteria, and in many unicellular as well as filamentous algae.

Essentially similar to fission is the *multiple fission*, or *sporulation*, exhibited by various Protozoa and Protophyta. Here the parent cell, instead of dividing into two (binary fission), divides to form many minute masses of cytoplasm and nucleus, each capable of growing into a full-sized organism. Simple fission, whether binary or multiple, constitutes *asexual* reproduction in unicellular organisms.

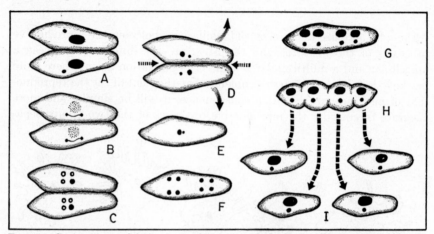

Fig. 15.2. Conjugation and fission in the slipper animalcule, *Paramecium caudatum*. Not all stages are shown. *A*, two individuals unite by their oral grooves (the groove leading to the "cell mouth"). *B*, the large nuclei (macronuclei) begin to disappear, and the small nuclei (micronuclei) divide. *C*, each micronucleus divides again, producing four daughter nuclei, three of which degenerate. *D*, the remaining micronucleus divides again, and one member of each pair thus formed migrates into the other paramecium. *E*, the two paramecia separate (only one is followed from here on), and the two micronuclei in each individual fuse (suggesting the fusion of sperm and egg nuclei in metazoa). *F*, the fusion nucleus undergoes three successive divisions, producing eight nuclei (suggesting the cleavage divisions in metazoa). *G*, four of these nuclei grow into macronuclei. *H*, the cytoplasm constricts in the middle and again in each half. *I*, four small individual paramecia are produced, each with one large and one small nucleus. (*Modified from Borradaile and others.*)

Sexual reproduction. Another common type of reproduction among protozoa and unicellular plants is *conjugation and fission, i.e.*, fission that is preceded by a temporary union or complete fusion of two individual cells. In conjugation the two cells either (1) effect a mutual interchange of nuclear material and then separate, or (2) fuse into a single cell, in which event they may be regarded as two *gametes* fusing to form a *zygote* in a process that closely resembles the fusion of egg and sperm in many-celled organisms. In either case, the resulting cell or cells contain at least nuclear material from both conjugants. Following conjugation, either binary or multiple fission of the conjugated cells (or cell) takes place. This differs from simple fission essentially in that the daughter cells contain material (at least nuclear material) from two different parent individuals.

Some unicellular organisms appear to reproduce chiefly or exclusively by fission; others reproduce chiefly by conjugation and fission; but many organisms utilize both methods, either alternately or as they are stimulated by varying environmental conditions.

"Potential immortality" of unicellular organisms. Since reproduction is accomplished by division of the entire cell, the parent organism is replaced by two (or more) new "daughter" organisms. Full growth and maturity are followed by division rather than by senility and death. In this sense, a unicellular organism is potentially immortal. Actually, of course, the great majority of unicellular organisms are killed either by other organisms for food or by adverse conditions of their environment. Such death is a matter of chance rather than necessity.

REPRODUCTION IN THE METAZOA

The variety and complexity of reproductive methods exhibited by multicellular organisms is much greater than those found in the Protista. Since there are some rather fundamental differences in detail between the reproductive adaptions of the Metazoa and those of the multicellular plants, we have chosen to treat reproduction in the higher animals and plants separately. It would be possible to classify metazoan reproduction into sexual and asexual on the same criterion that we used for the Protozoa, *i.e.*, on whether one or two parents are concerned. Although such a classification would be closer to our usage in everyday speech, a much more fundamental and useful basis for classifying reproduction in the Metazoa is found in the concept of germ and soma.

Germ and soma. We have seen that one of the chief features of multicellular organisms is the differentiation of their cells and tissues into diverse types, each differentiation accompanied by a corresponding division of labor. In the higher Metazoa there are hundreds of kinds of highly specialized cells, each fitted for some definite and limited function. The most fundamental specialization and division of labor is that between the cells reserved and later specialized for reproduction, and all the remaining cells of the body. The reproductive cells, or *germ cells*, have no contributing share in the functioning of the body; housed and nourished in it, their sole function is the production of a succeeding generation. All the other cells have some necessary share in the maintenance and functioning of the body of the individual they compose; they are known collectively as the *soma*. This distinction between *soma* and *germ* becomes progressively more clear-cut and definite as we consider progressively more complex organisms, and it is of great importance in the consideration of reproduction, inheritance, and evolution.

In the discussion that follows and in the section on genetics we shall use the term *asexual reproduction* for reproduction from soma tissues and the term *sexual reproduction* for reproduction by germ cells (or a germ cell). This will deviate from our everyday usage of the word *sexual* only in the case of one relatively unimportant type of germ cell reproduction (parthenogenesis).

Asexual (Soma Cell) Reproduction in Metazoa

Among the lower, less highly individualized Metazoa, there is slight development of cell differentiation and division of labor. In these organisms various methods of producing new individuals directly from the soma tissues of the parent individual are an important and often the most common method of reproduction. Such asexual reproduction shows considerable variation in detail among the lower Metazoa, but practically all types may be classified as either *budding* or *fission*.

Budding is the formation of new "daughter" individuals by growth and proliferation of some portion of the parent's body. The parent continues to exist as an individual. Budding is a common and extremely important method of reproduction and propagation in all groups of plants; but in animals it is confined to the lowest, least individualized groups of the Metazoa, especially the sponges and the coelenterates [Hydra (Fig. 13.5), corals, and their kin]. In the sponges a peculiar type of "internal budding" is the chief method of reproduction.

Fission is the production of two new "daughter" individuals by the self-cutting-in-two of the parent individual. In this process, the parent individual ceases to exist and is replaced by the two *new* daughter individuals. Fission is not so widely utilized a method of asexual reproduction as is budding, but it is characteristic of the flatworms and a few other forms.

Limitations to asexual reproduction. Asexual reproduction in the Metazoa is limited to those forms that have relatively little complexity of body parts, in which the tissues are comparatively few and generally distributed over the whole body. In such simple organisms, budding and fission are capable of providing a new individual with all the kinds of tissues and organs that are found in the parent. In the higher Metazoa, with their marked differentiation of soma tissues and highly integrated and interdependent organ systems, asexual reproduction does not occur.

Other limitations to asexual reproduction are as follows: (1) In many organisms asexual reproduction occurs only during seasons of continuously favorable environmental conditions and is stopped by seasons of unsuitable temperature or insufficient food or oxygen, when the species must resort to sexual production of eggs to survive. (2) In several groups that utilize asexual reproduction, it always alternates with sexual, so that each asexually produced individual reproduces by sexual methods, and vice versa. The alternation of sexual and asexual generations that occurs in most coelenterate animals is known as *metagenesis*. (3) Asexual reproduction does not produce so great a diversity and variation among the offspring as is produced by sexual, and especially by bisexual, reproduction.

There is considerable parallelism between asexual reproduction and the power of organisms to reproduce lost or mutilated parts. When a hydra or a sponge is cut into minute portions, each portion, if it contains cells of all kinds of essential tissues, is able to *regenerate* a complete new individual. Such an individual will be very small but will be able to grow to full adult size. A flatworm can also be cut into a number of portions, each of which is capable of forming a new, complete individual, provided that it contains all the considerably larger variety of essential tissues. We could, if it were desirable, propagate such animals from cuttings as we do plants. When we turn to higher animals, we find that the power to reproduce new individuals from severed portions of another individual rapidly decreases and is soon lost as we encounter progressively greater complexity of structure. In the lower ranks of the complex Metazoa, there is still, however, a marked ability to regenerate lost legs, tails, and other appendages. This ability, too, diminishes with further increase in structural and physiological complexity (or perhaps, more accurately, with increasing individualization of the organism) until in the higher vertebrates it is limited to the ability to heal a wound, knit a broken bone, and regenerate certain tissues.

Sexual or Germ-cell Reproduction in the Metazoa

Unlike the soma cells that are concerned in asexual reproduction, *germ cells* do not show differentiation into any sort of functional body tissue. They are to be classed neither as epithelial, contractile, sustentative, nor conductive tissue. All organisms that are reproduced by sexual means begin their existence as a single cell, and most of the multiplying descendants of this cell gradually differentiate into the various kinds of cells that make up the tissues needed in the formation of the new individual. However, not all the cells descended from the original germ cell become functional body cells. A few show no differentiation and constitute the germ cells of the new individual. In the higher Metazoa, at least, these germ cells soon migrate into the soma tissues that are destined to form the gonads (ovaries or testes) of the new individual.

MEIOSIS AND THE MATURATION OF THE GERM CELLS

When the metazoan approaches sexual maturity, its germ cells begin the characteristic processes by which they are formed into functional eggs or sperms. These processes include two successive, specialized nuclear divisions that together constitute *meiosis*, and also the cytoplasmic adaptations that fit the mature eggs and sperms for their respective roles. Although much of the nuclear and cytoplasmic change takes place concurrently, it will be simpler to consider first what happens in the nucleus and afterwards the cytoplasmic occurrences.

Meiosis

The nuclear divisions known as meiosis are identical in egg and sperm formation (and also in the formation of haploid spores in plants, Figs. 17.4, 17.5, 17.15). The meiotic divisions show many close similarities to mitosis (Fig. 2.2 and text)—the same chromosomes, the same formation of spindles, in animal cells the same appearance of amphiasters, and the same sequence of prophase, metaphase, anaphase, and telophase. However, there are a number of striking differences between meiosis and mitosis that have great significance not only for reproduction but also for the fields of genetics and evolution.

The account of meiosis, like that of mitosis, is illustrated by a series of diagrammatic drawings of successive stages (Fig. 15.3). Considerable detail is given, in the hope that this description will be adequate both for an understanding of reproduction and for an appreciation of the role played by meiosis in genetics and evolution.

We have already seen in mitosis that the chromosomes consist of two like sets, or in other words that there are two of each sort of chromosome. Such paired chromosomes are spoken of as *homologous*, or as being *homologues*, for their resemblance is due to the fact that they could have been derived from the same parent chromosome two or more generations removed, and, as we shall see, one member of each pair came from the individual's mother (the *maternal chromosome*) and the other from the father (the *paternal chromosome*).

The First Meiotic Division

Prophase. When the chromosomes first become discernable, they are in the form of extremely long, thin threads, even longer than in ordinary mitosis. Unlike mitosis, where each chromosome consists of two chromatids, the chromosomes in meiosis appear to be single—not divided into chromatids. This, the *leptotene* substage of prophase, is followed by a *zygotene* substage in which the two homologous chromosomes that constitute each chromosome pair come to lie closely side by side. The pairing takes place gradually, starting at one or more points and spreading along the whole length of the two chromosomes as though they were drawn together by a "zipper." At the completion of zygotene the paired homologous chromosomes are ordinarily so close together that it is difficult or impossible to see that there are two. Such closely applied pairs

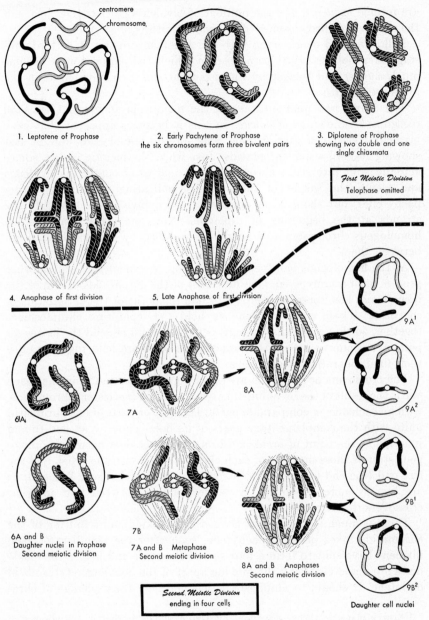

centromere
chromosome,

1. Leptotene of Prophase

2. Early Pachytene of Prophase
the six chromosomes form three bivalent pairs

3. Diplotene of Prophase
showing two double and one
single chiasmata

First Meiotic Division
Telophase omitted

4. Anaphase of first division

5. Late Anaphase of first division

6A

7A

8A

9A¹

9A²

6B

7B

8B

9B¹

9B²

6A and B
Daughter nuclei in Prophase
Second meiotic division

7A and B   Metaphase
Second meiotic division

8A and B   Anaphases
Second meiotic division

Second Meiotic Division
ending in four cells

Daughter cell nuclei

FIG. 15.3. A diagram of meiosis.

are termed *bivalents,* and the number of bivalents is, of course, just half the number of chromosomes to be seen in mitosis.

Following and overlapping with the zygotene substage is a third substage of prophase called *pachytene,* in which the chromosomes become much shorter and thicker by forming tight spiral coils, much as in the prophase of mitosis.

The fourth and final substage of the meiotic prophase that we shall recognize is known as *diplotene.* In this it becomes apparent that each bivalent consists of *four* strands, each of the homologues now at last showing its two sister chromatids. Just when the meiotic chromosomes actually split into sister chromatids is a matter of conflicting evidence and views (the weight of the evidence indicating some time during pachytene), but there is no doubt that each bivalent consists of four strands at the beginning of diplotene. Now the attraction between homologous chromosomes ends and is succeeded by a marked repulsion between them.[1]

As the homologous pairs separate it becomes evident that still another process has been involved. One (or both) of the chromatids of one of the homologues has "crossed over" with one (or both) of the chromatids of the other. These *crossovers* tend to hold the separating chromosomes together, so that although the regions between and beyond the crossover points continue to widen, the homologous pairs are held together until their final separation at anaphase.

The crossovers or *chiasmata* are of very great importance, in that each one is the result of the breaking of two homologous (*not* sister) chromatids, with an exchange of comparable parts. The part or parts of one chromatid unite with the complementary parts of its homologue by an end-to-end junction at the point of breakage. In a single crossover between homologous strands those portions of each chromatid between the break and the free end (the end lacking the centromere) are interchanged. When there are two or more crossovers, it is the portions between two adjacent crossovers that are exchanged.

There is much evidence that the actual breaking and reuniting of the chromatids takes place in pachytene, soon after the members of each bivalent have split to form a four-strand structure and before the chiasmata are made visible by the moving apart of the homologous strands in diplotene. It should be emphasized that normally the exchange of chro-

---

[1] A very plausible theory advanced by Darlington holds that in the absence of chromatid formation in early prophases of meiosis, the attraction that in mitosis holds the sister chromatids in close juxtaposition is expended in drawing the homologous chromosomes together. Then, when the meiotic chromosomes do finally split into chromatids, the attraction force is satisfied by the sister chromatids, and a repulsion is built up between the homologues.

matid segments by crossing over is a precisely equal exchange, and that the crossed-over chromatids are now composites, made up of segments from both of the original homologues.

Metaphase. Toward the end of prophase the nuclear membrane disappears and a spindle begins to form, quite as in mitosis; but as the nucleus passes into metaphase, the centromeres of the bivalents do not move into the equatorial plate but come to lie on either side of it, one centromere of a bivalent just above, the other just below the plate. *There is no splitting of centromeres at the first meiotic division.*

Anaphase. The centromeres now move toward the poles, drawing the crossed-over strands apart and toward the opposite ends of the spindle.

Telophase. This is essentially the same as in mitosis, although in certain organisms the chromosomes do not return to a resting stage but pass directly to the prophase of the second meiotic division.

The "daughter nuclei." Each of the two nuclei produced by the first meiotic division has just half as many chromosomes as were present in the mother cell—one chromosome from each homologous pair. This is termed the *haploid* number in contrast to the *diploid* number found in soma cells and in the germ cells before meiosis. Note that *no chromosome has yet undergone division* and that each of the haploid chromosomes consists of two chromatids united by an undivided centromere.

The Second Meiotic Division

The second meiotic division, which usually follows closely upon the first, is essentially a mitotic division. Here at metaphase the centromeres finally split into two, and the single chromatids are carried to opposite poles at anaphase. At the conclusion of this division each of the daughter nuclei contains a single chromatid from each of the bivalents that were formed at the pachytene substage of the first division, and meiosis is completed.

OTHER MATURATION PROCESSES

We have seen that the nuclear processes of maturation (meiosis) are the same for egg and sperm, but eggs and sperms are specialized for complementary roles in fertilization, and in consequence the other processes of maturation are markedly different for the two kinds of cells (Fig. 15.4).

Maturation of the egg (oögenesis). The unmatured eggs (*oögonia*) multiply by mitosis in the ovary to form a large stock of potential eggs before the beginning of sexual maturity of the individual. With the arrival of sexual maturity some (or all) of the oögonia begin to grow, both by an increase in the amount of their cytoplasm and by the storing up of food material in the form of minute oil droplets (*yolk*). This growth

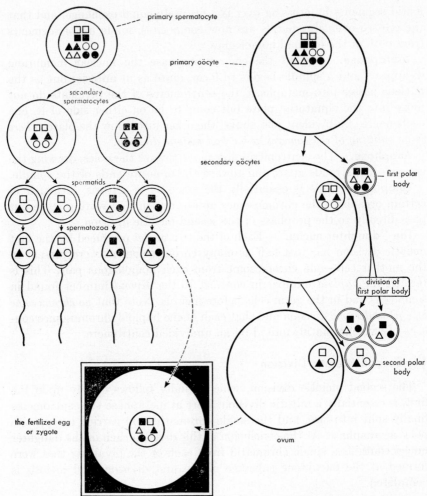

FIG. 15.4. Maturation of the sperm and egg, and fertilization. The meiotic divisions of the nuclei, which are much more completely shown in Fig. 15.3, are indicated by symbols for the same three pairs of chromosomes in the primary oöcyte and spermatocyte. The chromatids of each pair are given a special shape (square, round, triangular), with sister chromatids of the same color and homologous pairs contrasted in black and white. No crossing over is shown, and the symbols should be thought of as cross sections of chromosomes made very near their centromeres, since both first divisions are shown as separating homologous chromatids and the second divisions as separating sister chromatids. The diagrams of spermatogenesis and of the polar bodies are proportionately much too large as compared with the size of the egg.

process, which begins and is usually completed before meiosis, is followed by a migration of the egg nucleus (and much of the cytoplasm in eggs with large amounts of yolk) to a point near the cell membrane.

The enlarged egg is now known as a *primary oöcyte* and is ready for the first meiotic division. When this takes place, the cytoplasmic division that follows the nuclear division is so extremely unequal that all of the cytoplasm and yolk remain in one daughter cell, the *secondary oöcyte*, while the other nucleus is extruded onto the outer surface of the oöcyte and forms the *first polar body*. (The polar bodies are named from the fact that they are extruded at the point—nearest the egg nucleus—where the first embryonic divisions will begin, one of the "poles" of the embryo.)

The second meiotic division soon follows, and the cytoplasmic division of the secondary oöcyte is also unequal. Again one of the nuclei is extruded as the *second polar body*, and the cell that retains all of the cytoplasm and yolk is now a *matured egg (ovum)*, ready for fertilization.

The first polar body may also undergo a second meiotic division, in which event the egg will show three polar bodies instead of two, but the polar bodies soon disappear (either by reabsorption or disintegration) and have no further significance.

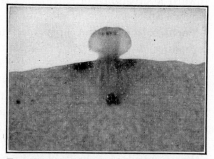

FIG. 15.5. A small part of a section through a whitefish egg undergoing maturation, showing the formation of a polar body. The enormous difference in size between the cell which will become the egg and the sister cell which forms the polar body is entirely due to the unequal distribution of the cytoplasm. The division of chromosomes between the two cells is equal. The cut section does not show all the chromatin of the polar body. (*Courtesy General Biological Supply House, Inc.*)

Oögenesis is evidently adapted to conserve the cytoplasm and food built up in the primary oöcyte within a single egg. It is a matter of chance which of the four daughter nuclei is retained in the egg, and which are extruded as polar bodies.

The matured egg. At the completion of oögenesis the egg has been or is ready to be shed from the ovary. It now consists of a nucleus with the reduced (haploid) number of chromosomes, a comparatively large mass of cytoplasm, and (in most eggs) a supply of stored food material or yolk. The egg is many times larger than the spermatozoon, and is invariably nonmotile. In several groups of animals the egg is also provided, either before or after fertilization, with such accessory parts as a "white" (additional food material secreted around the egg), a shell, and various supporting, attaching, or protecting structures.

The maturation of the sperm (spermatogenesis). The primitive male sperm cells (*spermatogonia*) also multiply in the testis by mitosis, so that enormous numbers of them are provided. Maturation of the spermatogonia is nearly synonymous with meiosis. As the cell enters the preliminary stages of the first meiotic division, it is known as a *primary spermatocyte;* the first division results in the formation of two similar haploid *secondary spermatocytes* with equal amounts of cytoplasm. Each secondary spermatocyte now undergoes the second meiotic division, again followed by an even division of the cytoplasm, to result in the formation of four *spermatids*. These develop without further division into functional spermatozoa. The nucleus becomes even more condensed, and the cytoplasm is organized into the whiplike propulsive tail of the *mature spermatozoon*.

The matured spermatozoon. At the completion of spermatogenesis the spermatozoon is ready to leave the testis and is capable of fertilizing an egg. It is very small, usually less than one-thousandth the bulk of the ovum, is capable of locomotion, and has the property of being attracted toward a substance or substances that diffuse from the unfertile eggs of its own species.

Fertilization of the egg. In the vast majority of animals sexual reproduction is *bisexual;* the matured egg is incapable of development until it has been fertilized by a spermatozoon. When spermatozoa are set free sufficiently close to such an unfertilized egg, they are chemically attracted by it and swim in its direction. Only one spermatozoon can fertilize an egg. The first one to reach it penetrates the egg membrane, and the head (nuclear portion) of the spermatozoon moves through the cytoplasm to meet the egg nucleus. Once within the egg membrane the sperm nucleus absorbs fluid and swells to the size of the egg nucleus, so that it soon becomes difficult to distinguish between the two. Soon after the two nuclei come into contact, they fuse to form a single diploid nucleus, which contains one haploid set of chromosomes from the egg and another haploid set from the sperm nucleus. The diploid number of chromosomes that characterized the unmatured germ cells (and soma cells) is thus restored. Fertilization is now complete, and the fertilized egg or *zygote* (Greek, *zygotos*, "yoked together") is ready to begin embryonic development.

BISEXUAL AND UNISEXUAL REPRODUCTION

We have already defined sexual reproduction as reproduction by germ cells and have seen that it normally involves the union of sperm and egg cells produced as a result of meiosis and maturation. Up to this point we have been concerned with the cells involved; now let us consider the individuals in which these cells are produced, and some of the variations in sexual reproduction.

Dioecious versus hermaphroditic conditions. We ordinarily think of bisexual reproduction as being correlated with the existence of two kinds of individuals—males that have testes and produce spermatozoa, and females that have ovaries and produce eggs. The sperms and eggs live, so to speak, in different "houses," and we speak of organisms with separate male and female individuals as being *dioecious* (Greek, *di*, "two," and *oikos*, "house"). The vast majority of bisexual animals are dioecious. But there are species, genera, and even families and classes of animals in which the sexes are not separate. In these groups individuals possess both testes and ovaries, and produce both spermatozoa and eggs. Such an individual or species is said to be *hermaphroditic*, and the condition is termed *hermaphroditism.*[1] Among many snails, annelid worms, flatworms, and certain other organisms hermaphroditism is the normal condition.

Fig. 15.6. A pair of earthworms in amplexus. The anterior ends of the worms are held together by a slime tube secreted by epidermal glands. Sperm from each worm are transferred to a storage chamber (spermatheca) in the partner; then the worms separate. Later each secretes a slime cocoon around a part of its body called the clitellum. This cocoon is slipped off over the worm's head, the worm's own eggs and the partner's sperm being deposited in the cocoon during this process. Fertilization and development occur within the cocoon in a liquid that provides the necessary "aquatic" environment. (*Courtesy General Biological Supply House, Inc.*)

It is unknown in vertebrates except as a rare abnormality, and most alleged examples in man and other mammals are not true cases where testis and ovary occur in the same individual. Even in true hermaphrodites cross-fertilization is often insured, as in the earthworm (Fig. 15.6) by arrangements of the reproductive organs such that the eggs of one individual can only be fertilized by sperm from another. In other

[1] From the Greek myth of Hermaphroditus, son of Hermes and Aphrodite, who was united with the nymph Salmacis to form a single androgynous (male + female) person.

species, including the hagfish and the oyster, the sperm cells and ova of a particular individual are not matured at the same time.

Unisexual reproduction (parthenogenesis). In several orders of insects and in certain other invertebrate groups there is a special and rather rare type of sexual reproduction called *parthenogenesis* (Greek, *parthenos,* "virgin," and *genesis,* "origin"). A part or all of the eggs are able to develop without fertilization. Such eggs are clearly germ cells; they have developed and matured in an ovary, have undergone meiosis, and are often outwardly and even microscopically indistinguishable from ordinary eggs. Unlike ordinary eggs, they undergo embryonic development without any stimulus from or union with a sperm.

There is much evidence that parthenogenesis is a derived condition, developed in groups that were once bisexual but that have become able to dispense with fertilization, wholly or in part. Males may be temporarily (or in a few cases permanently) absent. In some of the aphids or plant lice, for example, males appear only in the fall, to fertilize bisexual eggs that survive the winter in a resting state; during the spring and summer there are several generations consisting only of females. Here we see an alternation between bisexual and unisexual generations. In other instances, as in the honey bee, the eggs will develop either with or without fertilization. At her single union with the male the female receives a store of spermatozoa, which she can release or withhold at will as the eggs pass through the oviduct. The fertilized eggs produce females (workers or queens), the unfertilized eggs males (drones).

Artificial parthenogenesis. Among a few animals—starfishes, sea urchins, and frogs, for example—in which the eggs will not normally develop without fertilization, it has been found that unfertilized eggs can be made to develop by certain special treatments. Such treatments include placing the eggs in various solutions for a certain length of time or, in the case of the frog egg, pricking the egg membrane with a needle that has been dipped in frog serum. Usually the individuals produced by such methods are feeble and often fail to complete their normal development,[1] but these experiments indicate that one of the roles performed by the spermatozoon is to stimulate development. Another role, that of contributing paternal, inherited qualities to the offspring, will be considered under genetics and evolution.

BREEDING HABITS IN THE METAZOA

Bisexual reproduction is by all odds the most common and important way of producing new individuals. It is the sole method available to the vertebrates and most of the higher and intermediate metazoans, and it is at least occasionally utilized by nearly all the lower metazoans that

---

[1] Adult frogs, however, have been obtained by artificial parthenogenesis.

also reproduce asexually. There is good reason to believe that bisexual reproduction confers special advantages on the organisms that practice it. For one thing, it permits the development of a much more complex degree of body organization than appears to be reproducible by asexual means. The increased variability provided by biparental inheritance has doubtless been an important factor in the evolution of the most successful types of animal life.

Whatever its advantages, it is also apparent that bisexual reproduction encounters a complication not presented by asexual or unisexual methods.[1] Fertilization of the egg requires the cooperation of two individuals, which

FIG. 15.7. External fertilization with amplexus in the creek chub, Semotilus. The male (above) and female (below) are seen over a pit scooped by the former in the gravel of a stream riffle. As the eggs are laid and sink to the floor of the "nest" they are fertilized by "milt" from the male, who later covers them with pebbles. (*Redrawn, after Jacob Reighard.*)

not only must produce matured sperm and ova at the same season but must, by appropriate behaviors, bring the spermatozoa and eggs into close proximity. We find, therefore, that bisexual reproduction calls for special *breeding habits*, which lead the males and females of the species to abandon for a time their ordinary self-maintenance activities in order to perform their roles as parents of the next generation. Here we often find a clear subordination of the interests of the individual to the interests of the race. Many of the habits that have been developed to accomplish reproduction are highly dangerous or even fatal to the individuals that perform them and result in a heavy mortality of parent organisms.

Although the breeding habits of many species of higher metazoans include parental care for the fertilized eggs and developing young, all bisexual breeding habits begin with the special activities that lead to the fertilization of the eggs.

[1] Except in the rare, and relatively unimportant, instances of self-fertilization in hermaphroditic animals.

Methods of ensuring fertilization. With more than a half million bisexual species, variously adapted to live in so many diverse types of situations, we cannot hope to survey all the interesting behaviors that have been developed to ensure fertilization of the eggs. We can, however, classify practically all known *types* of habits into four groups that, although they somewhat overlap, illustrate something of the variety and the range in complexity and efficiency of these methods. The most fundamental distinction is that between external and internal fertilization.

External fertilization without amplexus is correlated with an aquatic (usually marine) habitat, a more or less sedentary type of life, and is usually associated with the congregating of large numbers of male and female individuals into a comparatively small area during the breeding

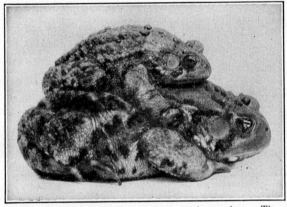

Fig. 15.8. A pair of toads, *Bufo terrestris americanus*, in amplexus. The male holds the female tightly, with his thumbs pressed deep into her sides. As the eggs are laid spermatozoa are poured over them by the male. (*Photo by Prof. S. C. Bishop.*)

season. There the females pour out their eggs into the sea water, and the males liberate tremendous numbers of sperms. The eggs drift about and diffuse out some substance that serves as an attraction to the spermatozoa of their own species. Sperms that chance to swim close enough to the egg to encounter this substance are attracted and guided to the egg and fertilize it. The approach of the sperm close enough to the egg to be attracted to it is a matter of chance, but chance that is very much increased by the proximity of the males and females and by the tremendous number of eggs and sperms that are produced.

External fertilization with amplexus[1] shows a much more elaborate and efficient development of breeding habits. Here, too, an aquatic situa-

[1] Literally, *amplexus* means "embrace" and is more correctly applied to the clasping of the female frog or toad in the arms of the male; however, its extension to include the behavior of many fishes during fertilization is physiologically if not morphologically justified.

tion is required, but, in addition, the male now actively seeks the female and clasps her or remains in very close proximity while eggs and sperm are discharged into the same very limited area, so that the eggs emerge from the female into a swarm of spermatozoa. A wide variation in details of this method is shown by the frogs, toads, and most of our fresh-water fishes.

Internal Fertilization without Copulation. Internal fertilization involves the liberation of the spermatozoa within the reproductive tract of the female. Here the sperms find a fluid medium in which to swim, and their path is so limited and directed that they are almost certain to encounter any eggs that are present. In a few forms, particularly some of the tailed amphibians, internal fertilization is accomplished by the males depositing sperm-filled capsules that the females find and take into their reproductive tracts. In some forms this is done without the males and females coming into direct contact with one another; in others, the sperm-filled capsule (*spermatophore*) is transferred from male to female during a behavior that involves amplexus but not copulation.

Internal Fertilization with Copulation. In nearly all other forms internal fertilization is accomplished by *copulation; i.e.,* by the direct transference of spermatozoa into the reproductive tract of the female by some intromittent organ (the penis, in the case of mammals) that forms a part of the male's accessory sex apparatus. In nearly all such forms the actual copulation constitutes but a small part of the complicated courtship and reproductive behavior that culminates in fertilization.

Care of the fertilized eggs and young. In many animals the peculiar adaptive breeding behavior is continued into nesting habits and various types of care for the young. Once the egg is fertilized, development begins. The materials and energy required for at least the early stages of development either are supplied by food contained in the egg (stored there before the egg left the mother's body) or are furnished by the mother as development proceeds. In the former case the egg is usually "laid," and we speak of such a habit as *oviparous.* Birds, amphibians, and most reptiles, fish, insects, and lower animals furnish examples of an oviparous habit. Among oviparous animals the amount of food that is stored in the egg varies widely. At one extreme we have such eggs as those of the starfish, which contain very little food material (yolk). Such eggs contain too little food to carry development very far, and the young are hatched in a very primitive (*larval*) condition that is quite unlike the parent form. Other oviparous eggs contain much food material, stored in one part of the egg. Frogs, fish, birds, and reptiles, as well as the arthropods and most of the mollusks, produce eggs of this kind. In the frog's egg the yolk forms little more than half the bulk of the egg; in the fish's egg the yolk forms a much larger proportion; and in the eggs of birds and reptiles the yolk forms all the true egg except a very small polar cap of cytoplasm, and the egg is supplied with additional food material, the "white," which is not truly a part of the egg but a secretion formed by the oviduct. In the frog the egg hatches into a larval form, a tadpole, while the better supplied fish, reptile, and bird eggs hatch into baby animals quite like the parents in all but size and minor features.

In the case of mammals and a few other animals the egg is not laid but is retained in the body of the mother, where it develops; the offspring is "born" with the embryonic stages already completed. This habit is termed *viviparous*. The mammal egg contains very little yolk, just

FIG. 15.9. Parental care. The obstetrical toad, Alytes, of Europe. The male carries the fertilized eggs until they hatch. (*Courtesy American Museum of Natural History.*)

enough to carry it through the first few stages of development. The early embryo very quickly develops a circulatory system and a large area of extraembryonic membrane, the *placenta*, which grows into very intimate contact with the mother's uterine wall. Through the placenta the embryo receives its needed supplies and rids itself of the by-products of metabolism.

A few organisms show a reproductive habit that appears somewhat intermediate between an oviparous and a viviparous habit. In some of the snakes, including the rattlesnake and its kin, and in some of the insects, an oviparous type of egg is formed that instead of being laid, is retained in the mother's reproductive tract until it hatches, although the embryo is "insulated" from any functional contact with the mother's tissues by the eggshell. This is essentially an oviparous habit but has outwardly the appearance of a viviparous one. This type of reproduction is termed *ovoviviparous*. In some of the sharks another type of ovoviviparous habit is shown that is more nearly like true viviparity. In this case, the egg has a fairly large yolk but no white or shell, and, when the yolk has all been utilized, the embryo develops a belated placental connection with the mother's tissues.

Even when embryonic development is complete and the young are born or hatched, they still have to undergo a more or less prolonged

FIG. 15.10. Parental care. Female, nest, and young of the ruby-throated hummingbird. (*Photo by Allan D. Cruickshank, courtesy National Audubon Society.*)

period of postembryonic development before they reach the adult condition. In nearly all animals this is a period of high mortality, and a large proportion, often a great majority, of the young perish. In general, animals have adopted one or both of two methods of offsetting this loss—a very high reproductive rate or some type of parental care of the young, at least while they are in the most helpless part of this period.

In the higher vertebrates and in most of the fishes, where the egg is either well supplied with food (strongly telolecithal) or viviparity occurs, the young are hatched or born in a highly developed condition and with a clear resemblance to the adult. Even among these forms, however, there is great variation as to the degree of precociousness or

helplessness that may be shown. To see this one has only to compare
the newly born kitten, pup, or mouse or the newly hatched songbird, with
equally young calves, colts, fawns, quail, chickens, or ducks.

In the amphibians and in most of the nonvertebrates, the young at
hatching do not at all resemble the parent forms that reproduced them.
Instead, they appear as larval forms that must pass through long periods
of finding their own food before they are able to transform into the adult
form. This transformation of *larvae* into adults is termed *metamorphosis.*
In many of the lower invertebrates the larval stage appears to be clearly
correlated with the small amount of food contained in the egg, a condition

FIG. 15.11. Parental care. Ostriches guarding their nest and newly hatched young from wart
hogs. (*Photo of African group, courtesy American Museum of Natural History.*)

that forces the young to become self-supporting at a very early stage; but
in the insects and many other groups, the larval stage is associated with a
highly successful type of life cycle in which the larval forms are as highly
organized for certain activities as the adult organisms are for others.

EMBRYONIC DEVELOPMENT

In the preceding paragraphs we digressed from a consideration of the
germ cells to look at some of the relationships and appropriate parental
behaviors that result in the fertilization of the egg and the care of the
developing young. We shall now return to the fertilized egg or *zygote*
and see something of its subsequent development.

The period between the fertilization of the egg and the birth or hatching of the young is a time of rapid growth and change. During this
period, in which the developing offspring is known as an *embryo* (Greek,
en, "in," and *bruo,* "bud"), it changes from a one-celled zygote into a

complex, many-celled organism more or less like the parent. It will be impossible for us to follow this development in detail for even one kind of organism, but we can see something of embryonic processes in general and learn to recognize embryonic stages that are common to all the metazoa.

Every zygote contains a *diploid nucleus*, a small mass of *cytoplasm*, and more or less stored food material in the form of *yolk*. The nucleus, as we have seen, was formed by the fusion of the haploid egg and sperm nuclei, but the cytoplasm and yolk were contributed solely by the egg, in which the proportions of cytoplasm and yolk and the details of their arrangement had been determined before fertilization. The proportions and organization of the cytoplasm and yolk are characteristic of the general group to which the animal belongs and will have two important consequences in the development of the zygote. Since in all oviparous eggs the yolk provides the chief or sole material and energy for growth, the amount of yolk will determine how far the purely embryonic development can go before the young individual will be thrown upon its own resources or before the parents will need to provide another food supply.[1] On the other hand, since the yolk is nonliving and inert, it cannot take any active part in development, and, if present in a considerable amount, it modifies or, so to speak, distorts the processes that are carried on by the living cytoplasm.

There is good reason to believe that the homolecithal egg, described below, shows the most primitive organization of cytoplasm and yolk. The other types of eggs are apparently modifications of this original organization caused by the inclusion of large stores of yolk, which, although they variously distort its early stages, provide for a more adequate embryonic development. On this hypothesis it is possible to correlate the many fundamental similarities that are common to the early embryonic development of all metazoans (except the sponges) and to interpret the relatively minor differences between them.

It should be noted that all eggs, and hence the zygotes derived from them, show *polarity; i.e.*, they are so organized that a certain point on the surface, the *animal pole*[2] is destined to be the center of the early externally visible embryonic activity. The opposite *vegetative* or *vegetal pole* marks the center of the region of greatest concentration of yolk and hence of least early activity.

---

[1] Parental care in the birds, certain of the insects, and a few other forms that have already provided a large store of food within the egg still further postpones the necessity of the young being "on their own" at the completion of embryonic development. The young of many of the Metazoa, however, must begin their independent existence long before development has reached anything like the adult structure of the parents.

[2] The egg nucleus is nearer this point than to any other part of the surface, and the extruded "polar bodies" are usually found here.

Homolecithal eggs contain a very small amount of yolk, and this is evenly distributed throughout the cytoplasm. Such eggs are very small[1] and undergo a markedly regular and symmetrical type of embryonic development that ends with the production of a postembryonic larval stage. This free-living larva must pass through a further period of development before attaining the structure of the adult. The eggs of starfishes, sea urchins, and marine worms are of this type, and those of the primitive chordate Amphioxus are very nearly so.

Telolecithal eggs contain an abundant store of yolk that is massed toward one pole of the egg. The greater part of the cytoplasm is concentrated near the opposite ("animal") pole, with the nucleus near its center. Telolecithal eggs vary widely in the amount of yolk they

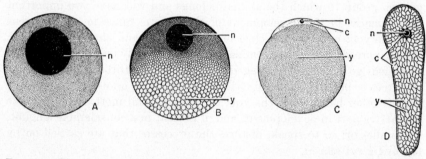

FIG. 15.12. Diagrammatic sections of eggs, showing differences in amount and distribution of yolk. *A*, homolecithal egg of starfish. *B*, mildly telolecithal egg of frog. *C*, strongly telolecithal egg of whitefish. *D*, centrolecithal egg of honeybee. The alecithal egg of mammals is exemplified by the human egg shown in Fig. 16.4. These eggs are not drawn to scale. Their relative sizes may be judged by the apparent size of the nucleus, which is actually about the same size in all. (*c*) Cytoplasm; (*n*) nucleus; (*y*) yolk. (*Modified from Turtox chart, courtesy General Biological Supply House, Inc.*)

contain. The frog's egg, which is mildly telolecithal, has little more than half of its bulk composed of yolk; the hen's egg (the "yolk" of the hen's egg is the true egg) is strongly telolecithal, with the yolk comprising much more than 95 per cent of the whole egg and the cytoplasm occupying a small superficial disk at the animal pole. Fish eggs are somewhat intermediate, although not much less strongly telolecithal than the hen's or reptile's egg.

Centrolecithal eggs are characterized by having a comparatively large central core of yolk surrounded by a peripheral layer of cytoplasm. The development of the centrolecithal egg is even more strongly modified by its yolk than is that of the telolecithal egg. Insects produce eggs of this type.

Alecithal eggs. The eggs of all viviparous mammals contain little if any yolk and superficially resemble homolecithal eggs. Their develop-

---

[1] Eggs of this type are usually correlated with a breeding habit that necessitates the production of huge numbers of eggs.

ment, however, is much more nearly—though not entirely—like that of a strongly telolecithal egg, and this is undoubtedly related to the fact that the mammals are descended from oviparous ancestors that laid telolecithal eggs.

Early Stages and Processes of Development

Except for such modifications and distortions as are evidently due to the varied amount and distribution of yolk, the early embryonic stages

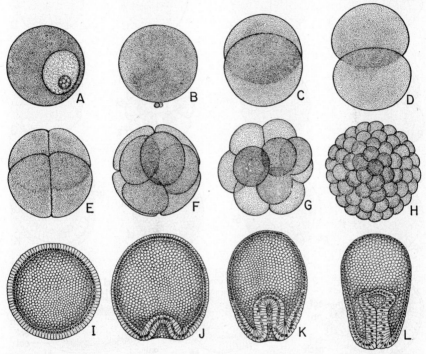

FIG. 15.13. Cleavage and gastrulation in the development of the starfish. *A*, the unfertilized homolecithal egg. *B*, the fertilized egg with two polar bodies. *C*, early two-cell stage. *D*, late two-cell stage. *E*, four-cell stage. *F*, eight-cell stage. *G*, sixteen-cell stage. *H*, morula ("mulberry") stage. *I*, blastula, optical section. *J*, early gastrula, optical section. *K*, later gastrula, optical section. *L*, late gastrula, optical section. (*Modified from Turtox chart, courtesy General Biological Supply House, Inc.*)

of all Metazoa (except sponges) are clearly similar. The brief account that follows is somewhat generalized but is based primarily upon the development of the homolecithal eggs of the starfish and the very nearly homolecithal eggs of Amphioxus. The latter animal (Fig. B.26) is a primitive relative of the vertebrates and shows the early development of certain characteristic vertebrate structures. The diagrammatic illustrations of the early development of the starfish (Fig. 15.13) and Amphioxus (Fig. 15.14) should be compared with that showing the somewhat modi-

fied cleavage, blastula and gastrula of the frog (Fig. 15.15) and the highly
modified development of the chick (Fig. 15.16).

Cleavage.   Soon after fertilization has taken place, the zygote divides
by mitosis to form a 2-cell embryo. The plane of the first division, or

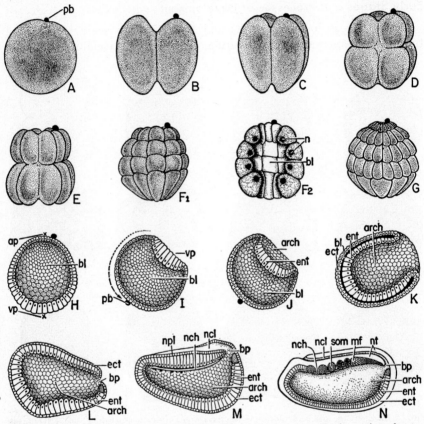

Fig. 15.14. The early development of the lancelet Amphioxus up to the formation of notochord, neural tube, and somites. *A,* the fertilized egg. *B,* 2-cell stage. *C,* 4-cell stage. *D,*
8-cell stage. *E,* 16-cell stage. *F₁,* 32-cell stage. *F₂,* 32-cell stage, optical section (as are all the
figures *H* to *N*). *G,* morula. *H,* blastula. *I,* flattening of vegetative pole. *J,* early gastrula.
K, gastrula. *L,* late gastrula. *M,* embryo at neural fold stage. *N,* embryo at neural tube
stage. *ap,* animal pole; *arch,* archenteron; *bl,* blastocoel; *bp,* blastopore; *ect,* ectoderm; *ent,*
entoderm; *mf,* mesodermal fold; *n,* nuclei; *nch,* notochord; *ncl,* neural canal; *npl,* neural
plate; *nt,* neural tube; *pb,* polar body; *som,* somites; *vp,* vegetative pole. (*Modified from
Turtox chart, courtesy General Biological Supply House, Inc.*)

first *cleavage,* passes through both poles of the zygote and divides it into
approximately equal cells. The next cleavage also passes through both
poles of the embryo, at right angles to the first cleavage plane, and divides
each of the 2 cells to form a 4-cell stage. In the next division each of the
4 cells divides in a plane at right angles to the first and second cleavage

planes, and this results in an 8-cell stage. At the fourth cleavage each cell is divided into two by planes that pass through both poles of the embryo, to produce a 16-cell stage. The fifth cleavage results in a 32-cell stage; the sixth, in a 64-cell stage, etc., but later cleavages are not likely to be so regular as the first four or five.

The blastula. The rapidly multiplying cells of the embryo show a marked tendency to round off their acute inner angles so that a cavity is formed at the center of the spherical mass of cells. As cleavage follows cleavage, this cavity increases in size until, by the end of the cleavage period, when the embryo consists of several hundred cells, it has the form of a hollow ball. At this stage the embryo is known as a *blastula* and its central cavity, which is filled with fluid, as the *blastocoele.*

Gastrulation. The completed blastula consists of a single layer of cells surrounding the blastocoele; but almost as soon as it is formed, it begins to change into a two-layered structure known as a *gastrula.* This change is accomplished by a flattening and then an indenting (invagination) of one pole of the blastula, until the blastocoele is obliterated and the cells of the indented side of the blastula wall are in contact with those of the opposite side. This indenting process, or invagination, is accompanied by a rapid multiplication of cells, so that the double-walled (*diploblastic*) gastrula has approximately the same outward shape and size as the blastula from which it developed.

The outside wall of the gastrula is known as the *ectoderm;* the inner wall, as the *entoderm;* the latter lines a new cavity, the *archenteron,* which opens to the outside of the embryo through an opening, the *blastopore.*

Modification of cleavage and gastrulation. In telolecithal eggs the processes of cleavage and gastrulation, although clearly comparable to those of the homolecithal egg, are modified by the large quantities of inert yolk. In the frog's egg the early cleavage stages are not markedly different from those described above, but the later cleavages are unequal and result in a blastula with many small cells at the animal pole and few and larger cells at the opposite pole. The blastula wall is much thicker in the region of these large yolk-filled cells, and the blastocoele is thus displaced toward the animal pole. In more strongly telolecithal eggs cleavage is confined to the small cytoplasmic disk at the animal pole, and the blastocoele forms a small shallow cavity beneath this disk. Gastrulation is correspondingly modified, considerably in the case of the frog embryo and greatly in embryos that develop from strongly telolecithal eggs. Nevertheless, a true gastrula is always formed with a distinct differentiation of outer ectoderm and inner entoderm and the formation of an archenteron and blastopore.

Mesoderm formation. In all but the two lowest phyla of the Metazoa the completion of the diploblastic gastrula stage is immediately followed by the development of a third fundamental cell layer, the *mesoderm*. At this point the similarity of development that is common to the embryos of all metazoans (except sponges) becomes less evident, and the embryos of various phyla begin to develop the diverse patterns of symmetry and organization that distinguish their respective groups. Here we can consider only very briefly the mesoderm formation in Amphioxus and the frog.

In Amphioxus, gastrulation is accompanied by an elongation of the embryo, which is beginning to show bilateral symmetry. On either side of the middorsal line of the elongating (head to tail) axis of the body the entoderm begins to evaginate (fold out) a linear series of connected

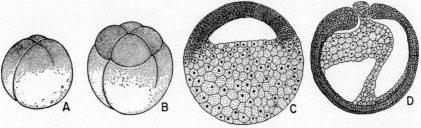

Fig. 15.15. The early development of the frog, showing the effects of a moderate concentration of yolk at the vegetative pole. *A*, beginning of second cleavage division. *B*, third cleavage division completed. *C*, section of blastula. *D*, section of gastrula. The projecting mass of cells is the yolk plug. (*Modified from Turtox chart, courtesy General Biological Supply House, Inc.*)

pouches. These outgrowths become the mesoderm; they rapidly enlarge and are soon cut off from the entoderm tube, which "heals" together to show no traces of its former connection with the mesodermal pouches. The right and left mesodermal tubes grow rapidly and soon meet and fuse along the mid-ventral line of the embryo, thus completely separating the ectoderm of the outer body wall from the entoderm of the gut. The cavity of the mesodermal tubes forms the coelom, or true body cavity, which is thus lined with mesoderm and forms the outer space of the "tube-within-a-tube" body structure.

Mesoderm formation in the vertebrates is clearly comparable to that in Amphioxus, but it is usually modified or distorted, either by the yolk-laden condition of the entodermal cells or, in the mammals, as a result of descent from ancestors that had such yolk-laden eggs.

The Primary "Germ Layers"

The *ectoderm*, *entoderm* and *mesoderm* constitute the so-called "primary" or "germ" layers, from which all the structures of triploblastic animals are developed. In all the higher metazoans the differentiation of these layers constitutes but a very small fraction of embryonic development. By far the greater portion is occupied with the formation of the tissues, organs, and systems of the finished embryo from the derivatives and combinations of these primary tissues. In general, the outermost layers of the body, the nervous system, and the sensory parts of the sense organs are derived from ectoderm, the lining of the alimentary canal and its derivatives—liver, pancreas, lungs, etc.—are derived from entoderm; the contractile and sustentative portions of the skin and the digestive tract, the muscular, skeletal, circulatory, and excretory systems, and sustentative and contractile tissues as a group are developed from mesoderm.

Some Special Vertebrate Structures

Somite formation. One of the fundamental devices of all vertebrate organization, the linear repetition of such structures as the vertebrae, ribs, spinal nerves, and certain blood vessels and thoracic muscles, is foreshadowed and determined by the early development of mesodermal *somites*. These are a linear series of paired, similar blocks that are formed as centers of condensation and more rapid growth in that part of the mesoderm that lies next to and on either side of the middorsal line of the embryo. The first pair of such centers forms on either side of what is to be the midbrain of the embryo, and the formation of additional centers proceeds rapidly backward (and slowly forward) from this point, each center contiguous to the one in front of it. This somite formation is so characteristic and regular that the number of somites that are visible at any given time gives one of the best indications of the stage in development reached by the early embryo, and much of the organization of the future body parts is a consequence of somite formation.

The notochord. In Amphioxus and in all vertebrate embryos the formation of a characteristic axial rod, the notochord, takes place at the same time as the formation of the mesoderm. In Amphioxus this rod is derived from the middorsal line of the entoderm by an evagination like that which produced the mesodermal pouches. The notochord, however, does not show any metameric arrangement into a linear series of pouches, nor does it develop a central cavity. It lies, as a cylindrical axial rod, dorsal to the alimentary canal. In the vertebrates (but not in Amphioxus) it is later replaced by the mesodermal tissues that form the centra of the vertebrae.

The hollow dorsal neural tube. Shortly after the beginning of the formation of the mesoderm and notochord, the development of the nervous system begins. The ectoderm along the middorsal line begins to grow rapidly, and a neural plate thicker than the rest of the ectoderm is formed. This development is most rapid in the region of what is to become the midbrain and progresses forward and backward from this point. The plate soon sags below the level of the remainder of the ectoderm and

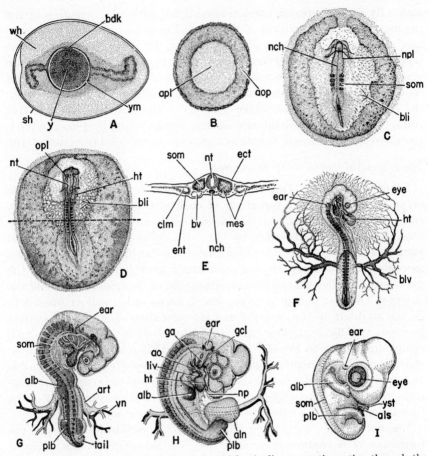

FIG. 15.16. Embryonic development of the chick. *A*, diagrammatic section through the hen's egg, showing relation of "yolk" (the true egg), white, and the shell and its membranes. Many details of structure are omitted. Note particularly the blastoderm (blastodisk), a small polar disk of cytoplasm enclosing the nucleus. The blastoderm alone undergoes cleavage and forms the embryo and its membranes. The huge mass of yolk is inert food material, which with the added white is used as a source of energy and raw materials for development.

B, the blastoderm. This is the blastodisk, now seen from above, after some hours of development while the egg is still in the hen's body. Cleavage has taken place, and first a blastula and then a gastrula have been formed. The blastula had the shape of a flat cap or plate of cells, and the gastrula was produced by the cell plate turning under at one point (the posterior end) and growing forward into the shallow space between the yolk and the upper layer. This made the blastoderm two-layered, with an upper ectoderm and a lower entoderm. Note the clearer inner space (area pellucida) in which the embryo proper will develop, and the outer region (area opaca) which will form part of the extraembryonic membranes.

C, the embryo after about 24 hours of incubation, viewed from above. Except for the clear space in front of the head there are now three layers of tissue—ectoderm on top, entoderm next to the yolk, and between them (except along the midline) a mesoderm which is in part split into two layers. The notochord lies between the right and left plates of mesoderm. Note the four pairs of somites formed from the denser part of the mesoderm, and the thickening neural ridges of ectoderm.

D, the embryo after 33 hours of incubation, viewed from above. Because the tissues are transparent, one sees both outer and inner structures. A neural tube has now formed by then folds, to form first a trough and then a tube that is cut off from the remainder of the ectoderm and lies beneath the outer ectoderm of the middorsal wall of the embryo, just above the notochord.

The rapid multiplication of the cells of the neural tube continues, and the tube soon develops a number of expansions that represent the early stages of the several brain regions. The longer portion of the tube posterior to the brain becomes the spinal cord.

The gill pouches.   Another peculiar and universal feature of all vertebrate embryos is the formation of several pairs of gill pouches and gill arches. The side walls of the fore portion of the early embryonic gut, which forms at a very early stage in embryonic development, soon produce a series of paired (right and left) pouchlike outgrowths that extend toward the body wall of the neck region. At a slightly later stage the outer body wall begins to grow inward in a series of lateral furrows, each furrow opposite the apex of an outwardly growing pouch. The partitions between these paired pouches become regions of rapid mesodermal growth, and a series of alternating *gill pouches* and *gill arches* is soon formed on either side of the fore-gut. In the fishes and amphibians the matched pouches and clefts soon unite (break through) to form *gill slits*, connecting the cavity of the fore-gut with the outside environment. In these groups the gill arches become the supporting structures on which the gill membranes are developed and through which the blood vessels (aortic arches) run that connect the dorsal and ventral aortas. In the higher vertebrates— reptiles, birds, and mammals—the pouches and furrows do not completely break through, but they and the arches between them do profoundly

junction of the neural folds and anteriorly is developing rapidly into the primary brain vesicles. The heart has also formed as a pulsing tube connected with the blood vessels developing from the nearer blood islands in the extraembryonic region. Note the increased number of somites.

E, a cross section through *D* along the line indicated. The neural tube was formed by an infolding and pinching off of the ectoderm; the inside of the tube was formerly the upper surface of the ectodermal sheet along the midline. (Compare *B* and *C*.)

F, the embryo after 48 hours of incubation, with the extraembryonic membranes removed. The rapidly developing neural tube has curved and twisted through nearly 90 degrees, so that the embryo now lies on its side anteriorly. Note the developing eye and ear, and the growing heart, which has elongated and looped. Note also the great development of extraembryonic blood vessels. The embryonic blood vessels are not visible except where they are somewhat indicated in the heart region.

G, the embryo after 72 hours of incubation, with the extraembryonic membranes removed. Note the appearance of limb buds and tail, and that the region above the heart shows gill arches and furrows.

H, the embryo after 96 hours of incubation.

I, the embryo after 5 days of incubation. The embryo is now much more opaque, and only surface features are shown. Note the great enlargement of the limb buds, and the appearance of digits on the forelimbs. Sixteen more days of incubation are required before hatching. *alb*, anterior limb bud; *aln*, allantois; *als*, allantoic stalk; *ao*, aorta; *aop*, area opaca; *apl*, area pellucida; *art*, artery; *bdk*, blastodisk; *bli*, blood islands; *bv*, blood vessels; *clm*, coelom; *ect*, ectoderm; *ent*, entoderm; *ga*, gill arches; *gcl*, gill clefts; *ht*, heart; *liv*, liver; *mes*, mesoderm; *nch*, notochord; *np*, nasal pit; *npl*, neural plate; *nt*, neural tube; *opl*, optic lobes of brain; *plb*, posterior limb bud; *sh*, shell; *som*, somite; *vn*, vein; *wh*, white; *y*, yolk; *ym*, yolk membrane; *yst*, yolk stalk.

modify embryonic organization and are variously utilized in the formation of subsequent adult structures.[1] The eustachian tube, for instance, which connects our mouth cavity with the middle ear, is derived from the first (foremost) gill pouch; and our lower jaw, the cartilages that support our tongue, and our thyroid and parathyroid glands are derivatives of various other gill arches or pouches.

The limb buds. A fifth set of characteristic vertebrate structures, the paired pectoral and pelvic limbs, also make their beginning in early embryonic life. The paired buds that are to develop into the pectoral girdle and forelimbs are the first to appear. They arise as lateral protuberances that show a very rapid growth, involving several of the paired somites and associated tissues in the shoulder region. The buds that are to form the hind limbs are markedly similar except for their more caudal (tailward) position and their at first more retarded development.

[1] The aortic arches of the various vertebrate groups owe their arrangement to that of the early embryonic gill arches, and our own pulmonary arteries and several of the important branches from the basal part of our aorta are derived from the embryonic blood vessels that traversed these arches.

CHAPTER XVI

HUMAN REPRODUCTION

In Part I of this book we dealt with the human body viewed as a self-maintaining individual organism. In that treatment the reproductive system was not included, for the primary functions of that system relate to maintenance not of the individual but of the race. Nevertheless the reproductive system does profoundly affect the development, structure, and functioning of the individual, as will be evident in what follows. Here we shall use man as a concrete example to illustrate some of the reproductive structures and processes described in general terms in the last chapter.

The reproductive system of the male. The male gametes, known as *spermatozoa*, are developed in the convoluted *seminiferous tubules* that make up the bulk of the *testis* (plural *testes*). In mammals, including man, the paired testes are suspended below the pubic region in a loose pouch, the *scrotum*, into which they descend from the abdominal cavity in late embryonic life.[1]

Certain cells of the seminiferous tubules, like the follicle cells of the ovary, nourish the germ cells while the latter are undergoing the changes that transform them into mature spermatozoa. The seminiferous tubules communicate by short ducts with a coiled tube, the *epididymis*, which lies in the scrotum alongside the testis and, perhaps with the aid of the seminal vesicles, acts as a storehouse for the spermatozoa until they are ejected. From each epididymis a duct, the *vas deferens*, passes from the scrotum up into the abdomen, over the symphysis pubis or junction of the pubic bones, and around to the lower rear side of the bladder. Here it is joined by the duct of an elongated saclike *seminal vesicle*, the principal function of which is to contribute a part of the fluid that, with the spermatozoa, makes up the *semen*. Beyond this point, the vasa deferentia are called the *ejaculatory ducts;* they open a short distance beyond the neck of the bladder into the common channel for urine and semen, the *urethra*. The *prostate gland* surrounds the ejaculatory ducts

---

[1] Mammalian spermatozoa are injured by the high temperatures prevailing in the abdominal cavity, and when descent of the testis fails to occur (as sometimes happens), spermatozoa are not formed.

and the base of the urethra and opens into the latter, as do the ducts of
the small *Cowper's glands*. The functions of the prostate gland and
Cowper's glands are not entirely understood, though they probably
contribute fluid to the semen; they are not, however, essential for
reproduction.

The distal portion of the urethra traverses the erectile copulatory
organ, the *penis*. This organ is composed chiefly of three *corpora cavernosa*,
two dorsal and one ventral, the latter enclosing the urethra and expanding

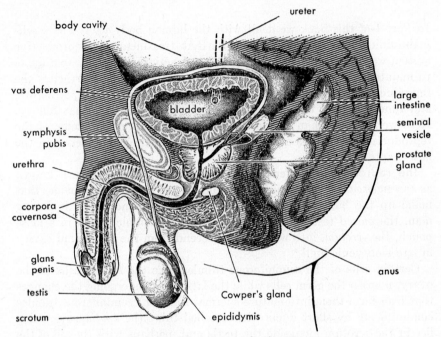

Fig. 16.1. The male reproductive system.

at its distal end into the glans penis. The two dorsal corpora cavernosa
diverge within the body and are attached to the pubic bones. The corpora
cavernosa contain large blood spaces; under the influence of sexual
excitement, the arteries carrying blood to the organ are dilated and the
veins are constricted at its base, causing the spaces to fill with blood under
pressure and the penis to become erect. Ejection of the semen is brought
about chiefly by rhythmic contractions of the vasa deferentia and the
bulbocavernosus muscle; the latter encloses the intrapelvic basal portion
of the ventral corpus cavernosum.

The reproductive system of the female. The paired *ovaries* are the
parts of the female reproductive system in which the germ cells are housed
and in which the mature germ cells, or *eggs*, are produced. The ovaries

are small, ovoid or almond-shaped bodies situated low in the abdomen and suspended in position by ligaments attached to the side walls of the pelvis and to the uterus. Like the uterus and the other abdominal organs, the ovary projects into the abdominal cavity and is covered by the peritoneum, which envelops the organ, and by its folds forms the supporting ligaments.

Within the ovary, the developing germ cells are surrounded by special soma or body cells that nourish them while they grow and mature. These accessory cells form a spherical structure imbedded in the ovary, known as an *ovarian follicle*. As the follicle enlarges, a split develops along one side between its inner and outer cell layers, and the space thus formed

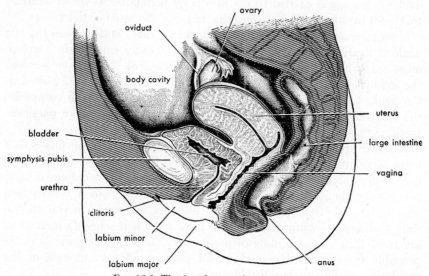

Fig. 16.2. The female reproductive system.

gradually fills with lymph and increases in size. When the egg is finally mature and ready to leave the ovary, it lies, surrounded by a layer of follicle cells, floating in the cavity of the much enlarged follicle. The latter has in the meanwhile pushed out to the surface of the ovary, just beneath the peritoneum that lines the peritoneal (or coelomic) cavity. The ovary has no duct for the discharge of eggs. Instead, the eggs are freed by a peculiar process called *ovulation*, which consists in rupture of the wall of the follicle and the overlying peritoneum and discharge of the follicular fluid and the egg into the peritoneal cavity.

Actually the egg does not ordinarily escape into this cavity but is discharged into or is at once picked up by the open end of the oviduct. The *oviducts* are a pair of tubes extending from the upper portion of the uterus to the vicinity of the two ovaries. There they end in enlarged, funnel-like, fringed openings that communicate directly with the peritoneal cavity. The open ends of the oviducts contain smooth muscle, have some freedom of movement, and can be applied to the surfaces of the ovaries. It is probable that shortly before ovulation occurs, they cup themselves over the surface of the ovary in the region of the follicle. Even if the egg is not discharged directly into the oviduct, the currents caused by beating cilia within the funnel tend to carry it in. Rare accidents are known, however, in which eggs have escaped into the peritoneal cavity and there been fertilized; or in which the egg from one ovary has traveled to the oviduct of the opposite side, when one ovary and the opposite oviduct had previously been removed by surgery. Once in the oviduct, the egg is carried to the uterus by peristaltic waves of contraction[1] and by the beating of the cilia that line the walls of the tube.

If copulation has occurred, sperm normally meet and fertilize the egg while it is still in the oviduct. In this event early embryonic development takes place during the several days required for passage through the oviduct to the uterus. If the egg is not fertilized, it is absorbed in the oviduct or uterus, probably through the agency of white corpuscles that pass through the walls of these organs and ingest foreign particles. In this event, there follow the phenomena of menstruation.

The ruptured follicle from which the egg has escaped soon fills with a mass of yellowish cells and becomes a gland of internal secretion called the *corpus luteum*. If fertilization does not occur, the corpus luteum persists for about 10 days and then dwindles away; but if fertilization does occur and the developing ovum becomes implanted in the uterine wall, the corpus luteum continues to grow until it reaches a diameter of about ¾ inch by the middle of pregnancy. The corpus luteum is indispensable for successful gestation and plays an important role in the regulation of the female reproductive cycle.

The *uterus* is the organ in which embryonic development takes place. It is an unpaired, median structure with very thick muscular walls and a central cavity. The two oviducts open into its inner end, and at the outer end a narrow passage extending through the neck of the uterus communicates with the *vagina*. The walls of the uterus are lined with a vascular and glandular epithelium to which the embryo becomes attached. During pregnancy the uterus becomes enormously enlarged, projecting far up into the abdomen. Birth of the child is accomplished by rhythmic contractions of the smooth muscles of the uterine walls, aided by the voluntary abdominal muscles. The neck of the uterus and the vagina are very distensible, and their openings are eventually stretched sufficiently to permit the passage of the child. The vagina communicates

[1] *Peristalsis* is the progression of bands of constriction along a tubular organ, pushing the contents in one direction. The intestinal movements furnish a good example.

with the exterior through the urinogenital sinus, bounded by the *labia* and containing the *clitoris*, a small sensory organ homologous with the penis of the male.

Sex hormones.   We have seen something of the nature of the endocrine glands and the coordinating role played by the hormones that they produce. The testes and ovaries (*gonads*) also produce hormones, in addition to their function of nurturing the germ cells. In general, these hormones affect the development of the male and female secondary sex characters, including degree of skeletal development, amount and distribution of hair, depth of voice, size of accessory sex organs, and sex behavior. They also regulate the sex cycles. The principal sex hormones and their roles are discussed below.

SEX HORMONES IN THE MALE

Androgenic hormones.   From bull testes there has been isolated an active hormone, *testosterone*, which has pronounced androgenic (promoting masculinity) effects. Testosterone has not yet been found in the testes of other species but is probably present. A very similar substance, *androsterone*, has been prepared from the urine of the human male and many other mammals. The chemical composition of both these hormones is known and both have been made in the laboratory. It seems probable that androsterone is formed from testosterone during the latter's excretion from the body. More than 30 other similar substances with androgenic effects have been artificially synthesized. There seems to be no doubt that the androgenic hormones are produced by the interstitial cells of the testis, but it is not yet certain that the seminiferous tubules do not also produce them.

The role of the androgenic hormones is demonstrated by castration and by injecting the hormones into castrated and normal animals. Castrated cocks, bulls, and men (known respectively as *capons*, *steers*, and *eunuchs*), as well as other castrated animals show characteristic effects of the operation. Young males fail to show the normal changes in body form, stature, external sex organs, and amount and distribution of hair at puberty; they are fatter and less muscular than normal males, and the body remains more like that of the young female. Castrated adults show a diminution of the peculiarly male characteristics, and their sexual behavior diminishes. That it does not disappear in men is probably due to the fact that such behavior depends partly upon purely psychological elements. Injection of testosterone into young castrated animals results in normal development of the male characteristics, and in castrated adults testosterone restores full sexual behavior. Such treatment does not, of course, enable castrated animals to produce spermatozoa. In caponized cocks the grafting of a testis within the abdominal cavity has the same results as testosterone injection. This has led to the popular belief that the grafting of testes into ageing men will prolong life and restore potency—an illusory hope. Such grafted testes, even when human, fail to become established and soon degenerate.

Gonadotrophic hormones.   The activity of the testis is under the remote control of the gonadotrophic hormones produced by the anterior lobe of the pituitary, as discussed in Chap. VIII. When the anterior lobe is removed from young male animals, they never become sexually mature. The testes cease to develop, spermatozoa are not formed, and there is no expression of the secondary sex characters. Injections of anterior lobe extract result in normal development of such animals. An excess of the hormones causes precocious sexual maturity; male chicks given repeated injections of anterior lobe extract grow large combs and begin to crow before they are fully feathered. Removal of the anterior pituitary from adults is followed by degenerative changes in the testes; spermatozoa cease to be formed, and the effects of castration appear.

The gonadotrophic hormones operative in the male are two. The *interstitial cell stimulating hormone (ICSH)* stimulates growth of the interstitial cells of the testis and thus indirectly causes the production of the androgenic hormones. The *follicle stimulating hormone (FSH)* stimulates the production of spermatozoa in the male, although it receives its name from its first observed effect, that of stimulating growth of the follicle in the ovary of the female.

In continuous breeders like man there is a constant output of ICSH and FSH at all times, maintaining a continuous production of androgenic hormones and spermatozoa. In seasonal breeders (the majority of vertebrates) the output of gonadotrophic hormones varies; the testes (and ovaries) are small and inactive except just before and during the breeding season. In many birds temperature and length of day have been found to provide the stimuli for increase in production of the gonadotrophic hormones and thus govern the time when mating and migration occur. Such birds can be made to breed and to migrate in midwinter by regulation of temperature and the daily ratio of light and darkness to which they are subjected in laboratory cages.

SEX HORMONES AND REPRODUCTIVE CYCLES IN THE FEMALE

Sexually mature females of all mammals, including the human species, show rhythms or cycles in the reproductive processes and activities. We have already seen something of these periodicities in the preceding section on the female reproductive system, but they require further description. We shall see how they result from alterations in hormone balance.

The menstrual cycle.   In the lower mammals mating occurs only during definite breeding seasons, when the female is said to be in "heat" or *estrus* (Greek, *oistrus*, "desire"). Estrus occurs at about the time the ripe ovum is ready to leave its follicle; the external genitalia become swollen and congested, and the female becomes receptive to attempts of the male at copulation. The vaginal membranes thicken and become more glandular, the mammary glands enlarge, and the uterine walls undergo changes preparatory to implantation of the fertilized egg. The uterine lining thickens, becomes more glandular, and its blood supply increases. At the completion of these changes ovulation occurs. If the egg is fertilized and implanted in the uterus, the estrus cycle gives place to the pregnancy cycle; otherwise the vagina, uterus and mammary glands return to their original state, and the animal becomes sexually quiescent until the start of the next estrus cycle.

Essentially the same sequence of events occurs in man and other primates, but with certain differences. Here ovulation is not accompanied by estrus, although the same changes occur in the uterine wall. If implantation fails to happen, most of the thickened uterine wall is sloughed off with bleeding, the cycle begins anew, and the uterus again makes ready for reception of an embryo. Since the bleeding comes at intervals of about 28 days, it is called *menstruation* (Latin, *menstruus*, "monthly"), and the special primate type of estrus cycle, which occurs only in mammals of that order, is called the *menstrual cycle*.

The pregnancy cycle. If a fertilized egg becomes implanted in the uterus, the menstrual cycle is interrupted and the 9-months pregnancy cycle intervenes.

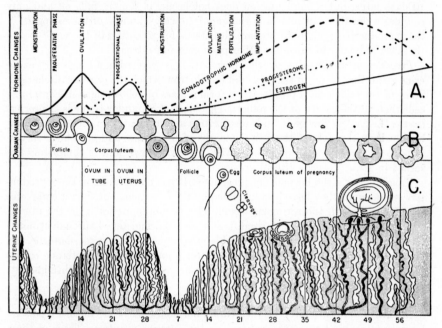

FIG. 16.3. Diagram of the changes occuring in the human menstrual cycle (left portion of figure) and in the first 8 weeks of the pregnancy cycle (right portion of figure). *A,* hormonal changes. These are only approximate and are not intended to show exact quantitative relationships. *B,* ovarian changes. *C,* changes in the thickness and blood supply of the uterine wall. *(From Amberson and Smith, Outline of Physiology, by permission The Williams & Wilkins Company.)*

The uterine lining remains thickened throughout this period, and various other changes occur in the body related to nutrition of the developing embryo and in preparation for its birth and postnatal care. Like those of the menstrual cycle, these changes are produced in response to a number of hormones which constitute an interrelated and balanced system of chemical control.

The ovarian hormones. During the first week following menstruation the ovum and the follicle in which it lies develop and ripen. The follicle becomes larger, and its central cavity fills with a fluid—the *follicular fluid*—which contains the hormones called *estrogens.*[1] These are a group of chemical compounds related to one another and to the androgens of the male and, like the latter, have certain

[1] Also called theelin or estrone.

general effects upon sex development. They can induce premature sexual maturity in young females and are responsible for the development of secondary sex characters, including the body form, breast development, hair growth, and voice timbre characteristic of women. They play an essential role in the menstrual cycle. As the ripening follicle approaches maturity the estrogens enter the blood in increasing amount and cause the epithelial lining of the uterus to thicken, become more glandular, and more richly supplied with blood. Production of these hormones reaches a peak just prior to ovulation and rises to a second peak about 10 days later; but if implantation does not occur, it shortly falls off and only resumes when the next follicle begins rapid growth. The role of the estrogens in the reproductive cycle is to prepare the uterus for reception of the embryo and (in lower animals) to cause the other phenomena of estrus.

Progesterone[1] is the other ovarian hormone. It is secreted in a temporary endocrine gland that forms in the ruptured follicle from which the egg was discharged. Some of the follicle cells proliferate to form a mass of yellow pigment-containing cells that fill the cavity of the follicle. This mass of glandular tissue is the *corpus luteum* (Latin, "yellow body"). If fertilization and implantation occur, the corpus luteum lasts throughout the first 7 months of pregnancy and continues all this time to produce progesterone; otherwise it breaks down and is completely absorbed in about 2 weeks after it appeared.

Progesterone is the hormone of pregnancy. It has no effect upon the reproductive organs until they have been modified by the estrogens, but then it completes the changes which the estrogens began. The membranous lining of the uterus, already thickened and vascularized, is softened and moistened through stimulation of its glands to secrete. A favorable environment for the spermatozoa and the developing embryo is thus created. After implantation progesterone causes physiological adjustments in the body that are related to childbirth and postnatal care.

The gonadotrophic hormones.   The periodic changes in the reproductive cycles are directly produced by the ovarian hormones; these are in turn regulated by gonadotrophic hormones produced by the anterior pituitary. Three of these are known: FSH and ICSH, already discussed in connection with the male, and luteotrophin, which acts only in the female.

In the female the *follicle stimulating hormone* (FSH) causes rapid growth of the follicle; the *interstitial cell stimulating hormone* (ICSH) causes the follicles to produce estrogens. Acting together these two hormones cause the follicle to produce the corpus luteum after ovulation.[2] The estrogen formed after ovulation comes from the corpus luteum under the stimulus of ICSH. The third gonadotrophic hormone, *luteotrophin*, acts to sustain the corpus luteum after it is produced, is responsible for the production of progesterone by this gland and may be the same as the lactogenic hormone to be mentioned later.

Relations of the ovarian and gonadotrophic hormones.   The various sex hormones are related to one another in a condition of fluctuating balance; those of the ovary affect production of the pituitary hormones, and the latter influence

---

[1] Also known as progestin.

[2] ICSH was formerly thought to be solely responsible for corpus luteum formation and was often called the *luteinizing hormone*.

the ovarian activity. It appears that the estrogens inhibit the release of FSH; at higher concentrations they stimulate the cells which produce ICSH, and at still higher levels they inhibit ICSH formation and cause disappearance of the corpus luteum. In the menstrual cycle the second (postovulation) peak of estrogen in the blood prevents release of FSH and ICSH. The resultant breakdown of the corpus luteum causes estrogen to fall to a very low level, and since this hormone is necessary to sustain the thickened uterine walls, the latter slough off and menstrual bleeding occurs. With the disappearance of estrogen from the blood, FSH is released once more, and another follicle starts to mature.

THE REPRODUCTIVE CYCLE IN THE HUMAN FEMALE[1]

Days after menstruation stops	Ovaries		Lining of uterus
	Follicle and ovum	Corpus luteum	
1st to 7th.......	Gradual ripening of ovum and increase in quantity of follicular fluid	Absent	Resting condition, then increasing thickness of lining with increased vascularity and gland formation
About 8th......	Ovulation and passage of ovum into oviduct (where fertilization may occur. Sperm entering oviduct 2 to 3 days before ovulation *may* remain and fertilize the egg)	Forms from the cells of the ruptured follicle	Uterine glands begin to secrete a viscid fluid
9th to 14th.....	Arrival of ovum in uterus	Grows	Ready for reception of fertilized ovum
Alternatives: (a) If fertilization has not occurred			
14th to 24th.....	Ovum can probably no longer be fertilized and disintegrates	Gradually disappears	Secretion subsides
24th to 28th.....	New follicle begins to develop in ovary	Absent	Menstruation—uterine lining sloughs off, with moderate bleeding
(b) If fertilization has occurred			
14th to 280th....	No follicle formation or ovulation during pregnancy	Remains during first 7 months of pregnancy	Fertilized ovum imbeds itself in uterine wall and grows

[1] Modified from *The Machinery of the Body*, by A. J. Carlson and Victor Johnson, courtesy of the University of Chicago Press. All figures are approximate and vary from individual to individual.

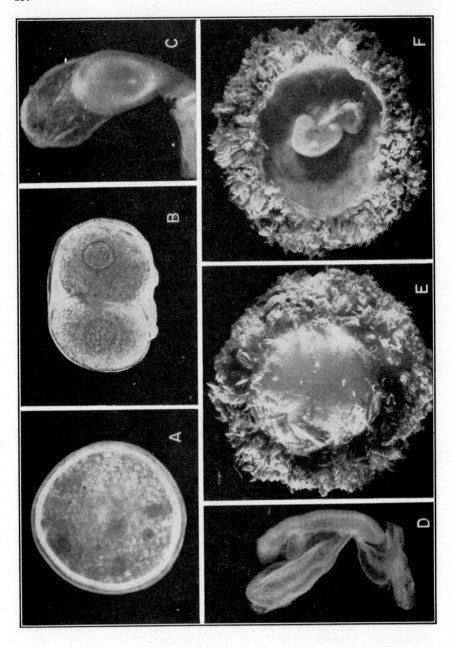

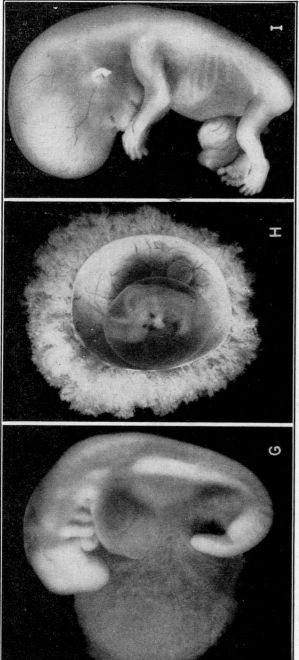

Fig. 16.4. Human embryology. The nine figures above are photographs of actual human embryos. They do not, of course, record the development of a single individual but show specimens in various stages of the process. They were taken by Mr. Chester F. Reather of the Carnegie Institution of Washington, to whom and to Director George W. Corner of that institution we are indebted for permission to reproduce them. Figures *A*, *B*, and *C* are used by courtesy of Dr. Warren H. Lewis, Drs. A. Hertig and John Rock, and Dr. Chester H. Heuser, respectively.

A, the matured but unfertilized human egg. Actual size 0.0054 inch, or about 0.135 mm. in diameter.

B, the two-cell stage, probably the youngest human embryo on record.

C, after 18 days of development. The embryo proper, now past the gastrula stage, forms the pear-shaped object at the lower right, attached to the maternal tissues; the somewhat wrinkled structure above and to the left of the embryo is the more or less vestigial yolk sac, and the other extraembryonic membranes (compare *E* and *F*) have been removed. The faint central line in the axis of the embryo is the primitive streak, which appears in the chick embryo at about 12 hours' development.

Legend continued on page 252

Embryonic Development and the Birth of the Child

When it is first implanted in the uterine lining, the embryo is microscopically small. It is soon enclosed by the growing maternal tissues. In a few weeks the embryo and its membranes have become large enough to cause the part of the wall containing them to bulge out into the cavity of the uterus and shortly thereafter to fill this cavity completely. Further growth of the embryo is accompanied by enlargement of the uterus, until at full term the latter has become about 400 times its original volume and occupies most of the space in the now greatly protuberant abdomen.

At an early stage of its development the embryo gives off an outer spherical layer of cells, which becomes the outermost of the embryonic membranes, the *chorion*. The embryo remains attached to the chorion at one point by the *body stalk*, which later becomes the *umbilical cord*, and is enclosed in a fluid-filled *amniotic sac* within the chorion. Blood vessels forming in the region of the body stalk grow into the chorion and there come to lie close to the blood-rich maternal tissues of the uterine wall. A circular area around the region of attachment of the body stalk develops into a richly vascular, pancake-shaped mass of intimately connected embryonic and maternal tissues, called the *placenta*. In the placenta there is no actual mingling of the blood streams of mother and child, but they are separated only by thin membranes through which dissolved substances can easily pass by diffusion. Oxygen, food substances, hor-

---

D, after 21 days of development. The embryo is at the right; the elongated yolk sac, at the upper left; and the umbilical cord that connected the embryo to the placenta, at the lower left. The embryo is now 0.117 inch long. Note the series of somites or segments, the slightly curved brain region at the upper end, and the saclike heart below the brain and between the yolk sac and the body of the embryo. The heart has already begun to beat faintly.

E, the embryo enclosed in its extraembryonic sac, the chorion. This specimen is twenty-eight days old and about an inch in diameter. The many long, slender projections (villi) of the chorion grow into the walls of the mother's uterus to form the placenta through which oxygen and food, carbon dioxide and wastes are exchanged.

F, this is the same embryo shown in *E*, with the chorion cut open to show the embryo floating in the cushioning embryonic fluid. The embryo is the large C-shaped object in and above the center of the cavity. Compare with *G*.

G, a four-weeks-old embryo removed from the chorion. This embryo is viewed from the left, that in *F*, from the right. Note the gill furrows just back (to the right) of the enlarged anterior end of the brain and separated by the gill arches or bars, the posterior curved tail, and the left posterior limb bud (leg) just anterior to the tail. The left anterior limb bud (arm) is barely visible to the right of the heart, which is the enlarged structure that projects outside of the body of the embryo anterior to the neck of the yolk sac.

H, a forty-day-old embryo inside a thin, intact membrane, the amnion, which in turn lies in the opened chorion. A third small extraembryonic membranous sac, the allantois, is seen as a small sphere just outside of the amnion. Both amnion and chorion are filled with fluids which protect the developing embryo. In the embryo itself the finger lobes of the developing left hand are plainly visible, as well as the now larger leg buds, the enlarged head, and the developing eye.

I, an eight-weeks-old embryo. The developing head, eye, ear, nose, and mouth can now easily be recognized, and the fingers and toes of the hands and feet are assuming their human form. Note the forming ribs. The entire skeleton is cartilaginous at this stage.

mones and antibodies from the mother's blood diffuse into that of the embryo, and carbon dioxide, nitrogenous wastes and hormones pass from the embryonic into the maternal circulation.

The details of human embryonic development do not differ greatly from those of other mammals, and it would be beyond the province of this book to discuss them at any length. All of the special vertebrate structures (somites, notochord, hollow dorsal neural tube, gill pouches, and limb buds) treated in the preceding chapter arise in man in the way there described. Nevertheless, because of our natural interest in all aspects of human biology, we have included photographs of human embryos in eight stages of development, with some explanatory notes, on pages 250–251.

At full term the fetus (as the embryo is called when it begins to be recognizably human) is enclosed within the greatly enlarged uterus and lies inside a fluid-filled sac composed of the chorion on the outside and the amnion on the inside. One side of this sac forms the placenta, to which the fetus is attached by the umbilical cord. Birth is accomplished by the periodic contractions of the powerful smooth muscles of the uterus, aided by the voluntary muscles of the abdominal walls. During the first stage of the process contractions of the uterus force the amniotic sac downward into the neck of the uterus, which gradually relaxes and expands. Finally the sac breaks, and the baby is gradually forced through the distended openings of uterus and vagina and is born. This is followed by freeing of the placenta from the uterine wall. With the ruptured embryonic membranes the placenta constitutes the "afterbirth."

Toward the close of pregnancy the mammary glands (breasts) enlarge, and their glandular tissue shows a marked increase in amount. These changes are produced by estrogen and progesterone, to the production of which the placenta increasingly contributes. Milk production begins about 3 days after the birth of the child and is caused by one of the gonadotrophic hormones, *prolactin* (which may prove to be the same as luteotrophin). So long as estrogens are present in the blood in large amounts, the secretion of prolactin is inhibited. The sudden fall in estrogen level at the time of birth releases prolactin into the blood. Continued secretion of this pituitary hormone is necessary for continued milk production, and this is apparently brought about by nervous impulses arising from sensory stimulation of the nipples in nursing the child. Soon after the infant is weaned, milk production ceases.

CHAPTER XVII

REPRODUCTION IN PLANTS

Although the reproductive processes of plants are fundamentally similar to those of animals, certain striking differences occur.[1] In animals we found it convenient to differentiate between reproduction in unicellular and in multicellular forms and to base our classification of metazoan reproduction upon the distinction between germ and soma. In plants the distinctions between unicellular and multicellular and between germ and soma are much less clear-cut, and other criteria have been adopted for the classification of reproductive processes.

The alternation of generations. Except for the most primitive forms, the typical life cycle of any plant includes two stages or generations—a *haploid gametophyte* generation, which reproduces sexually by gametes, and a *diploid sporophyte* generation, which reproduces asexually by means of spores. Here sexual reproduction involves the fusion of two gametes to form a diploid zygote, which develops into a sporophyte individual, and asexual reproduction involves the formation of minute haploid cells, which develop into gametophyte individuals.[2]

Simple vegetative reproduction. In addition to the reproductive processes that are associated with the alternation of generations, nearly all plants are capable of a direct and clearly asexual vegetative reproduction. By a process that is essentially like the budding or fission of the lower metazoans, individuals of the gametophyte generation may produce other gametophyte individuals, and individuals of a sporophyte generation may produce other sporophyte individuals. In many plants, both

---

[1] Among multicellular forms, the divergence in the plants' and the animals' ways of life has involved their reproductive practices. At least a part of the difference appears to be due to the fact that nearly all the nonmotile plants have utilized reproduction to provide for the dispersal of their progeny.

[2] This is perhaps the most fundamental difference between the reproductive cycles of the Metazoa and the multicellular plants. In the Metazoa, the haploid stage is confined to the unicellular gametes (sperm and egg), which immediately unite to form a zygote; in plants, the reduction division takes place at spore formation, and the haploid cells have a more or less prolonged existence as an often long-lived gametophyte generation.

high and low, this direct vegetative process forms an important or even the chief method of reproduction.

REPRODUCTION IN THE THALLOPHYTES

We have seen that the thallophytes include the algae, fungi, and bacteria, and form the lowest of the four great groups of the plant kingdom. Among the Thallophyta we find not only the most primitive of all types of reproduction but also encounter a graded series of reproductive processes, some of which appear to illustrate the origins of sex and the beginnings of the alternation of generations.

Reproduction by simple fission. In the blue-green algae, bacteria, and some of the most primitive fungi, the protoplasm of the cells shows little or no differentiation. There is no division into nucleus and cytoplasm. Here reproduction is by the simplest type of *fission* and does not even involve mitotic processes. In some of the lowest of the green algae, possessed of a nucleus and various cytoplasmic structures, all reproduction is still by fission, but by a type of fission that now involves mitosis.

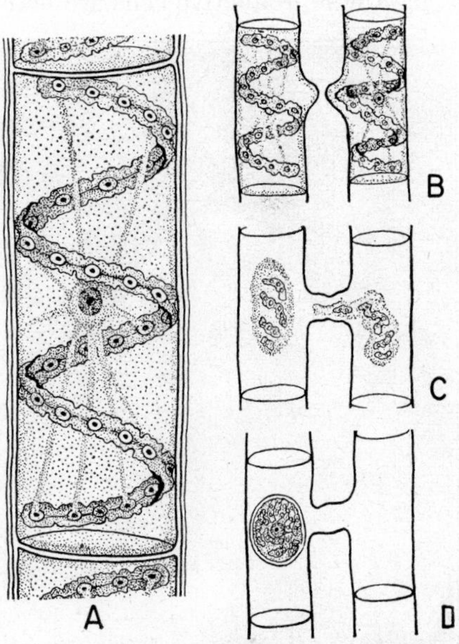

Budding is a variant type of fission illustrated by the reproduction of *yeasts*. It differs from typical fission in that the parent cell produces a small bud which grows gradually to full size and separates without the parent cell losing its identity. But it is like fission in that the yeast cell is able to produce a daughter cell without a stimulus from another individual.

FIG. 17.1. Sexual reproduction in the filamentous green alga Spirogyra. The structure of the vegetative cells is shown in *A*, with the characteristic spiral chloroplasts and a central nucleus. At *B* two cells in adjacent filaments are preparing to conjugate. At *C* the conjugation tube has been completed and the protoplasm of one of the two cells (corresponding to a male gamete) is passing through the tube. At *D* conjugation has been completed, a zygote has been formed, and a resistant wall has been secreted around the zygote to form a zygospore. The two conjugating cells in Spirogyra are isogametes. (*Modified from Turtox chart, courtesy General Biological Supply House, Inc.*)

Sexual reproduction in the thallophytes. In most of the green algae fission is not the only mode of reproduction, though it remains the chief method for rapid multiplication during the growing season. From time to time, however, sexual reproduction occurs, usually in response to unfavorable environmental conditions. Two alga cells fuse to form a *zygote*, which after a resting period will divide to form new individuals or a new colony. The two cells that fuse may be alike (*isogametes*) or unlike (*heterogametes*). Isogametes may not only be indistinguishable from each other but also from other vegetative cells (Fig. 17.1); more often they are small motile cells formed by the division of larger vegetative mother cells. In many algae the reproductive cells are heterogametes; that is, they are differen-

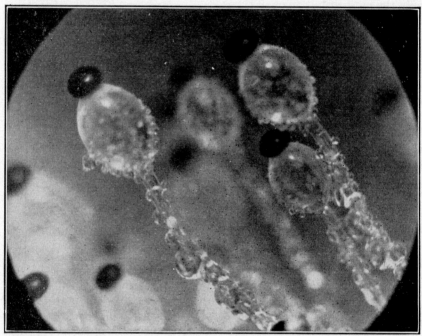

FIG. 17.2. Spore production by Pilobolus, an algalike fungus (phycomycete) that aims its spore-bearing organs (sporangia) and shoots the spores toward the light. The transparent bulb at the tip of the sporangium acts as a lens, concentrating light on the side opposite the light source. The light stimulates growth of that side of the filament, causing it to bend. When the shadow of the dark spore falls over the base of the bulb, the whole structure is aimed toward the light. Pressure gradually increases within the bulb until finally it explodes, shooting the spores toward the light. (*Photo by Prof. E. B. Mains.*)

tiated into small, motile, spermlike *male gametes* and larger, nonmotile, egglike *female gametes*. In every instance the fusing cells are haploid, and *the resulting zygote is diploid.*

Except in a few of the higher algae, the diploid condition in thallophytes is restricted to the zygote. At the first cell division the zygote undergoes a reduction division and so produces only haploid daughter cells.[1] Here

[1] In some green algae, the first division of the zygote produces two vegetative cells that continue to multiply by fission; in other species, two or more consecutive divisions result in the production of small haploid spores, each capable of giving rise to a new vegetative colony or individual.

we have not only the beginnings of sex in plants but, in the diploid zygote stage, a foreshadowing of the alternation of generations.

Reproduction in thallophytes in general. The algae and fungi show a wide range in structure, size, and appearance and have been variously modified for many modes of life. The details of their reproductive processes are correspondingly varied but may be grouped into three main types:

1. *Simple vegetative reproduction,* both in unicellular forms, such as the bacteria and certain algae, and in many multicellular algae and fungi, where fragments of alga filaments or fungus mycelia grow into new filaments and mycelia.

2. *Spore formation,* which may be subdivided into two types: the typical sporulation that follows the production of the diploid zygote, and a type of spore formation that results from the rapid and repeated division of a spore mother cell that was developed from haploid vegetative tissues without fertilization.

3. *Sexual reproduction,* which always involves the fusion of two gametes to form a zygote.

THE ALTERNATION OF GENERATIONS IN THE BRYOPHYTES

In the *mosses* and *liverworts,* which make up the second great division of the plant kingdom, an alternation of gametophyte and sporophyte generations is clear-cut

Fig. 17.3. The leafy gametophyte and capsule-bearing sporophyte generations of the moss Polytrichum. (*Photo by Prof. E. B. Mains.*)

and unmistakable. The gametophyte generation forms the more conspicuous part of the life cycle and is represented by the small green "leafy" plants that we recognize as mosses[1] or liverworts; but a sporophyte generation is now invariably a part of the cycle.

Sexual reproduction in the mosses. When the leafy stem of the gametophyte individual has reached its full growth, the upper end produces many-celled sex organs of two kinds. The female sex organs (*archegonia*) become vaselike in shape, and one of the cells near the bottom of the vase develops into a large *egg.* The male sex organs (*an-*

---

[1] "Spanish moss," so common a sight in the South, is not a moss at all but a flowering plant (spermatophyte), related to the air plants and the pineapple.

theridia) produce a huge number of ciliated *male gametes* or sperms. These, when released from the antheridium, are able to swim in water films provided by rain and dew and so reach the egg within the female sex organ. The union of a male gamete with the egg produces a diploid zygote that develops into a diploid sporophyte plant. This sporophyte genera-

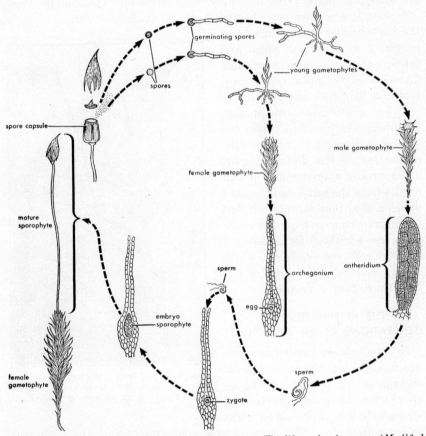

Fig. 17.4. Alternation of generations in the Bryophyta. The life cycle of a moss. (*Modified from Turtox chart, courtesy General Biological Supply House, Inc.*)

tion is not free-living but lives as a parasite on the green gametophyte. It forms a bulblike *foot* that grows down into the gametophyte tissues to obtain nourishment, and then sends up a stalklike structure that develops a conspicuous capsule at its distal end. The foot, stalk, and capsule, which lack chlorophyll and are usually somewhat longer than the leafy gametophyte stem from which they extend, constitute the sporophyte generation that begins with the zygote.

Spore formation. Once the sporophyte tissues are complete, spore mother cells within the capsule undergo maturation and repeated asexual divisions to form a large number of haploid spores. The ripe spores, when discharged from the capsule, may fall nearby or be carried a considerable distance by the wind. Those that chance to alight in a favorable environment absorb water and germinate to produce new gametophyte individuals.

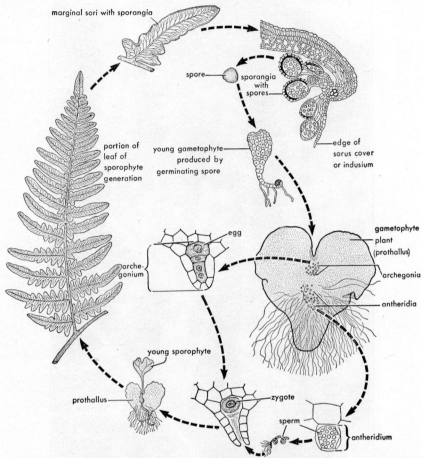

marginal sori with sporangia

spore

sporangia with spores

portion of leaf of sporophyte generation

young gametophyte produced by germinating spore

edge of sorus cover or indusium

egg

arche-gonium

gametophyte plant (prothallus)

archegonia

antheridia

young sporophyte

prothallus

zygote

sperm

antheridium

FIG. 17.5. Alternation of generations in the Pteridophyta. The life cycle of a fern. (*Modified from Turtox chart, courtesy General Biological Supply House, Inc.*)

THE ALTERNATION OF GENERATIONS IN THE PTERIDOPHYTES

In the *ferns*—and their relatives, the *club mosses* and *horsetails*—we find the most striking alternation of generations that occurs among plants. It is now the sporophyte generation that is the more accentuated and conspicuous, so that the plants we recognize as ferns, club mosses, or horsetails are members of the sporophyte generation. The gametophyte generation is reduced to small but free-living plants that persist only long enough to give rise to a new sporophyte generation.

Spore formation.   On the backs of the fronds of many ferns, one may often observe small fruit dots, or *sori*. These are composed of numerous minute spore cases, or *sporangia*, in which are contained a number of spore mother cells. These cells undergo reduction and division to form

Fig. 17.6. A fertile frond of the marginal shield fern, *Dryopteris marginalis*, showing "fruit dots," or sori, on the under surface. The sori of this species have a cover (indusium), which has been broken in some of those to the left, exposing the sporangia. (*Courtesy American Museum of Natural History.*)

spores that, when ripe, are thrown into the air by the violent bursting of the sporangium.

The gametophyte generation.   Such of the spores as chance to fall in favorable situations soon germinate. The spore wall cracks open, and the protoplasmic contents undergo repeated cell divisions that result in the production of a small, green, flat, somewhat heart-shaped structure known as the *prothallus*, which constitutes the gametophyte generation. Except for the region of the marginal notch, the prothallus is but one cell thick. It produces a number of threadlike structures (*rhizoids*) on its lower surface, which extend into the soil, where they take up water and salts.

Sexual reproduction.   The sex organs are borne on the lower surface of the prothallus. The female sex organs, or *archegonia*, are flask-shaped and are borne in the region of the thickened marginal notch. Each archegonium contains a single egg at the bottom of the open-mouthed

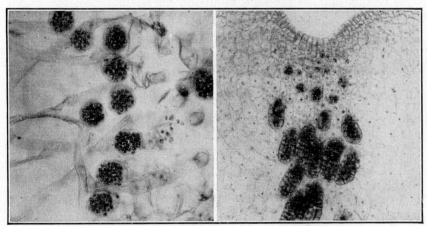

FIG. 17.7. The gametophyte generation of the fern. Photomicrographs of slide preparations of fern prothallus, showing at left the part bearing the antheridia, at right the part bearing the archegonia. (*Courtesy General Biological Supply House, Inc.*)

flask. The male sex organs, or *antheridia*, are more or less spherical in shape and are smaller than the archegonia; they are located near the apex of the "heart." A number of sperms are formed within each antheridium. When a ripened antheridium becomes wet with rain or dew, it swells and bursts, thus allowing the sperms to escape. The latter swim through the water film to the archegonia, which they enter by way of the open mouths. Within an archegonium, a single sperm fuses with the egg to form a zygote.

The development of the sporophyte.   The zygote begins its development within the walls of the archegonium and soon forms definite structures of its own: a "foot" that enables the developing embryo to absorb nourishment from the prothallus, and an embryonic root, stem, and leaves. When the latter have become functional, the prothallus shrivels, and the young sporophyte is left dependent upon its own tissues for maintenance.

REPRODUCTION IN THE SPERMATOPHYTES

In the *seed plants* (Spermatophyta), which constitute the fourth and highest division of the plant kingdom, the alternation of generations has become hard to detect. This is because the sporophyte generation has become overwhelmingly preponderant, with the gametophyte generation reduced to minute, short-lived structures nourished and borne by the spermatophyte tissues. There are three main groups of seed plants— cycads, conifers, and flowering plants. They differ in many details of their reproduction, but the essential features of the gametophyte-sporophyte relationship are the same in all and can be sufficiently illustrated by a consideration of the flowering plants, or angiosperms. We shall have

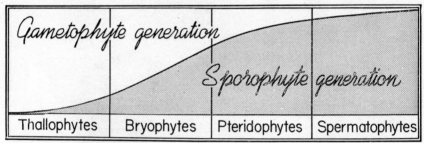

Fig. 17.8. A diagram to show the relative importance of the gametophyte and sporophyte generations in the four major divisions of the plant kingdom.

to begin by describing their characteristic reproductive structure, the flower, in which the gametophyte develops and through which sporophyte and gametophyte cooperate to perpetuate the race.

The Flower

The flower is a special reproductive adaption confined to and characteristic of the highest group of seed plants, the Angiospermae. Essentially it consists of an assemblage of parts derived from leaves, all more or less modified, borne upon a modified twig, and concerned with the production of the seed.

The modified branch that bears the flowers arises from a bud situated in the axil of a leaf, like an ordinary foliage branch. The leaf at the base of the flower branch, however, is not usually of the same form as the foliage leaves; it is called a *bract*. It is usually small and often deciduous but sometimes enlarges to enclose the flower or become a part of the flower. The flower-bearing axis may be either branched or unbranched. When unbranched it bears a single flower at its apex and is called a *peduncle*. Often, however, the axis is branched and the flowers are borne in clusters or *inflorescences*. In this event the usually short stems of the individual flowers are called *pedicels,* and the term peduncle is applied to the main stem of the entire flower cluster. A peduncle is thus the stem of a solitary flower or of an inflorescence, while a pedicel is the individual stem of a flower that is a part of a cluster. The flower-bearing branch differs from an ordinary foliage branch in important respects. It is often without

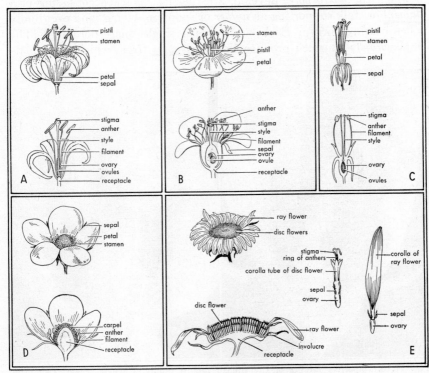

Fig. 17.9. Types of flowers. *A,* lily, a monocot (family Liliaceae), showing flower parts in threes, separate, and all arising separately from the receptacle, with ovary superior. All the other flowers are dicots. *B,* cherry (family Rosaceae), with sepals, petals and stamens united at base to form a cup, but ovary free and superior. *C,* gooseberry (family Rosaceae), with fused bases of sepals, petals, and stamens united to ovary wall, making the ovary inferior. *D,* strawberry (family Rosaceae), with enlarged receptacle bearing many small, separate pistillate carpels and scattered stamens. *E,* sunflower (family Compositae), with a head composed of many separate flowers on a common receptacle, sterile ray flowers at margin and fertile disk flowers in center. *(Modified from Turtox chart, courtesy General Biological Supply House, Inc.)*

recognizable leaves, though it may have green bracts at the bases of the peduncles or pedicels. Most of its "leaves" have been transformed into the flower parts, densely crowded together at the twig apex instead of being separated by distinct internodes, as in foliage branches. Lastly, in a flower-bearing branch, the meristem is entirely used up in making the floral leaves, instead of forming a persistent growing point, as in an ordinary branch.

The structure of a typical flower.   The parts that make up the flower may be divided into essential and accessory structures.

The *essential parts* are the *sporophylls*, which produce the small and large spores from which develop the male and female gametophyte plants and thus ultimately the male and female gametes. The *microsporophylls*, in which the <u>microspores</u> develop, are the <u>stamens</u>, each consisting of a *filament* or stalk supporting an *anther* or spore-producing (and eventually pollen-bearing) organ. Each stamen is a single microsporophyll. The *megasporophylls*, which produce the <u>megaspores</u> (from which the female

Fig. 17.10. Imperfect flowers of the squash (gourd family, Cucurbitaceae). Left, the staminate "male" flower; right, the pistillate "female" flower. Both these flowers are incomplete as well as imperfect. (*Photos by Prof. E. B. Mains.*)

gametophyte develops), form the *pistils*. Each pistil consists of a basal part, the <u>ovary,</u> in which the female gametophytes develop from megaspores within structures called <u>ovules;</u> a *style* projecting from the ovary, through which the pollen tube grows to effect fertilization; and a <u>stigma</u> or expanded tip of the style, to which pollen adheres. A pistil may consist of a single megasporophyll (<u>carpel</u>), in which case the ovary has a single chamber. More often the pistil is compound, consisting of several fused carpels and having an ovary with an equivalent number of ovule-bearing areas (<u>placentae</u>) in separate chambers or in a large chamber produced by fusion of those of the individual carpels.

The *accessory parts* of the flower include: (1) the <u>petals</u> (collectively called the *corolla*), often large and brightly colored, forming one or more rings outside the stamens; (2) the _sepals_ (collectively called the _calyx_), usually smaller than the petals, often green in color, enclosing the base of the corolla; (3) the _receptacle_, or expanded tip of the flower stalk to which the pistils, stamens, petals and sepals are attached; and (4) the immediate stalk of the flower, either a _peduncle_ or _pedicel_, as previously distinguished. This stalk and the receptacle are parts of the axis of the plant. All the remaining parts are modified leaves. In most flowers the pistils stand at the center, and the remaining parts are spirally or con-

FIG. 17.11. Spiral and cyclic arrangement in flower parts. Left, a mountain buttercup (_Trollius albiflorus_, family Ranunculaceae). Its petal-like parts are colored sepals and are cyclic in arrangement, but the numerous inconspicuous stamenlike petals, stamens, and pistils are spirally arranged and indefinite in number. Right, a lily (_Calochortus_ species, family Liliaceae), with all parts fixed in number and cyclic in arrangement. (_Photos by Prof. Alexander H. Smith._)

centrically arranged around them—first one or more rows of stamens, then the petals, and on the outside the calyx whorl.

Modifications in flower structure. Within the limits imposed by the scheme just described, flowers show innumerable variations in structure, arrangement, size, and appearance. They may be large and brightly colored or small and inconspicuous; they may be composed of a large number of parts or of few; they may possess both stamens and pistils or only one or the other of these; petals and sepals may be present or one or both of these sets of accessory structures may be lacking.

A flower is said to be _perfect_ if it possesses both stamens and pistils; if it has _only_ stamens or _only_ pistils it is _imperfect_. If it has a full set of parts—stamens, pistils, petals, and sepals, it is *complete*. Absence of *any* of these parts makes the flower *incomplete*. These terms are sometimes confusing, since we tend to think that if a thing is perfect it must also be complete, but in the terminology of flowers this not so. A complete flower is necessarily perfect, since it must have both stamens and pistils as well as the other parts; but, as a little consideration will show, an incomplete flower may be perfect, and an imperfect flower cannot be complete.

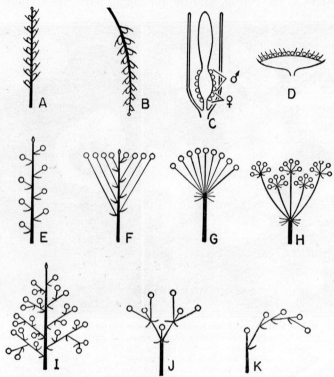

FIG. 17.12. Types of inflorescences. Flowers are indicated by small circles or ovals, leafy bracts by short curved lines. *A*, spike; *B*, catkin or ament; *C*, spadix; *D*, head; *E*, raceme; *F*, corymb; *G*, umbel; *H*, compound umbel; *I*, panicle; *J*, cyme; *K*, scorpioid cyme. (*Redrawn from Hill, Overholts and Popp, Botany, 2d ed.*)

The number, arrangement, and form of the flower parts vary much from group to group of the angiosperms and furnish the best characters for their classification. The parts may be arranged in a *spiral*, or in the much more frequent pattern of concentric circles called the *cyclic* arrangement. All the petals and all the sepals may be alike, in which case the flower is *regular*, like that of a lily or a wild plum; or some of the petals or sepals may be much larger or may be differently shaped than the others, making the flower *irregular*, like that of the sweet pea. Often the individual parts of one whorl or circle become fused together or fused with the parts of adjacent whorls. Thus several carpels may fuse to form a compound ovary, or the stamens may join into a solid ring, or the petals may unite into a tubular structure. Frequently the stamens appear to arise from the inner surface of a tubular corolla, their bases having fused with those of the petals. The pistil may be attached to the receptacle merely at the base, so that the ovary is exposed and is said to be *superior;* or the sides of the receptacle may grow up around the ovary and fuse with its walls, in which case the ovary is said to be *inferior.*

Arrangement. Besides the differences that exist in the flowers them-selves, their arrangement on the axis (*inflorescence*) varies greatly from plant to plant. Sometimes a single flower is borne at the end of the unbranched peduncle. Often the peduncle does not produce a flower at its tip but sends off lateral pedicels, each bearing a flower. If the pedicels and peduncle are both long, this makes a loose cluster of flowers called a *raceme*, as in wild plum; if the pedicels are very short or if the flowers are sessile, we have a *spike*, as in plantain, or various modified types of spikes, such as the spikelet of grasses, the catkin of willows, the spadix of white arum and Jack-in-the-pulpit, and the scaly strobilus of hops.

When, in this type of inflores-cence, the branching is continued, various kinds of compound

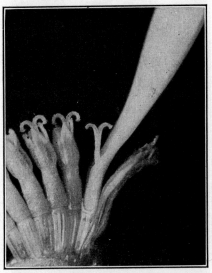

FIG. 17.13. Part of the head of the shasta daisy (*Chrysanthemum maximum,* family Compositae), showing perfect disk flowers with reduced corollas (left) and one of the imperfect ray flowers with strap-shaped, petal-like corollas (right). (*Photo by Prof. E. B. Mains.*)

racemes and spikes are produced. One very common form is the flower cluster (*umbel*) of the Umbelliferae, in which the axis is very short and the branches and pedicels are long and radiating. An-other common type of flower arrangement is the *cyme*, produced when the central axis terminates in a flower but sends off side branches, which themselves end in flowers; these may continue the branching process, giving rise to compound cymes.

Finally, we have in one very large group of plants, the *composites* (of which daisies and sunflowers are examples), flower clusters consisting of dozens or hundreds of small individual flowers borne crowded together on the surface of a greatly enlarged and conical or flattened receptacle.

The structure popularly regarded as a flower in this group is really a very dense mass of flowers, called a *head*. In such heads, the small individual flowers are often of two sorts—those in the center (the *disk flowers*) perfect, with inconspicuous corollas; and those around the margin (the *ray flowers*) imperfect and sterile, the tubular corolla of each forming a conspicuous strap-shaped projection or ray, which resembles a single petal of an ordinary flower.

Monoecious and dioecious conditions. All plants that possess perfect flowers are hermaphroditic, since male and female gametes or sex cells are both produced by the same plant. They are said to be *monoecious*, just as in the instance of hermaphroditic animals. In plants that have imperfect flowers, the *staminate* (pollen-producing or male) flowers and the *pistillate* (seed-producing or female) flowers may occur on different parts of the same plant, as in maize, oak, and maple. Here the plant as a whole is still *monoecious*, although the male and female gametes are produced in different flowers. In some species, however, each individual plant produces only staminate or pistillate flowers; this is true, for example, in the date palm, papaya, holly, and willow. Such species are said to be *dioecious*, since the male and female gametes are produced in separate individuals, as in most animals.

Fig. 17.14. The imperfect and incomplete flowers of hazelnut (*Corylus americana*, birch family, Betulaceae). The small pistillate flower appears near the tip of the twig. The large staminate flower (catkin) occupies the center of the picture. The male and female gametophytes are borne in separate flowers, but the plant as a whole is monoecious since it produces both types of flowers. (*Photo by Prof. E. B. Mains.*)

The Alternation of Generations in the Flowering Plants

The whole body of a flowering plant, including all of the flower itself except certain minute structures that develop in the stamens and pistils, is composed of sporophyte tissues with the diploid number of chromosomes. The gametophyte generation is reduced to the minute pollen grains that form within the anthers (the male gametophytes), and a seven-celled structure (the female gametophyte) that develops inside the ovule enclosed in the ovary. So reduced is the gametophyte generation that it might never have been recognized for what it is without the clues furnished by the lower plant groups. It has lost all importance save for its essential role in reproduction.

The *stamens* and *pistils* are the spore-bearing organs of the sporophyte generation. *They do not themselves produce male and female gametes.* The stamens produce asexual *microspores*, from which develop the male gametophytes; the pistils produce asexual *megaspores*, from which develop the female gametophytes.

Microspores and pollen grains. The *anther* that forms the apical end of each microsporophyll or *stamen* is in reality a spore case, though it is common to speak of it as the "male organ" of a flower. Within the anther a large number of spore mother cells is formed. Each of these undergoes a maturation process that results in the production of four haploid *microspores*. If our plant were like a fern, each of these could germinate and by cell division produce a small green gametophyte, which would in turn produce haploid male gametes. In the flowering plants this does not happen, but something comparable does.

Each asexual microspore "germinates" within its own spore case, by nuclear divisions unaccompanied by any cytoplasmic division. The first nuclear division produces two nuclei, one called the *tube nucleus*, which may be regarded as somatic, and the other called the *generative nucleus*, which may be regarded as a germ cell nucleus. The generative nucleus then proceeds to divide once more, producing two nuclei which function as male gametes and which are called the *sperm nuclei*. All this takes place within the original microspore case,[1] so that no external difference in appearance is visible after the nuclear divisions. Yet at this stage the whole structure has in effect become a three-celled male gametophyte, consisting of one vegetative (somatic) cell and two germ cells, although the cells are not cytoplasmically divided. This tiny three-celled gametophyte is the *mature pollen grain*. All of its nuclei are, of course, haploid.

Megaspores and the female gametophyte. The megasporophylls that produce the megaspores are called *carpels*, and the pistil is a structure consisting of a single carpel or of two or more fused carpels. At the base of the pistil is an enlargement called the *ovary*, within which each carpel produces one or several ovoid spore-cases called *ovules*. Each ovule is a thick-walled structure composed of several layers of cells and contains a single large diploid *spore mother cell*. By a maturation process not unlike that of the metazoan egg, this cell gives rise to four haploid cells; one of

---

[1] Sometimes the division of the generative nucleus does not occur until after formation of the pollen tube.

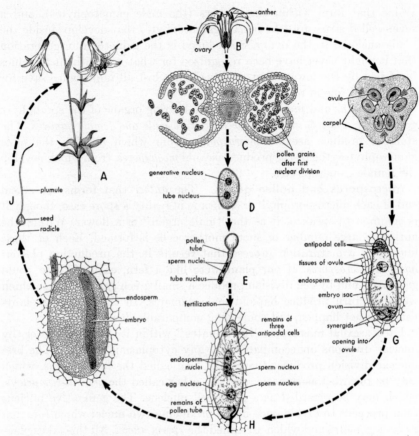

FIG. 17.15. Alternation of generations in the Spermatophyta. The life history of a flowering plant, the lily. The male gametophyte (pollen grain) develops from a microspore in the anther; the female gametophyte develops from a megaspore in the ovule within the ovary A, the mature sporophyte generation. B, the flower. C, a cross section through the anther, showing pollen grains. D, a pollen grain showing the tube nucleus and generative nucleus. In the lily the generative nucleus does not divide until after pollination occurs. E, the germinating pollen grain, with pollen tube containing the tube nucleus and two sperm nuclei formed by division of the generative nucleus. The pollen tube grows down through the style and ovary wall to the opening of the ovule. F, cross section of ovary showing ovules, two to each of the three carpels making up the stigma in this plant. G, the mature seven-celled female gametophyte, with egg (ovum). H, fertilization of the egg by one of the two sperm nuclei, and fusion of the other with the endosperm nuclei. I, development of the embryo from the egg, and of the endosperm from the primary triploid endosperm cell, within the ovule. J, the germinating seed. (*Modified from Turtox chart, courtesy General Biological Supply House, Inc.*)

these, the asexual *megaspore*, receives nearly all the cytoplasm, and the other three degenerate (like the polar bodies in animal oögenesis). Microspore and megaspore formation thus correspond closely to spermatogenesis and oögenesis in animals, with the difference that the spermatozoa and eggs of animals unite directly to produce the diploid zygote, while the microspores and megaspores of plants give rise asexually to a haploid gametophyte generation which produces the gametes.

The megaspore "germinates" within the ovule and undergoes three successive nuclear divisions unaccompanied by cytoplasmic division. At the conclusion of these divisions it is a large ovoid cell containing eight nuclei—four toward each end. One nucleus from each group of four migrates to the center of the cell; these two will later fuse to form the *primary endosperm nucleus*. One of the three nuclei at the end of the cell nearest the opening of the ovule grows larger than the other two and, with a portion of the surrounding cytoplasm, becomes enclosed in a cell

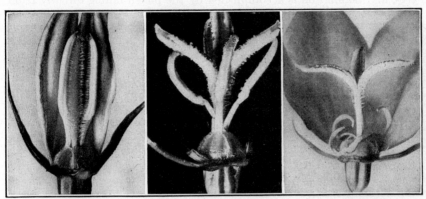

FIG. 17.16. The mechanism of pollination in the bellflower (*Campanula persicifolia*, family Campanulaceae). Normally cross-fertilized by insects, this plant can fertilize itself if necessary. The opening flower (left), with anthers closely applied to the sticky but non-receptive outer surfaces of the three stigma lobes. Later (center) the stigma lobes separate and the anthers pull away, leaving pollen adherent to the outer faces of the stigma lobes. The latter open wide (right), exposing their pollen-receptive inner faces to insect visitors. If pollination fails to occur, the lobes curl until their inner faces touch the pollen adhering to the pistil, so that self-fertilization takes place. (*Photos by Prof. E. B. Mains.*)

membrane; this is the *ovum*, or egg. The two other nuclei at this end (the *synergids*) and the three nuclei at the other end of the cell (the *antipodal nuclei*) may also form cell membranes, but all five are destined to break down and disappear.

The product of this entire process is a structure containing seven nuclei, corresponding to seven cells, and is the *mature female gametophyte*. The ovum is a germ cell; the other six may be regarded as somatic cells. The entire gametophyte is still contained within the ovule, or spore case, and all of its nuclei except the primary endosperm nucleus are haploid.

Pollination. Development of the egg is dependent upon its fertilization. To accomplish this, the first necessary step is transfer of a pollen grain with its contained sperm nuclei from the anther of the same or another flower to the adhesive tip, or *stigma*, of the pistil in which the egg lies.

We have seen that in the Metazoa bisexual reproduction is dependent upon some appropriate behavior of the parent organisms that brings the motile sperms within a short distance of the egg. Although the lower plants have male gametes that are motile and are capable of swimming short distances to meet the egg, in the flowering plants the pollen grains lack any means of locomotion and must be passively carried to the stigma.

Self-pollination. In contrast to the rarity of self-fertilization among the Metazoa, self-pollination is, for a number of important groups of plants, a normal and almost invariable process. In the bean or pea for example, the anthers and stigma are enclosed within the other floral parts, and pollination is accomplished by the pollen falling directly from

Fig. 17.17. The flower of a beardtongue (*Penstemon digitalis*, family Scrophulariaceae), showing adaptations to insect pollination. The outer surface of the flower (left) has sticky glandular hairs that discourage robber bees from puncturing the base of the flower for nectar instead of entering it. Shortly after the flower matures (center), the ripe anthers take a position in which pollen is shed on the backs of insect visitors. Later (right) the stigma pushes down into the position previously occupied by the anthers, and is thus ready to receive pollen brought by insects from other beardtongues. Ripening of pollen before the stigma becomes receptive, accompanied by mechanical devices such as this, is a common means of ensuring cross-pollination. (*Photos by Prof. E. B. Mains.*)

the ripe anthers to the stigma. In other self-pollinating flowers a properly timed growth of the pistil thrusts the ripe stigma against the anthers as they open to expose the pollen grains.

Cross-pollination. In most of the flowering plants cross-pollination is the rule, and here some other agent than gravity or the growth of the pistil must be utilized. In most flowers this is effected by animal visitors. The flowers are specially adapted to attract such visitors by having nectaries that secrete a sweet fluid called *nectar* and by producing quantities of pollen in excess of their own needs. Bees are the commonest pollinating agents, but other animals such as hummingbirds, butterflies, moths, beetles, and certain other insects also play a part. Almost all flowers that are not insect-pollinated are wind-pollinated; they produce vast quantities of pollen, which is broadcast in the air and reaches its destination solely by chance. The grasses are the largest group of flowering plants making use of this method.

Fertilization.   Pollination is not the same thing as fertilization, though we commonly think of it thus. It merely brings the male gametophytes (pollen grains) into a position which makes fertilization possible. As soon as it becomes attached to the stigma, each pollen grain begins to grow. It sends a slender, delicate-walled *pollen tube* down through the tissues of the style to the ovary; there the tube turns in and grows up through the

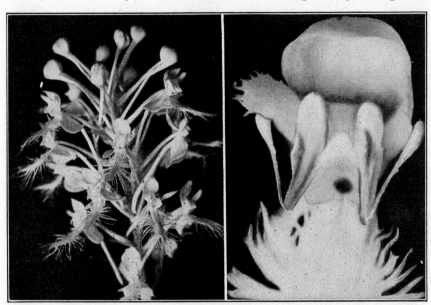

Fig. 17.18. The yellow-fringed orchid (*Habenaria ciliata*, family Orchidaceae) and its adaptations for insect pollination. Left, the entire inflorescence; right, a much enlarged view of a single flower from in front. The two large, down-pointing prongs are the stamens. The two erect, club-shaped bodies attached to their tips are the modified anthers (pollinia), containing masses of waxy pollen. Where each pollinium is attached to the stamen, it has a sticky gland. When an insect enters the flower, the two pollinia are glued to its head or thorax; during the flight to the next flower they bend forward and assume a position in which they will touch the stigma. (*Photos by Prof. E. B. Mains.*)

mouth of an ovule until it makes contact with the ovum and the female gametophyte. As the tube lengthens, the three pollen nuclei move forward near its tip. One, the tube nucleus, seems to control the growth of the pollen tube. As soon as the tube reaches the egg and the gametophyte, one of the two sperm nuclei enters the egg and fuses with the egg nucleus, fertilizing it and forming a diploid *zygote*. The other sperm nucleus enters the large endosperm cell and fuses with the double endosperm nucleus, producing a triploid condition in that cell and its descendants.

Seeds and fruits.   Immediately after fertilization the zygote begins to develop into an embryo within the ovule. The petals of the flower drop, and the style, stigma, and stamens wither away. The ovary, however, enlarges with the growth of the ovule or ovules within it. Each ovule becomes a *seed*, within which are contained an embryonic plant and a supply of food stored in the endosperm tissues or in the seed leaves of the embryo. The embryonic plant is a young sporophyte, with the diploid number of chromosomes in all its cells. When the seed is mature, the embryo has ceased to grow and has passed into a resting state, in which

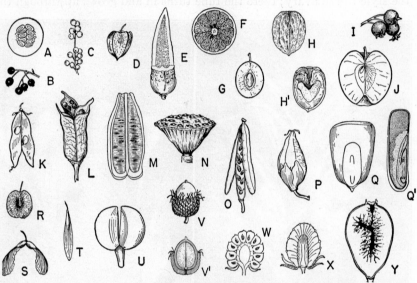

FIG. 17.19. Types of fruits. *A* to *J*, fleshy fruits; *K* to *O*, dry fruits that split open when ripe; *W*, *X*, aggregate fruits; *Y*, a multiple fruit. *A*, section through gooseberry (a typical berry). *B*, chokecherry (drupe). *C*, poison ivy (drupe). *D*, ground cherry (berry enclosed in papery calyx). *E*, cucumber (pepo), partly sectioned. *F*, orange (hesperidium), sectioned. *G*, plum (drupe). *H*, *H'*, walnut (drupe). *I*, hawthorn (pome). *J*, apple (pome). *K*, pea (legume). *L*, larkspur (three follicles), *M*, lily (capsule), sectioned. *N*, lotus (capsule). *O*, mustard (silique). *P*, buckwheat (achene). *Q*, *Q'*, maize or corn (caryopsis). *R*, wafer ash (samara). *S*, maple (samara). *T*, ash (samara). *U*, bedstraw (schizocarp). *V*, *V'*, acorn of oak (nut). *W*, raspberry (aggregate fruit of small drupes). *X*, strawberry (aggregate fruit of achenes on an enlarged receptacle). *Y*, fig (multiple fruit, achenes on inner surface of an enlarged hollow receptacle). (*Modified from Turtox chart, courtesy General Biological Supply House, Inc.*)

it can remain alive for a long time and await opportunity to resume its development. Around it are the hard protective seed coats formed from the ovule walls, protecting it from mechanical injury and too great water loss.

The matured ovary, enclosing its one or more seeds, together with any other parts of the flower, such as the receptacle, that have shared in the growth and maturation of the ovary, form the reproductive structure known as a *fruit*. This is the botanical definition of a fruit, which includes more than does popular usage. Thus botanically speaking, corn kernels, wheat, and other cereal grains are fruits, and so are the pods of beans and peas, nuts like walnuts and acorns, tomatoes, and many other things that are not popularly considered fruits.

According to whether the ovary was formed from one, two, or more ovule-bearing structures (carpels), the fruit may contain one, two, or more seed-producing areas, in one or more seed chambers. The matured ovary wall may remain thin, or it may thicken greatly; it forms what is called the *pericarp*. In many fruits the pericarp differentiates into three layers—an outer skin, or *exocarp;* a more or less thickened middle portion, or *mesocarp;* and an inner layer, the *endocarp*. In the stone fruits, such as the peach, the mesocarp is fleshy, while the endocarp forms a stony wall about the seed. In "nuts" like the pecan the mesocarp is a woody husk surrounding a hard endocarp. In the apple the mesocarp is fleshy and the endocarp thin and papery, forming the "core." Not all the flesh of the apple is mesocarp, however; in this and some other fruits, such as the strawberry, the receptacle enlarges and shares in formation of the fruit. The most important types of fruits may be classified as follows:[1]

I. *Simple fruits*, consisting of a single enlarged ovary, with which some other flower parts may be incorporated. Most of the common fruits, except those listed below under II and III, are simple fruits.

  A. *Fleshy fruits* (ovary wall fleshy, at least in part, or until maturity).

    1. *Berry*—the ovary wall fleshy, enclosing one or more seeds. Examples: grape, gooseberry, currant, pepper, persimmon, tomato, banana, date (the "stone" of the last being a seed).

    As special types of berries we have:

      a. *Pepo*—a type of berry with hard rind composed largely of the receptacle. Examples: squash, cucumber, cantaloupe, watermelon.

      b. *Hesperidium*—a type of berry with leathery, oily rind, and juicy pulp composed of numerous "cells." Examples: orange, grapefruit, lemon.

    2. *Drupe or "stone" fruits*—one-seeded, the seed enclosed in a "stone" or "pit" made up of the stony endocarp; mesocarp fleshy, exocarp thin, forming the skin. Examples: cherry, peach, mango, plum, olive. Such "nuts" as almond, walnut and pecan also belong here; the almond is the stone of a typical drupe, and the shell of walnuts and pecans is the stone of a drupe, the fleshy part of which is represented by the husk.

    3. *Pome*—outer part of the ovary wall fleshy and enclosed in the fleshy receptacle; inner part of ovary wall papery, forming the "core." Examples: pear, apple, quince.

  B. *Dry fruits* (ovary wall dry).

    1. *Dehiscent fruits* (splitting open when ripe).

      a. *Legume* or true pod—ovary composed of a single, modified, seed-bearing leaf (carpel), seeds attached along one side; splitting along two sutures when ripe. Examples: pea, bean, vetch.

      b. *Follicle*—ovary composed of one carpel; splitting along only one suture when ripe. Examples: milkweed, larkspur, columbine, peony.

[1] Reprinted by permission, with modifications, from Holman and Robbins, *Textbook of General Botany*, John Wiley & Sons, Inc., New York.

      c. *Capsule*—ovary composed of two or more carpels; opening when ripe in one of three ways—along the line of junction of the carpels (azalea), along the middle of each carpel (iris, lily), or by pores (poppy).

      d. *Silique*—ovary composed of two carpels, the sides of which split off at maturity, leaving a persistent middle partition. Examples: mustard, cabbage, turnip, radish, cauliflower.

  2. *Indehiscent fruits* (not splitting open when ripe).

      a. *Achene*—one-seeded, the seed attached to the ovary wall at only one point. Examples: buckwheat, sunflower, buttercup, ragweed.

      b. *Caryopsis*, or "grain"—one-seeded, the seed firmly united to the seed coat on all sides. Examples: Wheat, corn, rice, barley, broom corn, oats, and all other grasses.

      c. *Samara*, or "winged" fruits—one- or two-seeded, the ovary wall forming a winglike outgrowth that extends about the seed. Examples: ash, elm, maple.

      d. *Schizocarp*—carpels two or more, united during growth, splitting apart but not opening at maturity. Examples: carrot, parsnip, parsley, celery, mallow.

      e. *Nut*—a hard, one-seeded fruit, generally resulting from a compound ovary. Examples: acorn, chestnut, hazelnut. Many so-called "nuts" are seeds; others are achenes or the stones of drupes (see I, A, 2, above).

II. *Aggregate fruits*, consisting of a number of enlarged ovaries, belonging to a single flower and massed on or scattered over the surface of a single receptacle. The separate ovaries are spoken of as *fruitlets*. Examples: raspberry (the fruitlets are drupes and separate easily from the receptacle); blackberry (drupes, closely attached to the receptacle); strawberry (achenes, on a fleshy receptacle that consitutes most of the edible portion of the fruit); magnolia (conelike masses of follicles).

III. *Multiple fruits*, consisting of the enlarged ovaries of several or many flowers more or less coalesced into one mass. Examples: mulberry (achenes, each surrounded by a fleshy, juicy calyx); fig (achenes, on the inner surface of an enlarged hollow receptacle); pineapple (axial stem, with the fleshy receptacles and ovaries of many sessile flowers fused together); sweet gum (many partly fused capsules).

CHAPTER XVIII

MENDEL'S LAWS OF INHERITANCE

Thus far we have taken for granted that the new individuals of each generation will be like the parents that produced them and that the peculiar characters by which we distinguish one race from another will be perpetuated. Generally speaking, this is true, and the realization of its truth has given rise to such proverbs as "like begets like" and such metaphors as "a chip off the old block" and such folklore stories as that of the ugly duckling. The biologist has also recognized the general truth of "like begets like" in defining a kind or *species* of organism as "a group of like individuals that naturally perpetuate themselves by reproduction." Nevertheless, it is easily seen that offspring are not exact duplicates of their parents. Only very rarely is it difficult to see well-marked differences between full brothers or full sisters; some children appear to "take after their father"; others "take after their mother"; some are intermediate or are not very like either parent. Yet we do not hesitate to say that, on the whole, like does beget like.

We are here encountering two apparently contradictory phenomena that have been termed *heredity* and *variation*. By heredity is meant the passing of like qualities from one generation to the next. Many of these qualities are common to all the members of the race; others, not common to all the race, are likely to be common to or very frequent in a given parent-offspring sequence within that race. By variation, on the other hand, we mean all departures from a complete identity of qualities—the differences that permit us to distinguish between two individuals of the same race or of the same parent-offspring sequence.

The practical breeder, convinced of the general truth that like begets like, has long utilized these phenomena of heredity and variation. Selecting the most desirable variants from a litter, a herd, or a crop, he has utilized them for the parents of the next generation, eliminating less desirable individuals from the reproductive sequence. This process, repeated generation after generation, has led to the development of many distinct breeds of domesticated animals and plants, each characterized by the accumulation into a common inheritance of a desirable combination of formerly more variable qualities, and the elimination of other

Variations 1. hereditary
2. Environment

(undesirable) qualities that had regularly or frequently appeared in the original ancestral stock. One has only to consider some of the many existing breeds of dogs, cattle, poultry, corn, or tobacco to realize how effective such a practical manipulation of variation and inheritance has been.

Until the present century, however, the work of the practical breeder, although extremely productive, had been almost wholly empirical and by "rule of thumb," and the plight of the biologist was little if any better, in spite of the accumulation of much careful data from observation and experiment. Then, in 1900, with the rediscovery of Mendel's long-neglected pioneering work, the biologist was given a sound foundation and a powerful research method for the investigation and understanding of inheritance and variation.

Gregor Johann Mendel was an Augustinian monk and later the prelate or abbot of a monastery in Brünn (now Brno), Austria. In 1866, after 8 years of thorough study, he announced the results of his work on the inheritance of certain qualities in the garden pea. Many other workers before his time had made somewhat similar investigations, but Mendel's experiments were so carefully thought out and so painstakingly made and recorded that he was able to discover underlying principles of inheritance that could not have been disclosed by less precise methods. His procedure (which was to become one of the fundamental tools for modern genetic studies) is so important that it is necessary to describe it in some detail.

The selection of experimental material. At the beginning of his studies Mendel obtained as many varieties of peas as he could find. He tested each variety by growing it for several generations and then selected several that differed from each other in one or more distinct characteristics and that proved to breed true. For example, he obtained one variety in which all the individuals were tall (5 to 6 feet) and another in which all the individuals were dwarf (1½ to 2 feet); a variety with smooth seeds and another with wrinkled seeds; a variety in which the seeds were always green and another in which the seeds were always yellow; etc.

THE MONOHYBRID CROSS

Mendel's simplest experiments were concerned with crosses between varieties that differed from one another in a single definite quality. One of these was the cross between the tall and the dwarf varieties. The garden pea is normally a self-fertilizing species, so that Mendel's first step was to select one plant—a tall one, for example—and remove all its anthers before the pollen was ripe. The plant was thus completely emasculated and incapable of fertilizing itself. When the stigmas of this plant were ready for pollination, he introduced pollen from the anthers

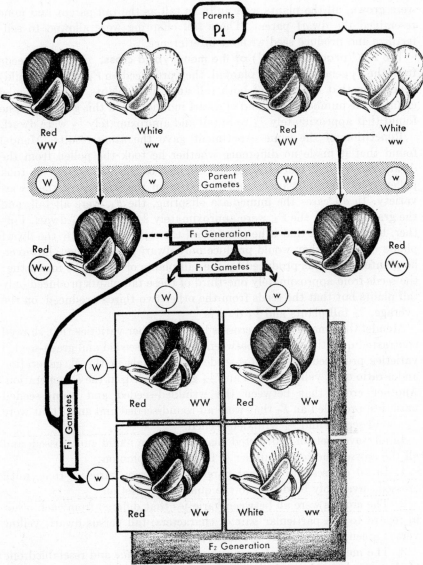

FIG. 18.1. The monohybrid cross. The results obtained in the F_1 and F_2 generations by crossing two types of pea differing by one character and each homozygous for that character —red flowers and white flowers.

of the dwarf variety and so effected a cross between the two varieties. The cross-pollinated flowers of the tall plant were then protected against the entrance of other pollen and allowed to mature their seeds.

The offspring (F_1) of the monohybrid cross. Mendel planted the seeds produced by crossing the tall and dwarf varieties, and when they were grown, all the plants were fully as tall as the tall parent and none resembled the dwarf parent. These tall offspring were allowed to self-fertilize and produce seed without interference.

The F_2 ("grandchildren") of the monohybrid cross. When the seeds from the F_1 generation were planted, they produced an F_2 (or grandchild) generation that consisted of both tall and dwarf plants. When Mendel counted the number of tall and of dwarf individuals in this generation, he found that approximately ¾ were tall and approximately ¼ were dwarf.

Repetition of the same experiment gave the same results. Mendel found that it made no difference whether he took the pollen from the dwarf variety and placed it on the stigmas of the tall variety or took pollen from the tall variety and placed it on the stigmas of the dwarf variety. In all cases the immediate offspring, the F_1, were all tall, and the grandchildren, the F_2, were approximately ¾ tall and ¼ dwarf. Further, he discovered that if he planted all the seed produced by the dwarf plants of the F_2, they would produce only dwarf plants. When, however, he planted the seeds produced by the tall plants of the F_2, he found that the seeds from approximately one-third of these tall plants produced only tall plants but that the seeds from the other two-thirds produced, on the average, ¾ tall plants and ¼ dwarfs.

Mendel then made similar crosses between other varieties that showed contrasted qualities. A cross between the yellow-seeded and green-seeded varieties produced only yellow-seeded individuals in the F_1 generation and a ratio of ¾ yellow-seeded and ¼ green-seeded, in the F_2 generation. Another cross, that between the wrinkled-seeded and round-seeded varieties, produced an F_1 that were all round-seeded and an F_2 that were ¾ round-seeded and ¼ wrinkled-seeded.

In all, seven sets of contrasted characters were found and crossed, and all the crosses showed a number of features in common:

1. In all crosses the original parents were from varieties that, until crossed, invariably bred true to the quality in question.

2. The crosses were all between varieties that differed from each other in regard to one particular pair of characters: tall versus dwarf, yellow versus green, round versus wrinkled, etc.

3. The members of the F_1 generation *were all alike* and resembled one of the parents to the exclusion of the other.

4. The members of the F_2 generation were always of two sorts, approximately ¾ like the F_1 and the parent that the F_1 resembled, approximately ¼ like the other member of the original parent cross.

5. The smaller group (the ¼) of the F_2 generation would breed true if allowed to self-fertilize; approximately one-third of the larger group (the ¾) of the F_2 would breed true, the other two-thirds again giving a ¾:¼ ratio of the same contrasted qualities.

It seemed evident that some basic principle was common to all these crosses, and Mendel now sought to discover what this basic principle might be. He assumed that each individual must have two factors for each quality but that a germ cell produced by the individual could carry but one factor from any pair present in the individual. It would follow, then, that factors would be separated at germ-cell formation and united into pairs at fertilization.

We can diagram this idea, using the cross between the tall and dwarf peas, by letting the capital letter D represent the factor for tallness and the small letter d represent the factor for dwarfness (which, as we have seen, acts as an alternative to tallness in inheritance in peas). (Mendel's original notation is here slightly changed to make it conform to modern usage.)

The following diagram shows that Mendel's hypothesis fits all the observed facts:

DIAGRAM OF MONOHYBRID CROSS

The original parent generation P_1..........	Tall	×	dwarf
Gene formula of P_1......................	DD		dd
Formulas of gametes produced by each parent.	D		d
Resulting formula of F_1 generation.........		Dd	
		(All tall, all alike)	

Gametes produced by each F_1 individual (two kinds in equal numbers)................. D and d

Union of gametes to produce F_2 zygotes, when { Female gametes $\quad D \quad\quad d$
F_1 is self-fertilized or interbred $\quad\quad$ { Male gametes $\quad\quad D \quad\quad d$

$$\begin{array}{ccc} DD & Dd & \\ & dD & dd \end{array}$$

Probable proportion of all possible combinations.......................

$$DD \quad (2)Dd \quad dd$$

The F_2 generation..................... 1 tall (DD)—2 tall (Dd)—1 dwarf (dd)

$$\underbrace{\qquad\qquad\qquad\qquad}_{3 \text{ tall}} \quad \underbrace{\qquad\quad}_{1 \text{ dwarf}}$$

1. Each of the original parents (P_1 generation) has both factors alike, DD or dd, because it came from a variety proved to breed true for its respective quality.

2. As a consequence, any germ cell produced by the tall parent could only receive a D, and any produced by the dwarf parent could only receive a d.

3. The cross must bring together a gamete with D and a gamete with d, and the resulting zygote that develops into an F_1 individual must have the formula Dd. (Since the individuals of the F_1, with the formula Dd, are as tall as the original tall parent with the formula DD, D is said to be *dominant* to d, and tall is said to be *dominant* to dwarf.)

4. When an F_1 individual produces its germ cells, there will be two kinds in equal numbers, D and d. This will apply to the formation of both male and female gametes.

5. Since half of the female gametes are D and half d and since half of the pollen grains are D and half d, there are four possible ways in which they can combine: (1) pollen D with ovum D—DD; (2) pollen D with ovum d—Dd; (3) pollen d with ovum D—dD; and (4) pollen d with ovum d—dd.

6. According to the laws of chance, the resulting combinations should be in the following proportions: $\frac{1}{4}DD$, $\frac{2}{4}Dd$, and $\frac{1}{4}dd$. Since, as we have seen in paragraphs 1 and 3, above, both DD and Dd produce an equal degree of tallness in the individual, $\frac{3}{4}$ of the F_2 should be tall and $\frac{1}{4}$ dwarf.

7. It is also evident that all the dwarf members of the F_2 should breed true but that only one-third (the DD individuals) of the talls should breed true; the other two-thirds of the talls (the Dd individuals) should produce a $\frac{1}{4}DD$, $\frac{2}{4}Dd$, and $\frac{1}{4}dd$ ratio when allowed to self-fertilize.

Here, then, is a hypothesis that explains all Mendel's monohybrid crosses. If we make exactly the same assumptions and diagram the cross between yellow-seeded (GG) and green-seeded (gg) peas, or the cross between round-seeded (WW) and wrinkled-seeded (ww) peas, we see how it comes about that they produce the same numerical ratios in the F_1, F_2, and subsequent generations.

MENDEL'S FIRST LAW: GAMETIC PURITY

The principle of inheritance that has just been discussed is now known as *Mendel's first law* and is often stated as follows: "Inherited pairs of factors segregate at germ-cell formation and recombine at fertilization." The first law is often referred to as the *principle of gametic purity, i.e.,* that a gamete can carry but one of any two alternative characters (for example, D or d) and hence can never be hybrid. It is also important to note that neither the D nor the d produced by the hybrid F_1 generation is in any way contaminated by their existence together in the F_1 generation and that each is just as "pure" as if derived from pure-breeding tall and dwarf individuals, respectively.

SOME NECESSARY TERMINOLOGY

In order to follow Mendel's further work, as well as post-Mendelian genetics, it is necessary to learn a number of definitions and timesaving genetic conventions and symbols. These not only make for greater clarity and preciseness but save much time in writing and thinking about genetic concepts.

gene (factor or determiner). An unknown entity carried in the germ cells that (under proper conditions) results in the development of a definite quality by the zygote. (The term *gene* is generally preferable to the synonymous terms *factor* and *determiner*.)

allelomorph or **allele.**   One of a pair of genes or characters that are contrasted in inheritance. Tall and dwarf are examples of allelomorphic characters; *D* and *d*, of allelomorphic genes. The term is applied to both characters and genes, but characters that are not inherited as alternatives are not allelomorphic.

gamete.   A germ cell, either male or female.

gametic formula.   The formula of a gamete in terms of the genes it is known to carry. Because of the principle of gametic purity, a gamete can have but a single gene from any allelomorphic pair. Examples: *d, D, Ab, AbC, abC,* etc.

zygote.   The product of the union of two gametes. By extension, it is also applied to the individual that is produced by the development of a zygote and is used in opposition to the haploid gamete.

zygotic formula or **zygotic constitution.**   The formula for a zygote or individual that it, he, or she is known to carry. Examples: *dd, DD, Dd, Aa BB cc,* etc.

homozygote.   An individual with like genes for the pair or pairs under consideration. Examples: *DD, dd, AA bb,* etc.

heterozygote.   A zygote or individual with unlike genes for the pair or pairs under consideration. Examples: *Dd, Aa Bb,* etc. NOTE: an individual may be homozygous for some genes and heterozygous for others. Example: *AA Bb.*

hybrid.   The result of a cross of unlike parents, a heterozygote.

monohybrid.   A cross that involves but a single pair of contrasting genes. Sometimes applied to the F_1 product of such a cross.

dihybrid.   A cross that involves two pairs of contrasting genes.

trihybrid.   A cross that involves three pairs of contrasting genes.

genotype.   The description of an individual in terms of the genes that he, she, or it is known to possess.

phenotype.   The description of an individual in terms of its visible characters. Tall is a phenotypic description, in the pea, and may be due to either of two genotypes, *DD* or *Dd.*

P_1.   The original parent generation; typically consists of a male and female that are each homozygous and differ in regard to one or more pairs of contrasting genes.

F_1.   The first filial generation, the immediate offspring of the P_1; always all alike and all hybrid.

F_2.   The second filial generation, the offspring of F_1 individuals, and the generation that shows various diagnostic phenotypic ratios.

THE DIHYBRID CROSS

Mendel's studies did not stop with the making and analyzing of monohybrid crosses. His experiments also included several dihybrid and trihybrid crosses that resulted in the discovery of a second great principle of inheritance. We shall examine one of these crosses in detail.

Among the varieties at Mendel's disposal was one in which the ripened seeds were round in shape and had a yellow color; another variety had seeds that, when ripe, were shriveled or wrinkled and retained their green color. The cross between these varieties was effected precisely as was the one between tall and dwarf—the pollen from an individual of one variety was transferred to the stigmas of an individual of the other variety and so produced a cross-fertilization.

The dihybrid F_1. The F_1 seeds were all yellow and round, as we should expect from the results already given for monohybrid crosses between round and wrinkled and between yellow and green.

The dihybrid F_2. On planting the F_1 seeds and allowing the flowers produced by them to self-fertilize, Mendel obtained four kinds of seeds—yellow and round, yellow and wrinkled, green and round, and green and wrinkled. Here were not only the original parent types—yellow and round and green and wrinkled—but also *two new combinations*—yellow and wrinkled and green and round. When the number of each of the four types was counted, it was found that 315 were yellow and round; 101 were yellow and wrinkled; 108 were green and round; and 32 were wrinkled and green. The proportion of yellow to green is $(315 + 101)$: $(108 + 32)$, approximately $\frac{3}{4} : \frac{1}{4}$; and the proportion of round to wrinkled is $(315 + 108) : (101 + 32)$, again approximately $\frac{3}{4} : \frac{1}{4}$; but how are we to account for 101 individuals that are yellow and wrinkled and 108 that are green and round?

MENDEL'S SECOND LAW: INDEPENDENT ASSORTMENT

Mendel saw that the two new combinations—yellow and wrinkled, and green and round—could be accounted for if he assumed that segregation between the genes for yellow and green was *independent* of the segregation that takes place between the genes for round and wrinkled. That is, although the hybrid F_1 received its genes for yellow and round from one gamete and its genes for green and wrinkled from the other, these genes would not tend to stay together when the F_1 generation formed its germ cells. Such independence in segregation would result in the F_1 individuals forming four kinds of male and female gametes in equal numbers:

1. Containing a gene for yellow and a gene for round.
2. Containing a gene for yellow and a gene for wrinkled.
3. Containing a gene for green and a gene for round.
4. Containing a gene for green and a gene for wrinkled.

If one of each of the four types of male gametes then fertilized one of each of the four types of female gametes, four classes of phenotypes should be produced, in the proportion of $\frac{9}{16}$ that are yellow and round, $\frac{3}{16}$ that are yellow and wrinkled, $\frac{3}{16}$ that are green and round, and $\frac{1}{16}$ that are green and wrinkled.

This can be more clearly expressed if we use a diagram to describe the various individuals and germ cells involved. We have already used

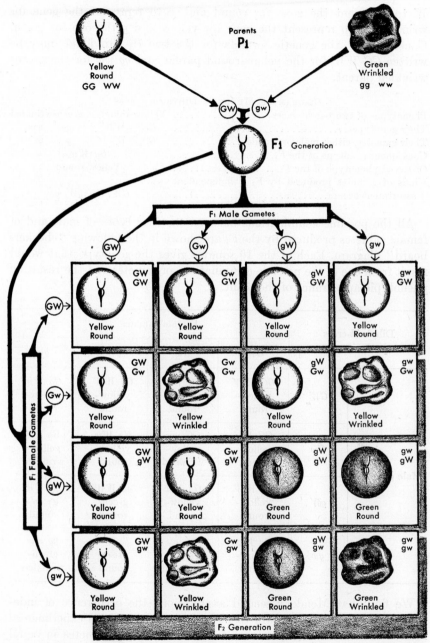

Fig. 18.2. The dihybrid cross between yellow-round and green-wrinkled peas. Yellow is dominant to green, and round is dominant to wrinkled. The F_2 ratio shows that the segregation of the genes for yellow and green must have been independent of the segregation of the genes for round and wrinkled.

W to represent the gene for round and w to represent the gene for wrinkled; G to represent the gene for yellow and g the one for green. Consequently, the genetic formula for the two P_1 individuals may be written $GG\ WW$ for the yellow-round parent and $gg\ ww$ for the green-wrinkled parent.

DIAGRAM OF MENDEL'S DIHYBRID CROSS

Phenotypes of two parent races.................	Yellow-round $\times$ green-wrinkled
Their genotypes..............................	$GG\quad WW\qquad gg\quad ww$
Their gametes, either male or female.............	$G\qquad W\qquad g\qquad w$
Consequent genotype of the F_1.................	$Gg\ Ww$
Observed phenotype of the F_1..................	Yellow-round
Kinds of gametes produced by F_1 if independent assortment occurs...........................	$GW,\ Gw,\ gW,\ gw$

All the possible combinations between the four types of male and of female gametes produced by the F_1 are shown in the following "checkerboard" diagram. Each of the 16 squares gives the genotype that would result from one of the possible combinations of gametes and the resulting phenotypic appearance of the plant.

Dihybrid-cross checkerboard		Female gametes			
		GW	Gw	gW	gw
Male gametes	GW	$GG\ WW$ yellow-round	$GG\ Ww$ yellow-round	$Gg\ WW$ yellow-round	$Gg\ Ww$ yellow-round
	Gw	$GG\ Ww$ yellow-round	$GG\ ww$ yellow-wrinkled	$Gg\ Ww$ yellow-round	$Gg\ ww$ yellow-wrinkled
	gW	$Gg\ WW$ yellow-round	$Gg\ Ww$ yellow-round	$gg\ WW$ green-round	$gg\ Ww$ green-round
	gw	$Gg\ Ww$ yellow-round	$Gg\ ww$ yellow-wrinkled	$gg\ Ww$ green-round	$gg\ ww$ green-wrinkled

We find that Mendel's second assumption—the occurrence of independent assortment—appears to fit and so "explain" his experimental results. If the dihybrid produces four kinds of male gametes in equal numbers and produces the same four kinds of female gametes in equal numbers, and if all possible combinations of male and female gametes take place according to the laws of chance, nine kinds of genotypes will result. We have already seen that in peas, yellow is dominant to green, and round is dominant to wrinkled, so that the nine classes of genotypes will produce four kinds of phenotypes as follows:

Genotype $GG\ WW$ 1 in 16 gives phenotype of yellow and round $\left.\rule{0pt}{40pt}\right\}9$
Genotype $GG\ Ww$ 2 in 16 gives phenotype of yellow and round
Genotype $Gg\ WW$ 2 in 16 gives phenotype of yellow and round
Genotype $Gg\ Ww$ 4 in 16 gives phenotype of yellow and round

Genotype $GG\ ww$ 1 in 16 gives phenotype of yellow and wrinkled $\left.\rule{0pt}{20pt}\right\}3$
Genotype $Gg\ ww$ 2 in 16 gives phenotype of yellow and wrinkled

Genotype $gg\ WW$ 1 in 16 gives phenotype of green and round $\left.\rule{0pt}{20pt}\right\}3$
Genotype $gg\ Ww$ 2 in 16 gives phenotype of green and round

Genotype $gg\ ww$ 1 in 16 gives phenotype of green and wrinkled. . 1

If we compare this theoretical expectation with the numbers of each phenotypic class of the 556 F_2 peas that were actually obtained, we find that the correspondence is very close:

Phenotypic class	Expected F_2 ratio	Actual F_2 ratio
Yellow-round.............	$\frac{9}{16}$, or 312.5	315
Yellow-wrinkled..........	$\frac{3}{16}$, or 104.25	101
Green-round..............	$\frac{3}{16}$, or 104.25	108
Green-wrinkled..........	$\frac{1}{16}$, or 34.75	32

The principle of independent assortment that Mendel assumed in order to account for the four phenotypic classes of the dihybrid F_2 was clearly substantiated by further breeding experiments and today is often referred to as *Mendel's second law*. It may be stated as follows: When more than one pair of allelomorphic genes are involved in a cross, each pair assorts *independently* of the others.[1]

THE TRIHYBRID CROSS

Mendel's most elaborate experiment was the crossing of homozygous parent stocks that differed in regard to three sets of characters, or three pairs of genes. One stock was characterized by having round seeds, yellow cotyledons, and a colored (gray-brown) seed coat; the other by having wrinkled seeds, green cotyledons, and a colorless (white) seed coat. This cross is given in diagrammatic form on the next page. It will be seen that the new trihybrid phenotypic F_2 ratio $27:9:9:9:3:3:3:1$ can be accounted for by the principles already encountered—segregation

[1] Later we shall see that under certain conditions Mendel's second law does not hold, and that it needs additional qualifications.

and recombination and independent assortment—but that the independent assortment of three pairs of genes results in the production of eight kinds of gametes and so requires a "checkerboard" with 64 squares. (The "checkerboard" is omitted in the diagram but may easily be constructed in the same manner as that given for the dihybrid.)

DIAGRAMMATIC DESCRIPTION OF TRIHYBRID CROSS

P_1 phenotypes.................. Yellow-round-colored × green-wrinkled-colorless

P_1 genotypes.................... GG WW CC gg ww cc

P_1 gametes .... GWC gwc

F_1 genotype..................... Gg Ww Cc

F_1 phenotype....................   Yellow-round-colored

F_1 male gametes................. GWC GWc GwC gWC Gwc gWc gwC gwc

F_1 female gametes............... GWC GWc GwC gWC Gwc gWc gwC gwc

The F_2 generation will consist then of:

27 Distinct Genotypes			8 Distinct Phenotypes
1	GG WW CC		27 yellow-round-colored
2	GG WW Cc		
2	GG Ww CC		
2	Gg WW CC		
4	GG Ww Cc		
4	Gg WW Cc		
4	Gg Ww CC		
8	Gg Ww Cc		
1	GG WW cc		9 yellow-round-colorless
2	GG Ww cc		
2	Gg WW cc		
4	Gg Ww cc		
1	GG ww CC		9 yellow-wrinkled-colored
2	GG ww Cc		
2	Gg ww CC		
4	Gg ww Cc		
1	gg WW CC		9 green-round-colored
2	gg WW Cc		
2	gg Ww CC		
4	gg Ww Cc		
1	GG ww cc		3 yellow-wrinkled-colorless
2	Gg ww cc		
1	gg WW cc		3 green-round-colorless
2	gg Ww cc		
1	gg ww CC		3 green-wrinkled-colored
2	gg ww Cc		
1	gg ww cc		1 green-wrinkled-colorless

CHAPTER XIX

THE PHYSICAL BASIS OF INHERITANCE

When Mendel announced the results of his experiments in 1866, nearly all biologists were engaged in the discussions and controversies that followed the publication of Darwin's *Origin of Species* in 1859. The few who knew of Mendel's work did not appreciate its importance, and it was soon forgotten. By 1900, however, many biologists had come to realize that a more precise evaluation of inheritance and variation was essential for the understanding of evolutionary processes and had turned to experimental studies. In that year, three botanists who were independently investigating inheritance in plants came across Mendel's paper, and, realizing its value, made it known throughout Europe and America. Almost at once a number of botanists and zoologists repeated Mendel's experiments, using a wide variety of plants and animals for breeding stocks. Nearly all these experiments verified Mendel's findings and soon established *segregation-and-recombination* and *independent assortment* as general principles of biological inheritance.

It must not be supposed, however, that modern genetics consists merely in verifying Mendel's laws and discovering that they apply to organisms in general. Mendel established two basic principles of inheritance and contributed an extremely useful experimental method. Since his time an ever-increasing number of workers and the combination of experimental breeding with other methods of research have carried modern genetics far beyond the point reached by Mendel.

In the interval between 1866 and 1900, tremendous advances had been made in another field of biology that was eventually to become closely knit with Mendelian breeding in the development of modern genetics. This is the science of cell study, or *cytology*. In 1866, the "cell doctrine" was in process of becoming established, but little was actually known about the detailed structure or the lineage of cells, and comparatively few biologists thought in terms of cells. Between 1866 and 1900, however, special techniques had been devised for fixing and staining cells to permit microscopic differentiation of their component parts; the microtome had been invented for cutting microscopically thin slices of tissues; and constantly increasing interest in cytological studies had led to the recognition of a number of fundamental and universal cell phenomena, particularly *mitosis, maturation (meiosis)*, and the details of fertilization.

The Sutton-Boveri hypothesis. The American cytologist W. S. Sutton, who was investigating the details of maturation, had, like nearly all other workers in biology, become greatly interested in the newly discovered "Mendelian heredity." About 1902, he realized that there was a striking parallel between Mendel's laws and certain details of maturation and fertilization. He saw that if we but conceive of the Mendelian factors or genes as being located in the chromosomes, then the latter provide a vehicle and a precise mechanism that will account for:

1. *Segregation* of the factors at gamete formation (gametic purity).
2. *Recombination* of the factors at fertilization (zygote formation).

And, if we can assume that the paired chromosomes at the metaphase of the first meiotic division (page 219) may have their paternal and maternal elements at random on either side of the equatorial plate of the spindle, then maturation will also provide a perfect mechanism to account for:

3. *The independent assortment of as many pairs of factors as there are pairs of chromosomes*, so long as each pair of allelomorphic factors is in a separate pair of chromosomes.

Sutton's reasoning was based upon the striking parallels between the phenomena of Mendelian inheritance and those shown by the chromosomes at meiosis. Another supporting fact cited by Sutton was the apparent lack of influence of cytoplasm upon inheritance. We have seen that it makes no difference which parent is tall or which is dwarf; in either case, the F_1 will be tall, and the F_2 will show a ratio of 3 talls and 1 dwarf. We also know that the only thing the male and female parents contribute equally to the zygote is their chromosome complex. All or nearly all the cytoplasm comes from the female parent, yet the male parent appears to contribute equally with the female to the hereditary qualities of the offspring.

Sutton's hypothesis, which came to be known as the *Sutton-Boveri hypothesis* (after Sutton and Theodore Boveri, the latter a cytologist who contributed much to our knowledge of maturation), at first met with much opposition, but gradually, more and more evidence accumulated to support it, until by 1920 to 1925 it was accepted as a proved principle in biology.

SEX DETERMINATION AND SEX LINKAGE

Shortly after the announcement of the Sutton-Boveri hypothesis, further studies on cytology brought to light still other parallels between chromosomes and certain peculiar modes of inheritance that did not precisely correspond to the original Mendelian types. Soon after chromosomes became well known, it had been found that the cells of each species or kind of organism have a definite and unchanging number of chromosomes. In man, for example, every cell (except matured germ cells) has 48 chromosomes (24 pairs); in the fruit fly Drosophila, every cell has 8 (4 pairs); and in the garden pea, every cell has 14 chromosomes (7 pairs).

Bug Type. But now certain exceptions were discovered. In some species of bugs (Hemiptera), the cells of the females have an *even* number of chromosomes and those of the male have an *odd* number, 1 less than in the female. Further study showed that all the eggs of such a species contain the same number of chromosomes (half the female number) but that the spermatozoa are of two kinds as regards chromosome number: half of the spermatozoa have the same number found in the egg; the other half of the spermatozoa have 1 chromosome less. For example, in one species of bug, the females have 12 chromosomes in each body cell, and all the mature unfertilized eggs have 6 chromosomes; but the body cells of the male contain only 11 chromosomes, and half of the mature sperm have 6 chromosomes and half only 5. It seems fairly evident from this that an egg (always with 6 chromosomes) fertilized by a sperm with 6 chromosomes will produce a 12-chromosome zygote and develop into a female, whereas an egg that is fertilized by a 5-chromosome sperm will produce an 11-chromosome zygote and develop into a male.

Drosophila Type. Later work brought to light other types of "sex determination." In Drosophila and in man, the number of chromosomes is the same in the two sexes, but in both these species one pair of chromosomes, the so-called "sex chromosomes," are alike (XX) in the *female* and unlike (XY) in the *male*. As a consequence, when the human egg is formed, it will always contain 23 ordinary chromosomes (*autosomes*) and 1 X chromosome, whereas the sperm are of two sorts—*female-producing* spermatozoa with 23 autosomes and an X chromosome, and *male-producing* spermatozoa with 23 autosomes and a Y chromosome.

Poultry Type. In poultry and in many of the Lepidoptera (moths and butterflies) a type of sex determination exists that appears to be just the reverse of that in man and Drosophila. Here the *male* has two X chromosomes (XX), and the female an X and a Y. Accordingly, all sperm are alike, containing one set of autosomes and an X chromosome, and the female produces two kinds of eggs—one with a set of autosomes and an X chromosome, the other with a set of autosomes and a Y chromosome.

The various types of correlation between sex and chromosomes that are well known in animals may be tabulated as follows (here AA denotes a diploid set of autosomes; A, a haploid set):

Type of sex determination	Chromosomes of female	Kinds of eggs	Chromosomes of male	Kinds of sperm
Bug type.........	AA + XX	(1) A + X	AA + XO	(2) A + X A + O
Drosophila type...	AA + XX	(1) A + X	AA + XY	(2) A + X A + Y
Poultry type......	AA + XY	(2) A + X A + Y	AA + XX	(1) A + X
Honeybee type....	AA + XX (32)	(1) A + X (16)	A + X (16)	(1) A + X (16) (no reduction division):
	Fertilized eggs develop into females, unfertilized eggs into males			

As soon as the correlation between sex and chromosomes was discovered, it was seen that such a mode of sex determination gave further evidence of the residence of the genes within the chromosomes. Long before Mendel's experiments were rediscovered, a peculiar type of inheritance had been noted in man, in which certain recessive traits were most frequently transmitted to the sons but not to the daughters, by a normal-appearing mother. *Color blindness*, the inability to distinguish red from green, is such a character; one type of *night blindness*, the inability to see in dim light, is another; and inherited *hemophilia*, a condition in which the blood lacks the ability to clot, is still another. The peculiar mode of inheritance of these characters is clearly accounted for if we suppose that the genes for color blindness, night blindness, and hemophilia and their dominant alleles are located in the X chromosome. This is shown by the accompanying diagram (Fig. 19.1), illustrating the inheritance of color blindness, in which the X chromosomes are represented as oval, the Y chromosomes as oblong, N is the gene for normal, and n the gene for color blindness.

Similar cases of sex-linked inheritance are well known in Drosophila. In poultry and in Lepidoptera the characters found to be sex-linked show an inheritance in exact keeping with the fact that in these groups the male has two X chromosomes and the female but one.

LIMITATIONS TO MENDEL'S SECOND LAW

Until 1906, all the rapidly accumulating crosses that involved two or more pairs of allelomorphs showed the independent assortment postulated by Mendel's second law. Some of the adherents of the Sutton-

Boveri hypothesis had speculated that two or more genes might reside within a single chromosome and had pointed out that genes so located should (from all evidence then available) remain permanently associated and invariably be inherited together. This idea was based upon theoretical considerations, not upon any actually known instances.

And then, in 1906, Bateson and Punnett encountered a supposed dihybrid cross in which neither independent assortment nor the permanent association of two genes would explain the F_2 progeny. They crossed a sweet pea that was homozygous for purple flowers and long

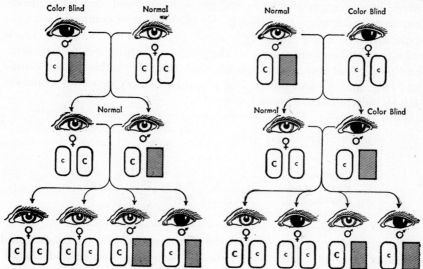

Fig. 19.1. Diagram of the sex-linked inheritance of color blindness in man. C represents the dominant gene for normal vision, c the recessive gene for color blindness. Note that only the X chromosomes carry C or c; the Y chromosomes (shaded) are represented as empty.

pollen grains with one that was homozygous for red flowers and round pollen grains. The F_1 had purple flowers and long pollen grains, showing that purple was dominant to red and that long was dominant to round. The F_2 generation, however, showed a marked deviation from that expected on the basis of independent assortment. The actual ratios and those expected on the basis of independent assortment in the 6,952 F_2 individuals that were obtained are tabulated below:

Phenotypic class	Expected F_2 ratio	Actual F_2 ratio
Purple-long...............	$\%_6$, or 3,910.5	4,831
Purple-round............	$\frac{3}{16}$, or 1,303.5	390
Red-long................	$\frac{3}{16}$, or 1,303.5	393
Red-round................	$\frac{1}{16}$, or 434.5	1,338

It is evident that there are far too many individuals like the original parents and not nearly enough of the two new combinations. There are, however, 783 (390 + 393) individuals that do show the new combinations, and they rule out the possibility that purple and long and red and round are invariably associated with one another.[1]

A sweet pea that was homozygous for purple flowers and round pollen grains was then crossed with one that was homozygous for red flowers and long pollen grains. (Note that this second cross starts with the other possible combination of flower color and pollen-grain shape.) Again, as would now be expected, the F_1 had purple flowers and long pollen grains, but once again, when the actual ratios of the F_2 were compared with the expectation for independent assortment, there were too many individuals with the combinations shown by the parents—in this case, red and long, and purple and round—and too few with the new combinations—purple and long, and red and round. The actual and the expected ratios for the 419 F_2 individuals are given below:

Phenotypic class	Expected F_2 ratio	Actual F_2 ratio
Purple-long..................	$\frac{9}{16}$, or 235.8	226
Purple-round..............	$\frac{3}{16}$, or 78.5	95
Red-long...................	$\frac{3}{16}$, or 78.5	97
Red-round................	$\frac{1}{16}$, or 26.2	1

No satisfactory explanation of the F_2 ratios obtained by Bateson and Punnett was found until after 1910. In that year Morgan and his colleagues at Columbia University began to find a similar lack of independent assortment in a number of crosses in the fruit fly Drosophila. Their method of attack was different from that of Bateson and Punnett in that they resorted to appropriate backcrosses to obtain a more direct test of independent assortment and more readily to permit measurements of the extent to which any kind of assortment might occur. They were also particularly fortunate in selecting Drosophila as their experimental organism.

The backcross as a test of independent assortment. As we have already seen, the direct effect of independent assortment is that the dihybrid or polyhybrid F_1 individual produces equal numbers of all the possible sorts of combinations of genes. If we return for a moment to Mendel's original dihybrid, it will be remembered that the F_1 yellow-round pea had the formula $Gg\ Ww$ and that to give a 9:3:3:1 F_2 ratio, it must have produced an equal number of GW, Gw, gW, and gw gametes.

[1] In such case, the 6,952 F_2 individuals should have shown a ratio of 5,214 purple-long and 1,738 red-round and no others.

In terms of percentages, it produced 25 per cent GW, 25 per cent Gw, 25 per cent gW, and 25 per cent gw. Now the simplest and most direct way to test this assumption is to cross the dihybrid F_1 back to its pure recessive parent or to this same pure recessive stock. Since the pure recessive can only have the genes $gg\,ww$, each of its germ cells must be

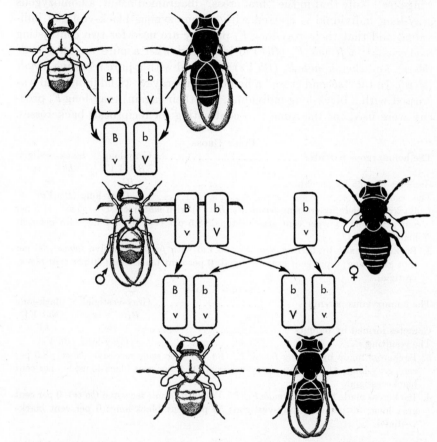

FIG. 19.2. The backcross of a male dihybrid Drosophila, from gray-vestigial black-long, and a pure recessive black-vestigial female. Note that black and long, gray and vestigial, show complete linkage. This is not true in the reverse cross, shown in Fig. 19.3.

gw, and the backcross progeny will show how many of each kind of gene combination occurred in the F_1 gametes. This backcross is tabulated below:

Gametes formed by the $Gg\,Ww\,F_1$..	25% GW	25% Gw	25% gW	25% gw
Gametes formed by the pure recessive............................	gw	gw	gw	gw
Backcross genotypes.............	25% $Gg\,Ww$	25% $Gg\,ww$	25% $gg\,Ww$	25% $gg\,ww$
Resulting phenotypes.............	Yellow-round	Yellow-wrinkled	Green-round	Green-wrinkled

Morgan adopted this type of crossing in order to study the assortment that took place between various genes in Drosophila, and the four following backcrosses show the actual results obtained for two of the pairs of allelic genes in that animal. Gray body color (*BB*) is dominant to black body color (*bb*), and long or normal wings (*VV*) are dominant to vestigial wings (*vv*). Note that in the "first cross," diagramed below, a homozygous gray-long individual is crossed with a homozygous black-vestigial individual and that their gray-long F_1 progeny are used for two contrasting backcrosses: a *female F_1* (*Bb Vv*) is crossed with a pure recessive *male* (*bb vv*), and then a *male F_1* (*Bb Vv*) is crossed with a pure recessive *female* (*bb vv*). In the "second cross" a homozygous gray-vestigial individual was crossed with a black-long individual, and their (again) gray-long F_1 progeny were used for the same two contrasting (or reciprocal) backcrosses.

FIRST CROSS

The homozygous parents............................ Gray-long × black-vestigial

BB VV   bb   vv

Gametes formed by parents......................   BV   bv

The resulting F_1................................   Gray-long (*Bb Vv*)

1. Backcross made by crossing *female F_1* (*Bb Vv*) with *male* recessive (*bb vv*): 41.5 per cent gray-long; 8.5 per cent gray-vestigial; 8.5 per cent black-long; 41.5 per cent black-vestigial.

2. Backcross made by mating *male F_1* (*Bb Vv*) with *female* recessive (*bb vv*): 50 per cent gray-long; 0 per cent gray-vestigial; 0 per cent black-long; 50 per cent black-vestigial.

SECOND CROSS

The homozygous parents.......................... Gray-vestigial × black-long

BB   vv   bb   VV

Gametes formed by parents......................   Bv   bV

The resulting F_1................................   Gray-long (*Bb Vv*)

3. Backcross made by mating *female F_1* (*Bb Vv*) with *male* recessive (*bb vv*): 8.5 per cent gray-long; 41.5 per cent gray-vestigial; 41.5 per cent black-long; 8.5 per cent black-vestigial.

4. Backcross made by mating *male F_1* (*Bb Vv*) with *female* recessive (*bb vv*): 0 per cent gray-long; 50 per cent gray-vestigial; 50 per cent black-long; 0 per cent black-vestigial.

These results, including the same percentage values, were found to be duplicated whenever the same crosses were made in these same ways. They thus appear to be regular and predictable (under the conditions given), but how are they to be explained? Note that in both the "first" and "second" crosses, the *female F_1* must form *four* types of germ cells, since when she is crossed to a pure recessive male, four types of progeny are produced, 83 per cent (41.5 + 41.5) like the combinations shown by her parents and 17 per cent (8.5 + 8.5) of the new combinations. When the reciprocal backcrosses are made, however, a *male F_1* being crossed with a pure recessive female, only *two* kinds of progeny appear, half of them like one of the male's parents, half like the other. Evidently the male forms but two kinds of germ cells.[1] The total lack of assortment in the male could be explained by adopting the Boveri-Sutton hypothesis and supposing that in the first cross, B and V were in the same chromosome and b and v were in its mate; and that in the second cross, B and

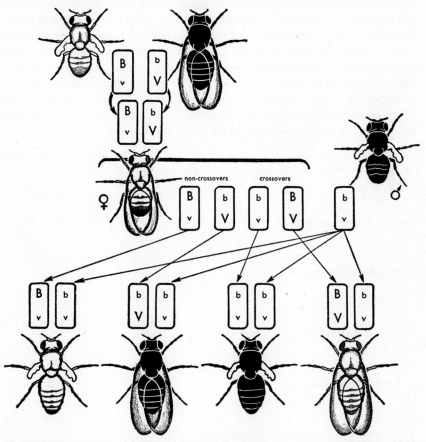

FIG. 19.3. The backcross of a female dihybrid Drosophila, from gray-vestigial black-long, and a pure recessive black-vestigial male. Note that black and long, and gray and vestigial, are neither completely linked nor do they show independent assortment. Compare with Fig. 19.2.

v were in one chromosome and b and V in its mate. But how are the 17 per cent of new combinations that are formed by the F_1 dihybrids to be explained?

Morgan and his associates were already strong proponents of the Sutton-Boveri hypothesis, and they consequently sought for some expla-

[1] This total lack of crossing over in the male of Drosophila appears to be peculiar to this group and is not characteristic of organisms in general.

nation that would make the new findings compatible with the evidence that the genes were in the chromosomes. A clue was found in some then recent microscopic studies on the details of early maturation, in which the pairing chromosomes appeared to be twisted about one another at the time they were "fixed" (killed) and stained. Morgan saw in these over-lapping chromosomes a possible explanation for his breeding results. If the chromosomes should break at the points where they cross over and interchange with each other the sections included between the crossings over, it would be possible to see how two or more genes could lie within one chromosome and yet occasionally become separated to form the new combinations that had been observed. Suppose, for instance, that we imagine the conditions and sequences diagramed below, in which the "first cross" in Drosophila is represented with the genes for body color and wing length situated within the same chromosome:

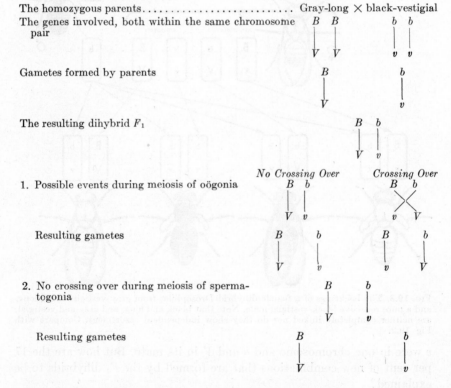

The homozygous parents.......................... Gray-long × black-vestigial
The genes involved, both within the same chromosome B B b b
    pair
                                                      V V v v

Gametes formed by parents B b

                                                            V v

The resulting dihybrid F_1 B b

                                                              V v

                                        No Crossing Over   *Crossing Over*
1. Possible events during meiosis of oögonia B b B b

                                                 V v v V

    Resulting gametes B b B b

                                    V v v V

2. No crossing over during meiosis of sperma- B b
    togonia
                                                         V v

    Resulting gametes B b

                                               V v

Here was a hypothesis that would explain the puzzling, partial, but not completely independent assortment that had been found in one cross in sweet peas and that was now being found in more and more crosses in Drosophila. Such a hypothesis depended upon a number of unproved assumptions about possible happenings in maturation. One marked difficulty was that it depended upon an active process, the twining of chromosomes and the exchanging of genes, which could not be watched under the microscope, since the chromosomes, in order to be seen in detail, had to be fixed and stained, with all processes stopped.

The establishment of this hypothesis involved many technical details that are beyond the scope of our treatment. A new type of genetic research was developed, in which appropriate breeding experiments were checked and compared with detailed microscopic studies of the chromosomes of the breeding stocks. These investigations, which are still actively in progress, have confirmed the supposition that the genes lie within the chromosomes. They have demonstrated the processes that provide and account for nonindependent assortment. They have also established a number of other principles that appear to be as fundamental as the original "laws" of Mendel. Some of the more important of these are summarized below:

Linkage.   Many groups of two or more genes do tend to be inherited together. Such genes are said to be *linked*, or to constitute a *linkage group*. Four linkage groups have been found in Drosophila, and three of them comprise more than 100 genes each. Linkage groups have also been found in most of the other organisms that have been extensively utilized for breeding experiments—corn (maize), garden peas, sweet peas, rabbits, mice, guinea pigs, and others. The mechanical explanation for linkage is now clearly established to be the fact that all the genes within any one linkage group reside within the same chromosome.

Crossing over.   Linkage was defined as the *tendency* for two or more genes to remain together without segregation. Most linked genes do not show an absolute or invariable linkage. As we saw in Drosophila, if the genes for black and vestigial enter a cross together, they tend to remain associated, but the linkage is occasionally broken (17 per cent of the time, in this instance), and black becomes associated with long and gray with vestigial. Such breakage of a former linkage association, with the consequent formation of a new linkage, is termed *crossing over*, and the new combinations that result are termed *crossovers*. Crossing over was once thought to be rather exceptional, but we now know that the processes that bring it about are a normal event in the very early stages of meiosis of many, and probably of all or nearly all, organisms. The essential features of this process and of linkage are shown in Fig. 19.4.

Linear order of the genes.   All the genes within any one chromosome are arranged in a definite linear order within (or along) that chromosome. Each gene thus has its own precise location, or *locus*, that will be occupied *only by that definite gene or its allele*, and the characteristic crossover percentage shown by any two linked genes is *a function of the distance*

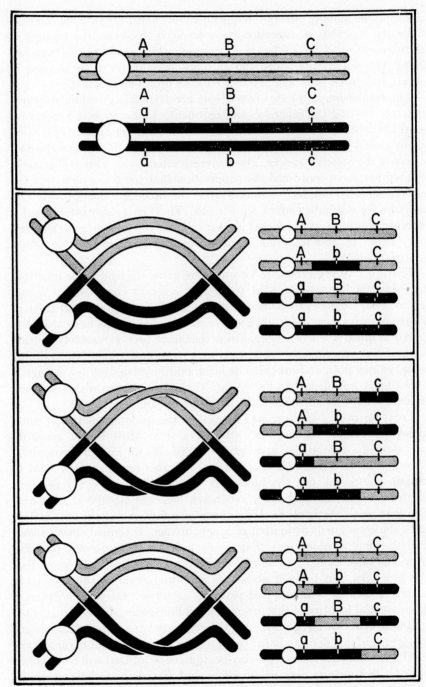

FIG. 19.4. Diagrams illustrating linkage and crossing over. Compare with Fig. 15.3. (*Based on White, Animal Cytology and Evolution, by permission Cambridge University Press.*)

apart of their loci. The loci for black and vestigial, for instance, are 17 crossover units apart, and since the one locus will contain *either* the gene for black *or* the gene for gray and the other will contain *either* the gene for long *or* the gene for vestigial, the crossover percentages between the genes for body color and for wing length will always be 17 per cent, whatever the original combination of the body color and wing length.

CHAPTER XX

SOME COMPLICATIONS OF MENDELIAN INHERITANCE

Although experimental studies on heredity since 1900 have abundantly verified Mendel's findings, it would be very misleading to imply that the present-day concept of inheritance is as simple and direct as might be expected from Mendel's original laws. We have already seen that the law of "independent assortment" is limited to special conditions and must be supplemented by the principles of linkage and crossing over when the genes of a di- or polyhybrid are located in the same chromosome. In the present chapter, we shall look at some of the simpler of other complicating conditions that have been discovered by post-Mendelian investigations.

Absence of dominance. In all the crosses made by Mendel the dominance of one allelomorphic gene over the other was a conspicuous feature. Soon after 1900, however, crosses were found in which dominance and recessiveness were not well marked. One of these was in the old-fashioned garden flower, the four-o'clock, in which a red variety crossed with a white variety gives an F_1 that is pale red or pink and an F_2 that consists of $\frac{1}{4}$ red, $\frac{1}{2}$ pink, and $\frac{1}{4}$ white. This F_2 ratio of $1:2:1$ is typical of a monohybrid cross when dominance is absent.

A similar case had long been known to poultry breeders, although it was not understood until after 1900. In the Andalusian breed of poultry there occur black, white, and blue varieties. Of these, the blue was most desired by fanciers, but although the black and white varieties breed true, mating two blues results in $\frac{1}{4}$ blacks, $\frac{1}{2}$ blues, and $\frac{1}{4}$ whites. It is thus evident that blue is due to a heterozygous combination of the gene for black and its allele, the gene for white, and the only way to obtain a brood consisting entirely of blue chickens is to mate a black with a white. Many other crosses that show lack of dominance are known, as well as a large number in which the heterozygote, although much more like one parent than the other, can be easily distinguished from it.

Lethal genes. Among the multitude of genes found to be inherited in various breeding stocks, a number are known that result in the death of the organism *if they are present in a homozygous condition.* The first example of such a gene was found in mice. Repeated experiments showed that when two yellow mice were bred together, the progeny always consisted of 2 yellows to 1 nonyellow, as though 1 individual of a 3:1 or a 1:2:1 ratio were persistently missing. Autopsies on pregnant yellow females that had been bred to yellow males showed that 1 embryo out

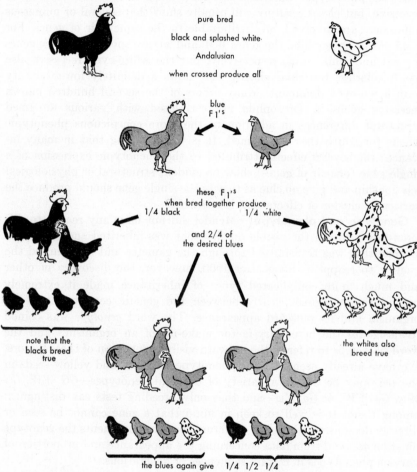

pure bred

black and splashed white

Andalusian

when crossed produce all

blue
F₁'s

these F₁'s
when bred together produce
1/4 black   1/4 white

and 2/4 of
the desired blues

note that the
blacks breed
true

the whites also
breed true

the blues again give   1/4 1/2 1/4

Fig. 20.1. The inheritance of blue as the nondominant monohybrid of black and splashed white in the Andalusian fowl.

of 4 always died; and genetic experiments proved this embryo to have been the homozygous YY individual. Here, apparently, is a gene that produces yellow coloration as a dominant and some lethal condition as a recessive. Just what this lethal condition may be is unknown, but it is fatal to the developing mouse at a fairly early stage in embryonic existence. Many other lethals are known, some producing death in early stages, some in later stages; but in all cases, such lethals are recessive and show little or no harmful influence when present in a heterozygous state.[1]

Multiple effects of a single gene. It is also now recognized that many genes are not limited to a single effect. We usually contrast (and name) the most striking or immediately evident character that differentiates the phenotypic expression of a dominant gene and its allelomorphic recessive, but closer scrutiny will usually show that several or numerous differences are involved, all attributable to the same pair of genes. For instance, in Drosophila, the genes WW and ww are spoken of as the genes for red and white eyes, respectively, but the white-eyed recessive also has a colorless testicular sheath and shows a definitely lower vitality than a red-eyed dominant. Many others of the several hundred known recessive genes in Drosophila are correlated with various unnamed structural differences in addition to the more conspicuous phenotypic effects for which they are named. It is worth noting that in many instances the several effects attributed to the phenotypic expression of a single gene (or pair of genes) show no evident structural or physiological relationship and give no clue as to why the single gene should produce the particular cluster of effects that is observed.

Genotype and phenotype. Mendel did not have any reason to differentiate between the visible quality that was inherited and the factor or gene that was transmitted through the gametes and that caused the quality to reappear. Soon after 1900, however, the discovery of other and much more complicated types of inheritance made it extremely helpful to distinguish clearly between the genetic constitution of an organism and its outward appearance. The word *genotype* was coined to designate the hereditary-factor make-up of an organism,[2] and the word *phenotype* to refer to the outward visible expression of these factors. We have already seen that the phenotype of round and yellow seeds in the pea may be due to a variety of different genotypes—*GG WW, GG Ww, Gg WW,* or *Gg Ww*—and that only breeding tests can distinguish among them. It is well to keep in mind that a gene cannot be seen or directly demonstrated, and in all actual genetic experiments the genotype must be *assumed* from data concerning the appearance and proportion of various phenotypes in certain sequences of generations.

THE INTERACTION OF GENES

So far we have been concerned with what have been termed *unit characters.* Here each gene or pair of genes appears to produce a distinct and evident phenotype, and, conversely, each phenotype appears to be due to one gene or one pair of genes. Soon after 1900, however, numerous cases began to be found in which a given phenotype was dependent upon

[1] Compare with the sex-linked condition in man known as *hemophilia.*

[2] The word *gene* was then coined to refer to a unit of the genotype.

the coincidence of two or more non-allelic genes in the same organism. Today many hundreds of such nonunit characters are known, and they form such a common and important type of genetic phenomena that we shall need to examine a number of representative examples.

Walnut comb in fowls.   The various breeds of the domestic chicken show a variety of comb forms. Among these are *rose comb, pea comb, walnut comb*, and *single comb*. Breeding experiments show that when a homozygous rose-comb fowl is mated with a homozygous single-comb fowl, the F_1 are all rose comb and the F_2 show a ratio of 3 rose comb to 1 single comb, a typical monohybrid cross. The cross between pea comb and single comb also forms a typical monohybrid cross, with an F_1 all

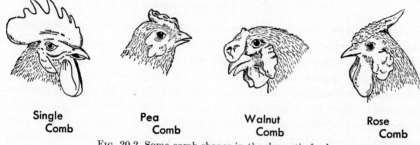

| Single Comb | Pea Comb | Walnut Comb | Rose Comb |

FIG. 20.2. Some comb shapes in the domestic fowl.

pea comb and an F_2 with 3 pea comb to 1 single comb. When, however, a homozygous rose-comb fowl is mated with a homozygous pea-comb fowl, the F_1 are all walnut comb, and the F_2 gives 9 walnut comb, 3 rose comb, 3 pea comb, and 1 single comb. Walnut comb is thus not a unit character but the phenotypic expression of the genes for rose and pea acting together. Here, if A is used to represent the gene for rose comb and a, its recessive allele, and B is used to represent the gene for pea comb and b, its recessive allele, we may diagram the cross as follows:

Parent varieties......................... Rose comb	$\times$	pea comb	
$AA\ bb$		$aa\ BB$	
F_1... $Aa\ Bb$			
Walnut comb			
F_2...................... 9 ($AA\ BB$, $AA\ Bb$, $Aa\ BB$, or $Aa\ Bb$)........ Walnut			
3 ($AA\ bb$ or $Aa\ bb$)......................... Rose			
3 ($aa\ BB$ or $aa\ Bb$)......................... Pea			
1 ($aa\ bb$).................................. Single			

Complementary genes—the 9:7 ratio.   Among the many types of sweet peas, there are two white varieties (the Emily Henderson and the Blanche Burpee) that differ from one another in several structural characters. When these two varieties are crossed, all the F_1 progeny have colored (purplish red) flowers, and when the F_1 are allowed to self-fertilize, the F_2 shows a phenotypic ratio of 9 colored to 7 white flowers. Further breeding has shown that this is really a ratio of $\frac{9}{16}:\frac{3}{16}:\frac{3}{16}:\frac{1}{16}$, in which the last three groups cannot be distinguished phenotypically, and that the genes concerned are C (dominant to c), the gene for chromogen, a colorless color base; and E (dominant to c), the gene for an enzyme that is capable of changing chromogen into a purplish red color.

This may be diagramed as follows:

Parent varieties.................................... White   ×   white
                                                     CC ee   *cc EE*

F_1.. *Cc Ee*
                                                         Colored

F_2........... 9   9 colored (*CC EE, CC Ee, Cc EE,* or *Cc Ee*)—chromogen, enzyme

7 { 3 white (*CC ee,* or *Cc ee*)—chromogen, no enzyme
    3 white (*cc EE,* or *cc Ee*)—enzyme, no chromogen
    1 white (*cc ee*)—neither enzyme nor chromogen

Here we have two sets of genes, neither able to produce a visible effect alone but together producing a visible effect. Numerous other examples of such complementary genes are known.

Modifying genes—the 9:3:4 ratio. A very common type of gene interaction is that associated with genes which do not themselves produce any visible effect but which have the faculty of modifying the phenotypic expression of some other non-allelic gene. Genes of this sort are very common in the inheritance of the various coat colors of mammals. Among the numerous domesticated varieties that have been developed from the common mouse are a pure white (albino) and a pure black variety. The "wild-type" mouse from which both of these were derived has a characteristic gray color known as *agouti*,[1] a peculiar pepper-and-salt color that is produced by each hair being banded with at least two colors, one basal and one apical.

If a black mouse is crossed with a certain type of albino, the F_1 are all agouti, and these, when mated among themselves, produce an F_2 that consists of approximately 9 agouti, 3 black, and 4 white mice. Here the genes involved are B (dominant to b), a gene for black hair pigment; and A (dominant to a), a gene that causes the pigment in the hair to become localized and not evenly distributed throughout the hair. When no pigment is present, the gene A can have no phenotypic expression.

Parent varieties..................................... Black   ×   white
                                                      aa BB   *AA bb*

F_1... *Aa Bb*
                                                          Agouti

F_2............................. 9   9 agouti (*AA BB, AA Bb, Aa BB,* or *Aa Bb*)
                                  3   3 black (*aa BB,* or *aa Bb*)
                                  4 { 3 white (*AA bb,* or *Aa bb*)
                                      1 white (*aa bb*) a new genotype for white

[1] The name of the color is derived from the agouti, a South American rodent in which this type of coloration is particularly striking.

Other types of gene interaction—the 13:3, 15:1, and other ratios. Another way in which genes interact to produce a modified F_2 phenotypic ratio is the *inhibition* by one gene of the phenotypic expression of another gene, the first gene producing no visible effect by itself. An example is found in poultry, where a gene A (dominant to a) for colored plumage and an inhibiting gene B (dominant to b), if brought together in a typical hybrid cross, result in a colorless F_1 and an F_2 ratio of 13 colorless (white) and 3 colored individuals.

A dihybrid phenotypic ratio of 15:1 is produced by what are known as *duplicate genes*. Here A is dominant to a, B is dominant to b, and either A or B alone or A and B together produce exactly the same effect. Consequently $AA\,Bb$, $AA\,BB$, $Aa\,BB$, $Aa\,Bb$, $AA\,bb$, $Aa\,bb$, $aa\,BB$, and $aa\,Bb$ are indistinguishable in their phenotypic expression and only the genotype $aa\,bb$ out of 16 shows a visible difference.

Modified trihybrid and tetrahybrid ratios are also known. Among the former are such modifications of the typical $27:9:9:9:3:3:3:1$ ratio as $27:9:28$, $63:1$ and $27:37$. Genotypically, such ratios are precisely of the same sort as those of the typical trihybrid, but various types of gene interaction make several of the groups phenotypically indistinguishable.

THE MULTIPLE-FACTOR HYPOTHESIS

One of the types of inheritance most difficult to understand is that illustrated by *skin color* in the cross between the White and Negro races. The color of the F_1 mulatto is more or less intermediate between that of the two parent races, but the F_2 generation fails to show any clear-cut pattern of segregation. Instead, there results a widely variable F_2, ranging from very light-yellow individuals to others almost as dark as the Negro grandparent. Similar cases are known in other animals and in plants, and for a long time they were regarded as non-Mendelian. That is, since they did not show a clear-cut segregation and recombination, it was assumed that some other and unknown type of inheritance must be involved.

The clue to an understanding of these crosses came from experiments on the inheritance of *seed color in wheat* and of *ear length in corn*, which furnish examples of this so-called "non-Mendelian," or "blended," inheritance. In a cross between a certain variety of red-kerneled wheat and a variety of white-kerneled wheat, the F_1 has pale red kernels; the F_2 is markedly variable, ranging from very pale red to much darker than the F_1, but with few if any kernels as white or as red as the parent generation.

It was finally seen, both by Nilsson-Ehle, who worked with wheat, and by East, who demonstrated a similar condition in the inheritance of ear length in corn, that such cases were probably Mendelian (involving segregation and recombination of genes) but that the Mendelian pattern

was concealed by the large number of genes involved. Suppose that
the red color in the wheat is due to three pairs of genes, $AA\ BB\ CC$, and
each of these genes contributes one-sixth of the total redness. Then Aa
$bb\ cc$, $aa\ Bb\ cc$, or $aa\ bb\ Cc$ will produce a kernel one-sixth as red as an
$AA\ BB\ CC$ individual, $AA\ bb\ cc$, $Aa\ Bb\ cc$, $Aa\ bb\ Cc$, etc., will produce
a kernel one-third as red, etc. In the original cross, the red variety has
the constitution $AA\ BB\ CC$, the white variety the constitution $aa\ bb$
cc, and the pale red F_1 individuals have the constitution $Aa\ Bb\ Cc$. The
gametes of the F_1 will be of eight kinds: ABC, ABc, AbC, aBC, Abc,
aBc, abC, and abc, and if all possible recombinations occur, 27 genotypes
will be produced, as shown in the following diagram.

1	AA	BB	CC	1 individual in 64 with 6 genes for red

2	AA	BB	Cc	
2	AA	Bb	CC	6 individuals in 64 with 5 genes for red
2	Aa	BB	CC	

4	AA	Bb	Cc	
4	Aa	BB	Cc	
4	Aa	Bb	CC	
1	AA	BB	cc	15 individuals in 64 with 4 genes for red
1	AA	bb	CC	
1	aa	BB	CC	

8	Aa	Bb	Cc	
2	AA	Bb	cc	
2	AA	bb	Cc	
2	aa	BB	Cc	20 individuals in 64 with 3 genes for red
2	aa	Bb	CC	
2	Aa	BB	cc	
2	Aa	bb	CC	

4	Aa	Bb	cc	
4	Aa	bb	Cc	
4	aa	Bb	Cc	
1	AA	bb	cc	15 individuals in 64 with 2 genes for red
1	aa	BB	cc	
1	aa	bb	CC	

2	Aa	bb	cc	
2	aa	Bb	cc	6 individuals in 64 with 1 gene for red
2	aa	bb	Cc	

1	aa	bb	cc	1 individual in 64 with 0 genes for red

Here is a hypothesis that seems consistent with many of the crosses
that appear to show a blended inheritance. It explains the rarity of the
appearance of either parent type in the F_2, the fact that the F_2 is much

more variable than the F_1, and the tendency of most of the F_2 individuals to be more or less intermediate. In some of these crosses, as in color in wheat, the parent type does appear in the F_2 about as frequently as once in 64 individuals. If it is argued that in other crosses the parent types are much rarer than once in 64 individuals (in some they are practically never obtained), we can refer to the ratios that would occur if four pairs or five pairs of genes had been involved.

Suppose that we are dealing with four pairs of multiple genes, AA BB CC DD, and that each gene contributed one-eighth of the total effect. There will be 16 kinds of germ cells produced by the F_1, and the F_2 will show:

1 individual out of 256 with 8 genes
8 individuals out of 256 with 7 genes
28 individuals out of 256 with 6 genes
56 individuals out of 256 with 5 genes
70 individuals out of 256 with 4 genes
56 individuals out of 256 with 3 genes
28 individuals out of 256 with 2 genes
8 individuals out of 256 with 1 gene
1 individual out of 256 with 0 genes

If five pairs of multiple genes, AA BB CC DD EE, were involved and each gene contributed one-tenth of the total effect, there would be 32 kinds of germ cells produced by the F_1, and the F_2 would show:

1 individual   out of 1,024 with 10 genes
10 individuals out of 1,024 with 9 genes
45 individuals out of 1,024 with 8 genes
120 individuals out of 1,024 with 7 genes
210 individuals out of 1,024 with 6 genes
252 individuals out of 1,024 with 5 genes
210 individuals out of 1,024 with 4 genes
120 individuals out of 1,024 with 3 genes
45 individuals out of 1,024 with 2 genes
10 individuals out of 1,024 with 1 gene
1 individual   out of 1,024 with 0 genes

The necessity of obtaining such large numbers[1] of F_2 individuals, together with the difficulty of separating and classifying all the various phenotypic classes, makes this type of inheritance difficult to study and has necessitated a special statistical or biometrical technique. By this means the multiple-factor hypothesis has been abundantly verified, although many cases are far less simple than the ones outlined above. The chief importance of multiple-factor inheritance lies in the fact that a great many of the qualities desired by the practical breeder are inherited

[1] In actual breeding experiments, the number of F_2 individuals obtained should be at least 10 times or, better, 25 times as large as the minimum number theoretically required to allow each genotype to show.

in this fashion. Among these are milk production in cattle, egg production in fowl, racing ability in horses, leaf shape in tobacco, and many types of disease resistance in crop plants. There is also much inferential evidence that many important human qualities are inherited in this way.

Breeding experiments are, of course, out of the question in human crosses; but from detailed observational data Davenport concluded that skin color in the Negro-White cross probably involves four pairs of genes, the genes in two of the pairs having a much greater effect than do the genes of the other two pairs.

CHAPTER XXI

VARIATION AS THE BASIS FOR HEREDITARY DISTINCTIONS

Variation is a common phenomenon among all organisms and includes many kinds and degrees of difference. Variations in size, in number of parts, in form, in color, and in physiological functions may be either large or small. They may be abrupt and discontinuous or, within large populations, may form minutely graded series. The difference in height between the tall and the dwarf peas of Mendel's experiment, for instance, was both great and abrupt; but we know that differences in height among men may be either large or small and that if we compare the heights of 1,000 men selected at random, we find an almost perfectly graded series between the tallest and shortest individuals of the whole group.

Practically all early attempts to classify variations were based upon some scheme of distinguishing between the degrees, or visible kinds, of differences among individuals. None of these schemes was very satisfactory, because no clear-cut distinction could be made between the proposed classes of variation. With the introduction of experimental breeding, however, it soon became evident that some variations are inherited and that others are not, but appear to be determined by the type of environment in which the organism is placed. This distinction, although often difficult to test, has proved to be a very fruitful one and has made possible a much more adequate knowledge of organic variation.

Environmentally produced variations. Once a number of clearly *noninherited variations* were known and could be studied as a group, it was seen that they were all produced by some environmental influence. Literally thousands of experiments and careful observations have shown that variations, slight or marked, may be produced in the form, size, color, functioning, habits, and longevity of organisms by modifying their environment. Changes in temperature, in the kind, duration, or intensity of light, in humidity, nutrition, water supply, amount of exercise, amount of crowding, etc., have all been used singly and in combination to produce such variations. *But none of these environmentally produced variations is ever inherited beyond the generation in which the soma is directly affected.*

Autogenous variations.   Another large assemblage of variations includes those known to be definitely inherited. Although many of these cannot by inspection be distinguished from environmentally produced variations, experiment shows that they are not due to a response to the environment but must be caused by some internal change in the organism itself. Such internal changes are spontaneous in the sense that they are not produced by any known cause and can neither be predicted nor duplicated by any effort of the experimenter.[1] Such variations first appear in but one or a few[2] of the many individuals exposed to the same environmental conditions; but once in existence the new variation may be passed on to an increasing number of individuals that are descendants of the original variant.

Detailed studies of autogenous variations by the parallel methods of the cytologist and the experimental breeder have shown that they are not all of one type. Broadly speaking they fall into two main groups: (1) variations that are correlated with various kinds of chromosome change and that show various patterns of inheritance; and (2) variations that behave as units in Mendelian inheritance but that are not accompanied by any detectable change in the chromosomes.

Autogenous Variations Due to Chromosomal Changes.   We shall dismiss this group of inherited variations rather summarily. This is not because they are rare or unimportant, but because at present they are of more interest and importance to the technical geneticist and cytologist than to the general student. It will be well to remember, however, that some autogenous variations are caused by gross changes in the chromosomes—changes that affect several or many genes at once—and that these changes provide valuable material for further studies of heredity and cytological processes. We can characterize the main types of known chromosomal changes associated with autogenous variations as follows:

1. Changes within a single chromosome including: loss of a small portion of a chromosome, duplication of a portion of a chromosome, and rearrangement of parts of a chromosome so that the normal linear sequence of a given block of genes is inverted.

2. Exchanges of parts between different (nonhomologous) chromo-

---

[1] The fact that exposure of organisms to X rays, radium, and other agents does very definitely increase the percentage of new inherited variations is not a real contradiction of this statement. Such agents do speed up the "mutation rate," but the variations that appear are still unpredictable, are quite like those that appear at a slower rate in the absence of radiation, and they have no discernible adaptation or relation to the agent that increased their frequency.

[2] The finding of a new variation in several individuals simply means that the variation was not *detected* until it had been inherited by the progeny of the original variant.

somes, with the result that the original linkage relationships and the meiotic behavior of the chromosomes are modified.

3. Losses or gains of whole chromosomes ("heteroploidy").

4. Gains of whole sets of chromosomes, or the loss of a single set, so that haploid, triploid, tetraploid, or higher polyploid individuals are produced by normal diploid parents.

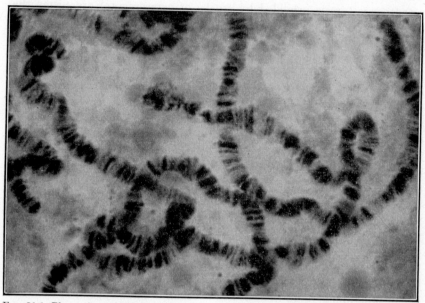

FIG. 21.1. Photomicrograph of giant chromosomes from the salivary gland cells of Drosophila larvae (stained preparation). In the salivary glands of most flies the chromosomes increase more than a hundredfold in length and considerably in diameter as compared with their size in the cells of other tissues. They appear as cross-striped cylinders or ribbons, the striations forming a constant pattern that permits identification of the chromosomes and of their parts. The stainable disks that form the bands may or may not correspond to single genes, but their longitudinal arrangement corresponds accurately to the gene arrangement in the chromosome. In addition, the homologous chromosomes in the salivary gland nuclei undergo a very intimate pairing, disk by disk, enabling identification of homologous disks and chromosome segments in the two chromosomes present in an individual. Losses, duplications, inversions, and the like (chromosome mutations) may be detected by abnormalities in the pairing of the chromosomes, which form loops or folds so as to bring the corresponding disks together as much as possible. (*Courtesy General Biological Supply House, Inc.*)

Autogenous Variations Due to Changes in Single Genes. We have seen that Mendelian inheritance is concerned with the transmission from generation to generation of differences in the genotypic constitutions of the original parent stocks. We have also seen something of the evidence that the genotypic constitution is made up of separable and combinable units—*genes* that occupy definite points within particular chromosomes. So far we have utilized gene differences that were found "ready made" in various Mendelian stocks, without question as to their origin. It is now time to see the evidence that the same sorts of variations are continuously coming into existence in many (probably in all) races of organisms, from which we must infer that all the allelic qualities available to the Mendelian breeder have arisen in the same way in the past.

The best evidence that a given inherited quality is actually new and was derived by some spontaneous change in the genotype of one of its recent ancestors is provided by stocks of experimental organisms that have been bred for many generations under laboratory observation. These stocks have a long history of continued *inbreeding*[1] that has eliminated any chance that an unknown ancestor might have introduced some hidden recessive into the germ plasm or that the appearance of a new character might have been caused by a new combination of genes already present. When the laboratory stock of the fruit fly *Drosophila melanogaster* was started, the "wild" parents were red-eyed. This normal red-eyed character persisted through many inbred generations before a white-eyed individual suddenly appeared in this purebred red-eyed stock. The new variant, a male, was bred to a red-eyed female, and the white-eyed condition reappeared in the inbred descendants of their offspring. White-eyed males and females were then bred together to establish a homozygous white-eyed strain of fruit flies. White-eyed proved to be a sex-linked recessive to red-eyed.

During the half century or so that Drosophila has been bred in the laboratory, hundreds of pedigreed generations and millions of individuals have been carefully scrutinized by the geneticist. Among this huge number of individuals more than 500 new variants have appeared, each new character proving to be an allele of some formerly homozygous character of the inbred stock. Similar though less numerous instances of the sudden appearance of new inherited characters have occurred in nearly all the stocks of organisms that have been intensively studied by the experimental breeder—numerous strains of mice, rabbits, poultry, insects, and plants. The field naturalist and the practical animal and plant breeder have likewise encountered hundreds of new variations that seem undoubtedly to be instances of the same phenomenon, though experimental proof is lacking.

The term *mutation* is applied and often restricted to the appearance of a new variation due to the origin of a new gene.[2] There is abundant

---

[1] Inbreeding is the mating of close relatives and results in progeny that have fewer than the theoretical maximum of recent individual ancestors. The mating of cousins, for example, reduces the total number of separate great-grandparents from eight to six, and the mating of brother and sister reduces the number of grandparents from four to two. The intensity of inbreeding varies from a maximum with self-fertilization to a minimum with cousin mating, with numerous intermediate degrees, but all degrees of inbreeding tend to disclose any recessive genes that may exist in the stock.

[2] Originally, the term *mutation* was applied to the appearance of any new, inheritable

evidence that each mutation is the result of a sudden change in some previously existing gene and that only a single individual gene is concerned. Since the gene that underwent the mutation occupied one definite point (*locus*) in a chromosome, the mutant gene will now occupy that

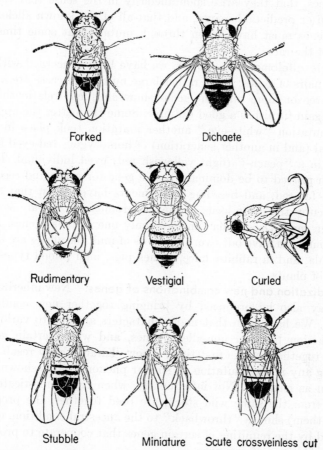

Forked   Dichaete

Rudimentary   Vestigial   Curled

Stubble   Miniature   Scute crossveinless cut

FIG. 21.2. Some of the variations which have arisen by mutation in Drosophila. (*From Sturtevant and Beadle, Introduction to Genetics, by permission W. B. Saunders Company.*)

point in all the chromosomes that are derived from the one in which the mutation took place.

We have no definite knowledge of what a gene may be and therefore cannot, of course, know what kind of change it is that produces a muta-

character, and it is still occasionally used in that sense, but today it is coming to be restricted to gene or "point" mutations, as distinguished from variations associated with chromosomal changes.

tion.[1] Most genes are remarkably stable, existing unchanged for hundreds or thousands of generations. When an occasional individual gene does change, the new mutant appears to have a stability very like that of the original gene from which it came. It is evident that mutations are real occurrences, that they arise spontaneously in the sense that they have no known or predictable cause, and that all of the known allelomorphic sets of genes must have arisen through mutation at some time in the history of the race.

Multiple allelomorphs.   So far, we have been concerned with allelomorphic pairs of genes; but a rather large number of cases are known in which three or more different genes show an allelic relationship. Drosophila again furnishes a good example. Some time after the appearance of the mutation "white-eye," another mutation took place in another individual (and in another generation) of homozygous red-eyed flies that resulted in a "peach-" (light yellowish red) eyed individual. The gene for peach proved to be dominant to the gene for white and recessive to the gene for red, and breeding experiments have shown that all these genes occupy the same locus in the X chromosome. All are sex-linked; any given male Drosophila can have only one of these genes, and any given female can have but two. Other sets of multiple alleles are known in Drosophila, and in rabbits, mice, guinea pigs, man (blood types), and a number of plants.

Hybridization and new combinations of genes.   New inherited variations may also be produced by bringing together new combinations of genes. We have seen that many characters are due to various types of interaction between non-allelic genes, and when certain genes are brought together for the first time, a new character may result without involving any recent mutation. A similar phenomenon is shown in what is known as *reversion*. Not infrequently, when two domesticated races, derived from the same wild stock, are bred together, the progeny (or some of them) show a "throwback" to the ancestral condition, evidently produced by the reuniting of certain genes that cooperate to produce the original wild type of organism.

HEREDITY AND ENVIRONMENT

We have distinguished among variations that are due to environmental causes and those that owe their existence and transmission to genes within the cells. This distinction, although thoroughly justified for analysis and study, gives an incomplete picture of the complexity of the whole prob-

---

[1] There is much inferential evidence that genes are some sort of protein molecules, or groups of such molecules, and that a mutation must be due to some change in the structure and hence in the reactions of the molecule or molecules that constitute the gene.

lem. Actually any organism is the product of both heredity and environment. We can produce variations either by keeping the heredity uniform and varying the environment or by keeping the environment uniform and varying (by crossing) the heredity, and many phenotypic qualities are demonstrably due to the coincidence of a particular genotype with a particular environment.

This is very clearly illustrated by the case of a garden flower, a red Chinese primula. In the primulas, there is a red race that, when crossed with a white race, gives a pink (pale red) F_1 and an F_2 with the ratio $\frac{1}{4}$ red, $\frac{1}{2}$ pink, and $\frac{1}{4}$ white—a typical monohybrid in which dominance is lacking. But if the red-flowered plant is taken from the garden and grown in a hothouse at a temperature of 95°F. or more, its flowers will be white. If 10 generations are kept continuously at this high temperature, they will produce nothing but white flowers in all this time; yet if the eleventh generation is returned to the garden, the flowers will again be red. Here the gene that distinguished the red-flowered variety from the white-flowered variety at lower temperatures is *not a gene for red but a gene to produce red at normal temperature and white at temperatures of 95°F. and above.*[1]

Many other genes are known that produce one quality in one environment but fail to produce this quality, or produce a different quality, in a different environment. There are also many other characters for which the phenotypic expression of the gene is dependent on the physiological condition (internal secretion) of the organism itself. This is well illustrated in the secondary sexual characters of animals. The natural type and color of a man's beard are inherited (through the mother as well as through the father), but if a man is castrated, he fails to have a beard, and although a woman has factors for a beard—as is shown by her transmitting to her sons the factors for her father's type of beard—she does not develop a beard. The same phenomenon is seen in the inheritance and appearance of horns in certain races of sheep and in the inheritance of the male plumage in birds. A very similar condition is seen in the case of at least certain types of goiter in man, where the development of goiter is dependent upon both genetic factors and the amount of available iodine in the environment.

What is inherited? In view of the foregoing considerations and of what we have seen of Mendelian inheritance, we can define inheritance as the transmission from generation to generation of a tendency to react in a certain way to (1) a given environment, (2) a given physiological constitution, and (3) a given complex of other hereditary factors; or, better, since (2) and (3) are also inherited, as the *transmission of a tendency to react in a certain way to a given environment.*

[1] Doubts that were cast upon this interpretation of the primula case have proved unfounded.

CHAPTER XXII

INHERITANCE IN MAN

Detailed and accurate knowledge of variation and inheritance in man would probably be of more practical worth than any other contribution biology has made or can make to humanity; but for practical as well as biological reasons, this is probably the most difficult and baffling of all fields of biological research. We have seen that the main key to a knowledge of genetics is experimental breeding—a method which is ruled out in our attempt to understand human genetics. Both cytological and statistical methods of investigation are most useful and efficient when they can be combined with breeding experiments upon the same stock of organisms. Moreover, human cells with their 48 chromosomes are much more difficult to study cytologically than are the cells of Drosophila, with their 8 chromosomes, or the cells of the other organisms from which our knowledge of cytology is mainly derived.

Most of our knowledge of human genetics comes from the scrutiny and statistical study of human pedigrees and from comparison of the modes of inheritance thus indicated with similar pedigrees in experimental organisms. Some special handicaps to this procedure lie in the following conditions: the small size of human families; the very slow reproductive rate, with an average of about 3 or 3½ generations per century; the markedly heterozygous constitution of most human stocks; and the extremely numerous and complicated factors that make up the environment of civilized man.

Heredity versus environment in relation to man. Perhaps the greatest difficulty of all lies in the fact that any individual man or woman is the product of *both* heredity and environment and that it is extremely difficult or impossible to know which of his or her individual qualities are chiefly due to heredity and which to environment. We can somewhat clarify the question by an attempt to analyze, define, and distinguish between the two effects.

Sir Francis Galton, who first attempted a careful analysis of the complementary roles played by heredity and environment in man, distinguished between what he termed *nature* and *nurture*. By *nature* is meant all the tendencies, limitations, and qualities that are bequeathed to the individual as maternal and paternal factors at the time of conception. Once a given sperm and egg are fused in fertilization, the full complement of factors is fixed, and the new individual's "nature" is irrevocably determined. From this time on, through the 9 months of embryonic development, through the early years of babyhood and childhood, with their psychological conditioning and training by example, through youth and schooling, many types of environmental influence are shaping the development and phenotypic expression of the particular set of factors that constitutes the individual's "nature." *The sum of all these environmental influences is nurture.*

Since both nature and nurture are absolutely necessary, there is no point in asking which is the more important for the *existence* of the individual. Their real antithesis lies in the different and complementary ways in which they determine the characters of the individual and in which they are or may be manipulated to modify the race. All the evidence from experiment, from checked observations, and from a detailed knowledge of embryonic development strongly supports the conclusion that only the individual's "nature" can be biologically inherited by his offspring. Not any of the influences of nurture, however much they modify, dwarf, or develop the individual, can in any appropriate way modify the factors in his germ cells. This is, of course, a declaration that *no characters, qualities, or modifications that are due to the environment or that are acquired by training, practice, or injury can be biologically inherited.* The only way an individual's nature can be determined is by controlling what factors shall be brought together when the zygote is formed, and this, of course, can be done only by selecting parents with the requisite genotypes.

It has just been stated that there is "no direct way" in which the environment can influence or change the nature of an individual or of a racial stock. There is, however, an indirect way in which various environmental influences can tremendously affect the genotypic qualities (average "nature") of a race. This is by *selection.* Whenever any environmental influence causes some group of individuals to reproduce more or less than its proportionate share of offspring, then that influence will increase or decrease, for the race as a whole, the proportion of whatever factors are peculiar to or are more concentrated in that group of individuals.

Among the numerous influences that civilization and social organization introduce and that indirectly and unconsciously cause selection in human stocks and in national or cultural groups are war, immigration, social and sanitary legislation, and a differential birth rate. We shall look at two of them very briefly.

War, as it was waged until very recently, must have exerted an adverse selection upon populations. The strongest and physically most perfect males were not only removed from the population during a part of their reproductive period but were also subjected to increased mortality hazards. Men unfit for military service were left to reproduce unchecked. Proportionately fewer of the (physically) better individuals and more of the poorer were able to transmit their genes to another generation.[1] Modern warfare, with its bombing of civilian populations, destruction of merchant shipping, intense industrial effort, and often general lowering of living standards, is a very different thing from the old conflicts between picked armies. What its hereditary effects may be is not clear.

The *differential birth rate* is one of the most subtle and persistent types of unconscious selection by society. Census returns from practically all civilized countries show that the various elements of the population do not reproduce their proportionate quota of offspring. On the contrary, there is almost invariably a definitely *inverse ratio* between the social, economic, and intellectual status of a group and the proportionate number of children it produces.[2] This is illustrated by the following tables.

NUMBER OF CHILDREN PER 100 WIVES IN SELECTED AREAS OF THE UNITED STATES

Areas and classes	Number of Children	
	Mothers of all ages at marriage	Mothers aged 20 to 24 at marriage
Urban sample		
Professional..................	151	148
Business.....................	152	146
Skilled workmen..............	178	170
Unskilled workmen............	213	206
Rural sample		
Farm owners.................	233	221
Farm renters.................	258	248
Farm laborers................	277	253

[1] Perhaps one of the clearest and least prejudiced discussions of the very complicated and controversial subject of the biological effects of war is to be found in *War's Aftermath*, by D. S. and H. E. Jordan, Houghton Mifflin Company, Boston, 1914. This is a study of our own Civil War and its effects on racial stocks.

[2] There is a huge amount of data in support of this conclusion, much of which has been summarized by S. J. Holmes in his *Human Genetics and its Social Import*, McGraw-Hill Book Company, Inc., New York, 1914. The tables here presented are taken from this work.

RELATION OF SCHOLASTIC RECORD AND ABILITY TO FAMILY SIZE
(Based upon a study of over 3,000 school children in one locality)

Scholastic record	Number of children per family	Rating for ability	Number of children per family
1 (best)	3.30	1 (highest)	3.28
2	3.47	2	4.03
3	3.81	3	4.43
4	4.24	4	5.05
5	4.11	5	5.15

The reasons for the differential birth rate are many, but most or all of them arise from the conditions and demands of modern civilization and particularly of urban life. Among the most obvious causes are the later age at marriage of those who are preparing for professional careers or who desire special and prolonged educational advantages; a sense of obligation on the part of more prudent and responsible parents to have no larger families than can be adequately provided with educational, social, and economic advantages; and the fact that large families are felt to interfere with various professional, social, and economic ambitions.

Whatever the cause of the differential birth rate, one thing is evident. A larger proportion of each new generation is produced by parents who have shown the least evidence of ability, and a smaller proportion by those who have shown the most—precisely the opposite of the method man has utilized for the continued improvement of his domesticated races of animals and plants. This leads to one more very important question that we can briefly examine. A question, unfortunately, for which clear-cut *human* data are very difficult to obtain, and in which many types of personal, religious, and social bias are likely to influence one's thinking.

Are the differences between men, which result in different grades of achievement and ability, dependent upon "nature" or upon "nurture"? Or, to put it another way, can society safely assume that it can maintain or increase the individual and social worth of its members by providing for the maintenance and improvement of *nurture* alone? If such differences as we see in physical vigor, longevity, temperament, mental ability, and social and individual worth can be explained by the differences in nurture, then selection by war, immigration, or a differential birth rate cannot produce any permanent injury to a racial stock. There is abundant evidence that such environmental factors as sanitation, medicine, education, material welfare, and a measure of leisure are of great importance, and that inequalities in sharing these advantages explain many of the differences among men. But the indications that the individual's *capacity* for mental, physical, and moral development is determined by his *nature* are even more clear-cut and unmistakable. Evidence from many sources indicates that men differ tremendously as to the kinds of genes they receive at fertilization and that this gene complement (nature) both limits and determines the extent to which they can utilize and profit from whatever type of nurture they encounter. There is, indeed, much evidence for the conclusion that the effectiveness of any nurture that society can provide is dependent upon the maintenance of a superior nature for at least a part of the population.

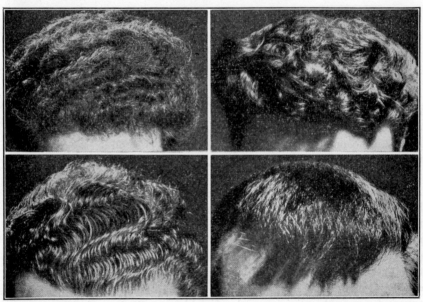

Fig. 22.1. The inheritance of hair texture. Kinky hair dominates curly hair, which dominates wavy hair, which dominates straight hair.

Some of the kinds of evidence for the biological inheritance of human qualities are as follows:

1. *Family pedigree*, in which physical and mental traits can be traced through many related individuals and the mode of inheritance correlated with known types of inheritance in experimental animals. By this method the inheritance of several hundred human characters has been clearly worked out. The difficulty here is that the method works best for simple cases of inheritance—unit characters and the less complex types of modifying and complementary factors. It is difficult to use in cases where there is complex interaction of genes or where environmental influences affect the phenotypic expression of the genes.

2. *Comparisons of the degrees of resemblance and difference between uniovular (identical) twins on the one hand and biovular (fraternal) twins*

on the other are a very good source of data because uniovular twins should have identical genotypes. Biovular twins should differ in genotypes as much as do ordinary brothers and sisters, and both types of twins should have the same degree of similarity of environment for the two individuals concerned. The evidence from these data very strongly emphasizes that most of an individual's capacities and qualities are determined by his nature; but this method gives little information as to the particular genes that are concerned or their mode of interaction.

3. *Results obtained by the experimental breeding of other animals may be applied to the interpretation of human heredity.* In all organisms in which experimental breeding and selection are possible there is positive and

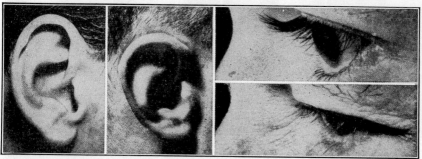

Fig. 22.2. Inheritance of ear size and eyelash length. Large ears dominate small ears, and long lashes dominate short ones.

unmistakable evidence of the role and importance of the genetic constitution (nature). Selection is demonstrably able to increase or decrease the learning ability of rats, the resistance or susceptibility of mice to cancer, and the longevity of Drosophila. It has been shown in these same animals that, so long as the genotype is unmodified, the environment can produce no permanent change in the stock. When we reflect upon how closely and invariably man's structure and functioning conform to the same laws and principles that apply to other organisms, it seems extremely unlikely that man would show a different relationship in the interaction of his nature and nurture.

The eugenics movement. Because of the promise for racial betterment that an application of human genetics would appear to hold out for society, many people have become actively interested in the effort to make such an application on the basis of our present knowledge. This practical program of improving the human stock through an application of the findings of human genetics has been termed *eugenics*—the science of being well born.

Theoretically, there is little reason to question the fact that *if* mankind could be subjected to the same procedures of rigid selection and controlled breeding that have produced our purebred strains of horses, dogs, cattle, and crop plants, he, too, could be molded into a wide variety of pure-breeding strains. Under this procedure, it would be entirely possible to develop a human race that would be homozygous for many desirable qualities and that would at the same time be free from many of the inherited liabilities that now affect many otherwise superior stocks. Actually, of course, this "if" is impossible, and it certainly would be undesirable. The qualities needed in a human society are far more complex and varied than those that are sought in any of the domestic breeds that man has developed; and the very uniformity so characteristic and desir-

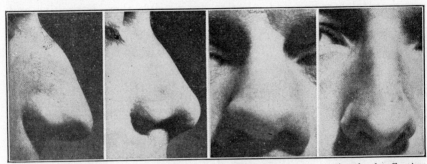

Fig. 22.3. Inheritance of nose form. At least three or four genes are involved, affecting different characteristics, of which two are here shown. Prominent nose dominates small nose; wide nostrils dominate slim (compressed) nostrils.

able in purebred races would probably be very undesirable in human society.

There are, however, many details and tendencies in human inheritance that do appear capable of practical management and control. A rather large number of human qualities or capacities that are known to be inherited can be clearly evaluated as definitely good or bad, no matter what the remainder of an individual's genotype may be. It is largely with such qualities that eugenics is concerned. It seeks to recognize and evaluate an increasing number of these qualities, to determine the precise mode of their inheritance, to discover the various ways in which they may affect the phenotype, and to weigh the practicability of the application of this knowledge by the individual, the family, and the state. Nearly every modern nation has its endowed or state-supported eugenics foundation, devoted to the discovery, dissemination, and ultimate application of the facts and principles of human genetics. Thus far, the practical possibilities of eugenics have hardly been evaluated, but within recent years new methods and statistical techniques have made possible a much more rapid accumulation of accurate knowledge. Here may be mentioned the increasing attention to human genetics in medicine and the importance that a knowledge of the patient's inherited constitution often has in diagnosing his condition and in indicating an advisable mode of treatment.

To date, much of the actual attempt to apply genetic procedures to race betterment has been of the sort known as *negative eugenics*, or the attempt to limit the undue increase of clearly defective stocks. A number of human qualities that are unquestionably undesirable in any individual or member of society have been shown to be inherited. Among such characters are certain forms of mental deficiency, various types of mental derangement, and several forms of severe structural or physiological deformity that condemn their possessors to feeble-mindedness, incurable insanity, or completely disabling physical handicaps. The individual who has inherited such defects not only constitutes a noncontributing burden to society (and often to himself) but also carries a germ plasm that will reproduce the same kind of unfortunate and unwanted individuals in the next generation or that will contaminate any better germ plasm with which it may be mixed. The fact that such defective individuals are often incapable of the personal or social responsibility that would lead them to refrain from reproduction places the responsibility upon society and the state.

Two possible methods of state control of defective potential parents have been suggested and to some extent practiced. Defective individuals who owe their condition to a defective germ plasm can be segregated from any opportunity for mating, or such individuals can be made permanently sterile by a surgical operation. The expense and difficulty of segregation are so great that it is hardly practical, but modern surgical techniques have perfected a relatively simple and safe operation that produces complete sterility without interference with the normal sex life of the individual. Here, of course, we encounter a number of legal, political, and religious considerations that, whatever their validity from biological point of view, must be taken into account in any practical eugenics program.

Part III: THE CHANGING GENERATIONS

THE EVOLUTION OF LIFE IN TIME AND SPACE

Darwin — The origin of Species

Readers Digest — march — 1947 — Gods
newest evidence — P. 39

CHAPTER XXIII

THE EVOLUTIONARY CONCEPT

In Part I of this book we began our survey of the world of life by examining individual organisms at close hand to see how they are built and how they work. Then, in Part II, we stepped back a little so as to see them, with their parents and progeny, as links in a continuous chain of heredity. Now we change our viewpoint once again. We climb to a hilltop, so to speak, whence we may see the whole panorama of life in broad prospect and trace the paths it has traveled since it emerged from the mists of primordial time. We shall see from the fossils of the dead how the processions divided and wandered, how their courses were guided by environment, what multitudes of them followed routes that led to extinction, and how the changed descendants of ancient stocks form the living populations of the present. We shall note how the generations changed by almost imperceptible degrees, through slow modification of the germ plasm over the eons. We shall consider especially the ancestral stocks from which the human species has emerged, and we shall examine the causes and conditions responsible for the changes, and the consequences of the blood relationship that exists among organisms by virtue of their common ancestry. All these aspects of life are summed up in the phrase *organic evolution*, which is the theme of this third section of the book.

The variety and multiplicity of living things.   One of the most striking phenomena of life is the tremendous number of different kinds of organisms that exists today. Just how many kinds of animals and plants there are we do not know. More than one million species[1] have already been described and named, however, and it is not improbable that an equal number remains to be discovered. Within this vast array we encounter the widest variations in size, form, degree of complexity, methods of self-maintenance and reproduction, and relation to other organisms. The size range extends from the ultramicroscopic to such enormous living things as whales and sequoia trees. At one end of the scale of complexity are the single-celled bacteria, in which not even a nucleus is visible; at the other are animals and plants made up of billions of special-

---

[1] According to a careful recent estimate, there are at least 750,000 described species of animals and more than 600,000 described species of plants.

ized, highly integrated, cooperating cells. Inside the limitations imposed by the two great nutritional methods—food manufacture in plants and food capture in animals—there are great differences in the arrangements for doing the tasks necessary for individual maintenance, accompanied by striking modifications in body form and organization. As for environment, animals and plants live in almost every conceivable type of terrestrial and aquatic situation. The seas, the streams and lakes, the soil, the forests and grasslands—all are populated by myriads of living creatures. Even the driest deserts, the arctic wastes, the lightless depths of the ocean, and steaming hot springs are not without their inhabitants.

Fig. 23.1. "One of the most striking phenomena of life is the tremendous number of kinds of organisms." (*Rearranged from a picture by Artzybasheff, jacket of Hegner, Parade of the Animal Kingdom, by permission The Macmillan Company.*)

The existence of so many and such varied forms of life poses important problems. How did all these kinds of animals and plants come into existence? What is the explanation of the orderliness that underlies their diversity—of the graded degrees of resemblance between organisms that permit us to classify them in a systematic hierarchy? How does it happen that each species is adapted to exist in some particular sort of environment? And that while adaptation is sometimes extraordinarily perfect, it is also sometimes faulty or incomplete? Why should each species inhabit only some particular part of the earth's surface and be absent from other places where it could equally well exist?

Such questions as these are of major concern to the biologist. To find their answers has been no easy task; many of the answers are still not fully known. Our present understanding of them has been obtained by putting together the results of a great many different lines of research. These include the study of fossil records of past life and their sequence in time; detailed comparisons of the structure and function of organisms in the search for fundamental similarities; analysis of the variation within species including its causes and mode of inheritance; and studies of populations with regard to environmental influences exerted by such factors as selection and isolation. All branches of biology and many of the other sciences have contributed important data. And from all this work, carried out by scientists of many countries over a long period of time, one great unifying concept has emerged—the *principle of organic evolution*. It will be worth while to review the steps by which this principle became established.

THE DEVELOPMENT OF THE DOCTRINE OF ORGANIC EVOLUTION

Practically all scientists and most educated persons now accept organic evolution as an established principle. It has not long held this status, however, and even today many people who lack biological background and the objective viewpoint of science refuse to admit its truth. The reason why this attitude toward evolution survives, while other scientific generalizations of similar scope are unquestioningly accepted, lies in the conscious or unconscious assumption that man is something wholly apart from the rest of the living world—that he differs qualitatively from other organisms and is, so to speak, the center and apex of creation. To people who feel thus, anything that shows man to be related to the rest of the animal kingdom, however remotely, is disturbing and objectionable, or even sacrilegious, if one takes the Mosaic account of creation literally.

In relation to organic evolution the *objectivity* of science has often come squarely into conflict with popular belief and emotion, producing bitter controversies that are now fortunately almost a thing of the past. The historic background of the unnecessary conflict between science and religion will be traced in brief outline, together with the nature of the evidence that forced men of science to accept the reality of evolution. Here we shall once again see the scientific method at work—the accumulation of observations that cried out for explanation, the somewhat groping formulation of hypotheses to account for them, the testing and revision of these hypotheses, and the eventual discarding of all but one, which became established in modified form as an accepted principle.

Early evolutionary speculation. From the earliest times men have sought a satisfying explanation of the universe and of their own place and significance in the scheme of things. Prior to the development of science it was natural that their explanations generally took the form of nature myths, in which plants, animals, and men were created by some supernatural agency. Such creation myths have arisen among nearly all primitive peoples. However, evolution has left so many clues and traces that we can scarcely suppose that they passed altogether unnoticed. It is probable that an occasional exceptionally acute observer and profound thinker must have caught glimpses of the truth even before the dawn of history.

However this may be, the oldest records of evolutionary speculations that have come down to us are the ideas of certain Greek philosophers of the sixth and fifth centuries B.C. These men had little biological knowledge to guide them and were groping in the dark. Their ideas were extremely vague, and, although interesting, were not really anticipatory of modern evolutionary doctrine as is sometimes claimed. During this early period of Greek philosophy a materialistic attitude prevailed, and purely natural causes were sought for all phenomena—a viewpoint not far removed from that of modern science. Later, under the influence of Socrates and Plato, a reaction took place. Material phenomena came to be regarded as the mere outward expression of abstract ideas, which were the true realities. Aristotle (350 B.C.), the greatest of the Greek natural philosophers, was the prime exponent of this view. Scientist as well as philosopher, Aristotle knew more about animals and plants than any man of his time or for generations to follow. He wrote a detailed treatise on the animals known to him, including many accurate observations on their anatomical structure. Through his wide acquaintance with organisms and his use of the comparative method of study, he was aware of the fact that they form graded series from lower to higher types of organization, and he drew from this the correct inference that they have evolved. He looked upon their evolution from lower to higher grades, however, as a striving toward the expression of an ideal "archetype" established by a supreme intellect.

The doctrine of special creation.   After this early flowering of science in Greece more than fifteen centuries elapsed before progress in biology was resumed. This long interval saw the rise and fall of Rome, with its essentially utilitarian philosophy, the barbarian conquests, and the confusion of the Middle Ages. During this time paganism was supplanted by Christianity throughout nearly the whole of Europe, and the church grew immensely in authority. Religion, commerce, and war were dominant in men's thoughts, leaving scant room for science.

The crusades during the eleventh to the thirteenth centuries brought the Western peoples into contact with the Arabs, among whom such sciences as mathematics, astronomy, and medicine had been carried to a rather high development. This may have had something to do with the intellectual revival in Europe that began in the eleventh century and culminated in the Renaissance during the fifteenth and sixteenth centuries. Now that men's interest and intellectual curiosity began once more to turn to the world of nature, they were furnished with a ready-made explanation of the origin of living things—the Mosaic account of creation given in the Bible. Not only was this the official and respectable belief but, infused during youthful training, it seemed to make any other explanation of the origin and diversity of life unnecessary.

For more than a millennium, from the Middle Ages until about the middle of the last century, the great majority of people in Christian lands thought that the world had been suddenly created only a few thousand years ago. The church eventually lent its authority to the literal interpretation of the story of creation told in the book of Genesis, according to which all the species of animals and plants were created to populate the newly formed earth, with the making of man as the last and crowning event. It was only about 300 years ago that Archbishop Ussher, a church authority, calculated that creation occurred in the year 4004 B.C., and even determined the day and hour when man was called into being. This date is still to be found as a marginal notation in some editions of the Bible.

The theory of catastrophism. From the time of the Renaissance onward, more and more persons became interested in the study of the earth and of the organisms that inhabit it. It had long been known that the rock layers were filled with objects that looked very much like shells, bones, and other parts of animals. Many of these *fossils*,[1] found far from the sea and even high up on the flanks of mountains, nevertheless had the appearance of creatures that once lived in the sea. Others were altogether strange; some of these were great toothlike or bonelike objects unlike the teeth or bones of any known creature.

With the renewal of interest in natural phenomena, a controversy sprang up over the nature of these "fossilia." As early as the fifteenth century the versatile artist, inventor, and scientist Leonardo da Vinci correctly interpreted them. Such interpretations were, however, so unorthodox that many curious hypotheses were advanced by others to explain in a less disturbing manner the occurrence of fossils. Eventually, however, the conclusion could no longer be resisted that they actually were the remains of animals long dead.

As knowledge of comparative anatomy increased it became possible to assemble and fit together fossil bones to form more or less complete skeletons, from which the appearance of the animals in life could be deduced. Many of the types so reconstructed proved to be unlike anything that now exists, either in Europe or, as exploration gradually showed, anywhere else in the modern world. The early reconstructions of fossils were, to be sure, often faulty and sometimes bizarre, but this served merely to exaggerate an essentially true conclusion—that many animals

[1] From the Latin *fossilium*, "something dug up."

which formerly existed have since completely disappeared. Today this idea of extinction is so familiar that we can hardly imagine how strange and revolutionary it then seemed.

At about this time many people realized that the occurrence of extinct types of fossil animals in the rocks need not conflict with but might actually support the Biblical account, if it were assumed that they were the remains of those killed by the Noachian deluge and buried in its sediments. Soon, however, it developed that each great rock formation had types of fossils that did not occur in the layers above and below it. Furthermore, there began to be much evidence that the earth had been in existence considerably longer than a few thousand years. Confronted by these difficulties, the adherents of special creation advanced the theory of *catastrophism*—the idea that there had been a succession of great catastrophes, in which all the life of the time was destroyed by flood or fire, followed each time by a new creation of other and higher types. According to this hypothesis the creation recorded in Genesis was the culmination of a series of such acts, and the Noachian deluge was the last of the great catastrophes. Unfortunately for this view, a new interpretation of earth history was shortly to appear and sweep away the assumptions upon which the whole concept was based.

The establishment of the uniformitarian principle.   While the leading geologists of the time were still engaged in heated debate concerning the nature of the catastrophes supposed to have overwhelmed the earth at intervals, there occurred an epoch-making event in the history of science. This was the appearance of a paper entitled "Theory of the Earth," presented in 1785 to the Royal Society of Edinburgh by James Hutton. In later years Hutton expanded and revised this treatise, and it was published as a two-volume work in 1795. It laid the foundation upon which the modern science of geology has been built.

Like so many of the great amateurs of science, Hutton had been trained in medicine. He was much interested in natural history and for many years devoted a great deal of time to the study of meteorology, mineralogy, and geology. His observations gradually led him to a new concept of earth history, in which catastrophism had no place.

Where others had seen in rivers merely streams of water which of course flowed in valleys, since these were the lowest parts of the land, Hutton realized that the rivers themselves had *made* their valleys by cutting down their beds and by carrying away the weathered rock washed down the valley sides by rain. In place of the accepted idea that the rock strata represented the deposits left by universal floods, Hutton's conclusion was that they were the weathered products of the land, eroded away and carried into former seas by former rivers. They had been laid down on the sea floor in the same way that muds and sands were being deposited in his own time off the mouths of the Scottish estuaries. He saw how the storm waves beat against the shore, undermining the sea cliffs and grinding up the boulders that fell from them into sand and mud that joined the other deposits on the bottom.

Nowhere did Hutton find traces of world-wide cataclysms or of the operation of any processes that could not be seen at work today. It was true that the lands showed evidence that sea-laid sediments, consolidated into rock, had been disrupted, upheaved, and injected with veins and masses of molten rock through the agency of subterranean heat. But these effects had been more or less local and were evidently akin to those produced by present-day volcanoes. Furthermore, earth processes appeared to *repeat* themselves in never-ending cycles. No sooner were new lands uplifted above the sea than atmospheric decay and stream erosion must once more begin to destroy them and make new rock layers from their debris.

Thus Hutton found evidence everywhere of the slow, long-continued, and orderly working of familiar everyday processes. He was forced to conclude that the geological forces that had been at work in the past were largely the same as those now operative. In a well-worn phrase, "study of the present is the key to the past." This thesis, christened *uniformitarianism*, is today accepted with but slight modification as a fundamental principle in geology, at least for all that part of earth history during which life has existed.

Let us pause here to note that the discovery of this principle resulted largely from two qualities of Hutton's work—continued, detailed, and critical observation of natural phenomena, unbiased by preconceptions; and a cautious and sober attitude in attempting to explain the facts thus gathered. It is perhaps significant in this connection that Hutton was Scotch in nationality. He and his followers merely applied in science a rule old in logic but often violated in early geological speculation and even today in ordinary thinking. This is the *rule of minimum hypotheses*,[1] which may be stated as follows: Of all conceivable hypotheses that can be made to explain a given set of facts, those are to be preferred which (1) are most consistent with the data, (2) remove the most difficulties, (3) are simplest, and (4) require the fewest assumptions. The hypothesis (now the principle) of uniformitarianism met these requirements admirably, whereas the hypothesis of catastrophism failed to do so.

Hutton's work at first attracted little attention, partly because the style of his writing was involved and difficult. The wide influence that

---

[1] Special application of the logical principle enunciated by Duns Scotus and later emphasized by William of Occam (1347 A.D.), after whom it is called "Occam's razor": *Entia praeter necessitatem non sunt multiplicanda*—"the number of entities should not be increased unnecessarily."

his ideas eventually exerted was brought about by two other men, John Playfair and Sir Charles Lyell. In 1802, Playfair published his *Illustrations of the Huttonian Theory of the Earth*, in which the uniformitarian thesis was further explained and developed, and documented with numerous detailed and concrete examples. Catastrophism held sway for another 30 years, until Lyell's *Principles of Geology* (1830 to 1833) converted most geologists to uniformitarianism. Lyell, the founder of modern geology, at the age of sixty, was one of the first to accept Darwin's ideas about evolution.

The length of geologic time.   Hutton, Playfair, Lyell, and the other men who helped to create the modern science of geology all served to prepare the way for the establishment of evolution as a fundamental biological principle. So long as earth history could be supposed to have comprised only a few thousands of years, or so long as men could take refuge in the idea that sudden departures from the "order of nature" were possible, the mind could still accept a belief in special creation without too much strain. But the establishment of uniformitarianism changed all this. Since, according to this principle, small and slowly acting forces have worn away mountains and filled up the seas with their debris, it must follow as a necessary corollary that geologic time has been immensely long. In our own day we have become inured to the incomprehensibly huge figures used by the modern astronomer and geologist in relation to space and time, and it is hard for us to realize the shock that it was to an earlier generation, accustomed to thinking in terms of mere hundreds or thousands of years, to find that the world was so immensely old. Hutton himself was awed by the vista that his studies had revealed. In his own words:

When, to a scientific view of the subject, we join the proof which has been given that in all quarters of the globe, in every place upon the surface of the earth, there are the most undoubted marks of the continued progress of those operations which wear away and waste the land, both in its heighth and in its width, its elevations and extensions, and that for a space of duration in which our measures of time are lost, we must sit down contented with this limitation of our retrospect, as well as prospect, and acknowledge that it is in vain to seek for any computation of the time during which the materials of this earth have been prepared in a preceding world, and collected in the bottom of a former sea.

The idea that geologic time has been very long, so revolutionary in those days, has now become a textbook commonplace. Although to Hutton the attempt to measure geologic time seemed vain, men have by now succeeded even in doing this. By combining all that astronomers, physicists, chemists, and geologists have learned about the subject, it has been determined that the earth was born from the sun, probably about 2 billion 500 million years ago, and that as early as 1 billion 800 million years ago it had reached something like its present physical state and may have been capable of supporting life. Actual traces of life have been found in rocks that, by the best methods of estimate, are between 600 and 900 million years old. One need not take these figures too literally; they are chiefly of interest as indicative of the general order of time magnitudes involved. Probably no one would be seriously perturbed if it were found necessary to cut the estimates in half. From the standpoint of the biologist it would seem of little moment whether life has endured for 1,800 million, 1,000 million, or even a mere 500 million years; any of these times seems amply long to have permitted the occurrence of the changes in life that are recorded in the rocks.

Attempts to formulate an evolutionary hypothesis. Although no satisfactory theory of evolution could be formulated prior to the establishment of the uniformitarian principle and recognition of the great age of the earth, one should not suppose that evolutionary speculation remained at a standstill until after the appearance of Hutton's work. All through the eighteenth century, developments in many branches of science made it increasingly evident that the doctrine of special creation was inadequate. As geological exploration widened, the abrupt breaks between the faunas of contiguous rock formations that were supposed to have been caused by catastrophic extinctions followed by new creations, were in many instances found to be bridged over in the rocks of other regions. In numerous groups fossils were seen to show a gradual transition from types quite unlike modern ones, in the older rocks, to other types increasingly like those of today in the more recent strata. Exploration of distant regions brought new knowledge of their faunas and floras. The tremendous number and variety of kinds of organisms came to be more fully appreciated, and it eventually became certain that most of the fossil types were no longer living anywhere on earth. Comparative anatomical studies were revealing a multitude of concealed but fundamental resemblances between superficially unlike animals and plants. Unexplained likenesses were being found between the early embryonic stages of animals that differed greatly as adults. The doctrine of special creation offered no satisfactory explanation of these and great numbers of other new facts, which were to fall so neatly into place and acquire so clear a significance under the theory of evolution.

More and more persons came to feel that these phenomena must have some meaning, if it could only be grasped; and by the latter part of the eighteenth and the first part of the nineteenth centuries a number of biologists and naturalist-philosophers were seeking some consistent and adequate theory that would account for them. The earlier of these men were merely feeling their way, their ideas being very vague, incomplete, and speculative. In 1790, the great German poet Goethe put forth a "theory of metamorphosis" to account for the transformation of leaves into the parts of flowers. Between 1790 and 1815, Erasmus Darwin (the grandfather of Charles Darwin), in England, and Lamarck, in France, attempted to account for modern organisms by appealing to a long sequence of changes and modifications from more primitive ancestral stocks. By the second quarter of the nineteenth century such evolutionary speculation had become rather general. In 1844, Robert Chambers, a popular Scotch essayist, in his *Vestiges of Creation* made a number of very bold and stimulating suggestions as to the origin of present-day organisms and their relations to the fossil forms of the past. The poet Tennyson was probably influenced by the *Vestiges* when he wrote the following part of *In Memoriam*, sometime before 1850:

> Nature . . .
> So careful of the type she seems,
> So careless of the single life . . .
>
> . . .
> "So careful of the type? but no.
> From scarpéd cliff and quarried stone
> She cries, "A thousand types are gone;
> "I care for nothing, all shall go."

All this pre-Darwinian work suffered from two defects—an insufficiency of factual evidence that evolutionary changes had actually occurred and failure to show any adequate causes for such change. Biologists therefore found themselves in the predicament of having to abandon the idea of special creation because of its inadequacies, while there was still no acceptable alternative. The proof of the reality of evolution, the formulation of a theory capable of accounting for it, and the testing of this theory against the background of accumulated biological knowledge were the work of Charles Darwin, and constitute one of the great achievements of science.

THE ESTABLISHMENT OF THE FACT OF EVOLUTION

Charles Darwin was born in 1809. His education, in preparation first for medicine at Edinburgh and then for theology at Cambridge, gave him a very meager training in technical biology. By natural inclination, however, he became a good field naturalist, with a strong interest in geology as well as in animals and plants. He was particularly stimulated by Sir Charles Lyell's *Principles of Geology*, in which Hutton's concept of uniformitarianism had been made the basis for a new interpretation of earth history and processes. In 1831, shortly after he had graduated and when he was only twenty-two years old, Darwin accepted the unsalaried position of naturalist on board the British cruiser *Beagle*, which had been detailed to spend 5 years in making oceanographic charts for the British admiralty. Most of this period was spent in mapping the harbors and coastal waters of South America, and Darwin took full advantage of his unusual opportunity to study the fauna, flora, and geology of this continent. All the way from Brazil to Patagonia and thence up the west coast to Chile, he made extensive collections and recorded his observations, both along the coast and on long trips inland. Later, the ship spent some time at the Galápagos Islands, some 600 miles due west of Ecuador in the Pacific, and then returned around the world to England.

It was his detailed observations of the animal and plant life of South America, especially of the distribution of species on this continent and in the Galápagos Islands, that first convinced Darwin of the inadequacy of the doctrine of special creation and started him on the search for a satisfactory substitute. Returning from the voyage in 1836, he occupied himself with publishing reports on his observations and in bringing out a number of zoological researches that established his reputation as a first-rate biologist. Most of all he strove to find an acceptable explanation of the diversity of organisms and the peculiarities of their distribution over the face of the earth.

In Darwin's own words:

On my return home in the autumn of 1836 I immediately began to prepare my journal [of the voyage of the *Beagle*] for publication, and then saw how many facts indicated the common descent of species. . . . In July (1837) I opened my first notebook for facts in relation to the origin of species, about which I had long reflected, and never ceased working for the next twenty years. . . . Had been greatly struck from about the month of March on character of South American fossils, and species on Galapagos Archipelago. These facts (especially latter) origin of all my views. . . .

In October (1838), that is fifteen months after I had begun my systematic inquiry, I happened to read for amusement *Malthus on Population*, and being well prepared to appreciate the struggle for existence which everywhere goes on, from long-continued observation of the habits of animals and plants, it at once struck me that under these circumstances favorable variations would tend to be preserved, and unfavorable ones to be destroyed. The result of this would be the origin of new species. Here then I had at last got a theory by which to work.

Malthus had attempted to show that most of the social and economic ills of society come from too high a reproductive rate in man relative to available resources. This concept furnished Darwin with the clue to many of the questions that had been puzzling him and served as the starting point for his theory of natural selection.

"The Origin of Species." For 20 years more Darwin accumulated data from all fields of biology, sifting and testing it, making new observations and experiments, and looking always for facts that might disprove as well as support his hypotheses. Gradually he built up, on the one hand, a vast body of *facts* that demonstrated beyond question that evolution had occurred and, on the other, a *theory* of organic evolution that seemed to fit the known facts. During nearly all this period of intensive work he was in ill health and lived the life of an invalid and recluse.

In 1857, he ventured to submit a draft of his theory to a number of his scientific friends for comment and criticism. The following year, he received a manuscript from Alfred Russel Wallace, a young naturalist who was studying the distribution of life in the Malay archipelago. Wallace, like Darwin, had been particularly impressed by the diversity and the peculiarities of distribution of living things, and he, too, had chanced to read Malthus. His conclusions, reached independently, were much like those of Darwin but had not undergone the searching criticism of 20 years' study. Wallace asked that, if the paper seemed of sufficient merit, Darwin should present it to the Linnaean Society, not knowing that the older man had been working along similar lines. Darwin might have done this, suppressing his own work, had not his friends persuaded him to make an abstract to present along with Wallace's paper at a meeting of the Linnaean Society in July, 1858. The joint paper created a tremendous turmoil—the first great debate on evolution. The following year, in November, 1859, *The Origin of Species* was published.

In many respects modern biology may be said to date from the appearance of this work. Although some of the older biologists refused to accept evolution, it rapidly became established as one of the basic principles of biology—perhaps the most fundamental of all, since this single concept affords a common explanation and correlating factor for the findings from all fields of biological research. Its influence has been equally far-reaching outside the field of biology and has profoundly affected all science and philosophy.

The proof of the fact of evolution. *The Origin of Species* really did two things, though they were not treated by Darwin as distinct. First and most important, it presented proof that evolution has actually occurred. This proof consisted of thousands of laboriously accumulated facts that are understandable only on the assumption that the species of animals and plants are of common descent and have become different from their ancestors. This conclusion is now unquestioned by biologists.

The theory of natural selection. In the second place, *The Origin of Species* offered Darwin's explanation of the mechanism of evolution. In formulating this theory Darwin found his essential clues, first in the effects of artificial *selection* of variations occurring among domestic animals and cultivated plants and second in the concept (derived from Malthus) of *competition* for success in an overpopulated world. His reasoning was as follows:

1. *The Effects of Artificial Selection.* From a few original kinds of useful animals and plants, men have succeeded in producing a great variety of cultural races by breeding from those individuals that possessed the most desirable charac-

Fig. 23.2. Some leaf-mimicking tropical insects. Darwin sought an explanation of such resemblance in the theory of natural selection. Above, green leaflike katydids (Orthoptera). Lower left, a green leaflike mantid (Orthoptera). Lower right, four species of butterflies that resemble dead leaves. (*Courtesy Ward's Natural Science Establishment, Inc.*)

teristics. As Darwin was aware, many of the improved varieties have appeared at a single leap as "sports." Others (and Darwin believed these to be the more numerous) were obtained by breeding from those individuals of a variable stock that showed the beginnings of desired modifications, by crossing of strains, and by repetition of the selection through subsequent generations. Darwin transferred the idea of selective breeding to events as they occur without human intervention and sought for selective agencies at work on species in the wild state.

2. *The Theory of Natural Selection.* This, the essential part of the Darwinian explanation of the causes of evolution, rests upon the following propositions:

a. Overproduction of offspring. Animals and plants are enormously fertile; the young produced by each generation are many times as numerous as the parents. Yet the number of individuals of each species remains approximately stationary under natural conditions, showing that most of the offspring of each generation must perish.

b. The struggle for existence. Since more organisms are produced than can survive, there is *competition* between individuals for food and space. Also, since not all situations are equally well suited for a particular kind of organism, each individual must pass an endurance test set by those factors of the environment that are unfavorable to it. Which individuals survive and which ones die depends upon the outcome of this struggle for existence.

c. Variation and natural selection. The different individuals of the same species are not all alike. Because of this variation, some will in one way or another be better fitted than others to succeed in the struggle for existence. There will thus be natural selection of the more fit for survival and production of the next generation.

d. Hereditary transmission of characteristics. The survivors of one generation will tend to transmit their own characteristics to their progeny, including those characters that ensured their own survival. The less fit, most of which will die while young, will in the long run fail to reproduce themselves.

e. Continued change inevitable. Because of this natural selection, each new generation will show an appreciable increase in average fitness to the environment. But since overproduction of offspring and the struggle for existence operate anew on each successive generation, and since the physical environment does not remain fixed, *complete adaptation can never be reached*, and continued change must result.

f. Formation of new species (speciation). Not only will the descendants of one stock change as time passes and thus become different "species" from their ancestors but also, if some of the members of this stock meet the conditions of life through change in one direction and others through change in other directions, the different groups must end by becoming *different species*, though descended from a single ancestral species.

g. Nonadaptive characters. Variations that prove neither useful nor harmful to their possessors will be unaffected by natural selection and will remain as fluctuating variations about an unchanged average condition.

3. *The Theory of Sexual Selection.* Darwin saw that there were differences between the sexes of many species (for example, plumages of male and female birds, presence or absence of antlers in deer, etc.) which could not be adequately accounted for by the theory of natural selection. In an effort to explain such differences he developed the theory of sexual selection, according to which competition for mates (through combat between males or through choice exercised by females) determines success in mating and hence perpetuates some characteristics at the expense of others. This is a subsidiary theory with which we shall not further concern ourselves.

Our knowledge of the causes and results of evolution has advanced far since Darwin's time, as will become evident in what follows; but here let us note that Darwin's demonstration of the fact of evolution assures him a place among the outstanding scientists of all time and makes him perhaps the greatest of biologists. *Evolution* and *Darwinism* are, however, not the same thing. Evolution is a fact; Darwinism is a term used by biologists to designate Darwin's own explanation of the occurrence of evolution. His theory of natural selection has stood the test of time but proves to be only a partial explanation.

SUBSEQUENT MODIFICATION OF DARWINIAN THEORY

Neither Darwin nor his immediate followers stressed the distinction between the historical fact of evolution and the Darwinian concept of the interplay of natural forces that brought it about. The first great debates and controversies were fought out over the question of whether evolution was a fact. Nearly all attacks on the proposed causal factors were incidental, and with the establishment of the doctrine of the common descent and blood kinship of organisms, the many lines of investigation opened to study proved so fruitful of results and so illuminating for an understanding of biological phenomena that the analysis of the evolutionary factors was neglected. Biologists chiefly concerned themselves with new studies and interpretations of the data of comparative morphology, embryology, and distribution. A very strong impetus was also given to the search for fossil evidence of earlier forms of life and to the tracing of actual evolutionary lineages.

Other theories of evolution were also recalled—earlier ideas that had been suggested by the great French naturalists Buffon and Lamarck, but *ideas* that had been dismissed and largely forgotten because the *fact* of evolution itself was not accepted. Buffon had suggested that the obvious differences between similar forms living in different climates and environments had been produced by direct and appropriate responses of the organisms to their particular environments. Lamarck (and Darwin's own grandfather, Erasmus Darwin) had developed the much more complete and far-reaching theory that the use or disuse of any part of the body resulted in the increased development or partial atrophy of that part, that the changes thus produced in an individual were transmitted to the offspring, and that if the same pattern of use or disuse were continued for many generations, the changes would be accumulative and result in marked modification. In Lamarck's view the stimulus for use or disuse lay in the *needs* of an organism to cope with its particular environment. This theory, presented in 1802 to 1809, came to be known as *Lamarckism.*

Darwin himself accepted both Buffon's and Lamarck's theories as contributing factors for evolution and often appealed to them to explain evolutionary changes which he had difficulty in attributing to the operation of natural selection. Still other theories were advanced by various post-Darwinians, some offered as supplements to and some as alternatives for natural selection. All these theories are now largely abandoned and forgotten or else (like orthogenesis) survive merely as descriptive terms for certain real or supposed evolutionary sequences.

None of the early work on evolution was either designed for or capable of throwing light on the nature and limits of variation, inheritance, or selection. To Darwin and his immediate successors these factors seemed evident in nature and were appealed to in terms of logic and plausibility to explain the facts of the past history of life. Then, in the period between 1880 and 1892, Weismann brought forward his concepts of the profound distinction between *germ and soma* and of the *continuity of the germ plasm.* As Weismann saw and stressed, here was a complete refutation of all theories based upon the inheritance of acquired characters. Weismann strongly championed selection (in conjunction with variation and inheritance) as the sole cause of evolution. Much of his work was highly theoretical; but his distinction between germ and soma and his concept of the continuity of the germ plasm were based upon good though not extensive experimental evidence and were destined to be further substantiated by subsequent workers. Nevertheless Weismann's ideas were dismissed or ignored by many biologists, and particularly by the paleontologists. As students of the fossil record the paleontologists felt that they had strong and convincing evidence, even though it was indirect and circumstantial, to prove that acquired characters had been and are inherited.

We have not space to describe the long, interesting, and often bitter controversies that followed Weismann's distinction between Darwinian and Lamarckian factors, nor can we outline the various alternative or subsidiary theories of evolution that were advanced in the period between 1890 and 1910. Biologists were, however, becoming increasingly aware that they had little more positive knowledge of the processes of evolution than had Darwin and his contemporaries and that they needed far more exact information concerning the details and limits of variation, inheritance, and selection.

It was only when investigators shifted their point of attack that rapid progress in understanding evolution began to be made. Instead of trying to decipher the events and processes of the past, many biologists undertook to study evolution in living organisms, using experimental methods as much as possible. This phase of evolutionary biology is often described as the study of *speciation,* to denote its concern with the relatively minor and detailed differences that distinguish closely related populations—the strains, lines, and stocks of the geneticist, and the races, subspecies, and species of the taxonomist. Most of the resultant progress has been due to the research methods and observations of the geneticist—experimental breeding, cytological studies, and statistical analysis—supplemented by the accumulating results of modern research in ecology, biogeography, and classification.

We shall see that the study of speciation leads to a reaffirmation of Darwinian (or neo-Darwinian) principles, as modified by our now greatly clarified concepts of the limits and nature of variation, inheritance, and selection, and as augmented by certain other evolutionary factors that were only vaguely foreshadowed in Darwin's own writings.

Variation as the "Raw Material" of Evolution

As we saw in the earlier discussion of genetics (pp. 311–316), variations in organisms result from two very different sets of causes. Variations of one sort, often termed "modifications," are due to environmental influence. Those of the other sort are the result of gene or chromosome differences within the organism itself. Often only breeding tests can distinguish between the two kinds, for they may be very similar in appearance or in extent. The one invariable difference between them is that variation produced by the environment is not heritable, while that due to gene or chromosome differences is.

If we use the term *mutation* in the broad sense that includes both the changes of a single gene—point mutations—and the microscopically visible changes in chromosome structure or complement, we can say that *all inheritable variations are caused by mutation*. Although spontaneous mutations have long been known to occur in laboratory populations of animals and plants, it was not until 1927 that a means of increasing the mutation rate was discovered. In that year Muller found that radiation would speed up the rate at which mutations appeared, opening the possibility for experimental study of evolutionary processes in living species. It is now established that nuclei exposed to various types of radiation show tremendous increases in mutation rate—increases that are roughly proportional to the amount of radiation received short of that which is lethal. Certain chemicals, and to a lesser degree temperature shock, will also increase mutation rate. Both gene and chromosomal changes can be thus induced. The gene changes can be recognized and studied by subsequent breeding tests of the radiated individuals; the chromosome changes can be seen by microscopic examination of nuclei, and their effects can be studied by breeding experiments.

It should be pointed out here that such induced mutations are in no sense Lamarckian. The changes they produce are just as random and unpredictable as are those caused by other mutations, and indeed many of the induced mutations are the same as those that occur spontaneously (though at a very much slower rate) in laboratory and wild populations. By far the greater part of these and of all mutations are detrimental or lethal.

On the assumption that radiation simply accelerates the mutation rate, it now becomes possible to measure rates of mutation. It is found that many known genes and certain specific arrangements of chromosome parts do have a characteristic even though very low mutation rate. As might be expected, different genes show widely different rates. A rate of 1 mutation in 100,000 genes is comparatively very high; 1 per million or 1 per several million would be more nearly an average rate, and some genes evidently have a much lower mutation rate than even this.

When we calculate the huge numbers of genes per individual—estimated to be between 5,000 and 12,000 in Drosophila, and from 15,000 to 25,000 in man—and multiply these numbers by the estimated size of population and number of generations in even a short stretch of geological time, it may be assumed that the supply of inherited variations is amply sufficient as material for evolution. In this connection we should take into consideration the possibilities of recombination. As different alleles accumulate in the total gene complement of a stock—or to put it another way, as the amount of heterozygousness of an interbreeding population increases—the new combinations possible for the genotype of any given individual increase exponentially with each new mutation. Even though the greatest number of new mutations are detrimental and destined to be eliminated sooner or later, there should still remain sufficient viable and neutral or potentially adaptive new genes and new gene combinations to provide an ample supply of variability upon which selection may act.

Inheritance and the Mechanisms of Gene Assortment

The entire field of Mendelian phenomena and of the cytological mechanisms that account for them was developed long after Darwin's time. We now know that inheritance is particulate—analyzable into the effects of individual genes that (barring rare mutations) are transmitted intact and unchanged from generation to generation. Ample evidence has accumulated to establish the fundamental difference between germ and soma and the continuity of the germ cell line. The phenomena of segregation and recombination and of linkage and crossing over have been verified both by breeding and by cytological observation and experiment.

Inheritance still remains as Darwin conceived it—the transmission of qualities from parent to offspring, but it is now revealed as having an even more effective and far-reaching role in evolutionary processes than he could have postulated from what was known in his time. Segregation and recombination, in conjunction with independent assortment and crossing over, form an exceedingly effective device for disseminating mutant genes and chromosomes throughout an interbreeding population. Linkage tends to hold various genes together long enough to "try out" various patterns of gene combinations. The phenomena of recessiveness permit many genes that are deleterious when homozygous in certain gene combinations to be carried and transmitted in a heterozygous condition. Eventually they may find their way into other genotypes where they may have adaptive advantages.

When we add to these conditions the almost limitless series of permutations and combinations of genes which results from the operation of bisexual reproduction, it becomes evident that biological inheritance not only provides for the transmission of variation but also tremendously increases the genetic diversity of a stock. From this diversity selection, isolation, and the statistical consequences of segregation and recombination can set apart and fix, modify, or eliminate various portions of a once continuous and uniform interbreeding population.

Selection

The concept of natural selection was the central and unique factor of Darwin's theory. Its efficacy (or even its reality) has been the most violently and persistently debated topic in the biological controversies about evolution. As mentioned previously, Darwin, in his search for the cause of the tremendous diversity in natural forms of life, was greatly impressed by the analogous diversity in domesticated animals and plants. Here the marked differences between related breeds were maintained by controlled mating and had unquestionably arisen through man's more or less conscious selection of inherited variation. This was a clue to diversity in nature, if some natural selective mechanism could be discovered and demonstrated. Darwin found a second clue in the Malthusian concept of ever-expanding populations faced with static limits to the number of individuals which could survive. Applied to wild populations, he saw that this must result in a struggle to survive and realized that this could be a continuous and powerful agency for selection.

The concept was clear and plausible but, like variation and inheritance, hard to limit or define. Darwin's own skilled, accurate, and abundant observations of the actuality of high reproductive rates accompanied by static population sizes have been confirmed and extended; modern naturalists have accurately measured the population sizes and reproductive rates of many organisms. There is no question that most zygotes are eliminated before they can in turn reproduce. To demonstrate that this process of elimination is selective, and capable of leading to organic change and diversity, is a different matter. Darwin had to appeal to such obviously adaptive variations as would give an individual organism an advantage over its fellows in the struggle for existence. This would appear to leave such inherited variations as are neutral or of only slight advantage or disadvantage outside the effective operation of selection. Yet variations of this sort are among the most common and obvious distinctions between closely related forms.

. Here again the data of genetics and of modern natural history have given clearer insight into the role of selection, both as an independent

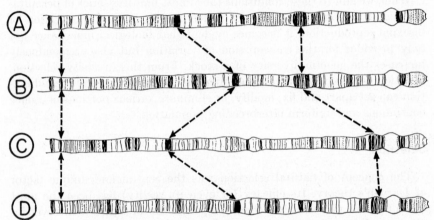

FIG. 23.3. Corresponding segments of one of the giant chromosomes in the salivary gland cells of four races of the fruit fly *Drosophila pseudoobscura*, drawn from photomicrographs. The differences between the four races, which occur at a single locality in southern California, are the result of rearrangements that have occurred in the section of the chromosome between the corresponding points indicated by arrows. Chromosome races *B* and *D* show little consistent seasonal variation in relative abundance. Races *C* and *A*, however, are best adapted to spring and to summer climates respectively. Selection therefore causes race *A* to decrease and race *C* to increase in spring, while the reverse change occurs in summer. (*From Dobzhansky, by permission Scientific American.*)

factor and as it acts conjointly with isolation, hybridization, and the play of mathematical chance. For one thing, this new knowledge has dispelled the faith of many of the earlier selectionists in the ability of selection to fix or make heritable the modifications due to environment. Today we know that selection cannot produce any change in a gene or chromosomal arrangement.

Selection *can* act as a screen or sieve, to favor or to eliminate any phenotypic expression of a gene or gene combination that is produced either directly or indirectly in an individual or a racial stock. We also now appreciate that nonadaptive or even deleterious characters may be favored in selection, when the same gene or gene complex also produces some advantageous quality or is closely linked to a gene that does. Numerous genes first known by their association with some visible phenotypic effect have been found to affect the fertility or the general viability of the organism and thus to be definitely vulnerable to the effects of selection.

Another (and largely modern) concept of the role of selection has to do with intergroup competition, as contrasted with the intragroup competition of classical Darwinian theory. A very large number of potentially interbreeding natural populations are from time to time segregated into more or less disjunct subpopulations, as will be briefly discussed in connection with isolation. After these subpopulations have been isolated long enough to develop some ecological or genetic deterrent to free interbreeding, they may again be brought into direct competition with each other. Here selection is particularly effective. It may result in establishing the better adapted stock throughout the common range, with disappearance of the less well adapted; or it may cause restriction and further fragmentation of the less favored population, which survives in those parts of a varied range where its particular characteristics are less disadvantageous.

Isolation

One of the great difficulties in the way of accepting segregation of inherited variations as an evolutionary process was to show how it could operate in nature. No mechanisms were known that would prevent the free spread of accumulating diversity throughout the whole of an interbreeding population. Accumulating mutations might well produce gradual change in a stock or increase its variability; but *speciation* requires segregation of variability into restricted portions of a population. What is needed is some type of isolating mechanism that is inherent in the conditions normally encountered by populations in nature.

This problem was recognized by Darwin and was emphasized by many of his immediate followers. They lacked, however, the data of genetics and ecology, and the detailed knowledge of geographical and ecological relationships of closely allied forms, that have enabled modern workers to deal with this difficulty.

Actually a wide variety of real and potential isolating mechanisms exists in nature. The most obvious and most fully studied and documented cause of isolation is spatial. Partial or complete separation in space (*geographic isolation*) has been a factor in the origin of many, probably of most subspecies and species. A once continuous range occupied by a continuous interbreeding population has often been divided by physiographic or climatic changes into two or more isolated areas, thus effectively restricting the spread of subsequently acquired genetic changes. Not infrequently a physiographic, climatic, or even a man-made change has extended the area or areas available to a population. When such new territories must be entered by way of narrow highways, or across partial barriers, the pioneer invaders will carry only a limited part of the gene diversity of the original population, and the barrier or restricted connection will tend to limit the spread of all subsequent mutations formed either in the parent population or in that descended from the immigrants.

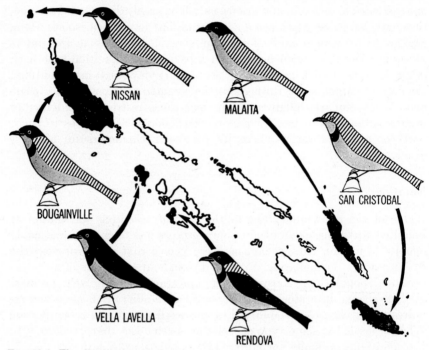

FIG. 23.4. The distribution of the geographic races (subspecies) of the golden whistler (*Pachycephala pectoralis*) of the Solomon Islands. The races are kept distinct principally by geographic isolation, which also permitted their original differentiation. In the bird figures barred is the symbol for green, gray for yellow. (*Modified from Dobzhansky, by permission Scientific American.*)

The changes that result from such isolation are neither necessarily permanent nor irreversible. There is ample evidence that changing geographic barriers or highways may first isolate parts of populations and later bring them once more together. Such changes may occur on both major and minor scales; microgeographic changes are constantly happening. What kind of change or how great a change is necessary to bring about isolation or reunion of populations depends on the physiological requirements and ecological limitations of the species population concerned.

Although geographic isolation can and does provide an efficient mechanism for speciation in itself, it appears also to be of great importance in conjunction with the other isolating mechanisms outlined below. It is the commonest (and some would maintain the invariable) first step in isolation. It provides an initial segregation, which may be maintained and strengthened by other mechanisms that continue to operate when populations more or less briefly isolated in space are once more brought into contact.

Many other kinds of isolating mechanisms have been discovered or have been postulated as a result of the findings of modern genetics and ecology. They may be broadly grouped as *physiological isolating mechanisms*, for in all of them it is some basically physiological difference that operates to prevent or reduce interbreeding with other groups. There may be some inherent difference in response to environment or to one another that reduces or eliminates opportunity or inclination for breeding. Or there may be structural differences that mechanically prevent mating, or genetic differences that make the offspring infertile or inviable.

Differences of all the sorts enumerated do serve to prevent effective crossing of closely allied forms that occupy the same geographic range. Whether such forms could have arisen from a common, freely interbreeding population without an interval of geographic isolation is a question not yet settled. There is little doubt, however, that all or nearly all of the physiological mechanisms mentioned are effective and important in maintaining the separateness of populations that are unquestionably closely related, although they now occupy the same or overlapping ranges.

Here also is an illustration of a fact that biologists are realizing more and more—*that there are many different evolutionary factors and that the sequence of events that has occurred in any one stock is not necessarily (and probably never exactly) the same as that which has occurred in another.*

Population dynamics

Another important factor or set of factors in the evolutionary process, which has only recently been appreciated and explored, lies in the mathematical combinations and permutations inherent in Mendelian inheritance. In the shuffle of heterozygous genes and gene combinations through successive generations, there are so many variables affected by the laws of chance that only the highly abstruse calculations of statistical genetics have revealed the importance of this new approach.

One of the important findings of these studies has been the phenomenon called *drift* by Sewall Wright, and referred to as the *Sewall Wright effect* by others. This is the tendency within a *small* interbreeding population for each gene that is represented by heterozygous alleles either to be eliminated or to become homozygous, even though neither of the respective alleles confers any adaptive advantage or disadvantage. Thus any small interbreeding population tends to become homozygous without benefit of selection; pure chance eliminates one allele and establishes the other.

If unopposed by a source of new genes (which may be either mutation or some degree of crossing with other stocks) or by sufficiently strong selection for adaptive value, genetic drift would result in the population becoming stable and unchangeable. Such a stock, stabilized without benefit of selection, would almost certainly show many poorly adapted or deleterious features and would be especially liable to extinction. It is probable that in most cases the conditions within a small population are such that drift is opposed by varying degrees of selection, mutation, and outbreeding. In this event drift will be effective only in establishing alleles of relatively small adaptive significance.

The real importance of the Sewall Wright effect comes from the fact that in nature most large populations are wholly or partly broken up into several or many subpopulations. The latter are often of sufficiently small size at some time or times in their existence to be affected by drift. Since drift is wholly random, it should result in producing a variety of differentiated subpopulations. The first phenotypic manifestations of many recessive alleles are likely to occur where these alleles have become numerous through drift. If isolation between the subpopulations is only partial, or if there are episodes of increase and spreading of the more successful ones, the existence of differentiated subpopulations sets the stage for modification of the whole species from centers where favorable modifications have become established, through *intergroup competition*. Sewall Wright has spoken of such centers as *population sources* and of the subpopulations which disappear as a result of intergroup competition as *population sinks*.

This résumé of the status of evolutionary concepts nearly a century after the publication of the *Origin of Species* has necessarily been partial and incomplete. Many of the most promising lines of investigation involve technical details beyond the scope of this book. Space prohibits any account of the interplay between mutation, isolation, selection, drift, and the changes in environment that may operate simultaneously or in sequence to produce diversity and change in populations of organisms.

Evolutionary theory is still essentially Darwinian or neo-Darwinian, with variation, inheritance, and selection playing vital roles. After this lapse of time the biologist knows far more than did Darwin about the source and limits (if not about the cause) of variation. With respect to inheritance, he has learned to distinguish between phenotype and genotype, and he knows now that inheritance is particulate. He has discovered the intricate and precise laws of combination and permutation that govern inheritance, and which are derived from the events, regularities, and random recombinations of meiosis and fertilization.

The large shift in emphasis from a study of macroevolution as it has occurred through great extents of time in the past, to the microevolution of today with its preoccupation with strains, races, and subspecies, is not so much a change in subject matter as of attack. Nearly all biologists are agreed that the process is the same and that the forces that are effective in breaking up more or less uniform, continuous populations into segregated, diverging subpopulations are identical with those that over longer extents of time have produced the many major adaptations and differences that distinguish the major groups of organisms.

CHAPTER XXIV

SOME CONSEQUENCES OF EVOLUTIONARY RELATIONSHIP

We have seen that one result of evolution has been the multiplication of species. This has resulted chiefly from the splitting of older species, and the geological record shows that this process has been operative throughout geological time. We may safely assume that a common ancestor could be found for any two species by going far enough back.

The blood relationships of organisms. We reckon kinship among men by the fact of common ancestry. Brothers and sisters are the closest of kin, only one generation removed from their common parents; cousins are more distant relatives, having common ancestors two or more generations back. So it is with species; the closeness of their blood relationship depends upon how far back in time their common ancestral species existed.

Of course, the kinship between even the most closely allied species is very remote compared to that which exists between cousins or even between all the individuals in a single species population. The common ancestor of species belonging to the same genus usually lived some thousands or millions of years and countless generations ago. We must go further and further into the past to reach the common ancestors of species belonging to different genera, to different families, and to different orders. When it comes to the origins of the plant and animal phyla, we can only surmise; they are older than the oldest geological records. Yet the whole trend of evolution suggests that life was once one, and that all creatures made of protoplasm are descended from the original living blob of that substance. If this is so, then every living thing is related to every other living thing by blood ties, near or remote.

What do we mean when we speak thus of "kinship" or "blood relationship" existing between individuals or species? Obviously this can mean nothing more or less than the presence of common genes, inherited from common ancestors. Close relatives share many or most genes; more distant ones have fewer genes in common. The amount of genic difference between any two species should, in a rough way, be a measure of the time that has elapsed since their ancestors were part of a single species population.

Viewed in this light, the existence of close and remote blood ties between species affords a genetic explanation for the homologous resemblances that they show. It accounts for the graded degrees of such resemblance, by means of which we can classify plants and animals in an orderly system of ranked categories. It explains the characteristic patterns of spacial distribution exhibited by groups of similar species. Lastly, it furnishes a rational basis for our use of homology, taxonomy, and biogeography for determining degrees of kinship among organisms.

HOMOLOGY AS AN EXPRESSION OF RELATIONSHIP

Determination of degree of relationship must be based upon detailed and critical comparisons of organisms with respect to their similarities and differences. The easiest comparisons to make are those of form and structure (comparative morphology). But we may apply the same methods to the study of development (comparative embryology) or of function (comparative physiology). Wherever we make such comparisons, we find a multitude of resemblances between species. However, we soon learn that the resemblances are of two different sorts, which must be clearly distinguished. Some are fundamental similarities which we assume are caused by the inheritance of a common stock of genes; these are *homologies*. Others are superficial similarities between only distantly related species, resulting from independent adaptation to similar environmental requirements and produced by wholly different gene complements. These are *analogies* and do *not* indicate relationship between their possessors. It is easy to distinguish these two kinds of resemblance in the abstract but sometimes not so easy in a specific instance. Let us look at some clear-cut examples of analogy and of homology; later we shall see how both may be involved in other cases of resemblance. Here we shall consider only form and structure.

Analogy. Structures that look alike and have similar functions but differ in fundamental plan and in embryological origin are said to be *analogous*, or to show analogous resemblance. Such analogous structures often occur in organisms that no one could mistake for close relatives. Thus both moles (mammals) and mole-crickets (insects) have digging front feet that are strikingly similar in form and function, but that differ fundamentally in plan and in embryonic origin. The foot of the mole is built like the hand of a man; its digging tools are the strong, flattened claws at the ends of the digits. The foot of the mole cricket is an insect appendage with characteristic exoskeleton and internal muscles; its digging prongs are spinous projections of the body armor. The similarity between these two feet is wholly superficial and relates to their use in burrowing. They show adaptive convergence in form.

Endless examples of equally obvious analogies could be cited. To name a few, there are the jumping legs of grasshoppers and kangaroos, the wings of butterflies and birds, the jaws of vertebrates and insects, and the "poison fangs" of snakes and spiders. Organs may be analogous without being very similar in form or they may be quite alike and yet unmistakably analogous, because they occur in organisms otherwise too unlike to be considered close kin.

Sometimes, however, closer study is needed to detect the analogous nature of a given resemblance. It is not surprising that the older natural-

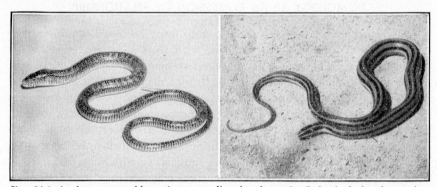

Fig. 24.1. Analogous resemblance between a lizard and a snake. Left, the legless burrowing lizard called the "glass snake" (*Ophisaurus ventralis*). Right, a true snake (*Conophis lineatus*) of similar appearance and habits. The two are both reptiles, but not at all closely related. (*Left, courtesy Zoological Society of Philadelphia; right, photo by Prof. Archie F. Carr, Jr.*)

ists grouped the whales and porpoises (mammals) with the fishes on account of their fishlike tails and streamlined bodies, or that they placed the bivalve mollusks with the bivalved brachiopods because of similarities in the shells. Some caterpillars could easily be mistaken for slugs (naked snails), which they closely resemble in form and in the possession of a creeping sole. The cephalopod mollusks (squid, octopus) have an eye which is very like that of a fish or other vertebrate. Certain legless burrowing lizards closely resemble snakes (Fig. 24.1); the burrowing blind lizards (Amphisbaenidae) and "worm snakes" (Typhlopidae) are blind and short-tailed and almost identical in appearance and habits. But all these cases of resemblance prove to be instances of analogy, when put to the test of structural plan and mode of development. All of them are the result of adaptation of very distantly related animals to similar modes of life.

Homology.   Structures that are built on the same basic plan and that arise embryologically in the same way are said to be homologous, or to show homologous resemblance. It is common to find homologous structures repeated in the body of a single organism. Examples are the spirally or cyclically repeated leaves and flower parts of angiosperms and the serially or radially repeated parts of vertebrates, arthropods, annelid worms, and echinoderms. Such repeated parts may be duplicates of one

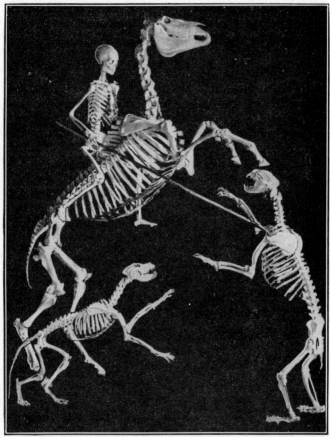

FIG. 24.2. "The Bear Hunt," showing skeletal homologies in mammals. Prepared by Charles H. Ward for the Chicago Fair of 1893. (*Courtesy Ward's Natural Science Establishment, Inc.*)

another or may differ strongly in form and function. Leaves, petals, and stamens are homologous in spite of their differences. The paired legs of centipedes are all much alike; but in such an arthropod as the lobster the homologous segmental appendages are modified into feelers, jaws, pincers, legs, copulatory organs, and swimming paddles.

Homology may also be seen in the corresponding structures of individuals belonging to the same species or to related species. In individuals of the same species the homology is complete, for the corresponding parts are nearly the same in all individuals. As the relationship grows less, however, so does the degree of homology that exists. When we speak of two structures as being homologous, it is not thereby implied that they are completely so. Homology ends where fundamental resemblance ends. This will become clear if we consider some examples.

The classic example of homology is that afforded by the forelimbs of air-breathing vertebrates. Whatever species we choose to examine—man, horse, dog, elephant, seal, whale, bat, bird, lizard, dinosaur, or frog—the skeleton and musculature of the forelimb prove to be fundamentally the same. All these limbs are modifications of one architectural plan—that

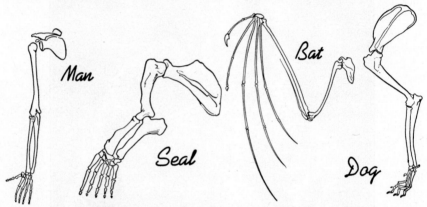

FIG. 24.3. Homologies between the bones of the forelimbs of mammals. (*Redrawn by permission from Schuchert and Dunbar, Outlines of Historical Geology, 4th ed., published by John Wiley & Sons, Inc., 1941.*)

of the *pentadactyl (five-fingered) limb*. All these limbs are therefore homologous.

Let us now carry the analysis a little further. Where relationship is close, as in dog and wolf, horse and ass, cattle and bison, crow and blue jay, or whale and porpoise, the resemblance extends even to minor details. Homology is essentially complete. In more distantly allied species, such as wolf and whale, man and blue jay, or elephant and dinosaur, the limbs are homologous in basic pattern but not in details of modification. In other instances the resemblances between vertebrate forelimbs prove to be compounded of homologous and analogous elements. An excellent example is that furnished by the winged vertebrates.

Three groups of vertebrates have the forelimb changed into a wing. In birds the flight surface is formed of feathers (modified scales) attached to an arm in which some of the digits are lost and the others are fused to form a stiff supporting axis. In bats the wing is a sheet of skin stretched between four elongate, outspread fingers and attached to the body and hind legs and usually to the tail. In the extinct flying reptiles, called *pterosaurs*, the wing was also a web of skin attached to the sides of the body and the hing legs, but anteriorly it was supported by an arm with a single enormously elongated finger, the fourth; the other fingers were small or lost. To the extent that all of these wings are modified vertebrate limbs based on the pentadactyl plan, they are strictly homologous. But considered as wings they are merely analogous; the adaptations for flight are unlike in basic design and do not indicate relationship. In terms of phylogeny this means that pterosaurs, birds, and bats have a remote common ancestry along with other terrestrial vertebrates but that each group independently acquired the power of flight, at different times and by different means.

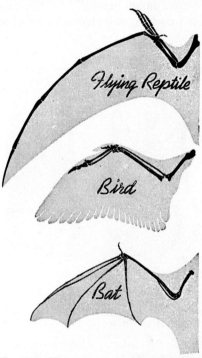

Similar instances of analogous resemblance superposed on more fundamental homologous resemblance are by no means uncommon. Various desert plants have succulent water-storing stems and a protective armature of spines. The stems and spines are fundamentally homologous with corresponding structures in other angiosperms; but their special adaptations to an arid environment have been independently developed in plants of different families and demonstrate only analogous resemblance. The digging legs of the Australian marsupial moles and of the true placental moles, the paddlelike forelimbs of penguins and of seals, and the lobed swimming feet of different groups of water birds (coots, grebes,

Fig. 24.4. Three vertebrate wings, to show that structures may simultaneously exhibit both homologous and analogous resemblances. Each of these wings is fundamentally a modified pentadactyl limb, and to this extent all three are homologous. Considered as wings they are merely analogous, for the modifications for flight are basically unlike and are known to have been independently acquired. (*Redrawn from Colbert, The Dinosaur Book, by permission American Museum of Natural History.*)

etc.) are examples of analogous modifications of fundamentally homologous structures. Failure to recognize the existence of such combinations leads to erroneous conclusions about relationship.

Vestigial structures. A special category of homologous resemblance is that which relates to rudimentary, or vestigial, structures. Both in plants and in animals it is common to find organs that perform no useful function. Usually they are reduced in size, and often they have lost essential parts. There are glands that do not secrete, appendages that cannot be moved, eyes that do not see, leaves that have no chlorophyll, and flowers that produce no seed.

The higher insects as a group are characterized by having wings. Yet a great many insects have wings that are too small for flight, or crumpled and useless, or reduced to small immovable pads. Sometimes the wings are completely lost, though the body wall shows where they were once attached. Most snakes have no trace of limbs, but in the python there are rudimentary hind legs projecting as blunt spines close to the vent. Whales have no external sign of hind legs, but within the body are a rudimentary pelvis and vestiges of leg bones. Birds typically have wings; but in some birds the wings are too small for flight, and in others only buried rudiments of the shoulder girdle and wing bones remain. Modern horses are one-toed, but traces of two additional toes exist in the form of splint bones along the sides of the foot. Many animals that live in the darkness of caves have eyes that are more or less reduced and often totally blind.

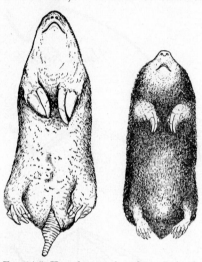

Fig. 24.5. Homology and analogy. Left, the African placental mole (Chrysochloris); right, the Australian marsupial mole (Notoryctes). In so far as these animals are both mammals, with all that this implies, they show a multitude of homologous resemblances. In their adaptations to a burrowing existence, however, they show only analogous resemblance, which does not imply a close relationship. The Australian mole is, in fact, more closely related to kangaroos than it is to the African mole. (*Courtesy American Museum of Natural History.*)

Man is no exception to the list of creatures possessing rudimentary organs. In fact, because his anatomy is so well-known, more vestigial structures have been described in him than in any other animal. Some authorities have recognized as many as 180; we can mention only a few of the more evident ones.

The *hair* on man's body is vestigial, since it is too sparse to prevent heat loss. Small *hair-erecting muscles* are attached to the base of each hair. In hairy mammals their homologues raise the hairs to make the fur coat thicker in cold weather; but when we feel cold, all that these muscles can do is to raise goose flesh. The *outer ear* of man is partly vestigial. It is not a good sound-concentrating funnel and cannot be turned toward the source of a sound. The *wisdom teeth* are becoming vestigial. There is hardly room for them in the jaw; often they never erupt, and sometimes they must be removed surgically. The *vermiform appendix* is notorious as a source of danger to its possessor. It is homologous with a large intestinal pouch or caecum that plays an important part in digestion among many herbivorous mammals. The *coccyx* is nothing more than a short, buried vestigial tail. The *pineal body* in the brain, although it may have acquired new functions, is morphologically a buried vestige of a third, median eye that was functional in the ancestral land vertebrates and persists in its original form in the lizardlike tuatera, a "living fossil."

The significance of vestigial structures is plain. They are homologous with structures that were fully developed in the ancestors of the species that possess them. Often we find their homologues still functional in related species living today. Organisms have rudimentary structures because they inherited the genes that produce them; the vestigial condition of these structures is the result of changes that have occurred in the gene complex. The presence of such organs demonstrates the kinship of their possessors to other species, contemporary or ancestral, in which the organs are or were fully functional.

Embryonic homologies.   When we compare the developmental stages of organisms belonging to different species, we find (1) that *embryos of related species resemble one another more closely than do the adults of those species* and (2) that *embryos of the "higher" groups resemble adults of the "lower" groups.* These phenomena are most clearly shown in animals, although the same generalizations apply among plants. We may illustrate them by describing an imaginary experiment.

Suppose we begin with a set of living zygotes, or fertilized eggs—one for each of the thousands of species of animals now living. Examining these zygotes, we find that although they differ in size and in the amount and distribution of yolk, all are single cells, and none shows any indication of the kind of animal it will be as an adult. Now we give the signal for development to start. Cell division begins at once. In some cases this is all that happens; the cells separate to take up life as single-celled organisms, which reproduce asexually until the time comes for conjugation and the production of new zygotes. These are the single-celled protozoans. Most of the zygotes, however, undergo rapid segmentation into smaller and smaller cells that stick together. The result is the production of a *blastula* (Fig. 15.13), which typically is a hollow ball of cells with its wall one cell-layer thick. A few colonial Protista, such as Volvox, drop out of the race at this point. As mature free-living colonies they correspond structurally to the blastula stage of higher animals.

Nearly all the remaining blastulae proceed to infold or invaginate and are thus converted into *gastrulae*. In its typical form the gastrula (Fig. 15.14) is cupshaped, with a central cavity (*archenteron*), a single opening (*blastopore*), and a wall two cell-layers thick (*ectoderm* and *endoderm*). The blastulae of sponges do not become true gastrulae but undergo a different type of infolding and soon transform into two-layered adult sponges. Some of the true gastrulae also soon change into adults without radical alteration; these are all coelenterates (Hydra, corals, jellyfishes, etc.). In them the blastopore becomes the mouth, the archenteron the gastrovascular cavity, and the body is two-layered (*diploblastic*).

Each embryo in the somewhat diminished company that remains now develops a third cell-layer (*mesoderm*) between the ectoderm and entoderm, thus becoming *triploblastic*. A few (comb jellies and flatworms) drop out of the procession at this point and become triploblastic adults with a gastrovascular cavity and a mouth but no anus. All the rest continue their development, but they begin to follow divergent paths. For our purposes we need trace only two companies of embryos— those following the chordate path, and those following the annelid-arthropod route.

In the embryos of each of these groups a new body cavity, the *coelom*, forms within the mesoderm; the body elongates and becomes subdivided into a linear series of repeated segments, or *somites;* and a central digestive tube, with anterior mouth and posterior anus is formed. In all other respects development follows quite different lines in the two assemblages.

In the annelid-arthropod group of embryos a solid, paired ventral nerve cord and a tubular circulatory system appear. The annelid and arthropod paths now diverge. In the annelids the coelom remains large, the blood vessels continue to be tubular, many somites are formed, and each somite typically gives rise to a pair of fleshy, jointless appendages. Further differentiation among these embryos results in the formation of adults of all the varied species of annelid worms. In the arthropods some of the blood vessels swell and fuse to form a huge blood cavity that surrounds the digestive tract and almost crowds out the coelom. A dorsal blood vessel is left to form the dorsal heart and aorta. A semirigid external skeleton forms from the skin, and some or all of the somites develop paired jointed appendages. Further differentiation separates successively the major and minor groups and finally the species of crustaceans, arachnids, insects, and so on.

In all the chordate embryos (Fig. 15.16) a tubular nerve cord forms along the dorsal side, with a brain at the anterior end. The heart develops ventrally; the somites become intimately fused; a stiff rod of cartilage, the *notochord*, appears beneath the nerve cord; and a matched series of pharyngeal *gill pouches* and external *gill clefts* is formed in the neck region. These things happen whether the embryos are those of fishes, frogs, snakes, chicks, pigs, or men.

Some of the embryos become adults at about this stage, and never develop a backbone. They are wormlike or vase-shaped marine creatures, whose kinship to the vertebrates might not have been recognized had it not been for the homologous resemblances between their embryos and those of higher chordates. The great majority of the chordates are vertebrates, and their embryos undergo further development. The notochord is replaced by a series of bony structures that become the vertebrae of the backbone, and eyes, ears, paired appendages, and other structures are added. By further changes the division of the vertebrates into fishes, amphibians, reptiles, birds, and mammals begins to appear, and the embryos of each group follow their own paths of development. Fish embryos have a shorter series of changes to undergo before arriving at the adult condition than do those of amphibians, which must pass through most of the stages shown by the fish before they develop their special amphibian characteristics. Similarly

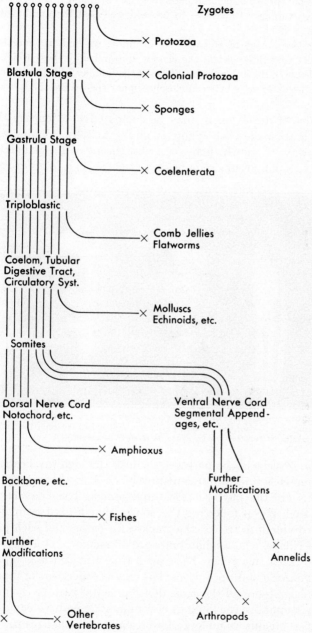

Zygotes

× Protozoa

Blastula Stage

× Colonial Protozoa

× Sponges

Gastrula Stage

× Coelenterata

Triploblastic

× Comb Jellies
  Flatworms

Coelom, Tubular
Digestive Tract,
Circulatory Syst.

× Molluscs
  Echinoids, etc.

Somites

Dorsal Nerve Cord
Notochord, etc.

Ventral Nerve Cord
Segmental Append-
ages, etc.

× Amphioxus

Backbone, etc.

Further
Modifications

× Fishes

Further
Modifications

×
Annelids

×
Other
Vertebrates

×   ×
Arthropods

Fig. 24.6. Diagram illustrating parallelism and recapitulation in embryonic development.

the embryos of reptiles, birds, and mammals have still longer series of embryonic changes to go through; they have to proceed well past the amphibian level of organization.

Whatever assemblage of embryos we examine, we find in general that the characteristics that differentiate the classes appear before those which separate the orders, those of the orders before those of the families, etc. Despite occasional exceptions, the differences between closely similar species are the last to appear.

The course of development may be compared to a journey that each individual must make from zygote to adult. At the beginning we have a broad highway, along which moves a vast throng of individuals traveling in company. Small groups soon begin to turn aside into lesser roads; but

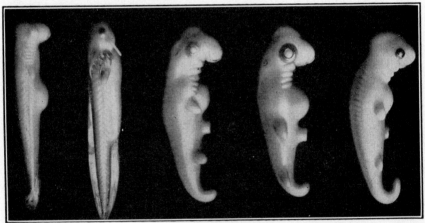

FIG. 24.7. Corresponding stages in the embryonic development of fish, salamander, reptile, bird, and mammal, showing the greater similarity that exists between the embryos than between the adults. (*Courtesy Chicago Natural History Museum.*)

most of the travelers keep on together until the highway begins to send off main branches toward different provinces. These provinces and their subdivisions are the phyla, classes, and orders. The body of travelers splits up, each group following the course that leads toward its home. The roads divide into tracks, the tracks into paths, and each path leads to a single village, whose inhabitants are all members of a single species. Those who reach this village have for a time traveled in company with others bound for distant provinces; but only the members of this particular species have followed the same developmental path to the end.

We may summarize the findings of comparative embryology as follows:

1. Simpler organisms undergo fewer embryonic changes to reach the adult condition than do more complex "higher" organisms.

2. Among the members of a given phylum the sequence of changes undergone by the embryo is (with few exceptions) invariable.

3. Within each phylum the "higher" forms undergo transformations that are similar to and follow the same sequence as those of the "lower" forms.

4. These "higher" forms attain their greater final complexity by (a) the *addition* of changes at the end of the original sequence and (b) the *modification* of earlier embryonic stages that they share with the "lower" forms.

5. The changes that every individual undergoes during its development from zygote to adult (*ontogeny*) run approximately parallel to the changes that occurred in the evolution of its ancestral stock (*phylogeny*).[1] This conclusion constitutes the *principle of recapitulation*. It holds true only in a very general way, as we shall see.

The meaning of recapitulation. To illustrate what is meant by recapitulation, let us consider the embryology of the frog. Beginning with the zygote, the frog embryo follows the beaten track of vertebrate development which we have already described. If we compare its successive stages with the adult forms of other organisms, the following series of structural resemblances can be seen:

Frog	Other Organisms
Zygote	Single-celled Protista
Blastula	Spherical colonial Protista
Gastrula	Coelenterate, such as Hydra
Very early tadpole	Primitive chordate, such as Amphioxus
Later legless tadpole	Fish
Late tadpole, with legs	Salamander (primitive amphibian)
Adult frog (unique)	

This does not mean that a frog is successively a protozoan, a coelenterate, a primitive chordate, a fish, a salamander, and finally a frog. It is truly a frog from the beginning, yet it does show these successive resemblances to organisms more and more advanced in the evolutionary scale —organisms which correspond structurally with ancestral stages in frog evolution. The geological record makes it certain that frogs came from salamanderlike amphibians, that amphibians evolved from fishes, and that fishes developed from more primitive chordates. There is no such direct evidence as to the earlier steps that led to the chordates, but the embryonic changes strongly suggest what some of them were.

Why should a frog (or any other organism) follow this long, complex, predetermined path of development and in so doing take on the temporary likeness of ancestral forms? And why is this likeness only partial? Perhaps

---

[1] "Ontogeny" (Greek *on*, "that which is," and *genesis*, "origin") refers to the origin of the individual. "Phylogeny" (Greek, *phylon*, "race," and *genesis*) refers to racial origins.

we can best answer these questions by considering the genetic implications of the observed facts.

We can trace the ancestry of the frogs back as far as the fishes, with some certainty; so let us begin there. Some hundreds of millions of generations ago there were no frogs or other amphibians but only various kinds of fishes. Some of these fishes, however, were the ancestors of the first amphibians, and from some of these amphibians came the frogs.

The ancestral fishes reproduced their kind according to the laws of heredity. They possessed a particular gene complex, which determined not only their characteristics as chordates, as vertebrates, and as fishes but

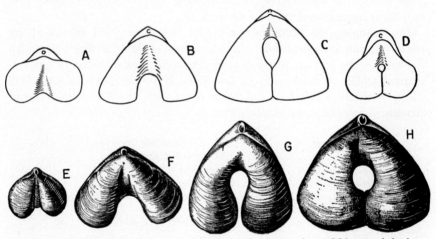

Fig. 24.8. "Ontogeny recapitulates phylogeny." Individual and racial history of the key-hole brachiopod. *A* to *D*, adult shells of species from four successive geological horizons in the Jurassic and early Cretaceous periods. *E* to *H*, successive developmental stages in the growth of a single Cretaceous species (*Pygope diphyoides*). *E*, young, *F*, somewhat older. *G*, more than half grown. *H*, adult. These growth stages correspond to the phylogenetic history as shown in *A* to *D*. (*Redrawn by permission from Schuchert and Dunbar, Outlines of Historical Geology, 4th ed., published by John Wiley & Sons, Inc., 1941.*)

also just what kind of fishes they were. This original gene complex was the basis of that now possessed by the frogs. Over great periods of time it was slowly modified by mutation, recombination, and selection. The descendants of the fish ancestors split into more and more kinds, each with a different set of modifications of the old hereditary complex. Today some of them are the frogs. The gene complex of these frogs is merely that of the ancestral fishes plus all the modifications that have taken place in it down through the endless generations. If the frog passes through fishlike stages in its development, it is simply because it has fish genes inherited from its ancestors. The same is true of the other resemblances its embryo shows. The fact that it fails to become a fish and instead goes through additional embryonic stages that make it a frog, is because of the gene changes and additions that have been incorporated into its gene complex.

Recapitulation is incomplete and distorted. Embryos are never replicas of ancestral forms but merely show a general resemblance to them. They often fail to show features possessed by their known ancestors and, as a rule, can scarcely represent any ancestral stage except in barest essentials. Ontogeny does *not* repeat phylogeny in detail.

It is easy to see why this must be so. Changes in the gene complex may affect the organism at any stage from germ cell to adult, and some or many are almost certain to affect embryonic processes. Furthermore, embryos have to live, just as do adult organisms. They must be adapted

FIG. 24.9. A larval insect highly modified for predatory aquatic life, shown seizing a mosquito larva. The adult is the familiar winged dragonfly (Odonata). The enormous enlargement of the lower lip and its adaptations for capturing prey are larval specializations added to the life history. (*Courtesy American Museum of Natural History.*)

to their environments if they are to survive and hence are subject to selection and evolutionary modification. The adjustments that embryos show fall into two principal classes—*changes in the rate of processes*, and *adaptations for life in special environments*.

Embryonic development must be completed in a matter of hours, days, or months, and yet it must accomplish the changes that are the result of millions of years of evolution. The developmental processes therefore tend to be "telescoped," partly by omission of stages, partly by the overlapping of processes which in phylogeny were successive. Such modifications tend to alter the historical sequence of changes, so that the embryonic record is not only condensed but often full of anachronisms. Thus in a vertebrate embryo the eye begins to form very early, far out of chronologic sequence, following the lead of the precocious brain.

Many embryos have developed special structures that enable them to feed upon stored food, to respire, and to dispose of metabolic wastes within an egg shell (Fig. 28.2). Obviously neither their ancestors nor themselves as adults could possess such structures. These are special embryonic organs, superimposed on the inherited ontogeny. Many other organisms become free-living in early stages of development. Such *larvae*, as they are called, must make their own living while they complete their development. Often they are enabled to live in environments unlike those inhabited either by the ancestors or by themselves as adults, through having special larval adaptations. Among many insects the larval structure has become so different from that of the adult that the change from one to the other is known as *metamorphosis*, or transformation. It is accomplished by the interpolation of a pupal stage into the developmental process. The larval body becomes enclosed in a protective case, the pupa, within which the entire internal and external organization of the larva is rapidly reworked into that characteristic of the adult.

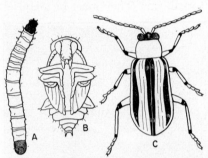

FIG 24.10. Life history of the striped cucumber beetle (*Diabrotica vittata*). *A*, stem-boring larva. *B*, pupa. *C*, leaf-feeding adult. This illustrates complete metamorphosis; the great differences between larva and adult are bridged over by the pupal stage, in which the anatomy is rapidly reworked. In such a developmental history as this the evidences of recapitulation are very much obscured and distorted. (*Modified from Turtox chart, courtesy General Biological Supply House, Inc.*)

Such modifications of the developmental stages as these may be thought of as things added to or lost from the original ontogeny. They often so alter and distort the pattern of development that the evidences of recapitulation become difficult to detect and interpret.

Physiological resemblances. Kinship is as clearly reflected in the physiology and biochemistry of organisms as in their structure and ontogeny. The well-nigh universal presence of chlorophyll in plants and of the process of photosynthesis dependent upon this substance is clearly a case of homology based upon common descent. Similarly we find in all vertebrates (and only in them) a type of respiratory-circulatory process dependent upon the presence of blood cells containing hemoglobin. In both these instances the portions of the gene complex responsible for the respective physiologic processes must be of great antiquity, since so many different kinds of organisms possess them.

Not all instances of physiological resemblance are homologies, however. Thus hemoglobin, present in the red blood cells of all vertebrates, also occurs in a few species of annelid worms and insects. This is clearly a case of physiological analogy, for the hemoglobin of these invertebrates differs chemically from any vertebrate hemoglobin and is diffused in the blood plasma instead of being contained in special cells. Furthermore, it occurs in organisms built on a structural plan very different from that of the vertebrates, so that there can be no question of close relationship.

Biochemical determinations of kinship. Since we know that each kind of zygote is predestined to develop into a particular kind of adult organism, it follows that the differences between organisms are inherent in the protoplasm of the zygote and of the cells formed from that zygote. These protoplasmic differences are the result of differences in the gene complex, just as truly as are the more obvious morphological and onto-genetic differences. Protoplasmic differences should manifest themselves in the nature of the chemical products of cell activity. Similar protoplasms should make similar products; unlike protoplasms should make unlike products. If we could test the degree of likeness in protoplasms and their products, it should give us a measure of the degree of kinship between the organisms tested.

Some very delicate tests of this sort have actually been devised and applied to a wide range of species. The most successful approach has been through the study of immunology, which deals with the reactions of blood to toxic foreign substances, chiefly proteins. Immunology is one of the borderline sciences with applications in many fields—medicine, physiology, biochemistry, genetics, and, as it proves, evolution.

In our treatment of the human body we have already touched upon the defenses against disease that are provided by the blood. One of these is the ability of the blood to form *antibodies* capable of neutralizing toxic foreign proteins and certain polysaccharides. These antibodies are formed after the entry of the foreign substance as a response to its presence and are *specific*—that is, made to order for each different protein or poly-saccharide. Any substance that can evoke this reaction is called an *antigen*. When we consider that for each of thousands of possible antigens a counterpart antibody can be formed in the blood of a single animal, the wonderful nature of this property of blood becomes apparent. It seems probable that the antigen must by its own chemical configuration in some way guide the formation of its counterpart antibody. Antibodies act in various ways. Those which furnish the basis for the tests of relationship here described are called *precipitins*, for they combine with the toxic foreign molecules to form an insoluble precipitate, thus rendering them innocuous. Analysis of precipitates formed with antigens of known chem-ical composition shows that at least some precipitins are typical serum proteins.

The general procedure for making precipitin tests of biochemical relationship is as follows. Some particular antigen-containing material is chosen as the basis with which others may be compared. Suppose that we select human serum as our base with which to compare the serums of other animals. First an *antiserum* (in this case an anti-human serum) is produced in the blood of some laboratory animal such as the rabbit, by means of repeated injections of small quantities of human serum or the proteins of human serum. When the anti-human precipitin has reached a high level of concentration in the rabbit's blood, the animal is killed, the blood is drawn off and allowed to clot, and the serum is sterilized by filtration and preserved for use as a chemical reagent. When a drop of this anti-human serum is added to a dilute solution of human serum, a dense white precipitate is formed. This simple and rather crude test has become routine procedure in crime investigation, for distinguishing human from other types of blood.

When the precipitin reactions were discovered in 1897, they were thought to be *absolutely* specific. A given antiserum was believed to react only with the serum used in its formation. If this were true, the reactions could be used for identifying serums but not for determining degrees of likeness among them. It was soon found that the reactions are instead *quantitatively* specific. An antiserum reacts most strongly with the antigen mixture used to produce it and progressively less strongly with related antigen mixtures in proportion to their degree of chemical similarity.

In the early years of this century Nuttall made some 16,000 precipitin tests of the blood serums of a large number of animal species. He used anti-human, anti-pig, anti-pigeon, anti-turtle, anti-king crab, and other antiserums as reagents. The general trend of his results was clear, and many of his findings have been substantiated by later work. His methods were not truly quantitative as he believed, however, and some of his conclusions have been shown by more precise later work to have been unfounded.

Some of Nuttall's more important conclusions were as follows: (1) the bloods of all mammals show chemical relationship; (2) man is most nearly related to the great apes and shows increasingly distant kinship to the Old World monkeys, the New World monkeys, the marmosets, and the lemurs, in that order; (3) all carnivores are more closely related to one another than to other mammals; (4) relationships are close within the families that include the pigs, the camels, the deer, and the cattle; (5) whales and porpoises are distantly related to pigs and much more distantly to other mammals; (6) among reptiles the turtles, crocodiles, and alligators form one assemblage and the snakes and lizards another; (7) all bird serums are chemically very similar and are closer to those of lizards and snakes than to the other groups of reptiles; and (8) the horseshoe, or king, crab, *Limulus*, is closer kin to the arachnids (spiders, scorpions, etc.) than to the crustaceans which it resembles. Except for (5), these conclusions are in accord with the indications of relationship given by morphology and taxonomy; but the relations of the whales and porpoises are probably with the carnivores and not with the pigs.

Modern techniques and instruments have greatly refined the precipitin tests and revealed sources of error in Nuttall's work. Using these new methods, the serums of many species of mollusks, crustaceans, insects, fishes, birds, and mammals have been compared. Within each of these groups degree of chemical likeness so closely parallels degree of taxonomic relationship that any marked exception calls for reexamination of both the serological and the taxonomic evidence. The amount of serological differentiation differs from major group to major group; all bird serums are much more similar than is the case in mammals, the differences between the *orders* of birds being comparable to those between *families* of mammals. This confirms Nuttall's conclusions as to the birds. The following tabulation, based on data from DeFalco (1942) and Boyden (1943), illustrates the parallelism between degree of taxonomic and of serological difference and the variation between major groups.

Level of Taxonomic Difference	Percentage of serological resemblance	
	Mammals	Crustacea
Species of distantly related families.........	5	4
Species of closely related families...........	45	15
Species of related genera.................	73	30
Species of the same genus................	85	46
Individuals of the same species.............	100 −	100 −

Methods similar in principle to those used in animals have also been applied to the study of plant relationships, with comparable results. It is now well established that the protoplasms and cell products of morphologically similar organisms are biochemically more similar than are those of unlike organisms. This is what we should expect if the protoplasm of each individual and species has its properties and functions determined by the inherited gene complex.

TAXONOMY AS AN EXPRESSION OF RELATIONSHIP

The classification and naming of organisms, or *taxonomy*, arose as a matter of convenience and necessity. If observations and experiments on animals and plants are to have any value, we must know the species to which they apply. One of the main functions of taxonomy has been and will continue to be the careful description, naming, and cataloguing of species. So multitudinous are the forms of life that identification of the species to which a given organism belongs is more often than not the task of a specialist. From this standpoint taxonomy is concerned chiefly with *distinguishing* among organisms and hence tends to emphasize their differences.

The description and naming of organisms began long before the doctrine of evolution was established. Since then taxonomy has become as much concerned with the discovery and expression of evolutionary relationships as with the description and naming of species. The system of classification rests upon the assumption that degrees of homologous resemblance correspond with degrees of relationship. A hierarchy of more inclusive and less inclusive categories is erected to express these degrees of relationship. The fact that living things fit into these categories and that we do not find organisms showing a jumble of inconsistent characteristics is understandable in the light of our preceding discussion of the meaning of homology.

Species and genus.   We often speak of "kinds" of animals, without any very precise meaning. Sometimes we use "kind" to mean a group of similar individuals, such as cows, or sheep, which breed together and form a population in a restricted and definite sense. At other times we use "kind" more loosely, to include broader groups such as snakes or fishes, which are obviously of more than one sort. In biology it is necessary to distinguish between the different kinds of "kinds"—to set up definite systematic categories of greater and lesser inclusiveness.

The basic systematic unit is the *species*. This term (spelled alike in singular and plural) is applied to populations of closely similar individuals, such as men, or English sparrows, or bullfrogs, which, in general, *are alike in most morphological, physiological, and embryological features, reproduce among themselves, and are of common descent.*

Actually it is very hard to give a good definition of species that is universally applicable. In many plants and some animals there is an alternation of generations (sporophyte-gametophyte, sexual-asexual, or bisexual-parthenogenetic), with marked differences between the generations. Widespread interbreeding populations of animals and plants often show local or regional differences, and instances are known in which the two ends of a chain of interbreeding populations are so different that the end populations cannot breed with one another. In such species as the dog the extremes of variation that have been produced by selective breeding are far more unlike morphologically than distinct species usually are. Even if species are hard to define, in a given group it is usually possible, with some experience, to tell definitely what are and what are not species. The following examples will illustrate the species concept.

Among the squirrels of the eastern United States there are two kinds known respectively as the gray squirrel and the fox squirrel. Each of these is a species; but both are squirrels, and hence "squirrel" is a larger category that includes both species. Another somewhat similar animal, the flying squirrel, also occurs in this region. It is also a species, but sufficiently different from the other two to be placed not in the "squirrel" category but in a separate one, "flying squirrel." Again, among the birds of this region are two sorts of crows, the fish crow and the common crow. Both of these are species, but they show so many similarities that we group them together as "crows." These larger categories in which we group similar species are called *genera* (singular *genus*). The fox squirrel and gray squirrel belong to one genus, the flying squirrel to another, and the two crows to a third.

The naming of organisms. People sometimes ask why biologists give strange Latin names to animals and plants, instead of using the common names "that everyone can understand." The reasons are two. First, only a few species have

Fig. 24.11. The gray squirrel, *Sciurus carolinensis*. (*Courtesy Zoological Society of Philadelphia.*)

Fig. 24.12. The flying squirrel, *Glaucomys volans*. (*Courtesy Zoological Society of Philadelphia.*)

common names; most are nameless and unknown until they are described by some biologist. Second, it is very naïve to think that the common names used in the United States will be intelligible to scientists in France, England, Germany, Russia, and Japan. Even within a single country the vernacular names are neither precisely used nor everywhere the same. A single species may bear a dozen or more names in different regions, while one name may be applied to many similar species and sometimes to very different ones. Thus in the North and West "gopher" means a small burrowing rodent, while in Florida and other parts of the South it means a tortoise.

Each species has only one valid technical or "scientific" name, by which it is known to scientists of all countries and all times.[1] This name consists of two

---

[1] This is the ideal. In practice a considerable number of names have to be changed at one time or another in order to eliminate synonymy or to conform to the rules governing nomenclature.

Latin or latinized words. The first is the name of the *genus* to which the species belongs; the second, that of the *particular species* of that genus. The name of the "squirrel" genus is Sciurus (from the Greek, meaning "shadow-tail"); the two species of squirrels mentioned above are *Sciurus niger* (squirrel, black = fox squirrel) and *Sciurus carolinensis* (squirrel, living in the Carolinas = gray squirrel). The "flying squirrel" genus is Glaucomys (Greek, meaning "blue-gray mouse"); the species is *Glaucomys volans* (gray mouse, flying). The "crow" genus is Corvus (Latin, "crow"); the two species are *Corvus ossifragus* (crow, that breaks bones = fish crow) and *Corvus brachyrhynchus* (crow, with a short beak = common crow).

This two-name, or *binomial*, system of nomenclature was the invention of a great Swedish naturalist, Linnaeus. He first used it consistently for plants in his *Species Plantarum*, published in 1753, and for animals in his *Systema Naturae*, 10th edition, published in 1758. These dates are taken as the starting points in botanical and zoological nomenclature respectively. The use of Latin names was natural at that time, for Latin was then the language of science; but it proved a fortunate choice. Latin has the advantage of being widely understood, and it does not change, since it is no longer a spoken tongue. It has been found necessary to draw up detailed rules to govern the making and use of plant and animal names—the International Codes of Botanical Nomenclature and of Zoological Nomenclature. The most important principle is that the oldest properly established name is that which must be used. No two genera in the animal or in the plant kingdom may bear the same name, nor can two species of the same genus. The name of the genus is always capitalized, while the second word that designates the species is generally—in zoology always—spelled with a small initial letter.

The higher taxonomic categories. Starting with the *species* as the basic unit in classification, we have seen that several or many similar and presumably related species are assembled to form a *genus*. The genus is a "kind" or category higher and more inclusive than a species. In similar fashion several or many genera may be grouped to form the next higher unit, the *family;* families are grouped into *orders,* orders into *classes,* and classes into *phyla.* The *phylum* is the largest division of the *kingdom,* and the plant and animal kingdoms together comprise all living things. Every species is thus at the same time a member of a genus, a family, an order, a class, a phylum, and a kingdom.[1]

Sometimes these categories are not sufficiently numerous to express all the degrees of relationship that can be distinguished among the species of a given category. In this event additional categories are inserted between the main ones and are designated as *sub-* or *super*species, genera, families, orders, etc. If still more categories are needed, they are interpolated into

---

[1] This is the system that has become established in zoology. Botanists frequently use other names for the categories above the rank of family, although some have proposed systems closely similar to that used in zoology. See Appendix A.

the scheme, and called by such names as tribes, sections, groups, and the like; there is no standard set of terms for such extra subdivisions. The principal taxonomic categories are illustrated in the accompanying diagram, which shows the classification of the five species previously mentioned.

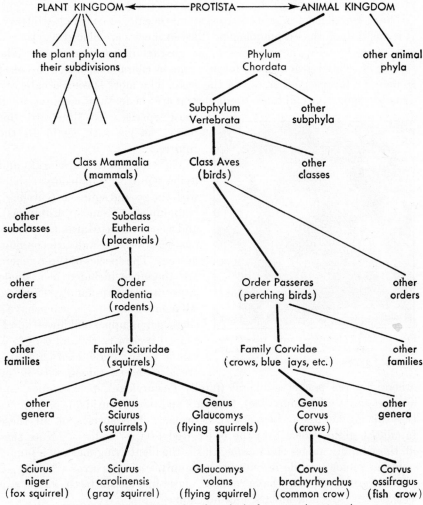

F&#x131;g. 24.13. Diagram showing the principal taxonomic categories.

The methods and aims of taxonomy. If the main object of classification were the naming, cataloguing, and identifying of species, any convenient artificial system would suffice. At this level taxonomy is no more a science than is a card file. However, modern taxonomy has the status of a science because it is an attempt to discover and express the relationships among organisms that are the result of evolution. To attain this end it may use any relevant data. Comparative morphology is necessarily the foundation of the system, for morphological data can be obtained for any species of which specimens are available. Wherever possible taxonomy also incorporates the findings of comparative embryology, comparative physiology, paleontology, biogeography, and genetics.

The assignment of organisms to systematic categories is not arbitrary. It is based upon shared homologies. Related species are placed together in one genus because they possess many characteristics in common. The species of related genera have fewer common characters, which are used to define a family, and so on up the scale. The more species a category includes, the fewer and more fundamental are the features common to all those species. To illustrate this point, let us turn again to the squirrels.

The tree squirrels (Sciurus) and flying squirrels (Glaucomys) share with the ground squirrels (Citellus), chipmunks (Tamias, Eutamias), and woodchucks (Marmota) numerous features that indicate common descent. The species of these genera are therefore included in a single larger category, the family Sciuridae. All members of the Sciuridae have a single pair of upper and lower chisel-shaped incisor teeth, and they lack canine teeth. These characteristics are also shared (along with many others) by the pocket gophers[1] (family Geomyidae), pocket mice and kangaroo rats (Heteromyidae), true rats and mice (Muridae), porcupines (Erythizontidae), and beavers (Castoridae). The species of all these families together constitute the order Rodentia, or rodents. (Note that all these family names end in *idae;* this is the identifying mark of a family name in zoology, while in botany the family ending is *aceae.*) Nearly all rodents are small. They have rootless, chisel-like incisor teeth, a long gap between incisors and molars, and no canines.

Fig. 24.14. A beaver, *Castor canadensis,* family Castoridae, order Rodentia. (*Photo courtesy Chicago Natural History Museum.*)

The pikas or conies (Ochotonidae) and the hares and rabbits (Leporidae) were long placed in the Rodentia, chiefly because they also have gnawing teeth. There were two suborders, the Simplicidentata for the true rodents and the Duplicidentata for the pikas, hares, and rabbits. The latter were

---

[1] The burrowing mammals known as "salamanders" in parts of the South, including Florida.

so named because they have a small second pair of upper incisors hidden behind the first pair. It now seems evident, on the basis of skull structure, reproductive organs, and teeth, that the two groups are only distantly related and their similarities due to analogous modification. The pikas, hares, and rabbits are now assigned to a separate order, the Lagomorpha.

None of these gnawing mammals possesses a pouch for the young. In all of them the coracoid bone is reduced to a projection from the scapula, the vagina is single, and the development of the young occurs wholly within the body of the mother, the fetus being attached to the wall of the uterus by a placenta. The same characteristics extend through the species of many other orders. These include the moles and shrews (Insectivora), flying lemurs (Dermoptera), bats (Chiroptera), lemurs, monkeys, apes, and man (Primates), sloths (Edentata), carnivores (Carnivora), elephants (Proboscidea), manatees (Sirenia), and the hoofed mammals (Perissodactyla, Artiodactyla). All of these are included with the Rodentia and Lagomorpha in a single subclass, the placental mammals, or Eutheria.

Thus it continues. All the groupings of the species of the plant and animal kingdoms are based on the same principle. Taxonomists do not create these groupings, which exist by virtue of the evolutionary relationships between species. Instead the student of taxonomy is trying to determine what the natural groupings are and to discover how they are related to one another. The fact that he is able to establish a system of classification based upon degrees of homologous resemblance and capable of a graduated and detailed grouping of all organisms is both a demonstration and a result of the fact of evolutionary kinship.

ADAPTIVE RADIATION AND ADAPTIVE CONVERGENCE

When we discussed homology and analogy at the beginning of this chapter, we were concerned chiefly with the criteria by which these two classes of resemblance might be distinguished. We then saw how these concepts gave meaning to the facts of comparative morphology, embryology, physiology, and classification. Now let us see how, in terms of adaptation to environment, they enter into the two contrasting evolutionary phenomena known as adaptive radiation and adaptive convergence.

The *adaptation* of organisms to particular modes of life has two aspects. On the one hand we see the great perfection of many adaptive structures and behaviors; on the other we note rather frequent cases in which species seem imperfectly adapted to their environments or fail to show adaptations that would appear desirable. Both aspects of adaptation are understandable if we remember that evolution consists in the *modification* of organisms. If a species has a structure or process or behavior which is suitable material for adjustment to new conditions, a new adaptation may result; but if it has nothing that could serve as a starting point, evolution cannot produce the desirable adaptation *de novo*. Much of the lack of adaptation in organisms is also probably due to evolutionary change lagging behind environmental change.

Adaptive radiation. Among the species of a single family or order it is usual to find a wide variety of ways of living and corresponding variety in the types of situations occupied. The members of the squirrel family (*Sciuridae*) are clearly related, although some are arboreal, others terrestrial, and still others burrowers in the soil. Yet they are all built on a common plan that is modified in relation to the mode of life of each species. As part of their basic inherited equipment, all of them have claws and tails. In the tree squirrels the claws have become sharp spikes by means of which the animals cling to tree trunks or run sure-footedly on

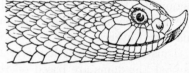

| Blue Racer | Hog - nosed Snake |

Fig. 24.15. Adaptive modification. The head of the black snake or blue racer (*Coluber constrictor*) is that of a typical snake. The head of the hognose snake or puff adder (*Heterodon platyrhinos*), is modified for burrowing in the soil. (*After D. Dwight Davis, Jr., courtesy General Biological Supply House, Inc.*)

branches, digging the points into the bark as a linesman uses his climbing tools. The tail has been modified into a graceful balancing organ, also useful as a cloak. The flying squirrels show the same changes, but in addition the skin of the sides of the body has become a loose flap which can be tightened by extending the legs, and the tail hair grows out in a horizontal plane. These modifications enable the animal to make his entire body a plane for gliding, simply by extending the legs and tail. The prairie dogs have become burrowers in the soil. Their claws are modified into strong digging tools, and the useless tail is reduced to a mere stub. None of these adaptations to different ways of life involves new structures but only modifications of the ancestral equipment. The phenomenon here illustrated is a nearly universal one—the spreading out of the descendants of a single original stock into more numerous and diverse types of environment, with accompanying adaptive changes. We shall encounter additional examples of adaptive radiation in our survey of the evolutionary history of life.

Adaptive convergence. Distantly related groups, each undergoing adaptive radiation, may contain species adapted to the same type of environment. The result may be a strong likeness in appearance and mode of life between the species concerned—but a likeness due to *analogous* rather than homologous modifications. The classic example of this common phenomenon is the convergence between the marsupial mammals and the placental mammals. In Australia, protected by isolation, the more primitive marsupial stock underwent adaptive radiation. A great variety of types evolved, fitted for nearly every mode of life available to mammals. Meanwhile in the other continents a similar adaptive radiation occurred among the placentals, which produced an even greater variety of adaptive types. Many of the Australian marsupials came to resemble closely their placental counterparts (or vice versa), though the similarities are analogies. Adaptive radiation within the marsupials and placentals

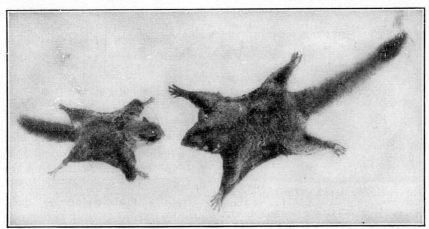

Fig. 24.16. Adaptive convergence. Left, the flying squirrel *Glaucomys volans*, a gliding placental mammal; right, the flying phalanger *Petaurus sciurus*, a gliding marsupial mammal. (*Courtesy American Museum of Natural History.*)

was accompanied by *convergence* between those species that adopted similar modes of life.

BIOGEOGRAPHY AND EVOLUTION

Everyone knows that species are not universally distributed. Lions do not occur in North America except in zoos, nor snakes in Ireland. In part the reasons are obvious; we should not expect to find alligators in deserts or sagebrush in wet regions. The ecological requirements of organisms account for much of their distribution. On the other hand, hardly any species is found in all parts of the world where it could exist. The chief exceptions are man and the creatures that man has carried about with him, on purpose or by accident. There were no rabbits in Australia until they were brought there by white men. This was not because they could not live in Australia; as soon as they were introduced they multiplied and became a plague. Evidently something besides ecological factors determines where species occur.

The ranges of organisms. The geographic distribution of animals and plants is not haphazard but follows definite patterns. Each species occupies a particular *range*, which covers a larger or smaller part of the earth. Size of range varies enormously. Man has the greatest range of any mammal—virtually the whole earth. Other species may have very restricted ranges, sometimes a few square miles or even less in extent. Subspecies and very closely related species seldom occupy overlapping ranges; instead they are generally separated by some sort of geographic barrier that prevents free intermingling. When they do occur in the same territories, some other sort of barrier to hybridization must exist. Whole families and orders may be absent from regions that have been long isolated from other parts of the world. The *biotas*[1] of such regions are composed largely of species peculiar to them.

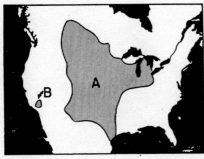

Fig. 24.17. Size of range of related species. *A*, the range of the 13-lined ground squirrel (*Citellus tridecemlineatus*), a species with wide ecological tolerance. The portions of the range occupied by the eight recognized subspecies are not distinguished. *B*, the range of the Mohave ground squirrel (*Citellus mohavensis*), a species confined to the western part of the Mohave desert. (*Based on Howell*, 1938.)

The phenomena of geographic distribution are in part an expression of the evolutionary relationships of organisms, but they also include the effects of ecological, spatial, and historical factors that are independent of organic evolution.

Factors that determine geographic distribution. The range of any species or higher group of animals or plants is the result of a unique combination of requirements and events. For this reason probably no two species or groups of species have exactly the same range. Analysis of the factors that determine the ranges of organisms shows that they always include the following:

    I. Ecological Factors.
        A. The constitution of the organism, including its ecological requirements and the changes produced in these by evolution.
        B. The nature and distribution of the physical and biotic environments in which it can live.
    II. Spatial and Related Factors.
        A. The place where the species or group originated, and from which it has spread.
        B. The means of dispersal available to the organism, and the spatial relations of barriers to and highways for its spread.

[1] *Biota* (Greek, *bios*, "life") is the term given to all the living things of one region or environment; it includes both the animals (fauna) and the plants (flora).

III. Historical Factors.
  A. The time of origin of the species or group, as a result of which it has been
     subjected to the effects of a longer or shorter sequence of changes.
  B. Changes:
    1. In the physical environment, both as regards ecological conditions
       within the range, and the spatial relations of barriers and highways.
    2. In the biotic environment, as modified by evolution and migration.

The present geographic and ecological distribution of any species or
higher group is the resultant of the operation of all these factors throughout the period of its existence. In so far as differences in the geographic
location of species and in the extent and form of their ranges are not the
direct result of the present distribution of their habitats, they have been
determined by the spatial and historical factors listed above.

Place of origin.   It is a fundamental assumption in biogeography that
each species originated in a single place and only once. This is simply a
working hypothesis; but it is borne out by the observed facts of distribution and has a basis in genetic theory. If new species were formed by single
mutations, there would be no reason why such mutant species might not
arise in distant portions of the range of the parent species. Such an origin
is conceivable for polyploid species of plants, but polyploidy is practically
nonexistent in animals. Most plant and animal species differ not in one
or a few but in many genes and gene groups. This implies an accumulation
of mutational differences between populations, and species formation by
changes in whole populations rather than by mutation of single individuals. It is in the highest degree unlikely that the gene complex in any
two separate parts of an ancestral species population would undergo the
same additions, subtractions, and alterations, thus giving rise to the same
new species.

The place where a species originated is often called the *center of origin*,
but it should not be thought of as a point in space. Instead it must have
comprised the range of the population that became the new species. This
area need not even be included within the present range of the species,
though doubtless it usually is. Many once widespread species are now
restricted to a small part of their former range, and the center of origin
may have been in a region where the species no longer occurs. Determination of a center of origin is often difficult or impossible, but its geographic
position is one of the main factors influencing location of range. A species
that arose in North America is much more likely to be there still than
it is to occur in Africa.

Dispersal in relation to barriers and highways.   Pressure of population makes every successful species tend to expand into more and more
territory—to extend its range. The gradual expansion of range that results
from the normal activities of animals and plants is called *spreading*. In

most animals spreading is *active*, caused by random wanderings in search of food, mates, and shelter. In plants and some groups of animals the mature organism cannot move about or has locomotor powers too limited to carry it a significant distance. In these cases spreading is *passive*. It is brought about by the transportation of seeds, spores, the resting stages of small aquatic organisms, or the organisms themselves. The transport-

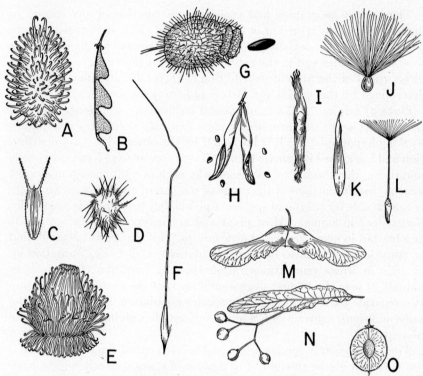

Fig. 24.18. Devices for passive dispersal of fruits and seeds. *A* to *F*, carried by animals. *G* to *H*, mechanically propelled. *I* to *O*, wind-borne. *A*, cocklebur, Xanthium. *B*, stick-tight, Desmodium. *C*, sticktight, Bidens. *D*, sandspur or sandbur, Cenchrus. *E*, burdock, Arctium. *F*, porcupine, needle, or wire grass, Aristida. *G*, squirting cucumber, Ecbalium. *H*, lupine, Lupinus. *I*, catalpa, Catalpa. *J*, milkweed, Asclepias. *K*, ash, Fraxinus. *L*, dandelion, Taraxacum. *M*, maple, Acer. *N*, linden or basswood, Tilia. *O*, wafer ash or hop tree, Ptelea. (*Modified from Turtox chart, courtesy General Biological Supply House, Inc.*)

ing agencies include currents of air and water, and animal carriers. Many or most of the species that depend upon passive spreading have a stage in the life history especially adapted for transportation. Examples are winged or fluffy wind-borne seeds, burrs that stick to the skins of animals, the drifting coconut, and the minute swimming larvae of many sedentary marine animals.

In some animals there is definite behavior directed toward dispersal; such behavior is called *migration*. It may be occasional, or *sporadic*, like the outpourings of the mouselike lemming from its home in the Scandinavian uplands. Or it may be regularly *periodic*, like the spring and fall migrations of birds. Migration is far less likely to cause permanent extensions of range than is spreading, though it may occasionally have this result. Its causes and effects are complicated, different in different groups, and only imperfectly understood.

Lastly, plants and animals are sometimes transported *accidentally*, by such agencies as hurricanes, floating rafts of vegetation, or mud sticking to the feet of water birds. With the advent of commerce, man has become the chief agent of accidental dispersal and has sometimes intentionally

Fig. 24.19. Seed dispersal. Left, burdock, Arctium; center, milkweed, Asclepias; right, dandelion, Taraxacum. (*Photos by Prof. E. B. Mains.*)

but usually inadvertently carried large numbers of species to regions distant from their original homes.

Barriers and Highways. Very new species may not yet have occupied all the available territory and may be seen to expand their ranges from year to year. In the islands of Tahiti and Moorea in the South Pacific, studies made in 1861 to 1884 and again in 1907 to 1923 showed that certain species of land snails of recent origin were steadily occupying more territory. The same phenomenon of expansion of range is more strikingly seen in the rapid dispersal of the English sparrow, the starling, and scores of insect pests after their introduction into North America.

Sooner or later, however, such an expanding population encounters obstacles to its further spread. These may be *physical barriers* such as the sea, a great river, or steep cliffs for a terrestrial species, or land for an aquatic one. The ranges of few species are enclosed on all sides by physical barriers. Usually they are bounded along much of their peripheries by zones wherein one or more ecological factors change past the limits of toleration of the species. The barrier is not a physical block to entry but an inability of the species to maintain itself permanently in the region beyond. A barrier of this sort may be called a *barrier to establishment*.

Sometimes there is a gap in the barriers that enclose a species population, permitting the species to spread along a relatively narrow highway into another region suitable for its existence. Many Great Plains species are barred to the west by the Rocky Mountains but have been able to pass through gaps, in Wyoming or in the Southwest, to reach the dry grasslands of the interior basin. Many Canadian species find southward leading highways along the crests of the Appalachian, Rocky Mountain, and Cascade-Sierra Nevada ranges. Central America has served as a highway for interchange of tropical species between northern South America and southernmost North America. During the latest of the geological eras the gap between Siberia and Alaska has several times been bridged by land, permitting exchange of species between the Old and New Worlds.

Historical factors in distribution. In the evolutionary time scale highways and barriers are shifting and ephemeral. Land connections emerge and again sink beneath the sea; mountain ranges are uplifted and eroded away; climates shift from arid to humid, from warm to cold, and back again. Forests become grasslands and again forests; and limiting biotic relationships undergo changes. This means that the longer a species or genus or family has been in existence, the more opportunities its members will have had to spread away from the region of origin. It also means that with increasing age of the species or group the more likely it is to have broken up into separately evolving populations. Spread followed by the formation of new barriers, or spread through narrow gaps in barriers, isolates descendants of the same stock and permits them to diverge along separate evolutionary paths.

The mingling of the species of previously isolated regions results in changes in the biotic environment—new enemies, new food organisms, new parasites and diseases, and new competition between species adapted to similar modes of life. The result of such invasions is generally the extinction of some species and always a readjustment of many biotic relations within the affected regions.

The ranges of closely allied forms. The ranges of closely related species and of the subspecies of a single species are found to show a rather consistent and orderly spatial pattern. David Starr Jordan first formally stated this as follows: "*In any group of related organisms, whether species or subspecies, the most closely related will be found, not in the same geographic area, nor in widely separated areas, but in adjacent areas separated by a barrier of some sort.*" This generalization, known as *Jordan's rule*, has had to be amplified as noted below, but it is found to hold true in the great majority of instances.

From what has already been said in this and the previous chapter about the role of isolation in species formation, it is easy to understand why this should be so. Most new species arise as populations, not from mutant individuals. A species population cannot split so long as interbreeding

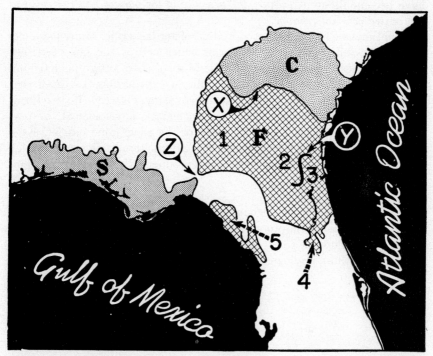

FIG. 24.20. An illustration of Jordan's rule. Three closely allied species of grasshoppers, *Melanoplus clypeatus*, *M. furcatus*, and *M. symmetricus*, occupy respectively the ranges indicated by *C*, *F*, and *S*. All three live in dense shrubbery on seepage slopes bordering streams and swamps. They can fly but seldom do so. They differ chiefly in the male genitalia, and do not intergrade. Their adjoining ranges are separated by barriers—the Altamaha River (*X*) between *C* and *F*, and a belt of uplands that at (*Z*) narrows to a 2-mile sand ridge between *F* and *S*. *Melanoplus furcatus*, which has the widest and most varied range, consists of five recognizably different subpopulations that occupy the numbered areas and are for the most part connected by intergrading populations. Whether some or all of these should be considered subspecies and given names is a matter of opinion. At (*Y*) is an intrarange barrier, a sand ridge along the St. Marys River east of the Okefenokee Swamp, which sharply separates populations 2 and 3, although they intergrade around its northern end. Populations 3 and 4 are the ends of a cline or gradient of change that parallels the St. Johns River. Population 5 is the most isolated and most distinct, and has not yet been shown to intergrade with any other. (*Based on unpublished data from field studies by T. H. Hubbell.*)

permits gene changes to spread through it. However, interpose a barrier to interbreeding between one part of the population and another, and the two isolated parts must inevitably become different in the course of time. By far the commonest isolating factor in species formation is geographic; some believe that geographic isolation is the *only* means by which the initial step in speciation is accomplished. This, then, is the genetic and evolutionary basis for the existence of the relations expressed in Jordan's rule. The different but related populations that occupy adjacent ranges have descended from a single ancestral population and have become different *because the presence of the barrier has prevented or minimized gene interchange.*

Sometimes we find apparent violations of Jordan's rule. Many instances are now known of closely allied forms which occupy the same territory and sometimes even the same habitat. Most of these situations have not been sufficiently investigated to permit an explanation. In those that have, it has usually been found that interbreeding between the two forms is prevented or minimized by some ecological, physiological, or psychological barrier that takes the place of the geographic barrier. Even so, it may be that such related forms living in the same area arose through geographic isolation and acquired their reproductive isolating mechanisms before coming together again.

Here we conclude our account of the evolutionary principle and its consequences. In the chapters which follow we shall trace the evolutionary history of organisms from earliest times to the present, with special emphasis on those phylogenetic lines which have led to man.

CHAPTER XXV

THE GEOLOGICAL BACKGROUND OF EVOLUTION

It is one thing to understand in principle the causes and consequences of evolution but quite another to know the actual evolutionary changes that life has undergone. The history of life would be only vaguely known by inference were it not that a record has been preserved in the rocks. This record consists of the fossil remains of animals and plants that lived in bygone eras. It is fragmentary in the extreme; yet surprisingly it is sufficiently complete to permit the main outlines of the evolutionary story to be clearly read. The fossils reveal the changes that life has undergone, and the rate at which such changes occurred. Often they permit us to reconstruct the ancestral creatures as they must have been in life, sometimes with a wealth of detail. Most dramatically, they tell us of the many blind alleys into which life has strayed, as shown by the great multitudes of fossil types that have left no descendants. We may compare the paleontological panorama of evolution to an enormous picture mosaic, begun long ago and still unfinished, faulty and defaced in its older parts but with its composition and significance plain and many of its finer details still clearly visible.

Before we can take up the story of life as told by the fossils, we shall have to know something of the geological background of evolution. The earth is the stage on which the life drama has been played; what has been its physical history? How were fossils formed, and what kinds of information do they furnish? How do we date events of the past and assemble the geological and paleontological facts into a connected history? In order to answer these questions it will be necessary to give some account of earth features and processes.

In Chap. XXIII we mentioned that it was formerly customary to attribute many geological phenomena to great catastrophic events of the past—universal floods, volcanic outbursts, or what were broadly referred to as "convulsions of nature." After Hutton, however, geologists came gradually to accept the idea that earth features had been molded by small forces acting over very long periods. Modern geology is founded on the Huttonian principle of *uniformitarianism*, and no one now doubts that earth history has been enormously long, that most changes have been gradual, or that past events must be interpreted in the light of what is going on today. These conclusions apply to evolution as well as to geology. Uniformitarianism does not mean, however, that the past was no different from the present or that the rate of geological and evolutionary change has remained constant. There was a time when the earth was molten and no life existed. Even since it has cooled and animals and plants have appeared upon it, the earth has undergone more or less cyclic physical changes because of which the rate of geologic and of evolutionary processes has varied from time to time.

The rocks of the earth's crust. The outer *crust* of the earth is a shell of rock about 60 miles thick, crystalline in its outer 20 miles or so and gradually becoming glasslike toward its lower limit. Beneath it are other denser layers surrounding the supposedly metallic core. Distributed about the surface are the continents—great masses of lighter rock floating low in the denser and heavier rock that makes up most of the crust. The places where the lighter rock is thin or absent are the ocean basins. The light crystalline rock of which the continents are chiefly made is *granite*, formed, like other kinds of crystalline rock, by cooling and crystallization of molten rock liquids similar to lava. Rocks formed in this way are called *igneous*[1] *rocks*, because heat was involved in their origin. Igneous rocks can obviously never contain fossils.

The land surfaces are exposed to the action of air, moisture, and changes of temperature, and to the influences of animals and plants. The combined effect of these agencies is to cause the superficial layers of rock to "decay" and disintegrate, a process termed *weathering*. The loose materials thus formed blanket the surface; they are blown by the wind, washed down slopes by the rain, and carried off by streams. Where the streams empty into lakes or the sea, the finely divided rock material (*sediment*) settles to the bottom and forms a layer of mud or sand. In the course of time earlier layers are covered by later ones, which in their turn are buried, until the accumulation may become very deep. Compacted by the weight of the overlying materials and cemented by slow chemical changes, the layered sediments harden into solid rock. Rocks thus formed are called *stratified* rocks in reference to their layered structure, or *sedimentary* rocks because they are formed from sediments.

The continents are almost entirely covered by overlapping sheets of sedimentary rock. Some of the sheets are very thin, and some very thick in places; some are local, but many extend over areas of hundreds or thousands of square miles. The widespread deposits bear evidence of having been formed in shallow seas that lay upon the surfaces of the continents, and they represent the mud and sand poured into the seas by rivers that flowed off the bordering lands. Once they were the muddy

[1] From the Latin, *igneus*, "fiery."

or sandy sea floors, where lived marine animals whose shells and bones are imbedded in the sediments, now hardened into rock. In portions of the seas distant from the ancient shores the water was clear, and there deposits consisting almost entirely of the limy shells and hard parts of organisms were formed and later consolidated into *limestone*.

In many regions the sedimentary layers, or *strata*, are still horizontal, as they were when laid down. But where they are piled up in the deepest accumulations (sometimes several miles thick), they are commonly folded and crumpled into great mountain ranges. This is the result of

Fig. 25.1. Horizontal rock strata in the San Juan River canyon, southeastern Utah. The canyon wall is more than 2,000 feet high. The lower strata are upper Carboniferous limestones, shales, and sandstones; the higher ones are Permian sandstones, limestones, and mudstones. (*Photo by Henry P. Zuidema.*)

a sequence of events described below, which has been many times repeated in earth history.

In all the ancient continents there were some areas that remained land most of the time. The rivers flowing off from these lands deposited the coarser and bulkier sediments only a little distance offshore. Under the weight of this accumulating sediment the crust sagged into long narrow troughs bordering the ancient permanent lands, and these troughs were filled with sediment as fast as they deepened. At various periods in earth history there has been intense and long-continued compression of the crust. At such times the weakest parts of the crust yielded, and the long, narrow troughs filled with water-soaked sediments were weaker than the masses of crystalline rock on each side.

In successive periods of deformation first one and then another such trough gave way, crumpling into mountains in such a manner that the sedimentary strata bent into corrugated folds or in places even broke and slid over one another. Where the pressure and the accompanying heat were intense, the nature of the rocks was greatly altered, becoming more or less crystalline, with the formation of new minerals and the destruction of all fossils. Thus shales or mud rocks were changed to slates, limestones to marbles, and sandstones to a much denser kind of rock called quartzite. Any rock, whether originally sedimentary or igneous, which has been thus altered by pressure and heat is called a *metamorphic rock*. Where the mountain-making forces acted less vigorously, the sedimentary rocks were thrown into folds without losing their sedimentary characteristics and without destruction of fossils.

Not all sediments have been laid down in the seas, though this is where the greatest accumulations have occurred. They may be deposited in lake basins or in swamps or as river deposits built up like land deltas on the plains at the foot of mountains. Much of our knowledge of the later steps in the evolution of life comes from fossils found in fresh-water and land deposits. From the geological standpoint, however, such sediments are far less important than the marine deposits because of their merely local extent and because they are so much more likely to be destroyed by subsequent erosion.

The order of the strata. In an undisturbed series of sedimentary strata the lowest layers are obviously the oldest, the uppermost the youngest. In regions such as Florida, where the strata lie relatively flat, and because of the low elevation streams do not cut deeply into the surface, only the uppermost layers are accessible to study. In such regions the nature of the deeper strata can be learned only from well borings. But in regions where the land has been elevated and the strata left undeformed or only gently tilted or warped, streams have often cut sections through the mass of layers so that their edges are exposed in the valley sides; or erosion may have stripped off parts of the surface, so that in crossing a region, one can traverse the beveled edges of the layers.

Each section thus exposed to study constitutes only a small part of the entire rock record. Nevertheless, by correlating the pieces of the story revealed in one area with those preserved in other areas, a fairly complete record of the last quarter or third of earth history has been worked out. Fossils are used for correlating distant exposures of rock strata in the following manner. Each stratum is found to have a peculiar assemblage of fossils different from that of other strata. The succession of these fossil faunas and floras can be determined in one region where the rocks lie undisturbed; then the sequence worked out in that region can be used to determine the relative ages of strata in other regions. This method is particularly important in studying the rocks of folded mountains, where the strata may be turned up into steeply tilted positions or even sometimes folded completely back on themselves, so that locally they may lie in reverse order—younger strata beneath older ones.[1]

The history of the continents. The results of studies that cannot here be discussed show that the continents and ocean basins have existed since the very beginning of that part of earth history recorded in the rocks. The ocean basins are a little more than brimful of water, so that the edges of the continents are generally covered by shallow seas. Such seas, resting upon the continents, are called *epicontinental seas*.

Geological cycles. On every continent a certain cycle of events has repeated itself many times with slight variations. At the *beginning of a typical geologic cycle*, the continent stands high; the epicontinental seas are restricted to the edges; and the high lands are being rapidly eroded by swift-flowing streams that carry their sediments to or over the edges of the continental shelves. As the lands are degraded and the sediments are deposited in the seas, the water level rises and slowly creeps in over the low parts of the land. Hudson Bay appears to be an example of such an advancing sea. By the *middle of the cycle* the lands are worn low, and the interior of the continent is occupied by widespread, shallow interior seas, in which are deposited the sediments from the remaining land areas. With warpings of the continent, the seas slowly fluctuate in form and extent, but they occupy the land for periods of one to several million years. Finally, toward the *end of the cycle*, readjustment sets in. The continents rise, often with the formation of a mountain range in some part where the sediments were thickest, the seas are spilled off, and the cycle is ready to repeat itself.

This cyclic series of events forms the basis for the subdivision of earth history into periods of time, corresponding to the systems of strata formed during the periods of sea invasion. Each spread of the sea left strata of rock on top of those formed during the previous cycles. There are breaks in the series, due to the times when the continent stood high. During these times there was no deposition of sediments on the continents, and streams were busy destroying the earlier depositions. These breaks (*unconformities*) in the rock record also appear to be breaks in the story of life, for the marine forms at least. Life was continually changing, and at each return the seas brought with them a fauna that was different from that of the previous cycle.

Geological revolutions. On the whole these cycles have affected all the continents simultaneously, so that the divisions of the rock record in one region hold good for other parts of the world. But there are generally

[1] Unfortunately, where such disturbance of the strata has been greatest, the fossils have been destroyed, and other methods of correlation must be used.

some places where rocks formed during the depositional gaps are still accessible. These give us a fragmentary record of what went on in the seas during the period of continental elevation. But at very long intervals unusually great "revolutions" occurred, in which all the continents stood so high and for so long a time that little or no record of the interval has been found. During these times erosion also destroyed a vast amount of the earlier records. These great breaks are taken as the dividing points between the major eras of earth history. For reasons pointed out later, they are also times when profound alterations occurred in the world of life, many ancient types becoming extinct, and the evolution of new types being accelerated.

The concept of time in relation to earth history. The student of science must become accustomed to thinking in terms of several quite different scales of time. Recorded history is only a few thousand years old, and in the historical sense an event of 6,000 years past is very ancient indeed. To the student of human evolution, whose field of inquiry comprises the Pleistocene or glacial epoch, an event of 6,000 years ago is quite recent, whereas really ancient events occurred 250,000 or 500,000 years ago. To the geologist years are of little moment; he deals with a vast period of time in which 6,000 years ago is the same as today and the Pleistocene in its entirety is an insignificant part of the whole. If years are insisted upon, he points out that the oldest known rocks, on the basis of recent physical estimates, are perhaps 1 billion 900 million years old, and that, since these do not record the beginning of earth history, a figure of 2 billion 500 million years may be taken as a working hypothesis for the age of the earth.[1] But the geologist and the biologist are much more concerned with the *relative age* and *relative duration* of events, and here they can speak with much greater assurance. Finally, to the astronomer, the whole period covered by the history of the earth is an insignificant fraction of the life of a single star such as the sun.

The Geological Time Scale. By fitting together the fragments of the rock record preserved in different regions, it has been possible to construct a detailed time scale, in which names are given to the periods of earth

[1] This is not a mere guess, but the result of prolonged and careful investigation of the problem from many angles. Data have been obtained based on the total thickness of sediments and the probable rate of their accumulation; on volume of rock removed in relation to rates of erosion; on amount of salt in the oceans relative to the amount added annually by present-day streams, etc. All such methods of estimate have been largely superseded by those based on the disintegration of uranium and thorium into lead, which goes on at a constant and known rate. Determination of the extent to which this disintegration has progressed in a sample of crystalline rock permits estimation of the time of formation of the rock. To this and related methods we owe our present concept of the magnitude of geological time. A discussion of the methods used in dating Pleistocene and postglacial fossils and events will be found in Chap. XXX.

history and their sequence is shown. This time scale includes both the known parts of the history and the gaps; the latter probably account for at least as much time as the periods of which there are records. The complete time scale of modern geology is nearly as complicated and

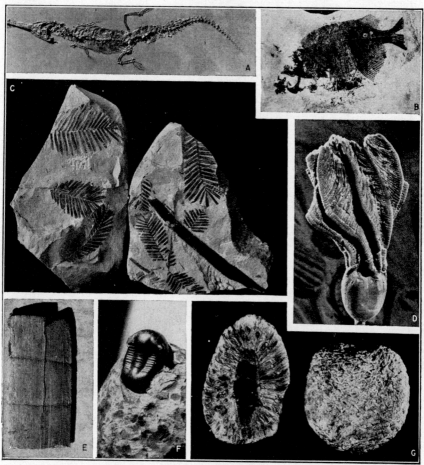

FIG. 25.2. Types of fossils. The symbols given after each refer to the table of modes of fossilization on p. 396. *A*, skeleton of phytosaur, I:A2a. *B*, fossil fish, I:A2a. *C*, fossil cycad leaves, I:B3. *D*, crinoid or sea lily, I:A2a. *E*, part of stem of giant rush, Calamites, I:A3. *F*, trilobite, *Illaenus americanus*, I:B2 + 3. *G*, cycad cones, I:A3. (*Courtesy Ward's Natural Science Establishment, Inc., except C, American Museum of Natural History.*)

contains nearly as many names and events as, for example, a moderately condensed treatise on the history of Europe. For our purposes only the most important periods and events are needed. A simplified time scale giving this information is presented herewith. Knowledge of the names of the periods and their sequence is essential to an understanding of the chapters that follow.

Geologic Time Scale

Thickness of Deposits	ERAS	Periods	Epochs and Events	Age in Millions of Years (estimated)	Duration in Millions of Years	PLANT LIFE	ANIMAL LIFE
5.0 miles coarse sediments	CENOZOIC	Quaternary	Recent = Holocene	0.01		Decline of woody plants and expansion of herbaceous types	Homo sapiens – Age of Man
			Pleistocene	0.6-1.0		Glaciation. Much shifting of ranges and extinction	Early man Widespread extinction of mammals and other animals
		Tertiary	Pliocene		70	Cool	Fauna increasingly modern. Reign of placental mammals, birds, insects, teleost fishes, molluscs, modern corals, foraminifera
			Miocene	30		Warm, drier Spread of grasslands — Modern genera mostly present but distribution different	First known anthropoids
			Oligocene			Warm	Increase of mammals; appearance and rise of placental mammals and decline of archaic types with coming of modernized forms Rise of birds.
			Eocene	60		Moderate becoming cool. First grasses	
			Paleocene	70		Moderate to warm	All major modern animal groups present

Minor Unconformity. Fourth Great Revolution (Rocky Mountain) with slight loss of record

Thickness of Deposits	ERAS	Periods	Epochs and Events	Age in Millions of Years (estimated)	Duration in Millions of Years	PLANT LIFE	ANIMAL LIFE
6.25 miles muds and sands	MESOZOIC	Cretaceous	First Andes and Rocky Mts Moderate, becoming cool	110	120	Rise of flowering plants. True ferns and cycads much reduced. Like Jurassic, but fewer ginkgos and more flowering plants. Climax of cycads	Culmination and extinction of dinosaurs, pterosaurs, and ammonites. Toothed birds
		Jurassic	First Sierra New Warm, Equable	150		Like Triassic, but seed-ferns die out; climax of ginkgos; first flowering plants	First birds Climax of sauropod dinosaurs, ichthyosaurs. First crocodiles and pterosaurs
1.25 miles limestones		Triassic	Warm, Equable, Deserts	190		True ferns, cycads, ginkgos abundant. Conifers and seed-ferns flourish	First non-placental mammals; first ichthyosaurs; first modern corals. Climax of mammal-like reptiles

Unconformity. Third Great Revolution (Appalachian) with some loss of record

Thickness of Deposits	ERAS	Periods	Epochs and Events	Age in Millions of Years (estimated)	Duration in Millions of Years	PLANT LIFE	ANIMAL LIFE
		Permian	First Appalachian Mts. Cool, Dry. Glaciation in Southern Hemisphere	225		Climax of horsetails; ginkgos abundant; conifers increase. Club-moss trees reduced. Seed-ferns continue abundant. Spread of Glossopteris flora	First modern insects. Increase of reptiles; amphibians first abundant, then decline; extinction of trilobites, eurypterids, Paleozoic corals

Era/Eon	Period	Mountains / Climate	Date (million yrs)	Plant Life	Animal Life
PALEOZOIC 4.6 miles muds and sands 3.6 miles limestones	Carboniferous	Mountains in Europe. Coal. Warm, becoming Cold at end	275	First cycads and ginkgos. Climax of horsetails. First conifers. Great coal-forming swamp forests.	First reptiles, winged insects, spiders. Climax of amphibians and shark-like fishes. Die-out of placoderm and ostracoderm fishes and decline of eurypterids.
	Devonian	Volcanoes in New England. Moderate, becoming Warm	260	First club-moss trees and horsetails. Die-out of psilophytes. First clubmosses, seed-ferns. First trees.	First amphibians. Climax of placoderms; Rise of crossopterygians and lung-fishes. Ostracoderms first abundant, then decline.
	Silurian	Warm. Salt Deserts	340	First known land plants – psilophytes.	First scorpions and wingless insects; First placoderm fishes; Climax of brachiopods, trilobites and eurypterids. Rise of ostracoderms.
	Ordovician	Mountains in Vermont. Moderate to Warm	390	Marine algae abundant.	First ostracoderms, corals, sea-urchins. Abundance of trilobites and brachiopods. Climax of graptolites.
	Cambrian	Cold, becoming Warm	450	Marine algae.	First foraminifera, graptolites, sea-lilies, star fishes, snails, brachiopods, trilobites, crustaceans, eurypterids, and other marine invertebrates. No land life known. First abundance of well-preserved fossils.

Major Unconformity. Second Great Revolution with much loss of record

| **PROTEROZOIC**
13 miles coarse sediments
1 mile limestones | Cryptozoic Eon | | 825 → 375 | Marine algae (concretions) | First radiolarian protozoans and worms; fossils few and poorly preserved. *Era of Primitive Life* |

925

Major Unconformity. First Great Revolution with great loss of record

| **ARCHEOZOIC**
9 miles muds and sands
9 miles limestones | | | 1750 | | *Era of Supposed Larval Life* |

1000?

AZOIC	No Record		?		*Lifeless*
PRE-CRUSTAL			?		
ORIGIN OF EARTH			?		

Dating based largely on Zeuner 1951

Fossils. The life of the past has left a great variety of records, and we can define a *fossil* as being *any trace of prehistoric life*. For obvious reasons fossils are never found in igneous or in strongly metamorphosed rocks. Most fossils have been preserved by burial in sediments, and many sedimentary rocks are literally filled with them. The things most commonly preserved are the hard parts of organisms, such as shells, bones, and teeth. Under exceptional circumstances even the more perishable soft parts may leave imprints on fine-textured muds, or be preserved by petrifaction, by impregnation with tar or resin, or by other means. Tracks left by worms or dinosaurs, mud-filled burrows, fossil excre-

ment, tooth marks on bones and holes drilled by snails in mollusk shells, deformities produced by parasites, and even objects made or used by animals, including ancient man, must all be regarded as fossils. Because fossils are so varied, both with respect to what is preserved and the means of preservation, the following scheme of classification will prove helpful.

I. Fossils giving evidence as to the form or structure of the organism:
   A. With preservation of both form and structure.
   1. Preservation of the actual remains, unaltered.
      a. By simple *burial* of hard parts. (Common.)
      b. By *freezing*. (Rare; Siberian mammoths, etc.)
      c. By *desiccation*. (R a r e ; ground-sloth mummies in caves, etc.)

Fig. 25.3. An aquatic relative of the scorpions, *Eurypterus lacustris*, preserved as an imprint in Silurian rocks at Buffalo, N.Y. (*Courtesy Carnegie Museum, Pittsburgh.*)

   2. Preservation of the actual remains, altered by *impregnation*
      a. With *mineral substances*, commonly lime or silica, filling the pores of bones and other hard parts; *permineralized* fossils. (Common; fossil bones that are heavier and denser than fresh bones, etc.)
      b. With *asphalt*. (Rare; animals trapped in tarpits.)
      c. With *resin*, which, on hardening, turns to copal or amber. (Rare; beautifully preserved amber and copal insects, flowers, and other minute fossils, mostly of Tertiary age. It should be noted, however, that many amber fossils are really molds, the impregnation not having been complete and the original material having almost disappeared.)
   3. *Petrifaction*, or molecular replacement of the original substance with another material, commonly silica, giving rise to fossils in which fine structural details are preserved, occasionally extending to microscopic cellular

structure. (Occasional; petrified wood; limy hard parts changed to flint, iron ore, pyrite, phosphate, or other substances.)

B. With preservation of form alone, details of internal structure lost.

1. *Molds*. Formed by percolating ground water dissolving away the original object, leaving a hole in the rock that records its form. In the instance of hollow objects like snail shells there may be an *external mold* and an *internal mold*, or core; the latter class of objects is often confused with natural casts. (Common.)

2. *Casts*. The interior of a mold may later be refilled with some mineral such as lime or silica, giving rise to a natural cast or *pseudomorph* (false + form), which has the shape but not the internal structure of the original

Fig. 25.4. A crane fly imbedded in Baltic amber of Oligocene age. See I:A2c in table on p. 396. (*Photo courtesy Chicago Natural History Museum.*)

object. A natural cast of a hollow object is formed in the space between the outer mold and the inner mold or core. (Moderately common.)

3. *Imprints*. Thin or soft parts may leave impressions of their form on the upper and lower surfaces of the rock layers that enclosed them, and these imprints may remain after the original object has disappeared or has been reduced to a layer of amorphous carbonized material. (Occasional; the commonest sorts of imprints are those of flat objects such as leaves, insect wings, or fish scales.)

4. *Footprints and trails*. Made on soft mud or wet sand and preserved by being covered with another layer of sediment. (Occasional.)

II. Fossils giving evidence of the existence and activities of organisms but not directly recording their form or structure.

A. *Coprolites*. Fossil excrement, sometimes giving direct evidence as to the nature of an animal's food and indirect evidence regarding the structure of its alimentary canal. (Occasional.)

B. *Lesions and deformities.* Such as bone lesions, giving evidence of microorganisms causing disease, and malformations due to the presence of animal parasites. (Relatively rare.)

C. *Habitations and artifacts.* Worm tubes, the cases of insect larvae, wood showing insect tunnels, mud nests built by insects, mammal burrows, and the like. This category also must include tools and ornaments made and used by prehistoric man. (Relatively rare.)

III. *Fossil-like objects (pseudofossils).* Objects are occasionally found in the rocks that are mistaken by untrained persons for fossils or are spoken of by geologists as "fossils" through analogy. Among the first class are chemically-formed nodules called *concretions,* which sometimes bear a striking resemblance to organic structures.[1] In the second class are such objects as "fossil" raindrop impressions, "fossil" ripple marks, "fossil" stream courses, and other normally ephemeral features of the physical world that have been preserved in some manner.

[1] An example is the so-called "dinosaur backbone," shown at the bottom of Silver Springs, Fla., by the guides. This is apparently the edge of a very large flint concretion. Dinosaurs had long been extinct when the upper Eocene Ocala limestone (in which the spring arises) was formed beneath the sea.

CHAPTER XXVI

THE HISTORY OF PLANTS

In this and following chapters we shall try to summarize what is known of the course of evolution from earliest times to the present. In so doing we encounter the historian's difficulty of selecting what is most significant without distorting and oversimplifying the story. Actually there are great gaps in our knowledge of the life of the past, and the fossils themselves are often hard to interpret. Nevertheless the general course of evolution is plain to be read in the rocks. In our brief account we shall have to make broad statements that are not without their exceptions, to omit all mention of many interesting and important matters, and to depend upon selected examples to illustrate what went on in all groups of organisms.

The story of evolution cannot be told without naming its characters. The names will be meaningless if they do not call to mind something of the appearance, structure, habits, and systematic position of the animals and plants to which they refer. All of the organisms discussed are included in the Appendix, where they are arranged in taxonomic order with brief descriptions of their most important characteristics.

THE BEGINNINGS OF LIFE

Our planet was born from the sun, along with the rest of the solar system, perhaps 2,500 million years ago. Nearly all authorities agree that the earth must have passed through a molten stage during which its internal constitution was established. We do not know how long it took for the earth to cool and solidify, for its deep and heavy atmosphere to thin by condensation of the water into the oceans, and for sunny skies and running water to usher in the reign of uniformity.

We do not and probably never shall know just how or when life appeared upon earth; but we can at least deduce something of the conditions and steps that led to the development of protoplasm. Organic substances must have existed in the first water that condensed around the cooling earth, for carbides from the molten interior, interacting with the super-heated steam of the atmosphere, would have produced a variety of carbon-containing compounds. These, dissolved in the envelope of hot water around the earth, would unite with oxygen and ammonia to produce hydrocarbons and nitrogenous compounds. With time in abundance for chance encounters between molecules, an ever-increasing variety of chemical substances, both organic and inorganic, would have come into existence, and among these we may suppose were the first simple *proteins*.

In generalized terms a protein consists of a polypeptide chain folded over on itself many times to form a three-dimensional particle, held together by chemical linkages and with exposed peripheral valences that can bind several or many such units into large colloidal particles. By chance meetings in the molecular soup of the primordial waters a certain proportion of the ancestral protein molecules may have made net gains in size and complexity, and some of these augmented molecules presumably had structures resembling those of *nucleoproteins*.

Nucleoproteins appear to be the essential stuff of life. Direct analysis and circumstantial evidence point to the conclusion that genes and viruses are wholly or chiefly composed of these substances. Chromosomes are largely nucleoprotein, which suggests but does not prove that this is true of the genes. Several viruses have been isolated in pure (crystalline) form, and these are all nucleoproteins. Genes and viruses probably approach one another in particle size, and both are able to duplicate themselves by organizing protein molecules from their environments and to mutate. These facts have led many biologists to the idea that the first life units were nucleoprotein particles similar to the viruses we know today. Beadle has proposed to call these hypothetical archetypic life particles *protogenes*.

Protogenes are compared with *viruses* rather than with genes, because the former are less complex and more uniform, are not grouped into assemblages of different but interacting units (chromosomes), can exist independently of cells and cytoplasm, and can be chemically isolated. The viruses cannot be regarded as surviving examples of protogenes, however, for all of them can multiply only within living cells. The *bacteriophages*, for example, can exist in a free state as submicroscopic, nonreproducing, physiologically inactive nucleoprotein particles. These particles are able to adhere to and penetrate bacterial cells. Entry of the particle disrupts the genetic, regulatory apparatus of the cell but leaves its metabolic system intact. The genetic material of the virus takes over control and guides the metabolic system of the cell in the production not of its normal products but of materials that become organized into new virus particles. These, barring mutation or recombination, are exactly like the particle that originally entered. Completion of the process is accompanied by breakdown of the cell membrane and liberation of perhaps 100 times as many virus particles as entered the cell. While the virus is within the cell, it is evidently dissociated into its components, with later recombination. This is demonstrated by the fact that if a bacterial colony is infected with two virus strains, one having the properties *Ab* and the other *aB*, the virus particles liberated on destruction of the cells include not only these types but also the new combinations *AB* and *ab*.

Whether virus particles are "alive" or not depends on how we define life. They can be crystallized without loss of ability to infect cells; but they also reproduce themselves and occasionally mutate. If we assume that the hypothetical protogenes were like viruses in these respects, we must accept the conclusion that the transition from nonliving to living was a gradual process and that there was no single instant at which life came into existence. Even if protogenes were the source of later life, we are wholly in the dark as how they acquired cytoplasm, how they ceased to depend upon the taking of organic molecules from the environment and passed to the synthesis of food from inorganic materials, and how they came to reproduce sexually. We can only assume that mutations occurred and that natural selection came into play.

The first *cells* must have been bits of protoplasm enclosed in semi-permeable membranes, containing genic particles and cytoplasm, but without differentiated nuclei and cytoplasmic structures. They would thus have been comparable to the simplest bacteria, and like some of the latter they were doubtless chemosynthetic. The complex sunlight-chlorophyll mechanism was almost certainly a subsequent development, and food-capturing (animal) cells may actually have arisen earlier than the green plants. One of the chief differences between the primordial cells and nonliving colloid systems was that, like all subsequent protoplasm, they must have been "open" instead of "closed" chemical systems, in which occurred continuous intake of simple food materials, synthesis of organic compounds by use of energy, and outgo of "waste" materials. A closed system tends toward a static condition of internal balance and fixed size; an open system in proper environment and with enough available energy must grow to a size limit imposed by the surface-volume ratio. If such a system were so constituted that it divided whenever it approached the limiting size, it would show the essential reproductive behavior of a cell.

Speculations such as these appear logical and reasonable and accord with what is known of the physics and chemistry of protoplasm and with the evidence as to the nature of genes and viruses. Yet they lie at present, and perhaps must always remain, in the realm of untestable hypothesis.

THALLOPHYTES, THE MOST ANCIENT PLANTS

The records of the first two-thirds of earth history are contained in two very ancient rock series, in most regions buried under layer on layer of younger rocks. These old rocks are exposed in some places, as around Hudson Bay and Lake Superior and in the bottom of the Grand Canyon. The older of the two series, formed during the *Archeozoic era*, which endured perhaps 900 million years, consists of highly metamorphosed sediments and enormous amounts of intruded igneous rock. Any fossils that may once have been present must have been destroyed by the heat and pressure of diastrophism and vulcanism.

One thing, however, suggests the presence of life during the Archeozoic. In New York, Ontario, and Quebec there is a vast body of metamorphosed limestones, shales and sandstones known as the *Grenville series*. The limestones of later periods were made largely through the agency of organisms, but since lime carbonate can also be precipitated chemically from sea water, this is not conclusive evidence that life existed in Grenville times. The deposits also contain flakes and masses of *graphite*, a metamorphic form of free carbon. The only known source of carbon in later rocks is the bodies of plants and animals. If this was the source of the Archeozoic graphite, we must infer that life was abundant in the seas of

Fig. 26.1. The general relations of Archeozoic, Proterozoic, and Cambrian rocks and the major unconformities between them shown in diagram. (*Redrawn after Chamberlin and Salisbury, Geology, courtesy Henry Holt and Company, Inc.*)

that time, for it has been estimated that there is more carbon in these rocks than in all the Appalachian coal beds.

The Archeozoic era closed with the first of the great "revolutions"; all the continents were uplifted, lofty mountains were folded up, and a long period of erosion followed, in which all the lands were worn low. When a new cycle of deposition began in the *Proterozoic era*, conditions had changed; igneous activity had lessened, and sedimentary rocks formed in interior seas were predominant. In most regions they have been metamorphosed, but in certain areas they remained unchanged and have come down to us as the oldest strata in which fossils could have been preserved. Many geologists have sought in vain for traces of life in these rocks.

Some fossils, however, have been found. In the Big Belt Mountains of Montana and in Canada there are extensive limestone deposits composed of rounded masses similar to those produced by certain lime-secreting algae of the present time. Much doubt has existed as to whether these were of organic or inorganic origin, but most authorities now agree that they were precipitated by algae, probably of the blue-green group. Other Proterozoic fossils that have been identified with fair certainty are those of bacteria, brown algae (seaweeds), a jellyfish, casts of annelid worm burrows, and what are probably silicious sponge spicules. Reports of protozoa and arthropods are as yet without good foundation. The absence of fossils in the Archeozoic and their great scarcity in the Proterozoic rocks has led to the grouping of these two eras into the *cryptozoic eon*, or age of hidden life, covering the first two-thirds of earth history.

Few though the Proterozoic fossils are, they prove not only that life was present but also that evolution was already far advanced before the end of the era. Cell structure had been perfected, animals had become differentiated from plants, multicellular types had evolved from unicellular ones, and at least some of the important groups of plants and animals

FIG. 26.2. Ancient algae. Natural exposure of a part of a reef of the lime-secreting alga Cryptozoon at Saratoga, N.Y. The Pleistocene glaciers have ground off the surface of these Cambrian rocks, forming natural cross sections of the rounded algal "heads." (*Courtesy American Museum of Natural History.*)

had come into existence. Among plants, we know or can reasonably infer the presence of many kinds of bacteria and algae; among animals, members of the phyla Protozoa, Porifera, Coelenterata, Annelida, Brachiopoda, and Arthropoda. Why, then, are pre-Cambrian fossils so rare? The answer seems to be that few organisms as yet secreted limy or silicious skeletons, and that pre-Cambrian plants lacked cuticle and woody tissues —in other words, there were no hard parts suitable for fossilization.

Some biologists, impressed with the high degree of organization shown by the cell, have maintained that evolution from the beginning of life to the perfected cell may have taken as long as all subsequent evolution. Others are of the opinion that it need not have taken long, in the geological sense, for the cellular stage to have been reached. In any event, as soon as the development of the cell made cell aggregation and multicellular organisms possible, there is reason to suppose that the pace of evolution increased and that the principal evolutionary lines were not long in appearing. As life has become more abundant and varied, the rate of evolutionary change in most groups seems to have continued to accelerate, through the interaction between gene complexes of increasing evolutionary potentialities and environments that became increasingly varied, competitive, and selective.

The Proterozoic era closed with the second great "revolution"; again the continents rose, the seas withdrew, and the lands were profoundly eroded during a very long interval of which almost no record remains.

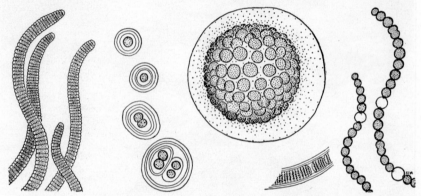

FIG. 26.3. Some types of modern blue-green algae.

When the seas finally came back over the lands in Cambrian time, their sediments, resting on the truncated surface of the cryptozoic rocks, were filled with a profusion of fossils. This return of the seas marked the start of the *Paleozoic era*, or age of ancient life—and the real beginning of the fossil record.

The Cambrian, Ordovician, and Silurian rocks were mostly laid down in the seas, so that the early Paleozoic record is essentially that of marine life. Apparently the lands were dreary, lifeless wastes at least until late Cambrian time and perhaps longer. The seas, however, swarmed with life—with many kinds of animals, among which trilobites and brachiopods were dominant, and what must have been an equal abundance and variety of simple plants. Unfortunately the plants left fewer fossil remains than did the animals. They lacked woody parts and surface cuticle (the most commonly fossilized parts of plants), while in contrast many of the early Paleozoic animals were well supplied with limy skeletons or armor. The plants were all members of the lowest division, Thallophyta, although all the animal phyla (except perhaps the Chordata) seem to have been present by Cambrian times. Since the fossil record of the thallophytes is meager, we shall have to piece it out with inference and deduction based on our knowledge of the group as it now exists.

The Bacteria (Fig. A.4) lack chlorophyll and are classed as plants chiefly because of their similarity in structure to the blue-green algae and the ability of some of them to use chemical energy for the synthesis of organic from inorganic substances. Most of them feed upon organic matter, and in the course of their evolution many have become parasitic, producing disease in plants and animals. We tend, therefore, to think of the bacteria as injurious, whereas in fact a great many are beneficial and essential in maintaining the balance of nature. They are the chief agents in the formation of soils, for without the acids and alkalies they

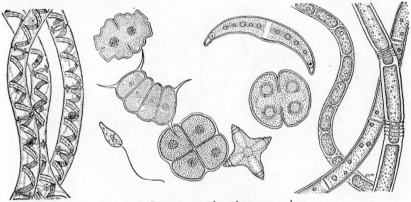

FIG. 26.4. Some types of modern green algae.

produce, the decomposition of rocks would be an exceedingly slow process. Certain bacteria have the ability to take nitrogen from solution in water and to build it into compounds which can be used by higher plants. They are alone among organisms in this ability. Of no less importance is the fact that bacteria are the chief agents of decay, breaking down dead bodies and returning their constituents to soil or water for use by new generations. Without the activities of the soil-forming and nitrogen-fixing bacteria, life could never have flourished on land, and without decay the supply of elements essential for life would have soon been depleted.

Because pre-Cambrian sediments show the same physical characteristics as those of later times, we must infer that bacteria have existed since the earliest periods of earth history. Objects believed to be fossil bacteria have been found in Proterozoic red iron ores of the famous Lake Superior mining district. The formation of these ores (some of which are of Archeozoic age) had already been attributed by some geologists to the action of iron-depositing bacteria, and the similarity of the supposed fossils to the modern iron bacteria strongly supports this view. Many supposed fossils of bacteria have also been found in later rocks. The best evidence of the presence and activity of bacteria, however, is that soils formed, dead bodies decayed, and plants flourished in the past as they do today.

The Algae rival the bacteria in their claims to antiquity and have greatly influenced the course of geologic processes and the development of life. The *blue-greens* (Figs. 26.3 and A.1) are the simplest and probably the most ancient; they have many similarities with bacteria, and as

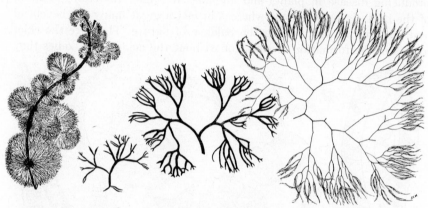

FIG. 26.5. Some types of modern red algae.

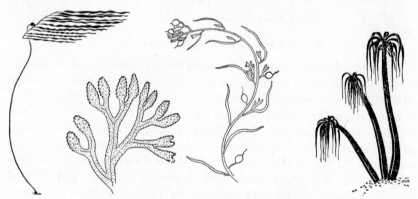

FIG. 26.6. Some types of modern brown algae.

previously mentioned, they are believed to have been the principal factor in the formation of the great limestone deposits of Proterozoic (and presumably also of Archeozoic) time. The *green algae* (Figs. 13.11, 13.12, 26.4, and A.2) are more important. Not only are they the probable ancestors of all the higher plants, but they also form a significant part of the drifting plant life of seas and lakes—*phytoplankton*, which is the basic food supply for all aquatic animals. Some of the green algae play a prominent role in limestone formation, adding to the calcium carbonate of coral reefs and forming marl deposits in fresh water. The group includes both unicellular and multicellular types, and some of the latter are known as far back as Cambrian time. The lime-secreting *red algae* form reddish or whitish incrustations on shells and rocks and are among the important rock builders in the tropical seas today, contributing as much to the formation of coral reefs as do the corals themselves. First known from the Ordovician period, the group has increased in abundance and importance to the present. The *brown algae* are the familiar seaweeds called kelps. They are the most highly organized of the algae, and some of them reach large size, but like the others they lack roots and leaves and take their sustenance directly from the water which surrounds them. Lacking hard parts they are seldom fossilized, but imprints ascribed to brown algae have been found in Proterozoic rocks.

Finally, the *diatoms* (Figs. 26.7 and A.3) require mention. These are microscopic unicellular plants with delicate siliceous skeletons. Various species of this group make up a large part of the phytoplankton of modern seas. A single quart of sea water may contain thousands of billions of diatoms during the reproductive season, and the millions of tons of diatom protoplasm present in the upper layers of the oceans constitutes the most important basic food source for marine animals. Diatoms and other phytoplankton are fed upon by protozoa, by the larvae of free-swimming and bottom-dwelling animals, and by other small fry at the base of a food chain that extends to the largest carnivores. Many diatoms occur in the plankton of lakes and ponds, and other species live attached to submerged surfaces in both fresh and salt water. The group is probably ancient, but fossils are unknown from the older rocks, doubtless

F I G . 2 6 . 7 . A modern species of diatom, *Navicula crabro*. (*Courtesy General Biological Supply House, Inc.*)

because the fragile skeleton is so easily crumbled by pressure or dissolved by ground water. In Cretaceous and Cenozoic strata, however, great beds of diatomaceous earth have been preserved, and similar deposits are being formed today.

The Fungi (Figs. 26.8 and A.5 to 9) are plants incapable of photosynthesis for lack of chlorophyll. For the most part they are scavengers, working with bacteria to destroy the dead bodies of organisms; but many have become parasitic on living plants or animals, and some have entered into a cooperative relationship with higher plants, serving the latter as functional replacements of root hairs. The fungi as a group are quite old; mycelia and fungus spores have been found in fossilized decayed stems of one of the oldest known vascular plants, of Devonian age, and many sorts have been described from the stem tissues or leaves of Carboniferous and later plants. The fungi are apparently an artificial assemblage in that they are not closely related but seem to have arisen at different times from different algal ancestors by loss of chlorophyll and assumption of saprophytic or parasitic existence.

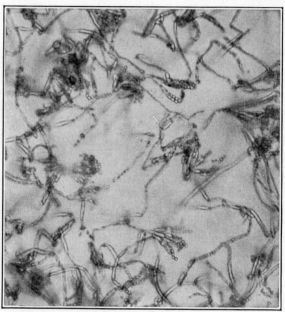

FIG. 26.8. Photomicrograph of the fungus Penicillium, showing filamentous hyphae and spores. (*Courtesy General Biological Supply House, Inc.*)

ANCIENT LAND PLANTS

To live upon land successfully a plant must possess certain things that are lacking in the thallophytes. It must have a protective cuticle to reduce loss of water by evaporation, and some means of absorbing water from the soil. If it is to attain any size, a third thing is necessary—a vascular system for carrying water from the buried to the exposed parts. At some time during the early Paleozoic one or more groups of plants made the transition from sea to land, but there are no fossils to show just how it was accomplished. The green algae are thought to have been the ancestors of land plants, because of similarities in cell structure and the absence in land plants of pigments other than chlorophyll, such as occur in the other groups of algae. Some of the multicellular green algae became adapted to life in fresh water, and in consequence became subject to seasonal fluctuations of water level which at times left them prostrate on the exposed muddy shores of ponds and streams. This would have been fatal to most of them; but if some developed a cuticle on the exposed parts and water-absorbent rhizoids on the lower surface, they not only could have survived but could have come to live on permanently moist ground away from bodies of water. A later evolution of vascular tissues would have permitted upward growth of shoots, exposing more surface to sunlight.

There is one surviving group of plants that remains in a stage which is approximately the same as this early adaptation to land conditions—the *bryophytes*. The simplest of these are the *liverworts* (Fig. A.10), most of which have flat, thin bodies that lie pressed against the surface of the moist soil or rock upon which they grow. Above they are covered with cuticle; below they have many fine hairlike processes that absorb water from the substratum. A few have erect shoots bearing small leaflike structures, but these liverworts are all very small, lacking any trace of a vascular system. The *mosses* (Figs. 17.3 and 4) are more advanced bryophytes, with stems and leaflike structures; but they also are without vascular tissues and in consequence are all small, being unable to transport water to any considerable height. Bryophytes bear their spore-producing organs on stalks, for wider dispersal of the spores, but the fact

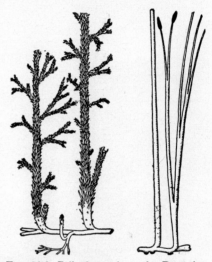

FIG. 26.9. Psilophytes from the Devonian of Scotland, restored. Left, *Asteroxylon mackiei;* right, *Rhynia major.* (*From Haupt, An Introduction to Botany.*)

that their sperm cells must swim in water films to reach the eggs has kept them from complete adaptation to land life. The living bryophytes show us what the earliest land plants must have been like, and the group is presumably very ancient, though fossil liverworts and supposed mosses are first known from the Carboniferous.

The first vascular plants. It is not bryophytes but simple vascular plants, which appear earliest in the fossil record. The oldest are from the mid-Silurian of Australia, but it was in the Devonian period that they first became numerous and varied. The simplest and probably the most ancient were the *psilophytes*, which may have been the ancestors of all the later vascular plants. They were slender green stems, a few inches to a foot or more in height, naked or covered with small leaves, and bearing spore cases at their tips. They had no roots but rose from horizontal underground stems bearing rhizoids. The shoots had a central strand of xylem surrounded by phloem, and possessed cuticle and stomata. Psilophytes seem to have formed meadowlike stands in swampy spots and along stream margins. With them occurred two slightly more advanced types of plants—*horsetails*, or scouring rushes, with fluted, jointed stems and whorls of leaves or branches at the nodes; and *club mosses*, or ground

Fig. 26.10. Restoration of the earliest known forest, at Gilboa, N.Y. (*Courtesy New York State Museum.*)

pines (lycopods), having stems densely covered with small pointed leaves and bearing spore cases in the leaf axils. The psilophytes became extinct by the end of the Devonian, but the other two groups prospered and some of their descendants increased greatly in size.

The first forests. By mid-Devonian times true *ferns* had appeared; of all the familiar present-day groups of plants these are the oldest. Throughout the late Paleozoic and Mesozoic they formed the undergrowth in moist, shady places, just as their modern descendants do. The ferns were spore bearers then as now, but some unknown member of the group gave rise to the first true seed plants. These were the *seed ferns*

(Figs. 26.11 and A.18), so similar to true ferns that they cannot be distinguished by their foliage. Many other types of plants of unknown relationships were also present. Some of the club mosses, horsetails, and other plants grew to tree size and formed the first forests. One of the best known of these forests was discovered at Gilboa in the Catskill Mountains of New York, where petrified logs and many large upright

Fig. 26.11. Restoration of a Carboniferous swamp forest in Illinois. The vertically ribbed tree trunks are those of Sigillaria. The trunks with spirally arranged leaf scars and the twigs with cones and grasslike leaves are Lepidodendron. Note the seed-fern fronds in center, some bearing seeds at the tips. The small plants with whorled leaves are Sphenophyllum. (*Courtesy Chicago Natural History Museum.*)

stumps were found. These trees were 40 feet tall, with crowns of slender branches that bore three rows of small pointed leaves. They were long thought to be seed bearers, but the supposed seeds have been found to contain spores.

The coal forests. The Devonian was followed by the Carboniferous period, so named because it was the time when most of the important coal deposits of the world were made. Vast swamps came into existence in eastern North America, Europe, China, South Africa, and Brazil. The climate of these regions was evidently mild, humid, and without marked seasons. Luxuriant forests of fast-growing, soft-tissued trees occupied the low wet lands. On the swamp floors partially decayed plant debris—logs,

twigs, leaves, spores, and seeds—accumulated in thick layers, and from time to time these were buried under sheets of mud during brief incursions of shallow seas. Where the plant layers were merely compacted by the weight of later deposits or were but slightly metamorphosed, they gradually altered to soft coal and are filled with fossils; but where they were subjected to the pressures that folded up great mountain ranges during the Permian period, they were changed to anthracite, and all fossils were destroyed.

A remarkable feature of the coal forests is the similarity of their species in all continents. These floras were as nearly cosmopolitan as have ever existed, suggesting wide land connections and absence of climatic barriers. Most of the great trees were spore bearers descended from Devonian horsetails and lycopods. Giant horsetails with fluted columnar stems (Calamites, Fig. A.14) grew 30 to 70 feet high in dense thickets like "canebrakes," and others of the coal-forest trees were even more imposing. The *scale trees* had trunks and branches covered with scalelike leaf scars. Though they were lycopods, related to the small club mosses, or ground pines, of today, they reached heights of 100 to 120 feet and had

Fig. 26.12. Restoration of Cordaites, with Calamites at right. (*Courtesy American Museum of Natural History.*)

trunks 4 to 6 feet in diameter at the base. There were two chief kinds—Lepidodendron (Fig. A.17), with slender trunk and a crown of stubby twigs covered with straplike leaves ½ foot long and with leaf scars running in spirals; and Sigillaria (Fig. A.16), with thicker trunk, few or no branches, longer leaves, and leaf scars in vertical rows. Another giant of the coal forests was Cordaites (Fig. 26.12), a primitive seed plant and forerunner of the conifers. It had soft wood resembling that of pines, but its leaves were bladelike and from several inches to 6 feet long, while its seeds were borne on branching stalks instead of in a cone. Some of the largest cordaites had trunks that rose 80 to 90 feet without a branch; their topmost twigs reached 120 feet above the ground. More familiar in appearance were the many small trees, herbs, and vines with fernlike leaves; some of these were true ferns, but a larger number were seed ferns. In these dank forests dwelt the oldest known winged insects and the primitive stegocephalian amphibians.

Permian changes in plant life. The third great earth disturbance, the Appalachian revolution, occurred during the Permian period at the end of the Paleozoic era. Once more the continents rose. Lofty mountain ranges were formed, and a world-wide change in climate set in. Great ice sheets covered parts of all the southern continents; in the northern hemisphere the climate became dry and cold. The coal swamps disappeared, and before the end of the Permian nearly all their character-istic spore-bearing plants except the ferns had died out. In their place came a flora of plants with smaller, more leathery leaves, better adapted to cold and drought, and probably derived from the unknown upland plants of Carboniferous times. There were many seed ferns, and ginkgoes and various primitive conifers appeared. A new flora of cold-tolerant plants, dominated by forms called *Glossopteris* on account of their narrow tongue-shaped leaves, spread over all the southern continents. Like most of the other successful

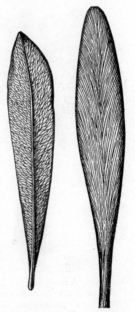

FIG. 26.13. Two charac-teristic leaves from the Permian Glossopteris flora. Glossopteris at left, Gangamopteris at right.

Permian types these are believed to have been seed plants; indeed the outstanding event of the time, so far as plants were concerned, was the rapid increase of seed bearers and marked decline of spore bearers. The reason for this seems evident. Possession of seeds gave the spermatophytes a distinct advantage over the spore bearers in this time of stress, for their gametophytes and embryos were protected and nourished by the parent sporophyte plant, while their seeds could remain dormant through periods of adverse conditions and use their food stores for rapid growth as soon as the proper season arrived.

THE RISE OF MODERN FLORAS

In the history of vertebrate animals the Mesozoic era was the age of reptiles, while mammals dominated the Cenozoic. Among plants and many invertebrate animal groups there was no such striking change at the end of the Mesozoic; the significant advances occurred at other times. Following the replacement of the Paleozoic spore bearers by seed plants in the Permian, three major events in the history of plants stand forth: the rise of the cycads and conifers in the first half of the Mesozoic era;

FIG. 26.14. A modern cycad, *Cycas revoluta*. (*Redrawn from Strassburger, Textbook of Botany, by permission The Macmillan Company.*)

the replacement of these by flowering plants in the Cretaceous period and early Cenozoic; and the rise and spread of herbaceous seed plants and of grasses in middle and late Cenozoic time.

The evergreen forests of the early Mesozoic. In the Triassic period the lands, drained and extended by the Permian uplift, were in many regions semiarid with strongly seasonal climates. Most of the plants belonged to groups which still survive. Ginkgoes, conifers and cycads were dominant; there were some tree ferns, and many small ferns and lycopods in the undergrowth. As a whole the flora was not luxuriant and had the aspect of scrub. Water was scarce, and extensive root systems developed for the first time. There were no flowering plants, and in the absence of grasses and weeds the vast plains which today would be prairie or steppe were then probably barren wastes. By Jurassic times the lands had become lower and climates more humid; plant life increased in abundance but continued to be dominated by the cycads and conifers.

The palmlike *cycads* (Figs. 25.2 and 26.14) were numerous and varied, though today they are represented only by a few surviving genera (Fig. A.19). They had thick trunks with a crown of large feather-shaped leaves; some bore their naked seeds in flowerlike structures, others in cones. They grew chiefly along the streams and on moist slopes. Their distant relatives, the *ginkgoes*, were also represented by various genera and species, though today they have but a single survivor, the curious maidenhair tree (*Ginkgo biloba*). The ginkgoes and cycads probably arose independently from some of the Paleozoic seed ferns, and both have swimming sperms within the pollen tube, reminiscent of the free-swimming sperms of their still more remote fern ancestors. Not all the early Mesozoic forests were scrublike; in some places there were dense stands of tall *pines*. Some of the silicified pine logs of the Jurassic Petrified Forest in Arizona are 10 feet in diameter and 100 feet long and give evidence of trees that towered to a height of nearly 200 feet. A striking feature of the Jurassic flora is the wide distribution of many of its species; excluding the cycads, the same kinds of plants occurred in the New and Old Worlds and from Alaska and Spitsbergen to the antarctic coasts. Obviously Jurassic climates were mild even in high latitudes.

The rise of flowering plants. One of the most dramatic events in the history of life was the sudden rise of the *angiosperms*, or flowering plants, during the Cretaceous period. No one has succeeded in finding their ancestors, and their origin is a mystery. Their oldest known fossils, from the early Cretaceous, are already trees of types now familiar—magnolia, fig, sassafras, and poplar, among the dicotyledons, and palms, representing the monocotyledons. By mid-Cretaceous times the forests had become essentially modern, including such other trees as beech,

FIG. 26.15. A relic from the Mesozoic. The maidenhair tree, *Gingko biloba*, lone survivor of its group. (*Redrawn from Strassburger, Textbook of Botany, by permission The Macmillan Company.*)

birch, willow, maple, oak, walnut, sycamore, tulip, sweet gum, breadfruit, and ebony, together with shrubs like laurel, viburnum, ivy, hazel, and holly Pines and other conifers persisted as in modern times, but they no longer dominated the landscapes as in the preceding period. The forest undergrowth was still made up of ferns and lycopods; herbaceous angiosperms did not appear until later, and the dry plains were still probably barren and desertlike in the absence of grasses.

The coming of the angiosperms had a profound effect upon the evolution of terrestrial vertebrates. All animal life is ultimately dependent upon plant food; but prior to the Cretaceous nearly all land vertebrates were carnivores—members of food chains in which larger organisms preyed upon smaller, and so on down to the smallest, which were the insects and other tiny creatures that fed on plants and plant debris. Under such circumstances the larger forms could never have been abundant. It is true that some of the Jurassic reptiles did become adapted to feeding upon the coarse leaves of cycads and other gymnosperms and gave rise to several lines of herbivorous dinosaurs in the Cretaceous; but such plants are poor fare. It was the angiosperms that made available the first abundant and nutritious plant food—seeds, fruits, nuts, and edible foliage in limitless quantity—and thus opened the way for a tremendous increase in the amount of animal life which the lands could

Fig. 26.16. A Triassic forest of giant pines, with an undergrowth of cycads. (*Courtesy American Museum of Natural History.*)

support. With the rise of flowering plants to dominance, many groups of animals became herbivores and multiplied in kind and number, as did the carnivores that fed upon them. The rapid evolution of the mammals and birds followed and was made possible by the evolution of the flowering plants.

Forests continued to dominate the scene until midway through the following Cenozoic era. Meanwhile the ancestral Rocky Mountains and

Andes had been uplifted at the end of the Mesozoic and worn down to level plains. During the Eocene and Oligocene epochs moist, mild, uniform climates prevailed over the world, with redwoods, beech, chestnut and elm occurring in Greenland and Siberia, cycads, magnolias and figs in Alaska, and palms and alligators in the Dakotas. But in Miocene times the continents began to rise in the first stages of the *Alpine* or *Cascadian revolution* from which the world is just emerging. This revolution brought with it great climatic changes and correspondingly great effects upon the life of the lands.

The spread of grasslands. Grasses and herbs appeared early in the Cenozoic era, but were at first of little importance. When the lands began to rise and mountains to be formed during the Miocene, however, large parts of North America and Eurasia began to receive less rainfall. Climates cooled and became more seasonal, and the vegetational belts shifted toward the equator. Many regions became too arid to support tree growth, and here the grasses and herbs found opportunity to spread. With their large root systems, small exposed surface, rapid growth and maturation, resistant seeds, and ability to grow in dense soil-protecting stands, the grasses are the best adapted of all plants for life in semiarid regions with strongly seasonal climates. By the time the Cascadian revolution reached its climax in the Pliocene, vast prairies and grassy plains like those of today had come into existence,[1] and the forests had become restricted to the moister parts of the continents. The whole of western North America, except in the mountains and along the Pacific slope, became grassland or desert, and similar changes occurred in the other continents. In the eastern half of North America and in eastern Asia and Europe, the forests continued little changed from those of the Cretaceous. Today there is less difference between the floras of England, Virginia, and China than between those of Virginia and Wyoming.

The development of the grasslands, though not comparable in importance to the rise of the angiosperms, was an event of major significance for land vertebrates. The new food source furnished by the harsh grasses and their seeds permitted the evolution of a host of grazing mammals, their multiplication to hitherto unheard of abundance, and the attainment of new levels of adaptation by both the herbivores and their predatory enemies.

[1] It is interesting to note that an increase in the grasslands during the Miocene and Pliocene was originally assumed largely from the grazing modifications shown by the teeth of horses and other groups that occurred at this time. Only recently has it been discovered that the middle Tertiary rocks of the plains regions are full of the fossilized seeds of grasses. These seeds show that the grasses were then undergoing much more rapid evolution than were the forest plants.

The effects of the glacial epoch. The cooling of climates that began in the Miocene culminated in the Pleistocene glaciations, in which ice sheets spread over about one-fourth of the land surface of the world. Four glacial ages occurred, with warmer interglacial intervals during which the ice melted away and climates became much as they are now. With each advance of the ice sheets all vegetation was destroyed over vast areas, which were later reexposed and repopulated. The ranges of plants and animals shifted and changed shape, not only in the glaciated territories but in the bordering regions as well. Many of the older and less adaptable species became extinct or were reduced to mere isolated remnants of what had been abundant and widespread populations. As yet we do not know whether the ice ages are over or whether we are living in one of the warm interglacial times. Parts of the Great Lakes region and New England were still ice-covered as recently as 12,000 years ago; the longest of the interglacial ages endured perhaps 100,000 years.

CHAPTER XXVII

ANCIENT ANIMALS

The history of animals really begins with the Cambrian period, when fossils were first preserved in abundance. This was a time far along in earth history, when life had already been in existence for countless ages— perhaps even for 1,000 million years. It is no wonder, then, that when the curtain rises, it reveals a scene crowded with living things of many kinds. Every important animal phylum except the chordates was already represented. Since the Cambrian fauna is the oldest known assemblage of animals, it deserves more than passing notice.

The Cambrian fauna. All Cambrian life was marine. What went on in the oceans we do not know; the record is that of the shallow seas that spread over the face of the lands. Their sands and muds are filled with the fossils of shell-bearing animals, and by a rare and fortunate circumstance a great many of the soft-bodied creatures were preserved as imprints in the Burgess shales of British Columbia. All told some 1,200 species of Cambrian animals have been described from North America alone, and while these are but a sample of the whole, they suffice to give us a clear picture of the life of the time.

Most of the animals were either small, delicate forms that drifted in the surface waters (*plankton*) or bottom dwellers (*benthos*) that crawled or swam over the sea floor, or attached themselves to some object for support, or burrowed in the mud. There was no group of strong swimmers (*nekton*) such as lived in later seas. In the plankton there must have been an abundance of protozoa and minute multicellular animals that fed upon the floating algae, but they have left few traces. The smaller plankton animals and plants furnished sustenance for larger animals—swimming annelid worms and shrimplike crustacea, of which many kinds have been found; these in turn were captured by jellyfishes very like those of today. On the sea floor lived simple sponges and possibly corals, together with short-stalked echinoderms, snails, bivalve mollusks, and primitive cephalopods. The dominant animals were the brachiopods and the trilobites.

A *brachiopod* has a hinged bivalve shell like a clam and, like a clam, gets its plankton food from a water current created by its beating cilia; but there the resemblance ceases. The two belong to different phyla and are easily distinguished by the features of the shell. In the mollusk the valves are right and left and each valve is asymmetrical; in the brachiopod the valves are upper and lower, and each valve is bilaterally symmetrical. Brachiopods were abundant and varied in the Cambrian seas and continued to flourish throughout the Paleozoic era. Some of the genera and species are important time markers for identifying Paleozoic strata. From Cretaceous times onward they declined until today only a few sur-

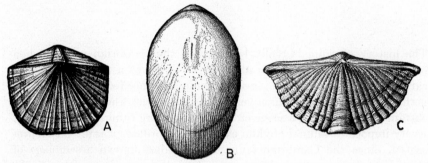

Fig. 27.1. Paleozoic brachiopods. *A*, Billingsella, Cambrian. *B*, Rensselaeria, Devonian. *C*, Mucrospirifer, Devonian.

Fig. 27.2. Silurian trilobites. Left, Arctineurus; right, Bumastus. Sponges and horn or cup corals are also shown. (*Courtesy Rochester Museum.*)

viving types remain. One of these (Lingula, the oldest known genus of animals) is remarkable in that it scarcely differs from its far distant Cambrian ancestors.

The *trilobites* (Figs. 25.2, 27.2 and B.17) were the highest form of Cambrian life. They were primitive arthropods, apparently close to the ancestral stock of the crustaceans. They had flattened, elongated bodies covered above with a firm shell. A large anterior "head" region contained the small brain and large stomach and bore two large compound eyes on the top; behind this were several or many free segments and finally a tail plate which might be broad or narrow. Along the top of the shell ran two grooves that divided the body into three lobes (whence the name trilobite). On the under side were two rows of legs, all alike, and running almost from end to end of the body. Each leg had an outer gill branch, an inner walking and swimming branch, and a jawlike spiny base. Apparently a trilobite could chew from stem to stern, crawling over its food and passing a continuous stream of food particles forward along the row of jaws to the scooplike mouth. The average trilobite was 2 or 3 inches long, though a few giants reached a length of 2 feet. Most of them were scavengers that crawled over the sea floor, but a few were swimming plankton feeders, and others became eyeless burrowers that fed upon mud. The peak of trilobite dominance was reached in the late Cambrian, but the group remained important until Devonian times and then dwindled to final extinction during the Permian.

We can scarcely comprehend the immensity of even 1 million years; this Cambrian fauna lived some 450 million years ago, and the most remarkable thing about it is that it was essentially modern in aspect. Its species were fewer and on the whole much simpler than those of today, but all belonged to phyla which still exist, and with the possible exception of the chordates no phyla not present in the Cambrian have since appeared. Post-Cambrian evolution has been largely an elaboration, a branching out, and a replacement of old by new, within the main evolutionary patterns laid down during or prior to the early Paleozoic.

In tracing the later history of animals we cannot even attempt to describe the changing faunas, period by period, nor to follow more than a few of the many evolutionary lines. Instead we shall have to confine our attention to selected groups that illustrate the general course of evolutionary change, with particular reference to the chordate stocks which include man's ancestors.

The record of life during the two periods following the Cambrian is still almost wholly that of the seas. The Ordovician fauna was more diversified and abundant than the Cambrian, and additional groups appeared in Silurian time. Trilobites and brachiopods continued to exist in large numbers, and graptolites, colonial corals, bryozoans, crinoids, starfishes, sea urchins, barnacles and eurypterids joined the older groups of invertebrates. Sometime during the Silurian the first land plants appeared, and some of the arthropods became land dwellers at about the same period. The most significant event in the animal world was the appearance of the first vertebrates in late Ordovician time.

The early vertebrates. The oldest known members of the phylum Chordata were small, fishlike creatures, with a heavy armor of bony plates and scales that gives them their name *ostracoderms* (meaning "hard-shelled"). Fragments of their armor have been found in late Ordovician rocks, and the group became common in the Silurian period. They are true vertebrates, though very primitive ones, and must have had a long line of simpler chordate ancestors of which no trace has yet been found. Of the many theories about the origin of the chordates, that

which derives them from a common stock with the echinoderms is best
supported by embryological and morphological evidence. The phylum
Echinodermata includes the sea lilies, starfishes, sea urchins and their
allies. It seems at first sight ridiculous to suppose that there could be any
relationship between these sedentary, five-radiate, armored, uniquely
constructed animals and the motile, bilaterally symmetrical, metameric
chordates. We find, however, that echinoderms possess small, free-swimming, bilaterally symmetrical larvae that have curved tubular digestive
tracts and external bands of cilia. A very similar larva occurs in the life
history of the acorn worm, Balanoglossus, which is a lowly though
specialized chordate that feeds on
the sand and mud of the sea floor.
The coelomic cavities in echinoderms appear as five pouches
pinched off from the archenteron;
in Balanoglossus and the more
advanced chordate Amphioxus they
develop in the same fashion. This
method of coelom formation is not
found in other phyla. For these and
other reasons it seems quite probable that there lived in the pre-
Cambrian seas a common ancestor
of the echinoderms and the chordates, in the form of a small, ciliated,
simple-gutted, bilaterally symmetrical plankton-feeder similar to the
larvae shown in Fig. 27.3. If such
a common ancestor existed, the

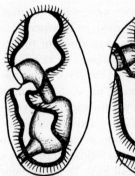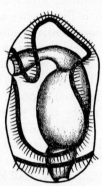

FIG. 27.3. Resemblance between an echino-
derm larva (left) and that of a primitive
chordate, the acorn worm (right), suggesting a remote common origin of the two
phyla. Note the curved tubular digestive
tract and the belts of propulsive cilia.
(*Redrawn from Buchsbaum, Animals without Backbones, by permission University of
Chicago Press.*)

chordate phylum is about as old as the rest. Since the ostracoderms all
occur in fresh-water deposits, it is presumed that the early evolution of
the vertebrates occurred in inland waters during Ordovician and perhaps
Cambrian times.

It used to be supposed that the ancestral vertebrates were boneless
types not unlike modern lampreys, and for this reason the heavily armored
ostracoderms were dismissed as an aberrant side branch off the main line
of vertebrate evolution. Recent anatomical studies have shown how
erroneous this interpretation was; the ostracoderms are now firmly
established as the ancestors of all later vertebrates, including man, and
as such deserve special attention.

The *cephalaspids* are the best known of the three orders of ostracoderms,
and may serve as examples of the group. By microdissection and the
study of ground sections Stensiö and other workers have deciphered the

detailed anatomy not only of the cephalaspid skeleton, but also of the brain and nerves, sense organs, branchial system, and other parts, so that these ancient organisms are actually better known than many living forms. The body was composed of a large "head" and a more slender, scale-armored tail. The "head" was crescentic in outline, convex above and flat beneath, and included what would be the shoulder region in later vertebrates. The upper surface was covered by a solid bony shield, in the center of which, over the brain, were two large eyes, a smaller median pineal eye, and in front of the latter an olfactory pit. Along each margin of the head shield and in the mid-line behind the eyes were specialized

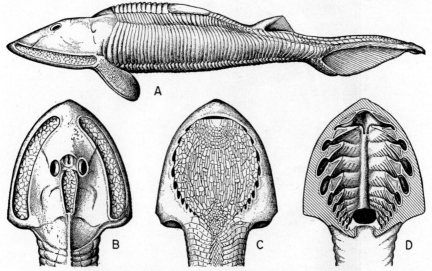

Fig. 27.4. The ostracoderm Cephalaspis, one of the earliest vertebrates. *A*, side view. *B*, dorsal view. *C*, ventral view. *D*, head region dissected from below to show the gill chambers. (*Redrawn from Romer, by permission The Williams & Wilkins Company.*)

areas which, from their structure, position, and enormous motor nerves, have been identified as electric organs analogous to those of the electric eel. On the flat under side of the head there was a slitlike anterior mouth without jaws, a pulsating scale-covered throat, and along the sides of the throat nine or ten pairs of gill openings. Most of the interior of the "head" was occupied by a series of very large gill chambers. The brain was complex, with all the characteristic vertebrate parts; and, as in modern lampreys, the organ of balance had only two semicircular canals, instead of the three of higher vertebrates.

The jawless mouth and great gill chambers show that the ostracoderms were food strainers, like their even more primitive modern relatives, the lancelets (Fig. B.26) and sea squirts (Fig. 27.5). Essentially they consisted of two parts—a pharyngeal gill apparatus for straining food particles from the stream of water entering the mouth, and for respiration; and a locomotor tail equipped with muscles, nervous system, and sense organs, to transport the gill system from place to place. Most ostracoderms were sluggish bottom dwellers, as shown by their flattened form. They

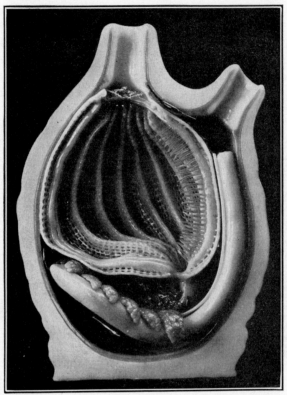

FIG. 27.5. Model of the tunicate or sea squirt Cynthia, a primitive marine chordate distantly related to the acorn worms, Amphioxus, and Cephalaspis. A stream of water is pulled in through the mouth (above) by the beating of cilia that line the walls of the enormously developed pharynx. The perforated walls of the pharynx strain plankton from the water and carry it to the funnel-like esophagus. The stomach (not here visible) lies beneath, with the tubular intestine looping forward and rising toward the lateral excurrent opening. The gonads can be seen draped over the intestine, their slender duct rising alongside of the latter. The circulatory system is unique; the ventral heart first pumps blood into the pharyngeal walls for aeration, then reverses its action and pumps the blood into the remaining viscera. The wrinkled brown covering or "tunic" that encloses the body is responsible for the name tunicate. (*Courtesy American Museum of Natural History.*)

served as the chief food organisms of the larger and more powerful eurypterids, and their bony armor and electric organs were probably defensive adaptations against these enemies. Since the ostracoderms were ancestral to later fishes, bone, rather than cartilage, must have been the primitive vertebrate skeletal material, and its absence in the lampreys and sharks is due to loss; bone was not acquired but merely retained by the ancestors of the bony fishes and terrestrial vertebrates.

We have just mentioned the *eurypterids* (Figs. 25.3 and 27.6) as enemies of the ostracoderms. Eurypterids were aquatic arachnids descended from trilobitelike ancestors, and included some of the largest, most active, and successful animals of the early Paleozoic. Their elongated bodies consisted of a small cephalothorax bearing compound eyes and a series of jointed appendages, and a segmented abdomen which was broad anteriorly and narrow posteriorly like that of a scorpion. As in all arachnids, the first pair of appendages was pincerlike, whereas in the Crustacea, which they somewhat resembled, the first appendage is always feelerlike.

Most of the eurypterids were less than a foot in length, but some of the later types were large; *Pterygotus*, of the Devonian, reached a length of 9 feet and was

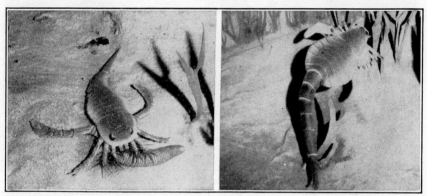

Fig. 27.6. Two types of Silurian eurypterids. Left, Eurypterus; right, Eusarcus. Compare Fig. 25.3. (*Courtesy Rochester Museum.*)

probably the largest arthropod that ever lived. The habits of eurypterids were probably much like those of modern hunting crabs, and most of them had swimming paddles as well as walking legs. The Ordovician eurypterids were marine, but most of the later ones were inhabitants of fresh waters. They reached their maximum development in the Silurian and Devonian periods and became extinct in the Permian; but they left descendants in the form of the terrestrial scorpions, spiders, and other arachnids. Primitive scorpions found associated with eurypterids in Silurian strata were long accepted as the first air-breathing animals but are now known to have been aquatic; land-dwelling scorpions are first certainly known from the Carboniferous.

The Devonian fishes. Corals, sea lilies and cephalopods were increasingly prominent groups in the Devonian seas, and brachiopods continued abundant, though snails and bivalves were few and the trilobites were on the decline. The dominance of invertebrates, however, was past; hordes of fishes lived in the seas and fresh waters of this period and left such abundant fossil remains that the Devonian is often called the *Age of*

Fishes. The little ostracoderms persisted for a time, only to be crowded out by their descendants. Among the newcomers were many strange types that did not long endure, but others were the ancestors of our modern sharks and bony fishes. All had jaws and fed on solid food.

The *placoderms* were the most primitive. They included a heterogeneous lot of bizarre forms, a step above the ostracoderms in organization but not very closely

Fig. 27.7. Life of a Devonian coral reef, showing crinoids or sea lilies, solitary corals, colonial corals, cephalopods, trilobites, and other organisms. (*Courtesy University of Michigan Museums.*)

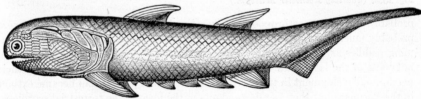

Fig. 27.8. The Devonian "spiny shark" or acanthodian, Climatius. (*Redrawn from Romer, by permission The Williams & Wilkins Company.*)

related among themselves. All possessed a well-developed bony armor of plates, or enameled scales, and had primitive jaws, the upper jaw being fastened directly to the brain case. The tail tapered to a point, which was usually bent upward with a tail fin projecting from its lower surface. The group included the acanthodians, the joint-necked fishes, and the strange antiarchs, as well as other oddities.

The *acanthodians* were small fresh-water fishes with numerous fins, and with a complete armor of bony scales. The fins were supported by stiff, immovable spines which are common fossils in Devonian rocks. Although these fishes are often called "the spiny sharks," they were not shark ancestors, as was once supposed, but are close to the stock from which the bony fishes arose. The *arthrodires* or joint-necked fishes included the largest and most powerful animals of the time. A complete bony armor covered the anterior parts of their bodies, the head armor hinged to that of the shoulder region by a joint at each side of the neck. The very large mouth was armed with powerful cutting and piercing "teeth" which were not teeth at all but projections of the bony jaws; in biting it appears that the lower jaw remained fixed while the upper part of the head moved up and down on the neck hinges. The earlier arthro-dires were small inhabitants of fresh water, but some of the later marine forms reached a length of more than 30 feet and had a tremendous gape of jaw. The whole group suddenly disappeared at the end of the Devonian. Another equally strange group of placoderms were the little fresh-water *antiarchs*. Like their arthrodire relatives they had a complete bony armor on the front part of the body, but

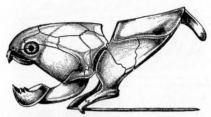

FIG. 27.9. The Devonian joint-necked fish or arthrodire, Dinichthys. (*Redrawn from Romer, by permission The Williams & Wilkins Company.*)

they lacked the neck hinge and had a pair of armored "flippers" with which they crawled and swam. They did not survive past the end of the period.

All later fishes, including those living today, belong to one or the other of two great groups which arose during the Devonian period. One of these includes the *cartilaginous fishes*—the sharks, rays, skates and their allies—the other, the *bony fishes*. Both groups possess modern-type jaws, the upper jaw being attached at the rear to the bones of the first gill arch

FIG. 27.10. The Devonian flippered fish or antiarch, Pterichthyodes (Pterichthys). (*Redrawn from Romer, by permission The Williams & Wilkins Company.*)

instead of solely to the brain case (Fig. 27.11); both have fins and body of more familiar and standardized type than those of the placoderms from which they were derived. However, the two groups evolved along quite different lines. In the sharklike fishes bony structure was lost, the scales were reduced to denticles imbedded in a tough skin, smell became the dominant food-finding sense, and the group became almost wholly marine. None of the cartilaginous fishes ever developed lungs, and the group played no part in the development of terrestrial vertebrates.

The *bony fishes* suddenly appeared in abundance in the fresh waters of Middle Devonian time, and since then have steadily increased in importance. By the end of the Paleozoic they dominated the lakes and streams and had invaded the seas, and today they comprise all the fresh-water and most of the marine fishes. The group probably arose from acanthodians or similar placoderms during the late Silurian. In the early forms the head was enclosed in a nearly solid case of dermal bones, the gill slits were covered by a bony plate (the operculum) as in all later bony fishes, and the body was armored with close-fitting, enameled scales of bone. There were paired pectoral and pelvic fins, and the tail was usually bilobed, with the spinal axis bent up into the larger dorsal lobe.

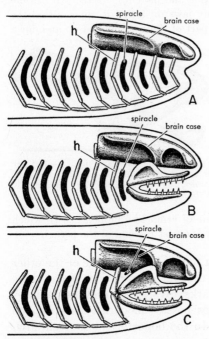

At their earliest appearance the bony fishes were already separated into two divisions. One of these, the *ray-finned fishes*, made a slow beginning but later expanded rapidly and today includes the great majority of all fishes. Their fins are supported by parallel rays of bone and cartilage, and they lack internal nostrils; primitive members of the group had a single dorsal fin and "ganoid" scales heavily covered with an enamel-like material called ganoine. The ray fins have been most successful as fishes but have given rise to no higher types. The other group comprised the *choanate*

FIG. 27.11. The evolution of fish jaws and the spiracle. The gill slits (black) are separated by gill arches, each of the latter with a hinged supporting bar of cartilage. *A*, the primitive chordate condition without jaws. *B*, jaws have developed, but only the brain case is involved in their support. The hyomandibular arch (*h*) and the gill slit in front of this arch are unaffected. *C*, the jaws extend farther back, the hyomandibular arch has become a jaw support, and the gill slit in front of this arch has been restricted to a small opening, the spiracle. (*Redrawn from Romer, by permission The Williams & Wilkins Company.*)

fishes, which possessed internal nostrils (choanae), two dorsal fins, and bony "cosmoid" scales covered with a *thin* outer layer of enamel. Some of the choanates were *lung fishes* (dipnoians) and others were *lobe fins* (crossopterygians); both groups were abundant in the Devonian and later Paleozoic but have since declined nearly to extinction. Though relatively unsuccessful as fishes, the lobe fins are of great interest as the stock from which the land vertebrates evolved.

Air-breathing fishes.   Remarkable as it may seem, all of the Devonian bony fishes possessed lungs in addition to gills and could breathe air. This can be inferred from the comparative anatomy of the fossil fishes and their descendants and is made certain by a fossil in which the outlines of the lung have been preserved. In the ray fins the primitive lung became transformed into the air bladder which enables them to float at any desired level in the water; but in the choanate fishes and their terrestrial descendants it retained its air-breathing function. The lung of the

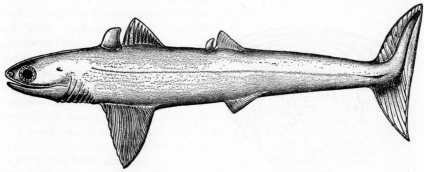

FIG. 27.12. The primitive Devonian shark, Cladoselache. (*Redrawn from Romer, by permission The Williams & Wilkins Company.*)

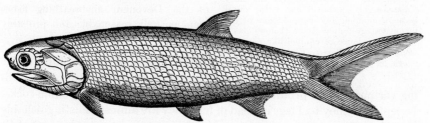

FIG. 27.13. The primitive Devonian ray-finned fish, Palaeoniscus. (*Redrawn from Romer, The Vertebrate Body, by permission W. B. Saunders Company.*)

Devonian fishes was probably an adaptation to life in ponds and streams which in dry seasons were reduced to stagnant pools, where ordinary fishes would die but those with lungs might survive until the next rains. The nature of the Devonian sediments supports this interpretation, for they are of a type which is formed under conditions of alternate submergence and exposure to air. The hypothesis is further strengthened by the habits of the five genera of air-breathing fishes which survive today as veritable living fossils. Two of these are primitive ray fins inhabiting African rivers; the others are lungfishes occurring in Australia, Africa, and South America.

The Australian lungfish lives in pools and water holes, cropping the aquatic vegetation to obtain the snails, insects, and other small animals found thereon.

During dry periods the pools become stagnant, low in oxygen, and foul with the decaying bodies of other fishes; but this does not seem to affect the lungfishes, though at such times they depend chiefly upon their lungs for respiration. The

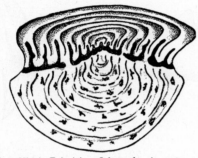

African and South American lungfishes live in marshes bordering rivers, where they feed on frogs, insects, and other animals. When the marshes are flooded they live much as does the Australian form, though they are more dependent upon their lungs and will drown if prevented from coming to the surface. During the dry seasons, when the marshes may be without water for months at a time, these fishes burrow into the mud and coil up at the bottom of their holes. There they secrete around themselves a moisture-holding "cocoon" of slime, tightly closed everywhere except over the mouth; and there they stay, breathing air and keeping moist in their slimy covering, until the return of water to the marshes. In the light of such facts our guesses concerning the habits of the Devonian air-breathing fishes seem entirely reasonable and probably correct.

FIG. 27.14. Primitive fish scales in cross section. The cosmoid scale of the early choanate fishes (above) has a thin outer layer of enamel. The ganoid scale of the primitive ray-finned fishes (below) has a thick outer layer of enamel-like ganoine. (*Redrawn from Romer, Vertebrate Paleontology, by permission University of Chicago Press.*)

The origin of amphibians. The oldest known four-footed, land-dwelling vertebrates are primitive amphibians found in Upper Devonian rocks. Except that they had legs instead of fins, they are almost indistinguishable from lobe-finned fishes, certain of which were without question their ancestors. The early amphibians and the lobe fins are parallel in the

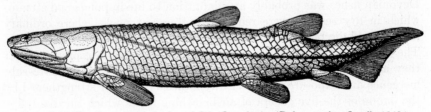

FIG. 27.15. The Devonian lobe-finned fish, Osteolepis. (*Redrawn after Jarvik, 1948.*)

arrangement of the bones of the skull, in the microscopic structure of the teeth, in the presence of internal nostrils, and particularly in the arrangement of the bones of the fish fin base and the amphibian leg. In the lobe fins there was a single proximal bone corresponding to the humerus or femur, followed by two bones corresponding to those of the forearm or lower leg, and beyond this an irregular subdivision which is roughly comparable to the foot skeleton of the primitive land vertebrates.

Fig. 27.16. Modern lungfishes. Upper, the Australian lungfish, Neoceratodus (Ceratodus). Center, the South American lungfish, Lepidosiren. Lower, the African lungfish, Protopterus. (*Courtesy Chicago Natural History Museum* (upper) *and American Museum of Natural History.*)

The steps that led to the adoption of land life by the ancestral amphibians can only be surmised, but Romer has propounded an interesting theory. He points out that many of the earliest amphibians were fairly large carnivores that still spent most of their time in the water, living alongside of lobe-finned fishes similar in habits and structure and differing only in the lesser development of the limb bases. Why did the amphibians leave the water? Not to breathe air, for that could be done by rising to the surface of the pool; not in search of food, for there was little food for carnivores on land; and not to escape enemies, for they were among the largest inhabitants of the fresh waters. Instead, their appearance on land was probably an adaptation for remaining in water. So long as there

remained any water in the pools, the lobe fins were probably the better off of the two groups, for they were better swimmers; but when the pools dried up completely the lobe fins had to burrow into the mud and would die if the drought were prolonged, while the ancestral amphibian could crawl out of the pool and walk overland on his stumpy leg fins to the next pool where water still remained. Once this habit had been formed, a land vertebrate fauna could be built up. Instead of seeking water immediately, the amphibian might linger on the banks and devour stranded fish; some might take to eating the primitive insects already present on land, and the larger ones might gradually come to prey on their smaller amphibian relatives. Although a true land fauna could thus be established, the amphibians remained tied to the water by their reproductive requirements. We can be certain that their eggs were laid in water and externally fertilized, and fossils prove that the young passed through a fishlike aquatic stage, as do those of most modern amphibians.

Fig. 27.17. From fish to amphibian. Above, the Devonian lobe-finned fish Eusthenopteron leaving the water to sprawl about on its stout, muscular fins. Below, one of the earliest known land vertebrates, the "stegocephalian" amphibian Diplovertebron of the lower Carboniferous. (*Courtesy American Museum of Natural History.*)

The dominance of the amphibians. For a geologically brief time the amphibians were the rulers of the lands. During the late Paleozoic they increased rapidly and branched out into many types adapted to different modes of existence—a phenomenon known as *adaptive radiation*, which has occurred in group after group as each attained temporary dominance in the world of life. Some of the Paleozoic amphibia were small, salamanderlike creatures; others were stout-bodied, with short tails and bellies protected by bony plates upon which they rested except while walking. Collectively they are sometimes called *stegocephalians* (meaning "roof-headed")[1] on account of their boxlike skulls without openings except for

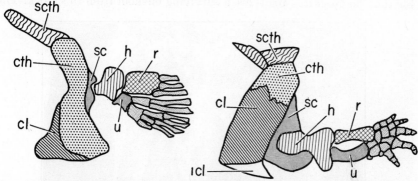

FIG. 27.18. Bones of the shoulder girdle and fin base in the lobe-finned fish Eusthenopteron (left), and the corresponding bones in a primitive amphibian (right). The basic similarity in limb pattern is evident. Some of the bones have been lost in the higher vertebrates. *cl*, clavicle; *cth*, cleithrum; *h*, humerus; *icl*, interclavicle; *r*, radius; *sc*, scapula; *scth*, supra-cleithrum; *u*, ulna. (*Redrawn from Romer, The Vertebrate Body, by permission W. B. Saunders Company.*)

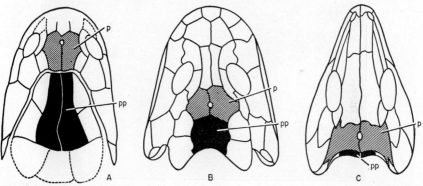

FIG. 27.19. Changes in the skull, fish to reptile. The same bones can be recognized through-out, but there is a steady decrease in the relative size of the posterior bones and enlargement of the anterior part of the skull. The parietal bones (*p*) with the pineal opening between them, and the postparietals (*pp*) have been shaded in the same way in all three skulls. *A*, the lobe-finned fish, Osteolepis. *B*, the primitive labyrinthodont amphibian Ichthyostega of the late Devonian or early Carboniferous. *C*, a cotylosaurian reptile, Romeria. (*Redrawn from Romer, by permission The Williams & Wilkins Company.*)

the eye orbits and nostrils. Most of them were carnivores like their an-cestors the lobe fins. The most important of the stegocephalians were the *labyrinthodonts* (Figs. 27.17, 19, and 20), which began in the Devonian as small, chiefly aquatic types, became stouter limbed land dwellers in the

[1] This is not a taxonomic group, but a broad term including a variety of types, many of which were not closely related to one another.

Carboniferous, and culminated in heavy-bodied, 5-foot long predators during the Permian, only to decline until their last Triassic survivors were small degenerate forms incapable of leaving the water. The reptiles are believed to have evolved from primitive labyrinthodonts, and it is possible that the frogs and toads are a surviving offshoot from this stock. The

Fig. 27.20. Eryops, a primitive Carboniferous amphibian. This labyrinthodont "stegocephalian" lived in the coal swamps of Pennsylvania. The trees in the background are Calamites, Sigillaria, and Cordaites; the herbaceous plants in the foreground are Sphenophyllum. (*Courtesy Carnegie Museum, Pittsburgh.*)

salamanders (Fig. B. 31), however, are descended from some other group of stegocephalians.

The winged insects of the coal forests. Although our account of the evolutionary history of animals centers around the vertebrates, we must occasionally take note of developments in other groups which were important for life as a whole. One such event was the appearance of winged insects, the descendants of which were destined to play a major role in the evolution of the flowering plants, and which today share dominance of the terrestrial world with the vertebrates. The origin of insects remains a mystery. The oldest fossils are those of primitive wingless forms (Collembola, or springtails) found in association with land plants (psilophytes) of early Devonian age. Then comes a great gap, until suddenly winged insects appear in abundance in the coal measures. How and when they acquired wings is completely unknown.

Many of the coal forest insects belonged to a primitive stock (Paleodictyoptera) which is apparently ancestral to all other winged insects. They had large net-veined wings which were outstretched at rest, like those of modern dragonflies. Another abundant group included the *ancestral cockroaches*, which differed only in minor respects from those of today. Very large insects occurred in the coal forests; one dragonflylike form had a wingspread of about 2 feet. There were, however, many small species as well, especially among the cockroaches, and if one includes the minute wingless springtails and similar forms, the average size of the Carboniferous insects was probably not much greater than in the modern fauna. None of these ancient insects had a pupal stage in the life history, and none of the modern insect orders was yet in existence during the Carboniferous period.

The end of the era of ancient life. The Appalachian revolution that closed the Paleozoic era was a time of profound changes in life, as we have pointed out in discussing the history of plants. Many ancient groups of animals died out during the Permian and were replaced by new and better adapted types, both in the seas and on the lands. Continental uplift caused withdrawal of the wide interior seas, and in the remaining narrow marginal seas crowding, competition, and lowered temperatures killed off a host of Paleozoic groups. The last trilobites disappeared; the brachiopods, sea lilies, old types of corals, and other invertebrates that had once been dominant were reduced to unimportant remnants; and the cephalopod molluscs, which had flourished since the Ordovician, died out, except for a few survivors, from which the dominant ammonites of the Mesozoic era were destined to develop.

On the lands the effects of the physical and climatic changes of Permian time were even more profound. The swamp forests disappeared, and with them most of their characteristic animal inhabitants. The ancient groups of winged insects were supplanted by new types, some of which were the ancestors of the modern insect orders with complete metamorphosis. In these the larva is very different from the adult insect, and there is an inactive pupal stage interpolated in the life history (Fig. 24.10); within the pupal case the larval body is transformed into that of the adult. This "invention" permitted the evolution of larval forms adapted to different environments and foods than those required by the adults and enabled insects to endure periods of drought or cold in the nonfeeding, quiescent pupal stage. The development of complete metamorphosis was as important an evolutionary step for the insects as was the development of the shelled egg for land vertebrates, for each of these advances overcame obstacles to full occupancy of terrestrial environments.

The "stegocephalian" amphibians reached their climax in the Carboniferous and early Permian and then rapidly diminished; their last survivors, as we have noted, were small aquatic forms that died out during the Triassic period. In part the decline of these amphibia may have been caused by the increasing aridity and lowered temperature of Permian times; but in greater measure it was probably due to inability to compete with the newly arisen reptiles, whose history is recounted in the next chapter.

CHAPTER XXVIII

REPTILES, BIRDS, AND MAMMALS

Thus far our account of the post-Cambrian evolution of animals has traversed some 260 million years of geological time. During most of the immensely long Paleozoic era the vertebrates lived in the waters of the earth, and only toward its end did some of them finally emerge onto the land. Once this step had been taken, the further evolution of the land dwellers was rapid, and the succeeding *Mesozoic era* saw the origin and establishment of all the truly modern groups of terrestrial organisms. This era is often called the *Age of Reptiles*, for a horde of reptilian types dominated the scene. It was also the time during which the birds, mammals, modern insects, and flowering plants arose and became established. The Mesozoic era seems brief and its evolutionary developments rapid by contrast with the interminable Paleozoic. How long it actually lasted can be better appreciated if we bear in mind that dinosaurs walked the earth during 120 million years, while the whole existence of mankind scarcely spans 1 million.

The evolutionary lines which lead from the early vertebrates to man form the main thread of our story. These lines do not, however, lead from evolutionary climax to evolutionary climax; they run along the edges of the picture, so to speak, until very recent times. Thus of the 20 or more reptilian orders that arose in the Mesozoic era, it was not the largest and most successful that lie in our own ancestry but an early and relatively obscure side branch from the primitive reptile stock. Nevertheless, the history of the reptiles as a group, and of their descendants the birds, was a most dramatic and instructive evolutionary episode, which warrants our attention.

The origin of reptiles. To see the start of the reptilian dynasty we must return to the Carboniferous coal forests, where lived, along with the dominant labyrinthodonts, other similar-appearing animals which were neither amphibians nor reptiles; they combined characteristics of both. One such form was Seymouria, a clumsy sprawling creature about 2 feet long. From this or some similar animal all the later reptiles evolved.

The success of the reptiles was based on their early acquisition of a reproductive device which made it possible for them to breed on land. This was the *shelled amniote egg*—actually a combination of several "inventions," some old and some new. The most important of these are the *yolk sac*, an embryonic stomach which grows around the food mass stored in the egg and is as old as the fishes; the *allantois*, a new organ

Fig. 28.1. The primitive protoreptile Seymouria from the Texas Permian. This creature was less than 3 feet in length. It retained many amphibian characteristics, and is close to the base of the reptilian stem. (*Courtesy American Museum of Natural History.*)

which, pressed against the inside of the shell, enables the embryo to respire and also serves for waste storage; the *amnion*, an enveloping sac that encloses the embryo in a fluid-filled space which is equivalent to the amphibian's pond; the *shell*, a gas-permeable protective covering secreted around the egg after fertilization; and *internal fertilization*, occasionally developed in fishes and amphibians but essential for reproduction on land. Whether or not Seymouria laid shelled eggs is unknown, though as our illustration shows it is often assumed to have done so. The shelled amniote egg is found in all true reptiles and birds and in some primitive mammals, and the shell-less, yolkless egg of the higher mammals (including man) has been derived from it. Perfection of the amniote egg freed the ancestral reptiles and all of their descendants from dependence upon water for reproduction and thus opened the way for complete conquest of land environments by the higher vertebrates.

THE MESOZOIC REPTILIAN RADIATION

By Permian times the evolutionary radiation of the reptiles was well under way, and almost every known reptilian order had appeared before the end of the Triassic period. This rapid expansion was accompanied by most diverse specializations for different modes of life, and there exists no more striking example of adaptive radiation than

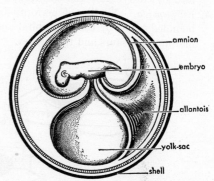

FIG. 28.2. Diagram of the shelled amniote egg, which freed vertebrates from dependence upon water for reproduction. (*Redrawn from Romer, Man and the Vertebrates, by permission University of Chicago Press.*)

that furnished by the Mesozoic reptiles. We may begin our account by defining the five great groups into which the numerous orders of reptiles may be assembled.[1]

The five reptilian stocks. All reptiles, living and extinct, may be classified in a broad, general way on the basis of skull design, as follows:

1. *Anapsida.* Skull roof solid like that of the stegocephalians, without any openings behind the eye. Includes the extinct "stem reptiles" (cotylosaurs) and the turtles.
2. *Synapsida.* Skull roof perforated by a lower opening behind the eye, bounded above by the postorbital and squamosal bones. Includes the Permian

---

[1] Unfortunately we shall have to use quite a number of unfamiliar names in this account of the reptiles. This cannot be helped but is not so bad as might appear at first sight. For one thing, most of them contain the root *saur*, which simply means reptile. Omitting a few which have no good translation, here is a brief list with meanings: *ankylosaur*, "reptile with hooks (spines)"; *archosaur*, "ruling reptile"; *Brachiosaurus*, "arm reptile"; *Brontosaurus*, "thundering reptile"; *Ceratopsia*, "of horned aspect"; *cotylosaur*, "reptile with hollows (cupped vertebrae)"; *dinosaur*, "terrible reptile"; *ichthyosaur*, "fish reptile"; *mosasaur*, "reptile first found in the Meuse river valley in France"; *Ornithischia*, "with birdlike hips"; *phytosaur*, "plant reptile" (a misnomer due to false interpretation of the first fossils of these crocodilelike animals); *plesiosaur*, "near reptile"; *pterosaur*, "winged reptile"; *Saurischia*, "with reptilian hips"; *stegosaur*, "roofed reptile"; *Triceratops*, "of three-horned aspect"; *Tyrannosaurus*, "tyrant reptile." The "*apsid*" part of Anapsida, Diapsida, etc. means "opening," and these terms refer to the number and position of the openings in the skull.

fin-backed reptiles or, "ship lizards" (pelycosaurs), and the Permian and Triassic mammal-like reptiles (therapsids) from which the mammals evolved.

3. *Parapsida.* Skull roof perforated by an upper opening behind the eye, bounded below by the postfrontal and supratemporal bones. Includes the fishlike ichthyosaurs and their allies, all extinct.

4. *Euryapsida.*[1] Skull roof perforated by an upper opening behind the eye, bounded below by the postorbital and squamosal bones. Includes the extinct marine plesiosaurs and their allies.

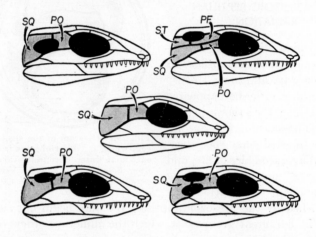

Fig. 28.3. The five basic types of reptilian skulls. The *anapsid* type (center) is the most primitive and that from which the others were derived. Upper left, *synapsid* type; upper right, *parapsid* type; lower left, *euryapsid* type; lower right, *diapsid* type. *PF*, postfrontal bone; *PO*, postorbital bone; *SQ*, squamosal bone; *ST*, supratemporal bone. (*Redrawn from Colbert, The Dinosaur Book, by permission American Museum of Natural History.*)

5. *Diapsida.* Skull roof perforated by *two* openings behind the eye, one upper and one lower, separated by the postorbital and squamosal bones. Includes the *scaly reptiles* (among which are the lizards, snakes, and extinct mosasaurs), and the *archosaurs* or "ruling reptiles" of the Mesozoic. The chief archosaur groups are the phytosaurs, crocodiles and alligators, dinosaurs, and pterosaurs, of which only the crocodiles and alligators still survive. The birds, however, came from one of the archosaur stocks.

The stem-reptiles and the turtles. The first reptiles were anapsids with solidly roofed skulls and sprawling legs—the cotylosaurs, or "stem reptiles," from which all the other reptilian stocks were evolved. This group arose in Carboniferous times from forms like Seymouria and reached its climax in the Permian, when it branched out into a number of varied lines—mostly lizardlike carnivores from 1 to 5 feet in length but some of them large plant-feeding types. One of the latter was as large as an ox and perhaps heavier, with a small head, great spraddled legs, and a massive

[1] Also called *Synaptosauria.*

short-tailed body. Cotylosaurs disappeared before the end of the Triassic, but one of their offshoots, the *turtles*, has survived to modern times. The turtles retained the primitive anapsid skull and sprawling legs of the stem reptiles but in other respects became highly specialized. They developed one of the most remarkable armors ever evolved by a terrestrial vertebrate, consisting of horny skin scales fused to the broadened ribs and sternum. The group first appeared during the Permian period; by Cretaceous times marine forms with reduced armor and paddlelike legs had appeared, from which the modern sea turtles have descended. The land tortoises and fresh-water turtles are the most primitive of surviving reptiles.

Marine reptiles of the Mesozoic. In addition to the Cretaceous sea turtles a number of other groups of Mesozoic reptiles became adapted to marine existence, some of them with marked success. Especially noteworthy were the fishlike parapsid reptiles called *ichthyosaurs*. These developed as perfectly streamlined a body as any fish or porpoise— deep, narrow, and spindle-shaped, with the legs modified into finlike

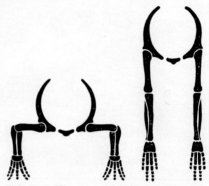

Fig. 28.4. The contrast in leg position between the earlier land vertebrates (stegocephalians and cotylosaurs, left) and the higher reptiles and mammals (right). (*From Romer, Man and the Vertebrates, by permission University of Chicago Press.*)

steering blades and the back furnished with a cartilaginous stabilizing fin resembling that of a shark. The jaws were beaked, with many sharp teeth; the eyes were very large, the nostrils set just in front of them, and the head was joined to the body with no perceptible neck. The propelling organ was a bilobed fishlike tail, though the vertebral axis turned down into its lower lobe instead of into the upper lobe as in fishes. The ichthyosaurs were fish feeders, occupying the ecological niche now filled by the dolphins and porpoises. They did not even need to go ashore for breeding, for as proved by fossil remains they were ovoviviparous, carrying the developing eggs in the abdomen until they were ready to hatch. These "fish reptiles" appeared in the Triassic period, became abundant in the Jurassic, and survived until late in the Cretaceous.

Another remarkable group of marine reptiles comprised the euryapsid *plesiosaurs*, which have been described as having the body of a turtle strung on a snake. They had a broad, flattened trunk plated with bony armor; the legs were powerful swimming paddles; and they had long necks and shorter tails. In some the head was small and the neck very long; others had a shorter neck and a large, often beaked head. Small

Fig. 28.5. One of the largest of the cotylosaurs. Bradysaurus, a South African pariasaur, was 8 feet long and as heavy as an ox, though it retained the primitive form and posture. Note the disproportionately small head, outbowed legs, and clumsy body. (*Courtesy Chicago Natural History Museum.*)

Fig. 28.6. A fossil ichthyosaur, or fish-lizard, *Ichthyosaurus quadricissus*, with imprint of soft tissues around the skeleton. Length, 5 feet 8 inches. (*Courtesy American Museum of Natural History.*)

plesiosaurs were 8 to 10 feet, large ones up to 50 feet in length. They fed upon fish, ammonites and other swimming creatures, as is shown by remains found within their skeletons. The group arose in Triassic times and persisted until the end of the Mesozoic era.

The diapsid *mosasaurs* were as close an approach to the mythical sea serpent as ever existed. They were huge marine lizards, some of them 40 feet long, which lived in the Cretaceous seas. They had short, paddlelike limbs, a powerful flattened swimming tail, and an immense mouth with many sharp recurved teeth for seizing such slippery prey as fish. During the Jurassic a group of crocodiles went to sea and developed paddlelike legs and a fishlike tail, and other short-lived attempts at marine adaptation were made by various reptiles; but the ichthyosaurs, plesiosaurs, mosasaurs, and sea turtles were the most successful of the sea farers.

The scaly reptiles. The lizards and snakes are the most abundant of modern reptiles, represented in the tropical and warm temperate regions by a host of genera and species. Although they are diapsids, they have lost the lower of the two skull openings characteristic of the group; but in

FIG. 28.7. Marine reptiles of the Jurassic. The long-necked plesiosaurs reached a length of 21 feet. The ichthyosaurs (right) were the most completely adapted to aquatic life of any reptiles. (*Drawing by Charles R. Knight, courtesy Chicago Natural History Museum.*)

other respects they are relatively primitive. The *lizards* (Fig. B.32) retain the sprawling gait of the cotylosaurs, though some can run rapidly. Most of them are small and lightly built, but some are large and heavy, the Komodo monitor being the largest living species, with a length of 12 feet. The lizards first appeared in the Jurassic. During the Cretaceous they gave rise to the marine *mosasaurs* described above and to the *snakes*. In the latter the body has become much elongated and the legs have been lost;[1] progression is accomplished by a sinuous twisting of the trunk aided by the backwardly directed points of the scales. Some of the true lizards have also lost their legs and become snakelike; but the snakes have a further peculiarity in that the structure of the skull and the loosely attached jaws permit very large prey to be swallowed without chewing. Snakes are probably more numerous and varied today than at any time in the past. The earliest were large, heavy snakes similar to their de-

[1] Except for rudiments of the hind legs in pythons and boas.

scendants the pythons and boas; small slender forms appeared during the Oligocene; and poisonous snakes with grooved or tubular fangs are first known from the Miocene.

One lonely survivor from the remote past deserves mention here—Sphenodon, the tuatara, found only on some small islands off the New Zealand coast, where through isolation it has been able to persist. It is close to the type from which all the diapsid reptiles arose and preserves some of the features of the ancestral cotylosaurs—in particular a rudimen-

FIG. 28.8. The tuatara (*Sphenodon punctatum*) is the only surviving member of the order Rhynchocephalia, which appeared in the Permian. It is the only reptile native to New Zealand, where it is now extinct except on a few small islands off the coast. Tuataras reach a length of 30 inches. They live in burrows and catch their prey both on land and in the water. (*Courtesy American Museum of Natural History.*)

tary third eye in the top of the skull, homologous with the pineal body of higher vertebrates.

THE HISTORY OF THE ARCHOSAURS

One of the most dramatic evolutionary histories is that of the archosaurs, or ruling reptiles, which from obscure beginnings in the Permian rose to dominate the lands, the seas, and even the air during the 120 million years of Mesozoic time, and then disappeared abruptly from the scene. The interest of this story is enhanced by the strange and monstrous animals which appear in it, like the dragons and giants of a fairy tale—except that these were real, and have left their bones to prove it.

Bipedal locomotion. The ancestral cotylosaurs had short, clumsy lateral legs and a slow, waddling walk. Various lines of reptiles improved

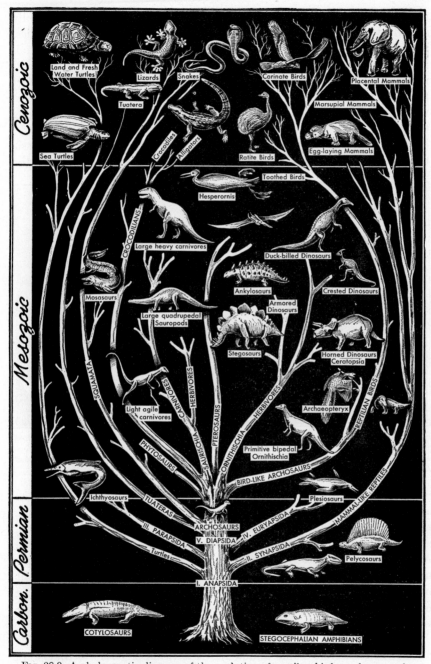

Fig. 28.9. A phylogenetic diagram of the evolution of reptiles, birds, and mammals.

upon this mode of locomotion, but the problem was most successfully solved by the archosaurs. The earliest archosaurs had lizardlike bodies; the front legs were short, the hind legs long and much modified, the tail massive and the pelvic girdle strong, and the legs had been brought under the body for better support. When resting or walking, all four feet touched the ground, but speed was attained by running on the hind legs, with the fore part of the body raised and balanced at the hips by the long tail.

From such a stem form there developed during Permian and Triassic times five major lines of archosaurs—the phytosaurs and crocodiles, the

Fig. 28.10. A Triassic phytosaur, Rutiodon. Some of these crocodilelike animals reached great size. They were an offshoot from the primitive archosaurs, and though relatives were not ancestors of the crocodiles that replaced them. (*Courtesy American Museum of Natural History.*)

pterosaurs, two distinct groups collectively known as dinosaurs, and the ancestors of the birds. Some of these continued their evolution as bipeds, though the phytosaurs and crocodiles failed to progress in this direction, and some of the dinosaurs later reverted to a quadrupedal condition. Among the bipeds the front legs had lost much of their original usefulness. In some groups they became much reduced or almost vestigial, but in others they took on changed functions and were altered into grasping hands, or defensive weapons with spikelike thumbs, or, even more drastically, into wings.

Phytosaurs and crocodiles. During the Triassic a group of primitive aquatic archosaurs became abundant. Known as *phytosaurs*, they were fish-feeding, crocodilelike creatures (Figs. 25.2 and 28.10), with long slender jaws armed with many sharp teeth and with the nostrils situated far back on the skull between the eyes. Some of them grew to great size. By Jurassic times the phytosaurs had been replaced by their distant relatives the *crocodiles*, in which, among other differences, there is a bony palate in the roof of the mouth that forms an air passage from the throat to nostrils placed at the tip of the snout. The crocodiles and related alligators have been among the least progressive of the ruling reptiles but are the only members of the archosaur stock which survived beyond the Mesozoic era. The marine crocodiles of Jurassic time, already mentioned, are the only archosaurs that ever took to the sea.

FIG. 28.11. The American crocodile (*Crocodilus acutus*, narrow snout) and American alligator (*Alligator mississippiensis*, broad snout) are surviving representatives of the subclass Archosauria. (*Courtesy American Museum of Natural History*.)

The pterosaurs, or flying reptiles. Twice in the history of the archosaurs the front legs, freed from walking, were modified into wings —once by the ancestors of the birds, as will be described later; again, and for the time being, more successfully, by the pterosaurs. These were light-bodied flying reptiles, with membranous wings supported by the enormously elongated fourth finger of the forelimb; the bones were hollow and air-filled as in birds. Since they had no large breastbone for the attachment of strong flying muscles, they are believed to have flown by soaring, taking off and landing on high cliffs or trees. They varied from the size of sparrows to the largest flying animal that has ever existed, the giant Pteranodon of Cretaceous times, which had a wingspread of 27 feet.

The saurischian dinosaurs. Of all extinct animals, the dinosaurs are those most generally known. The great size and bizarre forms of some of them appeal strongly to the imagination, and the fact that the last dinosaurs disappeared some 70 million years before the coming of man has been no deterrent to science-fiction writers, who have created a widespread impression that dinosaurs and early man were contemporaries. Another misconception is that all dinosaurs were immense ferocious carnivores; some of them were, it is true, but the largest were ponderous, slow-moving herbivores, and there were a great many medium-sized and small dinosaurs, some no larger than chickens. Finally, even the name

dinosaur is misleading, for dinosaurs were not a single group but belonged to two distinct and rather distantly related archosaur stocks, the Saurischia and the Ornithischia.

The most obvious difference between the two groups of dinosaurs lies in the structure of the pelvis. In the Saurischia the three bones of each half of the pelvis formed a triradiate structure, as in the primitive archosaurs, with the pubis projecting downward and forward from the acetabulum. In the Ornithischia the pubis had swung back until it lay along the lower margin of the ischium, as in the birds (whence the name of the group); but as a support to the belly a new bony process developed from the front edge of the base of the pubis, so that the pelvis became four- instead of three-pronged.

Fig. 28.12. The pterosaur mural by Constantin Astori. A large tailless type (Pteranodon) is in flight above; tailed forms (Rhamphorhynchus, etc.) appear below. (*Courtesy American Museum of Natural History.*)

Among the Saurischia there were two great divisions, the first of which included the bipedal *carnivorous dinosaurs*, or *therapods*. In the Triassic period these were mostly small, swift-running types, rather lightly built. In one line (Fig. 28.16, Struthiomimus) the claws of the forelegs were lost, the fingers became grasping organs, and the teeth disappeared; it has been conjectured that the members of this group fed upon the eggs of other dinosaurs. The main stock grew increasingly large and culminated in the enormous Tyrannosaurus of the Cretaceous period—the largest carnivore that ever ruled the lands. This beast stood 19 feet high, reached a length of 47 feet, with a skull 4 feet long, and is estimated to have weighed approximately 10 tons. Its powerful armament of teeth and the great claws of its three-toed hind feet were obviously adapted for attacking large, thick-skinned or armored prey—doubtless the large Cretaceous ornithischian dinosaurs.

The other saurischian stock included the quadrupedal *amphibious dinosaurs* or *sauropods*, which were plant-feeders. The line probably began in the late Triassic, but is first known from the Jurassic period, in which it reached its climax; it had nearly died out by late Cretaceous time. It included the largest

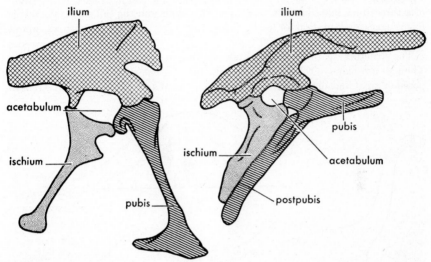

FIG. 28.13. The structure of the pelvis in the two dinosaur stocks. Left, a saurischian; right, an ornithischian. (*Redrawn from Romer, The Vertebrate Body, by permission W. B. Saunders Company.*)

FIG. 28.14. Upper Cretaceous dinosaurs in Wyoming, as reconstructed by Charles R. Knight. A pair of *Tyrannosaurus rex* (right) is about to attack one of the herbivorous horned dinosaurs, Triceratops (left). Tyrannosaurus was the largest of the carnivorous bipedal saurischians, with a length of 47 feet and a standing height of 19 feet. Triceratops grew 20 to 30 feet long and to 8 feet in height, with a skull some 8 feet in length. (*Courtesy Chicago Natural History Museum.*)

land animals that have ever lived, whose chief protection against the attacks of the great carnivores seems to have been sheer bulk and weight. Diplodocus was the longest of all dinosaurs, relatively slender in build but stretching almost 90 feet from its nose to the end of its whiplike tail. Apatosaurus (formerly known as Brontosaurus) was a heavier creature, only 70 feet long but weighing some 30 tons. The giant of them all was Brachiosaurus, known from North America and Africa. Unlike all other sauropods, which showed their bipedal ancestry in their long hind legs and massive tails, Brachiosaurus had short hind legs but long fore legs which, with the very long neck, would have enabled it to look over the top of a three-story building. The body was very stout and the tail short; the whole form suggests adaptation for life in rather deep water. The total length was about 80 feet and the weight about 50 tons.

The structural features of these sauropods are marvels of mechanical efficiency. The legs are massive columns for the support of great weight; the spine is composed of great vertebrae so hollowed and perforated as to give maximum strength

Fig. 28.15. Sauropod saurischian dinosaurs. *A*, Apatosaurus (Brontosaurus); *B*, Diplodocus; *C*, Brachiosaurus. Not drawn to scale. (*Modified from W. D. Matthew, Schuchert, and Colbert.*)

for the weight of bone used; and the entire skeleton is built on the lines of a double-piered cantilever bridge. Even so, such great creatures must have been clumsy on land, and there is evidence that they were chiefly inhabitants of swamps and streams where their weight was partly water-borne; their peglike teeth, furthermore, seem best fitted for feeding upon soft aquatic vegetation.

The ornithischian dinosaurs. The second order of dinosaurs, the Ornithischia, arose in the late Triassic but did not undergo rapid evolutionary expansion until during the Cretaceous. Its members never attained the great size reached by some of the saurischians but are even more interesting on account of the variety of bizarre forms which they exhibit. From their earliest appearance the ornithischians were plant feeders. The front teeth were lost and replaced by horny beaks; the back teeth became more numerous and changed from the primitive conical type to flattened leaflike blades pressed together in long rows so that

Fig. 28.16. Upper Cretaceous dinosaurs in western Canada, as reconstructed by Charles R. Knight. The only saurischians shown are the two ostrichlike forms in the background—Struthiomimus, a specialized toothless type. All the rest are ornithischians. Paleoscincus, an ankylosaur is in the left center foreground. At the right are crestless Trachodons, on the extreme left the crested Corythosaurus, and in the background Parasaurolophus. These last three had webbed front feet and seem to have been amphibious. (*Courtesy Chicago Natural History Museum.*)

their roughened edges formed a grinding surface. One group, the ornithopods, remained bipeds; the other three groups reverted to the quadrupedal state.

Some of the *ornithopods* or *bird-footed dinosaurs* were small, light, apparently
arboreal creatures, but most were larger forms from 10 to 35 feet in length that
browsed on shrubs and trees, or lived in swamps and fed on aquatic plants. Among

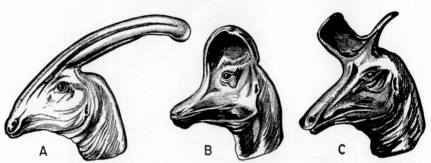

FIG. 28.17. Heads of crested dinosaurs. *A*, Parasaurolophus; *B*, Corythosaurus; *C*, Lambeo-
saurus. The peculiar crests contain the long, looped nasal passages, which are thought to
have served as air storage chambers permitting the animals to remain longer submerged.
(*Redrawn from Colbert, The Dinosaur Book, by permission American Museum of Natural
History.*)

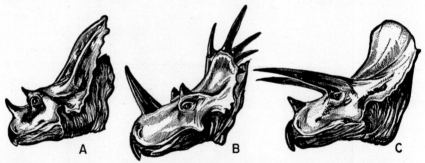

FIG. 28.18. Heads of horned dinosaurs. *A*, Chasmosaurus; *B*, Styracosaurus; *C*, Triceratops.
These are some of the highly specialized end types of a line that began in the early Cretaceous with small forms that had no horns and only the suggestion of a frill or neck
shield. (*Redrawn from Colbert, The Dinosaur Book, by permission American Museum of
Natural History.*)

the semiaquatic types were the duck-billed and crested dinosaurs of the Cretaceous (Figs. 28.16 and 17), which had birdlike horny beaks, immense numbers
of teeth (as many as 2,000 in the mouth at one time with replacements as they
wore out), and in some forms webbed feet for swimming. The *stegosaurs* were
four-footed Jurassic dinosaurs about 20 feet long, with a tiny head, a double row
of upright triangular plates down the middle of the back, and a powerful tail
armed toward the tip with four heavy spikes. The Jurassic *ankylosaurs* were built
like tanks, their large depressed bodies armored above with bony plates and

lateral rows of spikes and their stiff tails ending in a huge clublike mass of bone.

The *ceratopsians* or *horned dinosaurs* were the last group to appear; their entire history was confined to the Cretaceous period. They were heavy-bodied quadrupeds with an enormous skull which projected as a bony shield over the neck and shoulders. The earliest known member of the group was about 6 feet long and had merely the rudiment of a nasal horn. From such a type came several lines of horned dinosaurs, one of which culminated in *Triceratops* of the late Cretaceous—a 30 foot monster with a skull 8 feet long armed with three sharp horns. Like all the ornithischians the horned dinosaurs were herbivores, and their armament was purely defensive.

The end of the Age of Reptiles.   The Cretaceous reptiles were abundant and diversified, and their rule seemed firmly established. Ichthyosaurs, plesiosaurs, and mosasaurs dominated the seas, the various archosaur groups held sway over the lands, and pterosaurs soared in the skies. Yet all this varied reptilian life disappeared with apparent suddenness at the end of the era. Only the turtles, the lizards and snakes, the crocodiles, and the relict tuatara are known to have survived the transition to Cenozoic times. What caused this downfall of a whole dynasty? Many hypotheses have been advanced in explanation, but there was probably no single, simple cause. Basically the cause was inability of the reptiles to adapt to change; and there were many changes that came toward the close of the Cretaceous period. The first effects of the revolution that ushered in the Cenozoic era began to be felt; climates slowly shifted from the uniformly warm, equable conditions of Mesozoic time toward cooler, more zonal ones with fluctuating temperatures, and tropical lowlands gave place to rolling uplands. With these physical changes came alterations in the biotic environment. Cycads and conifers retreated before the advance of the newly arisen hardwood forests; and a host of small, active, warm-blooded and bigger-brained mammals appeared to compete with the cold-blooded, smaller-brained, less efficient reptiles. The changes occurred slowly; no individual would have noticed them, nor several generations, but they continued and their effects were cumulative. Not any one of these things, but all of them together and doubtless others still unsuspected, probably caused the disappearance of the reptilian hordes.

THE HISTORY OF BIRDS

There is little in the appearance or actions of modern birds to suggest the reptile. These alert, active, highly coordinated creatures share dominance of the modern world with the mammals and higher insects and seem a far cry from the dinosaurs and their kin. Yet it was long ago pointed out that aside from their special modifications for flight, with which are to be associated their warm blood, high metabolic rate, and probably their nesting habits, the birds are little more than "glorified reptiles." Feathers are their most distinctive feature, yet even these seem

to have been derived from horny reptilian scales in which the edges have developed into a large number of fine, interlocking subdivisions. The fossil record gives conclusive proof of their archosaur derivation.

The oldest known birds. At Solnhofen, in Bavaria, a very fine-grained Jurassic limestone is quarried for use in lithographic printing. Many beautifully preserved fossils have been taken from the quarries, and among these are two primitive birds about the size of crows, in which even the outlines of the feathers may be seen. Although placed in different genera, they are very similar and are usually referred to under the name *Archaeopteryx*. So reptilian are their characters that if the feathers had not been preserved they would doubtless have been classified as small, primitive ornithischian dinosaurs. Their

Fig. 28.19. The earliest known bird, *Archaeopteryx*. (*After von Meyer.*)

differences from modern birds are shown in the following tabular comparison.

Archaeopteryx	Modern Birds
Jaws with many sharp teeth	Jaws toothless, with horny bill
Tail long, reptilian, with row of feathers on each side	Tail short, with fanlike spread of feathers
Wings feeble, the 3 anterior fingers clawed, projecting from front margin of wing; digits not fused together	Wings strong, the digits fused together, and claws lost (except in the primitive hoatzin)
Bones not hollow and air-filled; air sacs presumably not developed	Bones hollow and air-filled; air sacs in body, connected with lungs
Breastbone (and by inference the flight muscles) weakly developed	Breastbone large and keeled for insertion of powerful flight muscles
Pelvis of ornithischian type, bones showing only incipient fusion	Pelvis derived from ornithischian type, but fused with vertebrae into a rigid structure

Though *Archaeopteryx* could probably fly, it certainly could not have flown well and may have used its wings chiefly for gliding. The fossils give no clue as to how birds first acquired feathered wings. One theory is that their ancestors were tree dwellers with projecting scale fringes on the edges of the limbs and tail; that, jumping from branch to branch, they spread their arms as parachutes to break their fall, and thus in time progressed to gliding flight. A second theory is that they were light-bodied runners, and that the fringed arms and tail helped, by acting as planes, to increase speed in running by lifting the animal somewhat off the ground.

Fig. 28.20. Penguins have lost the power of flight; the wings have become swimming paddles. A group of the Snares Island crested penguin (*Eudyptes atratus*); one of the birds is feeding its young. (*Courtesy American Museum of Natural History.*)

Unlikely as either hypothesis may seem, flight itself is unlikely, and yet it did somehow come about.

Other characters in which modern birds differ from reptiles are: possession of warm blood, a four-chambered heart and double circulation, and greatly increased development of the sight, balance, and coordination centers of the brain—all these being features related to the demands of flight, incubation of the eggs, and increased complexity of behavior, including such phenomena as song, migration, social habits, etc. Archaeopteryx was probably more reptile than bird in most of these respects.

Later evolution of the birds. Bird fossils are rare. Two birds known from Cretaceous time represent an intermediate stage between Archaeopteryx and modern birds. They still had toothed jaws but in other respects were much more birdlike than reptilelike. One, Ichthyornis, was a small form with well-developed wings; the other, Hesperornis, was a large marine diving bird without external traces of wings; only a reduced shoulder girdle and rudimentary humerus remained. By the beginning of the Cenozoic, birds had become completely modernized; teeth had disappeared and the mouth had become a horny beak adapted to pecking and biting. Most of the modern families of birds appeared early in Cenozoic time, and the group has continued to expand up to the present.

Flight is the most characteristic attribute of birds; yet many times in the history of the group ability to fly has been lost, generally among birds which grew very large or adopted aquatic habits. Sometimes the reduced wings took on new functions, as in the penguins (Fig. 28.20), where they became swimming paddles, or the ostriches (Fig. 15.11), which use them as sails to increase speed in running. In the early Cenozoic there was a considerable development of large, flightless birds, similar in habits to the ostriches, rheas, and moas. The mammals were then still in the earlier phases of their development, and it appears that these early giant birds were for a time serious competitors with mammals for dominance of the ground. Diatryma, a wingless predatory bird from Wyoming, was a contemporary of the earliest horses. The horse, at that time, was the size of a fox terrier; this bird was 7 feet tall.

FIG. 28.21. Diatryma, a large Eocene flightless bird of prey from Wyoming, and Eohippus, a contemporary horse, drawn to the same scale. The horse is about a foot high at the shoulder. (*Redrawn from Raymond, Prehistoric Life, by permission Harvard University Press.*)

THE HISTORY OF MAMMALS

Although the mammals arose from synapsid reptiles far back in Mesozoic time, they remained inconspicuous until the close of the age of reptiles. Then they began their spectacular rise to dominance; the Cenozoic era was the age of mammals. Geologically speaking the Cenozoic was short, comprising but a single full period (the Tertiary) and enduring a mere 70 million years; but it was crowded with events, as was described in Chap. XXVI. The climax of mammalian evolution was reached in the Miocene and Pliocene epochs. The Pleistocene glaciations caused the extinction of many lines, so that our modern mammal faunas are mere remnants of the preglacial ones.

Man is one of the mammals, and in taking up the history of this group we return from our digression on reptiles and birds to a consideration of the line of human ancestry. By way of introduction let us review the distinctive features of mammals.

Mammalian characteristics. Just as feathers make the bird, so does hair make the mammal; but hairiness is only one of the more obvious mammalian characters. All but the most primitive mammals are viviparous; the young are "born alive" in a more or less helpless state and are cared for by the mother and fed on milk secreted by her mammary glands. Mammals are warm-blooded like the birds and have a hairy coat and sweat glands which help to maintain a constant body temperature. Except for the birds, they are the most active and alert of vertebrates; their metabolic rate is high, maintained by rapid respiration and an efficient circulatory system with a four-chambered heart.

In structure mammals show many advances over reptiles. The brain is much larger, owing to the great development of the cerebral hemispheres; the remaining parts are not much changed. The skull has lost some of the bones present in primitive reptiles and has been modified from the type found in the synapsid reptiles; the brain case is much enlarged, it articulates with the spine on two bony processes (condyles) instead of one, the nostrils open into an upper chamber cut off from the mouth by a shelflike palate, and the jaw is formed from a single bone (the dentary) instead of from several. The teeth are not all similar as in reptiles but are differentiated into four kinds. In primitive mammals each tooth row contains 3 incisors, 1 canine, 4 premolars, and 3 molars—11 in all, or 44 in the entire dentition. Most modern mammals have lost a part of this complement.

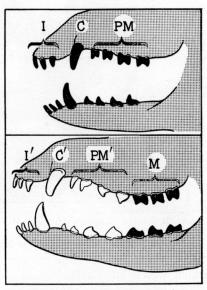

Fig. 28.22. The two sets of teeth of a generalized placental mammal. The first set (black) develop in succession from front to rear; before the rearmost members of this set (the permanent molars) have erupted, a wave of replacement brings the second set of teeth (white), again in anteroposterior succession. This wave, however, proceeds no further than the premolars; the molars of the first set are not replaced. I, incisors; C, canine; PM, premolars; M, molars. I', C', PM', the teeth of the second set. (Modified from Romer, The Vertebrate Body, by permission W. B. Saunders Company.)

A set of deciduous or "milk" teeth precedes the permanent ones. Reptiles have one small bone (stapes) between the inner ear and the eardrum (which lies at the surface); mammals have three. One of these is the old reptilian bone, the other two (malleus and incus) are parts of the old reptilian jaw hinge, which, with the eardrum, have sunk into the head and been enclosed by the parts of the outer ear. An ear flap is developed which concentrates sound waves. The legs of mammals are swung under the body into a fore-and-aft position, elbows back and knees forward, so that less energy is used in lifting the body and more in propelling it. The bones of the digits have been reduced in number from the reptilian 2-3-4-5-3 to 2-3-3-3-3, beginning with the thumb.

Fig. 28.23. Permian fin-backed reptiles ("ship lizards," or pelycosaurs), as drawn by Charles R. Knight. (*Courtesy American Museum of Natural History.*)

Reptilian ancestors. The earliest animals showing traces of mammalian characters were the primitive synapsid reptiles called *pelycosaurs*, which lived in late Carboniferous and early Permian times. They included

the bizarre "fin backs," or "ship lizards," some of them 7 feet long and with a 3-foot high membranous dorsal "sail," supported by enormously elongated vertebral spines. It was not, however, these specialized pelycosaurs but more primitive ones with lizardlike bodies and sprawling limbs that lie in the mammalian line. Features that indicate their relationship to mammals are the position of the skull opening and the fact that the skull is nearly closed behind.

Fig. 28.24. Lycaenops, a mammal-like reptile or therapsid from the Permian of South Africa, restored by E. H. Colbert. This is one of the cynodont or dog-toothed reptiles, the stock from which the mammals probably arose. (*Courtesy American Museum of Natural History.*)

The next step in the development of mammals is represented by the *mammal-like reptiles* or *therapsids* common in late Permian and Triassic strata; most of them have been found in South Africa. They were a varied group, some quite like the pelycosaurs from which they came, others specialized in peculiar ways. The most typical were active carnivores, about 5 feet long, with limbs already shifted toward the typical mammalian position, and mammal-like changes in the skull. In them many of the skull bones that are lost in mammals were becoming small or had already disappeared; the dentary was enlarged and the other jaw bones reduced in size; a double occipital condyle had developed, and also a palate separating the nasal and mouth cavities; the teeth had differentiated into incisors, canines, and cheek teeth. There was still only a single auditory bone. In spite of their mammalian characteristics the therapsids were still reptiles in most respects. Whether they were warm-blooded, or had hair, or nursed their young is a matter for conjecture.

Egg-laying mammals. Two very specialized survivors of an egg-

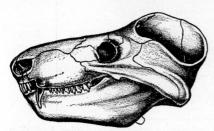

Fig. 28.25. The skull of Cynognathus, a Permian dog-toothed reptile. Note the mammal-like differentiation of the teeth, increased size of the dentary bone of the lower jaw, and reduction of the bones of the jaw hinge region (*Redrawn from Romer, Vertebrate Paleontology, by Permission University of Chicago Press.*)

Fig. 28.26. The duckbill or platypus. Ornithorhynchus, a primitive egg-laying Australian mammal. (*From Burrell, The Platypus.*)

laying stock of mammals occur today in Australia, where they have been able to persist through the protection afforded by their geographic isolation and their retiring habits. These are the *duckbill* (Platypus) and the *spiny anteater* (Echidna). They have fur and nurse their young but lay shelled eggs. Neither has teeth. The duckbill has webbed feet and is mainly a stream dweller, nesting in burrows in the banks; the anteater has a covering of stout spines, strong digging feet, and a slender snout. It is probable that viviparity appeared early in mammalian evolution, and that the viviparous stocks prevailed over the egg-laying types even during the Mesozoic era.

The marsupials or pouched mammals. By late Mesozoic time the viviparous mammals had divided into several lines, of which two have survived—the more primitive *marsupials* and the more advanced *placentals*. In both of these the embryo develops for a time as a parasite within the body of the mother, but this stage is brief in the marsupials and prolonged in the placental mammals. Marsupial young are born in a very immature state—practically as embryos—whereupon they crawl to the nipples of the mammary glands and attach themselves. The nipple swells within the mouth until it can be removed only by force, and the windpipe of the young animal grows up into contact with the nasal chamber so that breathing is possible even while milk is being swallowed. In all but a

Fig. 28.27. The spiny anteater or echidna. Tachyglossus, a primitive egg-laying Australian mammal, with a model of its egg. (*Courtesy American Museum of Natural History.*)

very few marsupials the region of the nipples is covered by a skin pouch, the *marsupium,* and within this pouch the young complete their development.

Except for the North American opossum, living marsupials are confined to Australia, Tasmania, and South America. The group was probably numerous and widespread in the late Mesozoic, although no fossils except those of opossums have been found in North America and Europe. Regardless of where they originated, the marsupials were evidently present in Australia and South America by Cretaceous times. In South America they were later overrun and largely supplanted by the higher placental mammals; but submergence of the Asiatic-Australian land bridge during the Cretaceous prevented most of the placentals from entering Australia. The marsupials had the entire continent almost to themselves until the coming of man and the animals introduced by him,

Protected by their isolation from competition with higher types, they underwent an *adaptive radiation*, which we have already cited as a classical illustration of this phenomenon.

The ancestral marsupial was apparently a small, arboreal, opossum-like animal. From such a stem form, a great variety of types evolved, adapted to almost every sort of habitat and mode of life. Among living Australian marsupials (Figs. 24.5 and 16; 28.28 and 29) there are "mice," "shrews," "squirrels," "cats," a "wolf," "moles," an "anteater," sloth-

Fig. 28.28. Representative Australian marsupials. *A* and *B*, two kinds of wombats, Phascolomys. *C*, anteater, *Myrmecobius*. *D*, koala, Phascolarctus. *E*, kangaroo, Macropus, with young in pouch. *F*, marsupial "wolf," Thylacinus. *G*, "tiger cat," Dasyurus. *H*, phalanger or "opossum," Trichosurus. (*A* and *E*, *courtesy Zoological Society of Philadelphia, remainder, American Museum of Natural History.*)

like "bears," badgerlike wombats, the wolverinelike Tasmanian devil, and other types like nothing else on earth, including kangaroos, bandicoots (suggesting rabbits with long tails), and the flying phalangers. Many of these show extraordinarily close resemblance to the unrelated placental mammals whose names they were given by the European settlers of Australia. On the main continents the placental squirrels occupy one ecological "niche," or way of life, the placental moles another, and so on; in Australia the corresponding niches are occupied by marsupial "squirrels," marsupial "moles," etc. In the one region the various niches have been filled by adaptive radiation of the placentals, in the other by adaptive radiation of the marsupials, and the superficially similar end products exemplify the phenomenon called *adaptive convergence.*

The placental mammals.   The young of the placental mammals are
retained within the body of the mother for a long time, while they pass
through their embryonic and fetal stages of development. During this
period they lead a parasitic existence, nourished within the uterus by
means of an organ called the *placenta*, formed from the old reptilian
allantois. For a time after birth they are cared for by the mother and fed
upon milk secreted by her mammary glands. Not only is their chance of
survival better than that of the young of egg-laying and marsupial
mammals, but the prolonged period of embryonic development makes
possible and is required for the attainment of the higher levels of com-

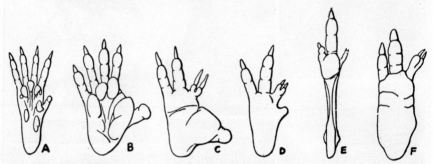

Fig. 28.29. The hind feet of a series of marsupials, showing the extraordinary history of the
feet of the tree kangaroo, Dendrolagus. The forms shown do not represent the actual
ancestral line but illustrate its successive stages. *A*, Caenolestes, a primitive walker. *B*,
opossum, a primary climber. *C*, phalanger, a specialized climber. *D*, bandicoot, a secondary
walker derived from climbing ancestors. *E*, kangaroo, a specialized leaper derived from
types like *D*. *F*, tree kangaroo, a climber derived from kangaroos. (*After D. Dwight Davis,
Jr., by permission General Biological Supply House, Inc.*)

plexity which characterize the placental mammals, particularly in the
organization of the nervous system.

The earliest known placentals were small late Cretaceous *insectivores*
related to our modern shrews and moles. They had long skulls with many
sharp teeth, small brains, and flexible feet with pointed claws; they were
agile, and may well have been nocturnally active tree dwellers. From such
an ancestral stock the placental mammals rapidly developed along many
lines during the Paleocene, and by Eocene times the principal directions
of their later evolution had become established.

In all of the groups that arose from the insectivores there has been a
tendency toward increase in relative brain size and in size of body, accompanied by modifications of the skull, teeth, and limbs. In each stock some
archaic groups early became specialized and attained temporary dominance, only to be replaced later by more advanced modernized types with
better brains, that rose from the ranks of the less specialized. Several
different groups of early placentals became herbivores, taking advantage

of the new abundance of plant food provided by the angiosperms; others retained the more primitive omnivorous or carnivorous food habits.

Much of the evolutionary history of the placentals was controlled by the interplay between *carnivore* and *herbivore*. Since the slower, more stupid, and less well protected of the herbivores were the easiest prey, selection continually operated to make the survivors speedier and more alert, or to give them improved means of protection. Some stocks evolved into fast runners; others developed great size and strength, with tough

FIG. 28.30. Pleistocene life in southern California, reconstructed from the fossils of the tar pits at Rancho La Brea in the suburbs of Los Angeles. Great numbers of animals were trapped in the sticky tar when they came to drink at the pools or to feed upon mired creatures. Among the forms evidently common in the region were mastodons, horses, lions, saber-toothed tigers, dire wolves, giant vultures, and many smaller mammals and birds. (*Courtesy Carnegie Museum, Pittsburgh.*)

skins; protective weapons appeared in wide variety, the commonest being horns and striking feet. Meanwhile the carnivorous types kept pace. Some, like the wolves, specialized on the long chase; others, like the cats, on the pounce from concealment; size and strength grew to match the size and strength of the prey. All this is reminiscent of what we have seen among the dinosaurs—a race between offense and defense. But among the mammals one result of this competition was something quite new—the development of social behavior. Family groups and organized herds among the herbivores, and hunting groups among the carnivores, have had no counterparts among the reptiles.

A great deal is known of the history of the placental mammals. It makes a fascinating story, but one which is far too complex for treatment in a book of this nature. For those who would like to learn something of the knob-skulled, tusked unintatheres, giant horned titanotheres, huge-clawed horselike chalicotheres, club-tailed armored glyptodonts, blood-drinking saber-toothed tigers, and many another group as strange, Scott's *History of Land Mammals in the Western Hemisphere* (The Macmillan Company, New York, 1937) will make good reading. Here we shall have to content ourselves with an account of the development of the horses, perhaps the most completely known of evolutionary histories.

THE EVOLUTION OF THE HORSES

The fossil record of the horses constitutes one of the classic examples of evolution. Not only is the record extraordinarily complete, but the important changes that occurred in teeth and skeleton are easily seen and understood. The horses constitute one of the families of the hoofed mammals, or *ungulates*, and it will be best to begin their story by a survey of the history of this group.

The hoofed mammals. During the Paleocene epoch there appeared among the primitive herbivores some which had small hoofs instead of. claws on their toes. These were the ancestral ungulates. They all began as five-toed animals. In some of them the third and fourth toes were of equal length and the foot axis passed between the two; from such forms arose the *even-toed* ungulates, or *artiodactyls*. In others the middle toe was the longest and lay in the axial line of the foot, and these forms gave rise to the *odd-toed ungulates*, or *perissodactyls*, including the horses.

Ungulates have always been the main food of the larger carnivorous mammals. Under selective pressure from these predators the members of all the ungulate groups tended to increase in size and to attain greater speed in running by rising on the toes instead of planting the whole foot on the ground. As the heel was raised, the side toes were lifted from the ground, as can be seen by placing the hand flat on a table and raising the wrist. With loss of function the lateral toes dwindled and in the end some-times disappeared. Some of the ungulates early developed into large, ponderous animals which no longer depended upon speed for protection. In these toe reduction did not proceed far; the legs became pillarlike, and the spread toes buttressed the stumpy feet, as in the elephants. In other ungulate lines, size increase occurred more slowly, and speed continued to be the main defense; in them development of the running leg was carried further.

What happened to the feet of the even-toed artiodactyls can be visual-ized by raising the wrist, as before, keeping the two middle fingers on the table. First the thumb lifted and was lost, leaving a four-toed foot; then the second and fifth digits were lost, leaving the typical two-toed condition seen in the cloven-hoofed pigs, camels, deer, giraffes, and cattle. By lifting the hand on the axis of the middle finger one may imitate the changes that occurred in the odd-toed perissodactyls. First there was loss of the thumb and then of the little finger, leaving a three-toed foot such as is found in tapirs, rhinoceroses, and most of the fossil horses. In later horses this was followed by loss of the second and fourth digits, giving the ultimate in toe reduction, the one-toed foot.

Characteristics of the modern horse.   The nature of the evolutionary changes in the horse group will be most easily comprehended if we first consider the principal adaptive features of the familiar horse of today.

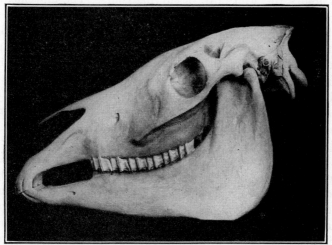

Fɪɢ. 28.31. The skull of a modern Arabian horse. (*Courtesy American Museum of Natural History.*)

The horse is a large, swift-footed grazing animal. Its most distinctive characters are those of the teeth and feet. The skull is long and consists mostly of face; the part in front of the eyes is extended far forward to accommodate a powerful battery of grinding cheek teeth and a set of cropping teeth in front. The grinding teeth include the molars and all but the first of the premolars; they are all much alike—square prisms with a complex pattern of infolded enamel on the grinding surface. These teeth are tall, with high crowns and short roots, and are set deep in the jaws; the rear part of the lower jaw is much deepened to accommodate them. The grinding surface is worn away by the chewing of abrasive foods, and the nearly vertical harder enamel layers form little ridges supported by the inner dentine of the tooth on one side and by cement on the other. Cement is a limy material deposited on the surface of the tooth and between its folds by secretions of the mouth. The cheek teeth continue to grow at the base until the animal is between five and eight years old; then the roots close, growth stops, and the teeth are thenceforth simply pushed up as fast as they are worn away. When they are used up, the horse dies from inability to chew its food. The fossil record shows that these high-crowned, complex grinders evolved from small, short-crowned simple teeth more like the molar teeth of man.

The adaptations for swift running are equally striking. The body of the horse is narrow, deep-chested, and powerfully muscled at the shoulder and hip; the neck is long, as is necessary in a long-legged grazing animal. The legs are placed close against the body, and when in rapid movement, the feet are brought almost under the body axis, giving maximum support and the ability to "lean into" a curving course. The movement of the legs is restricted largely to a fore-and-aft swing; the radius and ulna of the foreleg and the tibia and fibula of the hind are fused into single bones so that the foot cannot be rotated. The heel is lifted high off the ground, adding the length of the foot to that of the leg proper; and most remarkable of all, the foot is reduced to a single functional toe, on the toenail of which (the hoof) the horse is perched. From the fossils it is evident that this highly specialized leg and foot have evolved from the primitive five-toed type found among the early ungulates.

Fossil horses.   More than a score of genera and a great many species of fossil horses are now known, representing every age from lower Eocene through Pleistocene time. Many of the species are represented by hundreds or thousands of specimens. The genera form an almost unbroken gradient of change, which makes them little more than groupings of convenience; many of the species could equally well be placed among the advanced members of one genus or among the primitive members of the genus next higher in the scale. For full descriptive purposes it is customary to recognize about ten stages in horse evolution, but we shall describe only five.

Eohippus, the dawn horse, is the first stage to be considered.   The earliest known ancestral horses were creatures the size of a cat or small dog, which became numerous in the lower Eocene. There were many species, all very similar and mostly members of the genus Eohippus. From the structure of their teeth it is judged that they fed on leaves and tender shoots, and they probably inhabited the undergrowth of the Eocene forests. These dawn horses were slender-bodied, with pawlike feet, but with tiny hoofs instead of claws on the toes. The front feet had four toes, the hind feet three; the missing "thumb" of the forefoot was gone without trace, but rudiments of the side toes were still present on the hind foot. The radius and ulna and the tibia and fibula were still separate bones. The skull was short, with the eye sockets situated at about mid-length, and open behind. The molar teeth were small and low-

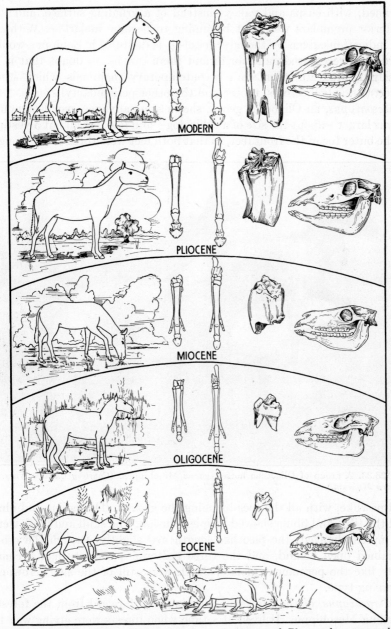

Fig. 28.32. Diagram of the evolution of the horse. Lowest panel, Phenacodus, a generalized "archaic" ungulate of the Paleocene. The remaining figures are horses. From bottom to top those shown are Eohippus, Mesohippus, Merychippus, Pliohippus, and Equus. Within each panel, from left to right, appear a reconstruction of the horse, the fore and hind foot showing the progressive reduction in lateral digits, one of the permanent molar teeth, and the skull. Only the teeth are drawn to scale.

crowned, with cusps and valleys instead of a grinding surface, and the posterior premolars were just beginning to become molarlike. Without the indications given by the later fossils it is doubtful if Eohippus would have been recognized as a horse; and there can be no doubt that it is closely related to other similar contemporary mammals which were ancestral to rhinoceroses, tapirs, and the other perissodactyl stocks.

Mesohippus, an Oligocene genus, shows some advance over Eohippus. It was larger—about the size of a collie dog—and had lost all but a vestige of the outer toe of the front feet, so that both feet were three-toed, though

.Fɪɢ. 28.33. A group of Oligocene horses, genus Mesohippus. (*Courtesy Chicago Natural History Museum.*)

still pawlike, with all the toes touching the ground. The radius and ulna and the tibia and fibula showed incipient fusion. The skull and teeth were not much changed; the face had lengthened slightly, though the orbit remained open behind, and the three posterior premolars had become quite like the permanent molars, which were still of the short-crowned browsing type.

Merychippus, of the Miocene, is a long step forward from the forest-dwelling Mesohippus. It lived at a time when forests were giving way to grasslands, and its structure shows that Merychippus had taken to the plains and to a diet of grass. Its height had increased to 3 feet. The legs were stronger, with the two bones of the lower leg firmly fused together in the adult though still separate in the colt. There were still three toes, but the center one had become much larger and stronger than the side toes, which did not ordinarily touch the ground. Functionally this was a one-toed foot, which, though less well adapted to rough going than the earlier three-toed type, was better for running on the hard surface of the plains. The teeth for the first time showed a heavy deposit of cement on the sides and in the folds. The milk premolars were still low-crowned, but the permanent molars and premolars were now all alike, moderately high-crowned and with an enamel pattern similar to that of modern horses. High crowns imply grass-feeding habits; the silica content of grass is highly abrasive and would rapidly destroy low-crowned teeth. As the cheek teeth enlarged, the face elongated, and the orbit became closed behind for the first time. Merychippus is regarded as a direct ancestor of modern horses.

Pliohippus, like the preceding, was a widespread genus of many species which occurred during the Pliocene. Some of its members were three-toed horses, but others were the first horses with a single toe. In these, fusion of the lower leg bones was complete, and the two side toes had been reduced to mere splint bones buried in the tissues of the leg. The grinding teeth of both milk and permanent sets were moderately high-crowned, with a more complicated enamel pattern than that of Merychippus. The average size was that of a small pony.

Equus, the genus to which modern horses belong, appeared in the Pleistocene and represents the last stage in the evolution of the horses. Its characteristics have already been described rather fully above.

Most of the evolution of the horse group occurred in North America, which was the developmental center throughout Tertiary time. An occasional offshoot succeeded in reaching the Old World or South America, but for the most part these soon died out. Pliohippus is evidently the stock from which the modern horses and their relatives have come. Some of its progeny reached South America and there became specialized types, which later disappeared; but the main line of descent was that which led to the genus Equus, which first appeared at the beginning of the Pleistocene. Equus arose in North America and rapidly spread to every continent except Australia. It subdivided to form the zebras, now confined to Africa; the asses, still found wild in the Old World tropics; and true horses, of which a wild species still exists in central Asia. Numerous species of zebras, asses, and true horses existed in North America until late in the Pleistocene. It is a strange fact that although North America had been the evolutionary center for so long, the entire horse group became extinct in the New World by the end of the Pleistocene. The horses that now range the Great Plains all came from the horses brought by man from the Old World back to their ancestral home.

CHAPTER XXIX

MAN'S RELATIVES: THE PRIMATES

The order of mammals that interests us most is the Primates, for we ourselves belong to this order. Unfortunately the fossil record of primate evolution is very fragmentary; primates have been chiefly inhabitants of tropical forests, and this environment is not one in which fossils are likely to be preserved. On the other hand various primitive groups of primates still have living representatives to which we can turn for help in interpreting the fossils.

The origin of primates. In early Cretaceous times the lands were covered with forests, but there was little development of a ground vegetation. This may explain why the early placental mammals, like the early marsupials, were tree dwellers. Their arboreal habit is not directly evident from the Cretaceous fossils, which are mostly skulls and teeth. Instead it is deduced from the fact that in all the stocks descended from the Mesozoic insectivores the earliest types had the first toe set apart from and differently hinged than the other toes. This condition indicates that they came from ancestors possessed of grasping feet, an arboreal adaptation. During the late Cretaceous a ground flora began to appear, and at this time many mammalian stocks forsook the trees and took to the ground. From these the clawed carnivores and the hoofed herbivores developed. Some of the insectivores, however, remained in the trees, and among these were the ancestors of the primates.

The beginnings of the primate line are found in a group called the *tree shrews*—small arboreal mammals intermediate between typical insectivores and true primates. Only a single fossil tree shrew is known, from the Oligocene of Asia, but the group fortunately still survives in the Malayan area. These creatures are squirrel-like in appearance. The foot has a grasping first toe, and claws instead of nails (except on the hind foot of the Oligocene fossil). The skull is long and low, with an eye orbit which is partly or completely closed behind by a bar of bone. The teeth are similar to those of the insectivores, with molars suited for mincing and slicing rather than grinding. The brain is intermediate in size between that of typical insectivores and the lowest of the primates.

From such ancestors the further evolution of the primates has been a history of increasingly perfect adaptation to life in the trees, until the direction of modification was partly reversed among the larger and heavier apes and more completely in man. Although man is not a tree dweller, the arboreal life of his ancestors has left its mark deeply upon him and is perhaps in great measure responsible for his attainment of his present estate. Some of the more important primate characteristics, most of which are related to this arboreal habit, may here be considered.

Primate characteristics.   The primates fall into three groups—*lemurs, tarsioids,* and *anthropoids,* the last being highest in the scale and including

Fig. 29.1. A Philippine tree shrew, Tupaia. The members of this group are intermediate between insectivores and the more typical primates and are placed at the base of the primate family tree. (*Courtesy Zoological Society of Philadelphia.*)

the monkeys, apes, and man. All share the following features: hands and feet prehensile (grasping), or evidently derived from the prehensile type; a clavicle, or collarbone, present; some or all of the fingers and toes with flattened nails instead of claws; breasts as a rule restricted to a single anteriorly situated pair; and brain relatively large, often attaining great size and intricacy of pattern.

For locomotion in trees, flexibility of the *limbs* is essential. This is particularly true of the forelimb, which reaches for new holds, grasps and clings, while the hind limbs support the weight of the body. The result has been the differentiation of a more mobile arm with a more prehensile hand, and of a more stable leg with a less supple foot. There has been no restriction of limb movement to one plane and no solidification of the foot into a strong supporting structure as in terrestrial quadrupeds. The digits, instead of having sharp claws, are protected by flat nails in all but the most primitive forms. In many of the higher primates *brachiation*—swinging through the air from branch to branch by use of the arms—has largely superseded climbing and jumping; and this has been accompanied by a strengthening of the arms and hands at the expense of the legs and feet. On the ground most primates walk on all fours; but all except the lemurs rest in a squatting position, and since their hands are thus freed from the supporting function, they can be used to pick up food and other objects. The primitive long tail is retained in the lemurs, tarsioids, and more primitive monkeys, and in some of the latter it has been modified into a prehensile organ. In the higher anthropoids the tail tends to shorten and become rudimentary, and no external signs of it remain in the great apes and man.

Arboreal life has profoundly affected the *nervous system* and *sense organs*. Smell, so important to terrestrial mammals, is of little value to a tree dweller. This sense shows progressive deterioration in primate evolution and is probably more rudimentary in the apes and man than in any mammal of terrestrial descent. On the other hand good eyesight and well-developed touch and muscle senses are of the utmost importance for life in trees. In the higher primates two great improvements have been made in the visual apparatus. The first was the shifting of the eyes from the sides to the front of the head in the tarsioids and anthropoids, so that *the visual fields overlap or coincide*. This makes possible stereoscopic vision and accurate distance perception. The second, found only in the anthropoids, was the development of a centrally located "yellow spot" (*macula lutea*) in the retina, which acts as a color filter to strain out those light rays that cause color aberration. Together with the fovea, or central pit, this gives ability to see a maximum of fine detail and greatly increases acuity of vision.

The *brain* has been greatly enlarged and modified in relation to the requirements of arboreal life and the accompanying changes in the sense organs. Brachiation requires good eyesight and accurate judgment of distance. It also demands the most perfect muscular coordination of any type of locomotion except perhaps flight. Correspondingly we find the motor and coordination centers of the brain greatly developed in the higher primates. The volume and variety of sensory impressions are much increased by keen vision and the ability to grasp and handle objects. This is probably correlated with the disproportionate size increase of the cerebral hemispheres, where the sensory areas of the brain are located. Throughout primate evolution the size of the brain has continually increased.

The changes in sense organs and brain have been accompanied by changes in *skull* and *teeth*. The facial region has tended to shorten and become smaller (Fig. 30.6), and the brain case has become larger and rounder. The shortening jaw has lost a part of the original mammalian complement of 44 teeth; in the higher primates, including man, only 32 remain. Primate teeth have stayed quite primitive in form, the molars being low-crowned with rounded cusps, like those of the early ungulates and of the omnivorous pig. The canine tooth is a projecting tusk in most primates, but in man it scarcely rises above the level of the other teeth.

In primitive placentals the *eye socket* is not separated from the temple opening, but in more advanced forms a bony bar bridges the space and separates the two openings. Such a bar is present in all primates. Beneath this bar in the tarsioids and anthropoids, a thin sheet of bone is formed which completely closes off the eye socket at the rear—a structure found in no other animals. Presumably the complete bony socket gives better muscle attachment and support for the eyes in their forwardly rotated position and prevents disturbances of vision caused by movements of the jaw muscles.[1]

The lemurs. These are the simplest of the primates, recognized as fossils from the Paleocene and Eocene of Europe and North America. They survive today chiefly on the island of Madagascar, where they have been protected by isolation. Typical lemurs are small four-footed arboreal animals, somewhat squirrel-like in appearance, with fluffy hair and a long bushy tail. In structure they are only a little more advanced than their ancestors the tree shrews. The muzzle is long and pointed, the teeth suggest those of insectivores, the eyes are directed outward and lack a complete bony socket, and although some of the toes have flat nails, certain toes typically have clawlike ones. The placenta is very simple; projections inserted into the uterine wall occur in scattered groups over its surface and are pulled free at birth. Some of the early Cenozoic lemurs appear to be transitional to the

Fig. 29.2. The ruffed lemur of Madagascar, *Lemur varius*. (*Courtesy Zoological Society of Philadelphia.*)

tarsioids, and the latter were evidently derived from some lemur stock.

The tarsioids. This group is represented today by a few species of the highly specialized genus Tarsius, a relict type found in the East Indies. These tarsiers are small, nocturnal, arboreal creatures, with ratlike tail and furred body. The hind legs are specialized for hopping, and all the toes are very long and slender, with flattened clinging disks at the

---

[1] A very good and complete account of the changes that have occurred during the evolution of the primates is to be found in Hooton's book, *Up from the Ape*, The Macmillan Company, New York, 1947.

tips, that suggest those of tree frogs. The nail of the first toe is small and flattened, but the other nails are pointed and clawlike. The eyes are immense, directed forward and almost touching above the small nose; they are enclosed in a complete bony socket with flaring margins. The sense of smell is much reduced; tarsiers are insect feeders, and catch their prey by sight, the great eyes being adapted for night vision. The teeth are much like those of lemurs and insectivores. The brain is large, the brain case rounded, and the face reduced. The placental connections with the uterus are concentrated into a disk-shaped structure, which is shed at birth as in the higher primates. Although highly specialized in some features, in other respects Tarsius is intermediate between the lemurs and the anthropoids. Primitive tarsioids occurred with lemurs in the Paleocene and Eocene epochs, and the higher primates are believed to have come from some early tarsioid line.

Fig. 29.3. A Philippine tarsier, Tarsius species. (*Photo by Isabelle deP. Hunt.*)

The anthropoids. The remaining primates form the suborder Anthropoidea—the "manlike animals." They comprise the monkeys, apes, and man, which share many important characteristics. Compared with lemurs and tarsioids the anthropoids show numerous advances. The brain is much larger and more complicated. The eyes are directed forward and have complete bony sockets as in Tarsius, but the tear ducts open within the sockets instead of on the face. Acuity of vision is increased by the presence of the specialized "yellow spot" on the retina. The facial region has been progressively reduced and the brain case expanded. The spinal column is attached beneath instead of at the back of the skull, and the face is turned more nearly at right angles to the spine. The placenta is disk-shaped and shed at birth.

The anthropoids are divided into two groups, geographically separated today and in the past. The more primitive of the two includes the flatnosed monkeys (platyrrhines) of the New World; all the Old World primates (advanced types of monkeys, apes, man) belong to the narrow-nosed group, the catarrhines.[1]

In the *New World monkeys* the nostrils are directed forward and separated by a low, wide septum; each jaw has three premolar teeth on

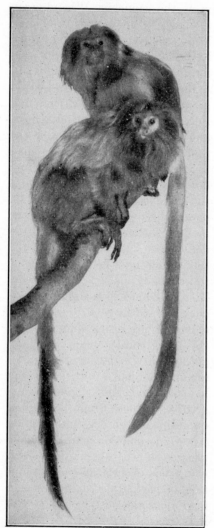

FIG. 29.4. Lion-maned marmosets, or tamarins, Leontocebus. (*Courtesy Zoological Society of Philadelphia.*)

FIG. 29.5. A South American spider monkey, Ateles, family Cebidae. (*Courtesy Zoological Society of Philadelphia.*)

each side; and there are no callous areas on the buttocks as in the Old World monkeys. The *marmosets* (Hapalidae) are primitive platyrrhines quite

[1] "Platyrrhine" simply means "flat-nosed"; "catarrhine" means "with down-wardly directed nose."

like the lemurs in appearance. They are squirrel-like forms with short fur and bushy tails; the first toes have flat nails and are not opposable, while the other toes have claws. The remaining platyrrhines (Cebidae) are more familiar types of monkeys, such as the capuchins ("hand-organ monkeys"), howlers, squirrel monkeys, woolly monkeys, etc., which have flat nails on all digits, and most of which have prehensile tails.

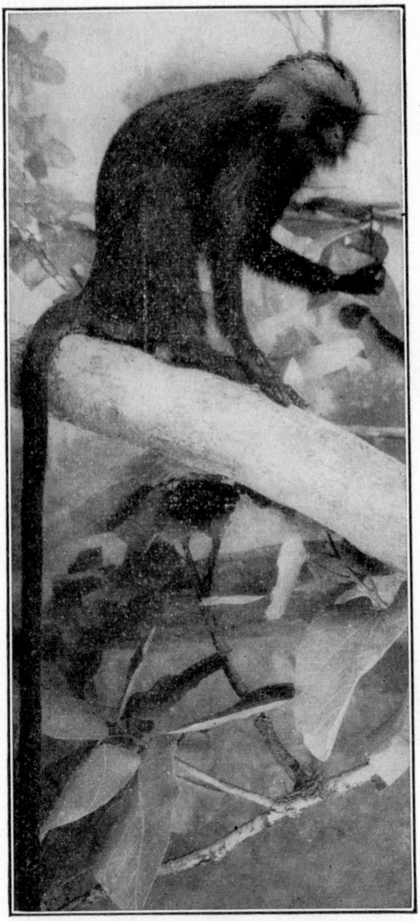

The catarrhines. This Old World group includes the African and Asian monkeys, the manlike apes, and man. In all of these the nostrils are placed rather close together and open forward and downward. The tooth formula is the same as in man—two incisors, one canine, two premolars, and three molars in each tooth row. All the digits have flattened nails, and the tail (which may be long, short, or rudimentary) is never prehensile. The catarrhines show a general tendency toward increased size, which among living forms culminates in the chimpanzee, man, and the gorilla. Most members of the group are arboreal, but a few, such as the baboons and man, have become ground dwellers. From the original quadrupedal climbing and jumping mode of locomotion some lines have progressed to brachiation, with elongation of the arms and assumption of partially erect posture. In man alone the posture has become fully erect.

FIG. 29.6. A langur monkey, Semnopithecus, from the Nilgiri Hills of India. These monkeys, of the family Cercopithecidae, lack cheek pouches and have a complicated stomach for food storage. (*Courtesy American Museum of Natural History.*)

The Old World monkeys. The earliest known member of this group is a tiny monkey called *Parapithecus*, from the lower Oligocene of Egypt. Judging from the characters of its jaw and teeth (Fig. 29.14), it may well have been the ancestor of all the later catarrhines. Today the Old World monkeys comprise many genera and species, all placed in the family Cercopithecidae. They are easily distinguished from the American platyrrhines by the shape of the nose, the lack of a prehensile tail, and the presence on the buttocks of bare callous areas which are often brilliantly colored, especially in the males. There are two groups, one of which includes plant-feeding arboreal monkeys in which the thumb has become vestigial, the hind legs are longer than the front ones, cheek pouches are lacking, and the stomach has become large and complicated, as in animals that chew their cud.

Most of the Old World monkeys, however, belong to the other group in which the thumb is well developed, the front legs are at least as long as the hind ones, there are cheek pouches for holding food, and the stomach is simple. Many members of this second group, such as the guenons and mangabeys, are typical tree-dwelling monkeys. Others—the mandrills, drills, and baboons of Arabia and Africa—have taken to the ground. They walk and run as quadrupeds on the palms of the hands and soles of the feet but retain the grasping thumb and big toe. Their muzzles have become elongated and doglike, and the canine teeth are large tusks. The Old World monkeys as a group show many similarities to man, but they have obviously played no part in his evolution and are no more than very distant cousins.

FIG. 29.7. A male mandrill, one of the large West African baboons of the genus Papio, family Cercopithecidae. These apes have become completely terrestrial and wholly herbivorous. The tooth row is much elongated, forming a doglike muzzle armed with large canine tusks (see Fig. 29.8). (*Courtesy American Museum of Natural History.*)

The manlike apes. Of all animals, the apes of the family Simiidae come closest to man in structure, physiology, and behavior, and the fossil record shows our own ancestry converging with theirs as we go back in time. For this reason we shall take up their evolutionary history in connection with that of man and shall here consider only the modern representatives of this highly interesting group. There are four living types— the gibbon, the orangutan, the chimpanzee, and the gorilla. The gibbon is considerably smaller than man, while the other three types, called the great apes, weigh as much as or considerably more than man. In all of them the skeleton is quite manlike. The chest is broad, in contrast to the deep chest of monkeys and of mammals in general. The arms are longer than the legs; the hands are quite similar to those of man but with relatively longer fingers and shorter thumb; and the feet are used mostly for walking but are still well fitted for grasping, with the toes long and the big toe opposable and thumblike. The tail is even more rudimentary than in man, and does not project externally.

These features of the body are related to the mode of locomotion. As the weight increased, the monkeylike four-footed running on a single branch was abandoned in favor of placing the feet on one branch and the hands on a higher one; from this to brachiation was an easy transition. As it swings from the hands, the body necessarily hangs vertical; and because the arms are long and the legs are short, an inclined, suberect position of the trunk is maintained even in quadrupedal locomotion on the ground. These are steps in the direction of the erect posture characteristic of man.

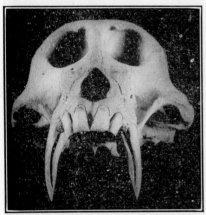

Fig. 29.8. The skull of a baboon in front view, showing the tremendous fighting tusks. (*Courtesy American Museum of Natural History.*)

The gibbon. The smallest and most primitive of the manlike apes is the gibbon, of which several kinds inhabit Malaya. This ape averages about 3 feet in height and has extraordinarily long arms, which reach to the ground when the animal stands erect. The body is very slender and light, covered with fur rather than with coarse hair like that of the great apes. The skull is low, with prominent brow ridges, a rather flat nose, and protruding jaws; the canine teeth are long tusks; and the hand is long and narrow with a short thumb. Gibbons are the only apes which customarily walk erect, extending the arms to the sides as balancers. They are seldom seen on the ground, however; it is in the trees that they are truly at home. The gibbons have developed brachiation to its highest perfection. They hurl themselves through the air from branch to branch, easily clearing distances of 20 feet, and on occasion making 40-foot leaps. In such progression the feet are doubled up close to the body and the arms are used alternately, taking off with the right, catching momentarily with the left to obtain impetus for a new leap, and so on indefinitely. Brachiation calls for the greatest agility, exact coordination, precise judgment of distance and of strength of branches, sharp eyesight, and general alertness; the penalty for failure is injury or death.

The orangutan. Next above the gibbon in the scale of living primates is the orangutan, or "man of the woods" of Borneo and Sumatra. It is a bulky and powerful animal, though short-legged and standing only 4 to 5 feet tall. The arms are very long, with a span of over 7 feet, and the hands and feet are long and narrow, with a short thumb and great toe. The skull and brain are relatively larger than in the gibbon; the muzzle is large and protruding, the brow ridges scarcely prominent, and the nasal region deeply concave. The canine teeth are large, tusklike, and inter-

Fig. 29.9. A group of gibbons, genus Hylobates. There are a number of kinds differing in coloration, but all are probably varieties or subspecies of one or two species. (*Courtesy Chicago Natural History Museum.*)

locking. The body is sparsely covered with long, reddish-brown hair. This ape is almost exclusively arboreal, but on account of its weight (up to 160 pounds) is not an expert brachiator; it climbs deliberately and tests the strength of branches before venturing upon them. Orangutans build nests on which to sleep and on rainy nights are said to cover themselves with leaves. They feed on fruits and foliage. One young is produced at a birth, and the life span is about 45 years. The orangutan, while more advanced than the gibbon, is probably far off the line leading to the two higher manlike apes and man.

The chimpanzee and the gorilla. These two apes, which inhabit tropical Africa, are closely related and may be discussed together. Of all

existing animals they are those most similar to man, and both show a
change from arboreal to terrestrial life, though far less complete than in
man. They are large, powerful, and heavily built animals. The male
chimpanzee may be 5 feet tall and weigh 175 pounds, while the male
gorilla attains a height of more than 6 feet and a weight up to 600 pounds.
Weight for weight both are several times as strong as the strongest man.
The chimpanzee is an expert climber but spends much time on the

Fig. 29.10. The "man of the woods," or orangutan, Simia (= Pongo). Left, a young individual; right, the face of a five-year-old male. (*Courtesy Zoological Society of Philadelphia
and American Museum of Natural History respectively.*)

ground, where it runs on all fours or walks semierect for short distances.
The gorilla is largely terrestrial, though it climbs trees for fruit and to
sleep; it also is normally a quadruped, but stands erect for attack or
defense. Both animals have a coat of coarse black hair which is thin on
the chest and absent on the face, hands, and feet. These apes are chiefly
herbivorous, though the chimpanzee, at least, sometimes eats animal
food. There is some degree of family organization. Young are produced
singly, maturity is reached at eight to twelve years of age, and the span
of life is comparable with that of man.

Some of the original arboreal adaptations of these apes have been
modified in conformity with the changed mode of life. The arms have

become relatively shorter and the legs stronger. In the more arboreal chimpanzee the hands and feet are still long and narrow, with small thumbs and great toes. In the more terrestrial gorilla the arm, hand, and foot have become more like those of man, the thumb being larger and more opposable, the foot shorter, and the weight of the body being carried more on the sole of the foot and less on the outer edge than in other apes.

The brain attains a volume of 500 to 600 cubic centimeters, which is about half that found in the most primitive men. The skull (Figs. 29.13, 30.4 to 6 and 13) is large but low vaulted, and in older individuals it develops bony crests on top and at the rear for the attachment of the

FIG. 29.11. An African chimpanzee, Pan (= Anthropopithecus). (*Courtesy American Museum of Natural History.*)

FIG. 29.12. A large male gorilla of the mountain species, *Gorilla beringeri*. (*Courtesy American Museum of Natural History.*)

huge jaw and neck muscles. There are prominent bony ridges above the eyes (especially in gorillas); the nose is depressed and the muzzle prominent. The canine teeth form projecting and interlocking tusks. The molar teeth are quite similar to those of man; but they are larger and somewhat elongated from front to rear instead of being quadrate and are further distinguished by having five cusps instead of the four cusps usual in modern human teeth. In each jaw the teeth are set in a long narrow U-shaped arch (Fig. 29.15), with the molars in parallel rows, while in man the arch is shorter and broader, forming a parabola with the molar rows divergent behind. The chimpanzee, the gorilla, and man are similar in that they lack a certain bone in the wrist which is present in nearly all other primates.

THE ANCESTRY OF MAN

Man is unquestionably one of the giant primates and more closely allied to the chimpanzee and gorilla than to any other living animals. Nevertheless he differs from the great apes in important respects and is placed in a separate family, the Hominidae. The distinctions grow less as we trace the ancestry of man and of apes back in time. In order that we may better appreciate the changes that occurred in the line that gave

Fig. 29.13. Skulls of the four living genera of anthropoid apes, family Simiidae. From left to right they are gibbon, orangutan, chimpanzee, gorilla. (*Courtesy Ward's Natural Science Establishment, Inc.*)

rise to modern man, let us consider the features that set him apart from the great apes.

Characteristics of man. Some of the anatomical characters that distinguish modern man from the apes and lower primates are: (1) the posture is fully erect; (2) the legs are much longer than the arms; (3) the great toe is not opposable to the other toes and is in line with them, instead of being set off on the side like a thumb; (4) the foot is more rigid, and is arched both transversely and from front to rear; (5) the spine is doubly curved, with a forward convexity in the small of the back, called the *lumbar curve;* (6) the human nose has a prominent bridge and a well-developed, elongated, peculiar tip; (7) there is a median furrow in the upper lip of man, and the lips are rolled outward so that the mucous membrane is visible as a continuous red line; (8) the brain is from two to three times as large as that of the gorilla, which has the largest brain of any living ape; (9) the jaws and facial region are much reduced (Fig. 30.6), instead of forming a prominent muzzle; (10) man has a chin; (11) the anterior root of the tongue is attached to a bony prominence in the angle of the jaw, instead of in a "simian pit"; (12) the canine teeth project slightly if at all above the level of the other teeth, and the upper and lower canines do not interlock nor are there gaps in the tooth arch for reception of the canines of the opposing jaw; (13) the tooth arch is short, broad, and parabolically curved, instead of being long and U-shaped; (14) the molars are subquadrate and typically four-cusped, instead of somewhat elongate and five-cusped; and (15) the body is relatively hairless and completely devoid of long tactile hairs. This is not an exhaustive list; most of the characters mentioned are ones that can be seen or inferred in fossils and hence can be used to estimate degrees of similarity to man and to ape.

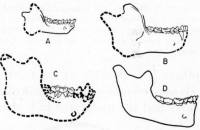

Tertiary ancestors. As we have mentioned, the oldest known catarrhine monkey, Parapithecus (Fig. 29.14A), was found in the lower Oligocene of Egypt. The stock which led to man and apes was already in existence at that time, for a small gibbonlike animal, Propliopithecus (Fig. 29.14B), was found in the same deposits. Though very primitive, this animal was either on or not far removed from the direct line of human ancestry. If Propliopithecus was an ancestor of man, he must also

Fig. 29.14. The lower jaws of fossil primates and man. A, the most primitive known monkey, Parapithecus from the lower Oligocene of Egypt. B, the most primitive known anthropoid ape, Propliopithecus, also from the lower Oligocene of Egypt. C, the Miocene anthropoid Dryopithecus (subgenus Sivapithecus). The human branch of the anthropoid stock probably came from some species of this genus. D, modern man. (Redrawn from Howells, Mankind So Far, by permission Doubleday & Company, Inc.)

have been an ancestor of the higher apes. From such a form it is inferred that true gibbons early appeared and went off on their own evolutionary course, which has nothing to do with that of man; a fossil gibbon is known from the Pliocene of Germany.

Fossils of arboreal primates are exceedingly rare, but in the Miocene the ape stock began to develop larger size and to adopt more terrestrial habits, and the fossil record becomes a little better. Until recently the Miocene apes were known only from numerous fossil teeth and jaws found in India, Egypt, and several European localities. Teeth are fortunately among the most characteristic parts of mammals and yield considerable information about their possessors. One of the Miocene fossils, Paleosimia from India, seems clearly ancestral to the orangutan. Most of the other fragmentary Miocene fossils are placed in the genus Dryopithecus (Fig.

29.14C and 29.15B). Careful study has shown that the members of this genus show divergent evolutionary trends. Some represent lines that have since disappeared; some suggest the chimpanzees and gorillas; in

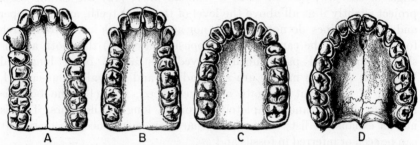

Fig. 29.15. Human and near-human dental arches, showing the widening of the arch, shortening of the tooth row, and reduction in size of canines and molars from ape to man. *A*, gorilla. *B*, Dryopithecus. *C*, South African Sterkfontein man-ape, Plesianthropus. *D*, modern man. (*Redrawn from Howells, Mankind So Far, by permission Doubleday & Company, Inc.*)

others it is possible to see faint suggestions of human characteristics. All were certainly apes and not primitive men, for the canines are strong tusks and the tooth arch is U-shaped. It is highly probable that among these Miocene apes are to be sought the beginnings of two divergent evolutionary lines, one leading to the chimpanzees and gorillas and the other to man.

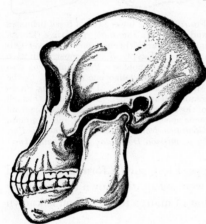

This hypothesis is given support by an interesting discovery made by Leakey in Africa. As a climax to 17 years of search for fossil anthropoids, in 1948, he found on an island in Lake Victoria Nyanza the nearly complete skull of a Miocene ape, which he has since christened *Proconsul*. It seems to belong near the base of the human stock, for while it was a small, primitive, chimpanzee-like creature, it lacks brow ridges and shows certain other prehuman features in teeth and skull which put it a step beyond Dryopithecus in the direction of man.

Fig. 29.16. The skull of the South African Kromdraai man-ape Paranthropus, restored. (*Redrawn from Howells, Mankind So Far, by permission Doubleday & Company, Inc.*)

The man-apes of South Africa. Little is known of primate evolution during the Pliocene, when the human stock was taking shape. In South Africa, however, Broom and Dart have discovered a number of fossil anthropoids which almost bridge the gap from ape to man. Found in cave deposits, the fossils are difficult to date with accuracy; they may be late Pliocene or more probably early Pleistocene in age. By 1950, five different types of man-apes had been found. Each possesses a somewhat different

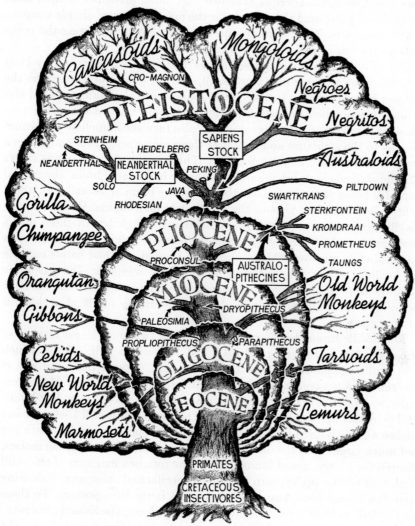

FIG. 29.17. The evolution of the primates.

combination of primitive and advanced characters, so that they do not form a linear series; they are clearly related to one another, and to man, but in just what way is still a matter for debate. Together they form a group known as the Australopithecines. These creatures were apelike in appearance, with heavy jaws, protruding muzzles, and low-vaulted skulls. Their brains, however, were relatively large and more human than anthropoid in type, and the teeth were very similar to those of man, with the canines reduced and the molars of human type, though the tooth arch was still U-shaped. There is evidence that these man-apes walked erect on their legs, and used their hands for the manipulation of simple weapons and implements. They were ground dwellers that lived among the rocks and on the plains and sought shelter in caves.

The first to be discovered, the Taungs man-ape,[1] was described by Dart in 1925, from a single immature skull, and for years thereafter was the subject of controversy. In 1948, Dart found more abundant material of a related form, called *Prometheus*,[2] which not only verified his earlier conclusions regarding the Taungs skull but also furnished much new information as to the structure and habits of these man-apes. Prometheus was a small creature only about 3 feet tall. The structure of the pelvis shows that he walked erect; for so small a being he had a large brain, the cranial capacity being 480 cc., or about the size of the brain of a small gorilla and a little less than half that of the smallest human brains. He was a cave dweller and a hunter; his fossil remains are mingled with those of his prey, among which are pig and antelope bones which had been split open to obtain the marrow. This implies that Prometheus had hands capable of holding stones for pounding and use as weapons. Dart believes that he knew the use of fire (whence his name), for some of the split bones are charred; but this might have been the result of accidental ground fires.

Meanwhile Broom had found the remains of two much larger man-apes, those of Sterkfontein (Fig. 29.15C) and Kromdraai (Fig. 29.16), which had skulls comparable in size to that of man, though the brain size is intermediate between that of gorilla and the primitive Java Man presently to be described. In these two man-apes the cheek bone, jaw hinge, and dentition approach those of man. The tooth row is still U-shaped but makes a slightly broader arch than in modern apes; the canine teeth are not much larger than the others and are very human in shape; the molars, though very large, are of human type. The foramen magnum of the skull is also set farther underneath than in the gorilla and chimpanzee, showing that like Prometheus these man-apes had a fairly erect posture. To these was added, in 1949, a related but much larger form, the Swartkrans man-ape,[3] of which three skulls and a complete jaw were found. From the size of the teeth and massiveness of the skull it is evident that this creature

---

[1] *Australopithecus africanus.*

[2] *Australopithecus prometheus.*

[3] The technical names of these man-apes are: Sterkfontein, *Pleisanthropus transvaalensis;* Kromdraai, *Paranthropus robustus;* Swartkrans, *Paranthropus crassidens.*

was of monstrous size, larger and heavier than the largest gorilla, and comparable only to the Asiatic giants later to be mentioned.

The exact relationship of these South African man-apes to man is far from settled. One group of investigators believes that they were actual ancestors of man and would place their occurrence in the late Pliocene; others think that they are of early Pleistocene age and that they lived too late to have been more than the unprogressive descendants of the true human ancestors. This would make them merely contemporaneous "cousins" of early man. Regardless of differing views the fact remains that these fossils unmistakably show the kind of changes by which our apelike ancestors were transformed into creatures recognizable as men.

CHAPTER XXX

PREHISTORIC MEN

At a time when remains of apelike men were unknown, Darwin postulated that such creatures must once have existed. Before his death in 1882, the first fossil men had been recognized, and since 1895, scarcely a year has passed without significant new finds. Our own species, *Homo sapiens*, has been traced far back into the Pleistocene, and other now extinct kinds of men have been discovered in Europe, Africa, and Asia. The known fossils are more and more apelike as we go back in time, although even the oldest are still "men," if we define "man" as a big-brained anthropoid built much as we are who had well-formed hands and made recognizable tools. Future discoveries will almost certainly bridge the remaining gap between the most apelike men thus far found and the manlike Pleistocene apes described in the last chapter.

The Pleistocene epoch. Although man is presumed to have arisen during the Pliocene, his known history is wholly comprised within the Pleistocene epoch—the "great ice age." This latest episode in earth history was a time of unrest. Continents were uplifted, mountain making was active in many parts of the world, and climates fluctuated extremely. Four times vast ice sheets spread over the northern lands, and four times the ice melted away. The temperature and rain belts shifted their positions, and with them moved whole floras and faunas. The last melting of the ice took place only a few thousand years ago. We speak of the time since then as *postglacial* and designate it as the *Recent epoch;* but this "epoch" is perhaps no more than a warm spell in the Pleistocene winter. According to one theory of glacial causes the ice will be back in some 50,000 years.

The Sequence of Glacial and Interglacial Ages. It is well established that there were four major Pleistocene glaciations, separated by warmer interglacial ages. In each glacial age ice sheets arose in the north and advanced southward over Europe and North America. No two glaciations had exactly the same limits, but in general the ice covered Europe as far south as Germany and England, and North America to the present Missouri and Ohio rivers. Between glaciations climates became at least as warm as those of today; the ice melted back, and the displaced floras and faunas reoccupied the northern lands.

The glacial and interglacial ages are given different names in Europe and in North America. For our purposes it will suffice if we keep their sequence in mind. We may call the glacial ages the *first, second, third,* and *fourth glacials,*[1] and the interglacials the *first,* the *great,* and the *last interglacial ages.*[2] The great interglacial was several times as long as either the first or the last. Each glacial age had minor climatic fluctuations, with glacial maxima and milder interstadials.

Pleistocene Changes in Life. A great many species living today have come down with little change from early Pleistocene times, and few major

Fig. 30.1. The mammoth and woolly rhinoceros spread far south into Europe during the glacial ages of the Pleistocene. Both were hunted by men of the Old Stone Age. (*Drawing by Charles R. Knight, courtesy Chicago Natural History Museum.*)

evolutionary developments occurred during the epoch, which was after all a very brief period of time from the standpoint of earth history. However, in many groups there was active speciation, and a great amount of extinction occurred owing to the rapid and extreme climatic fluctuations. Floras and faunas were displaced. The ranges of species contracted and expanded, changed shape and position, fragmented and reunited, and fragmented once more. Under such conditions species populations tend to become more variable and opportunity is given for the formation of new species and subspecies at a rapid rate. Man was himself involved in this evolutionary flux. Isolation and differentiation among human populations through much of the Pleistocene, followed in postglacial time by enormous increases in man's numbers, with migration and

[1] Called respectively Günz, Mindel, Riss, and Würm in Europe, and Nebraskan, Kansan, Illinoian, and Wisconsin in North America.

[2] Called Günz-Mindel, Mindel-Riss, and Riss-Würm in Europe, and Aftonian, Yarmouth, and Sangamon in North America.

hybridization on a grand scale, resulted in his present racial and individual diversity.

The Interglacial Ages. The general distribution of plant and animal life during the interglacials was not unlike that of today, although warmth-loving species at times occurred much farther north. The Arctic tundras were bordered to the south by coniferous forest. The interiors of the continents were chiefly grassland and desert, and the marginal lowlands—China, Europe, and eastern North America—were humid and covered with temperate hardwood forest. Then, as now, the Mediterranean region and Near East were warm and dry, with winter rains, and with scrubby chaparral-type forests. Deer, bison, hairless elephants,

Fig. 30.2. The musk ox is a northern animal that came as far south as France during the Pleistocene glaciations. (*Courtesy Chicago Natural History Museum.*)

and lions lived in France, the hippopotamus reached southern England, and wild asses, gazelles, and horses were abundant around the borders of the Mediterranean sea.

The Glacial Ages. During the glaciations so much water was frozen in the ice sheets that sea levels fell hundreds of feet, exposing broad coastal plains and uniting islands with mainlands. Tundra stretched along the ice front. Beyond were dry, cold grassy steppes where wind-blown loess accumulated, and forests of spruce and pine. In the Mediterranean region and over much of Africa the glacial ages were cool, rainy periods called *pluvials*, during which hardwood forests increased and the Sahara desert was partly covered by grassland and scrub forest. Cold climate animals such as reindeer, musk ox, woolly mammoth, and woolly rhinoceros occupied southern Europe, and herds of small northern horses roamed the central European steppes.

Postglacial Extinction. Many species, especially among the larger mammals, died out both in Europe and in North America toward the end of the Pleistocene epoch. Man's too efficient hunting may have contributed to the disappearance of some of them. Among the Old World forms that vanished were the woolly mammoth, woolly rhinoceros, Irish deer, and cave bear. Among the North

American animals that died out were mammoths of several kinds, some of them enormously large, and the wide-ranging mastodon. The once abundant saber-toothed tiger (Fig. 28.30) disappeared with the mastodons which may have been its chief prey. Camels and horses, giant bison and lions vanished from the plains and savannas. The giant beaver became extinct, as well as certain bizarre immigrants from South America—ground sloths as heavy as elephants that reached Alaska during the interglacials and huge armadillolike glyptodonts with tails like spike-knobbed war clubs that lived in the southern states. Man reached the New World in time to encounter some at least of these now extinct species, for remains of ground sloths and giant bison have been found with his campfires and weapons.

Fig. 30.3. Giant ground sloths and club-tailed glyptodonts lived in North America until late in the Pleistocene. (*By Charles R. Knight, courtesy Chicago Natural History Museum.*)

Pleistocene chronology. Whether the Pleistocene lasted 1 million years, as most geologists think, or was only two-thirds that long, it represents only an insignificant fraction of earth history. Brief as it was in terms of geological time, it covers the whole period of man's known evolution, and from his viewpoint it stretches interminably into the past. For our account of human origins we must change time scales. To appreciate the vast duration of the Pleistocene we need only make some simple calculations. If we let the whole epoch be represented by one 24-hour day, then Christ was born about 5 minutes ago, history began about 10 minutes earlier, and the last climax of the fourth glaciation occurred about an hour past. According to one theory of glacial climates the ice should return in about 2 hours. Again, figuring 20 years to an average human generation among primitive peoples, Julius Caesar lived 100 generations ago, history began 250 generations back, and there are more than 30,000 generations between us and the men who lived early in the ice age.

Before we can interpret the fossil record of human evolution, we need to know the relative ages of the fossils and their relation to the events of the Pleistocene. There are various ways of establishing a Pleistocene chronology and of dating the fossils.

The basic chronological data are *geological* and are derived principally from the glaciated regions and adjoining (periglacial) areas. Each advance and melting back of the ice sheets, and each warm interglacial interval, left its traces, though many of the earlier evidences were destroyed by later glaciations and subsequent erosion. The ice sheets left around their borders deposits of boulder clay and outwash from glacial streams; in the periglacial zone wind-blown dust formed characteristic loess deposits; stream terraces in unglaciated territory record changes in elevation and climate; coastal terraces show the various levels of the sea; and soil layers retain evidence of the climates under which they were formed. From such data the sequence and relative duration of the glacial and interglacial ages and of their subdivisions have been worked out. Fossils found in association with identifiable geological features can be assigned relative though not absolute ages on this evidence.

The so-called "astronomical" dating is based upon a hypothesis as to the cause of glaciation which was elaborated by Milankovitch in 1930. This hypothesis holds that the temperature changes responsible for ice ages are due to the periodic variations in the amount of solar radiation received in one hemisphere, caused by precessional changes in the earth's axis and the known cyclic variations in the path of the earth around the sun. It assumes that the cold maxima will produce glaciation in the affected hemisphere (northern or southern) only when continents stand high and oceanic circulation is impeded, as during a geological revolution. Milankovitch's laboriously calculated radiation curve for the northern hemisphere purports to give the temperature fluctuations over the 600,000 years which according to this hypothesis is the length of the Pleistocene. The astronomical theory has been widely accepted in Europe and was made the basis for a detailed world-wide Pleistocene chronology by Zeuner.[1] It is not, however, the only theory as to the causes of glaciation[2] and, as noted below, is not supported by the radio-carbon dating of the last glacial advance.

Radio-carbon dating is one of the most remarkable scientific achievements of recent years. It promises to give accurate and reliable dates up to a maximum of about 35,000 years past. It has no geographical limitations; but it can be used

---

[1] In a most interesting and ambitious book, *Dating the Past*, Longmans, Green & Co., Inc., New York, 1951.

[2] A second widely held hypothesis assumes that ice ages are caused by variation in the amount of radiation emitted by the sun, or, alternatively, by variation in the amount received by the earth because of passage of the solar system through cosmic dust clouds. A third assumes purely terrestrial causes for ice ages, suggesting that locally produced glacial nuclei may set off a runaway reaction and grow into continental glaciers through the siphoning of water by evaporation from the oceans to the glacial centers. The recent demonstration by radio-carbon dating of the simultaneity of the late glacial warm intervals in North America (Cary Mankato) and in Europe (Alleröd), suggests an extraterrestrial cause.

only on materials containing carbon derived from the carbon dioxide of the atmosphere. Such materials include all organic remains, and limestones of recent origin. In 1946, it was discovered that a small but constant fraction of the carbon in the atmosphere is the radioactive isotope C_{14} (radio-carbon) instead of the ordinary C_{12}. The radio-carbon is formed in the upper layers of the atmosphere by bombardment of nitrogen by cosmic rays. It becomes uniformly dispersed in the air and is built into the bodies of all living things through their dependence upon photosynthesis. Tests prove that the same percentage of C_{14} is present in the bodies of animals and plants the world over. When organisms die the accumulation of carbon ceases, and the radio-carbon originally present in their bodies gradually disappears through radioactive decay of the C_{14} atoms. The rate of this disintegration is known, its half life being $5,568 \pm 30$ years. Therefore the age of a carbon-containing fossil or rock that is not too old can be determined within narrow limits by measuring the amount of radioactivity remaining in a standard sample by means of electronic counters.

The first extensive series of radio-carbon dates was published in 1950–1951. It included age determinations on various historic and prehistoric objects made by man and on fossil bones, shells, charcoal and wood. The date of the last (Mankato) ice advance of the fourth glacial age in America was found (by tests made on buried trunks of spruce trees) to be about 9,000 B.C. or 11,000 instead of the previously assumed 25,000 years ago. This casts doubt on the Milankovitch theory, since there is no minimum at this date on the radiation curve. Where the radio-carbon dates can be checked by historical records or tree-ring dates, they generally show close agreement, although some unexplained discrepancies occur.

Certain other methods of dating, applicable to postglacial and late Pleistocene times, require only brief mention. The *tree-ring* record has been carried back some 3,000 years, giving a graph of climatic variation, chiefly that of rainfall. Analysis of the *pollen content* of bog layers has revealed much of the vegetational and climatic history of the glacial and periglacial regions during the past 15,000 years. Measurement of the thickness of the annual layers of sediment (*varves*) deposited in lakes and bays that received glacial melt-water has given an equally long record of postglacial temperature variations and the rate of ice recession. Other time correlations for the late Pleistocene are based upon Baltic Sea levels and similar phenomena. Finally, where other means of dating are unavailable, sometimes the faunal assemblage itself gives a clue to the climatic conditions under which it lived, by means of which it can be tentatively assigned to a particular age or subage.

FOSSIL MEN

Our knowledge of prehistoric man comes from two sources—his fossil bones, and remains of the things he made and did. From his bones the physical anthropologist reconstructs his bodily characteristics; from his tools, weapons, ornaments, dwellings, and even his refuse the archeologist reconstructs his way of life. The first of these studies is concerned with the evolution of man's body; the second with the evolution of his mind and culture. They tell separate stories which run parallel and merge only when fossil man is found together with the remains of his cultures. We shall have to concern ourselves chiefly with the evolution of the human body. Even from this standpoint, however, we cannot wholly ignore culture, for culture has had important genetic consequences upon man as a species.

Fossil men can be divided into two broad groups—*paleanthropic* or *old-type* men, and *neanthropic* or *new-type* men. The first group includes the earliest known fossil men and the Neanderthaloids. They had an outthrust head buried in heavy shoulders, a snouted face, heavy brow ridges,

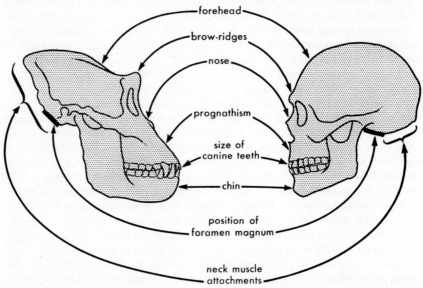

Fig. 30.4. Skull of gorilla showing generalized anthropoid characters contrasted with skull of man showing specialized characters. (*Redrawn from Howells, Mankind So Far, by permission Doubleday & Company, Inc.*)

a massive jaw with receding chin, large teeth, a low vaulted skull, and less erect posture than modern man. Neanthropic or new-type men are those of our own species, *Homo sapiens*, characterized by erect head and slender neck, pushed-in face, weak brow ridges, a small jaw with prominent chin, small teeth, a larger and more domed brain case, and fully erect posture.

The earliest men. The most primitive men we know lived in Asia some ½ million years ago. *Java man*, discovered in 1891, is now represented by four skulls, four jaws, and some odd teeth and leg bones, all dug from river terraces near Trinil in Java. *Peking man* was found in 1927 in a cave at Choukoutien near Peking, China; many skulls and other bones have since been recovered from this cave. These two ancient types of man are much alike, and although they were originally assigned to different species and genera, anthropologists are now inclined to place them in the genus Homo and treat them as subspecies of a single species.[1] Both possess many apelike characteristics.

Java man stood about 5 feet 6 inches in height. He was of stocky build, and though he stood erect, he was bull-necked, with outthrust head. The spine was attached rather far back on the skull, which was long and

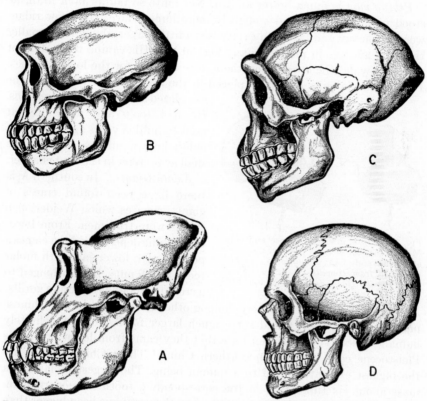

Fig. 30.5. Skulls of old and new type men compared with that of the gorilla. *A*, gorilla. *B*. Java man, Pithecanthropus. *C*, Peking man, Sinanthropus. *D*, modern man, *Homo sapiens*, (*Redrawn from Howells, Mankind So Far, by permission Doubleday & Company, Inc.*)

narrow, very thick-boned, very low-vaulted, and had a brain cavity only two-thirds as large as ours (Fig. 30.5B). There was a tremendous undivided brow ridge continuous with the low, receding forehead. The jaws were big, massive, and protruding, with large teeth. The upper canines

[1] Java man was named *Pithecanthropus erectus* by Dubois; Peking man, *Sinanthropus pekinensis* by Davidson Black. Weidenreich and others would call them respectively *Homo erectus erectus* and *Homo erectus pekinensis*. In the naming of fossil men, anthropologists often used to magnify differences and to erect genera for what would be considered species or subspecies in other branches of zoology.

were somewhat tusklike, and the dental arch was narrower and more apelike than in modern man, with distinct gaps in the upper tooth row for reception of the lower canines. By our standards Java man must have been an extraordinarily ugly, brutish creature. There is no telling whether he could speak, and no direct proof that he used tools, though some of the skulls had been crushed as though by a club or stone ax.

Peking man is much better known. Not quite so tall as Java Man, he stood more erect and had a slightly more human face. His brow ridges were less heavy and his brain cavity was a little larger, though far smaller than the average in modern man (Fig. 30.5C). His canine teeth did not project beyond the others, and there were no gaps for the lower canines. Peking man is quite definitely placed in the first interglacial age by the associated animal and plant remains. He had tools and used fire—at least ½ million years ago! His is the oldest known culture, to which we shall again refer in the next chapter.

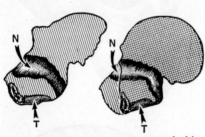

Fig. 30.6. How man got a nose and chin. Median sagittal sections through the skulls of gorilla and man. *N*, nose; *T*, tongue. (*Redrawn from Howells, Mankind So Far, by permission Doubleday & Company, Inc.*)

Asiatic Giants. In southern Asia there have been found traces of giant primates which Weidenreich thinks were true men. From lower Pleistocene deposits of Java comes a portion of a lower jaw with molar teeth which must have belonged to a creature about as large as a gorilla.

And in a Hong Kong drugstore, among other fossils used in the Chinese pharmacopoeia, were found some much larger fossil teeth of definitely human aspect. The indications are that they came from lower or middle Pleistocene cave deposits in southern China.[1] These Chinese teeth are the biggest ever attributed to a human being. The largest molar has a mass about six times that of the corresponding tooth in modern man. Whether man or ape, the owner of these teeth must have been bigger than the biggest gorilla. Weidenreich believes that such giants are ancestral to Java and Peking man and that man has grown smaller. Others regard the giants as extinct side branches of the human stock. Perhaps they died out because they specialized on size and strength rather than on brains.

The Neanderthaloids. Many fossils of more advanced old-type men have been found in Europe, Asia, and Africa. These men, though not all alike, were evidently related and can be grouped as the *Neanderthaloids*. The earliest is Heidelberg man, who lived in Europe during the second glacial age. Neanderthal man is by far the best known; he was the typical

---

[1] Von Koenigswald, who found both, named the Javanese giant *Meganthropus paleojavanicus*, and the Chinese giant *Gigantopithecus blacki*.

"early cave man" of Europe and the Near East and dominated those regions during the great interglacial and the first part of the fourth glacial ages. Solo man, from Java, was contemporary with Neanderthal, while Rhodesian man from South Africa is of undetermined Pleistocene age.[1] The Neanderthaloid group of men probably descended from the Java-Peking stock.

Heidelberg man is known from a single jaw, found under 80 feet of river deposits near Heidelberg, Germany. Dating apparently from the interstadial of the second glacial age, it may be 450,000 years old. The jaw is extremely large and massive, chinless and quite apelike in appearance; but the teeth, the open dental arch, and the short tooth row are unmistakably human. Except for its greater size and very broad ascending ramus, this jaw resembles that of Neanderthal man, as do its teeth. On the other

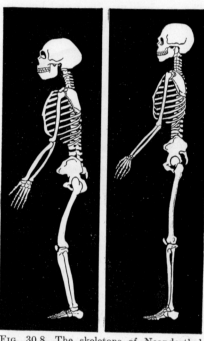

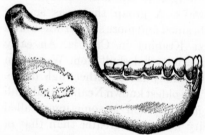

FIG. 30.7. The Heidelberg jaw, *Homo heidelbergensis.* (*Redrawn from Howells, Mankind So Far, by permission Doubleday & Company, Inc.*)

FIG. 30.8. The skeletons of Neanderthal man and *Homo sapiens* compared. (*After Boule, redrawn.*)

hand it is not very different from the jaws of Java and Peking man, except for being heavier and having smaller canines and a broader tooth arch. Heidelberg man seems to have been descended from men of Java-Peking type and may well have been an ancestor of Neanderthal man. Unfortunately no implements were found with this fossil.

Neanderthal man was the first discovered and is still the best known of prehistoric men. A skull and other bones were found near Dusseldorf in the Neander valley, Germany, in 1856, and since then many other skeletons have been unearthed in various parts of Europe and Palestine.

[1] The technical names of these fossil men are, respectively, *Homo heidelbergensis, H. neanderthalensis, H. soloensis,* and *H. rhodesiensis.*

True Neanderthal man has not yet been found in Asia or Africa and may not have occurred in those regions.

Typical Neanderthalers (Figs. 30.8 to 10 and 13B) were stocky, barrel-chested, brutish men of short stature. They averaged about 5 feet 3 inches in height and stood less erect than we do. The spine had almost no lumbar curvature, and the knees were slightly bent. The head jutted forward from a short, massive neck and heavy, hunched shoulders. The skull and brain were as large as or larger than ours but differently shaped. The cranium was long and low, angulately projecting behind, and with scarcely any forehead. The eyes were deep set under heavy bony brow ridges, and the large, strong jaws protruded muzzlelike, without much chin.

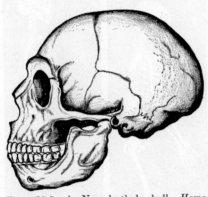

FIG. 30.9. A Neanderthal skull, *Homo neanderthalensis*. (*Redrawn from Howells, Mankind So Far, by permission Doubleday & Company, Inc.*)

Not all Neanderthalers were alike. Those that lived in European caves during the fourth glacial age, and some of the earlier ones, were of the sort just described. Others that lived during the last interglacial age differed in various ways. A group that was smaller brained and more slender was found at Krapina in Croatia. An early Neanderthal skull from Weimar in Germany has a rather high dome. The oldest known Neanderthal skull was found at Steinheim, Germany, in 1933, and is sometimes called *Steinheim man*[1]; it has a brain capacity not much greater than that of Java man, but a much less snoutlike face and more rounded cranium than in the typical Neanderthalers. This skull dates from somewhere between the end of the great interglacial and the beginning of the last interglacial ages.

The people who lived in the Mount Carmel caves in Galilee were peculiarly variable. Some were quite typical Neanderthalers, but others possessed in varying degree features more like those of *Homo sapiens*— greater height, smaller face, rounder skull, interrupted brow ridges, moderately full forehead, and more rounded and less projecting occiput. Some investigators think this Palestinian group was evolving into modern man.   Others believe the variation was caused by hybridization between Neanderthal man and *Homo sapiens*.

Two other Neanderthaloids deserve brief mention. *Solo man* is known from several skulls found in Java not far from the place where Java man

[1] *Homo steinheimensis*—probably only a form of *Homo neanderthalensis*.

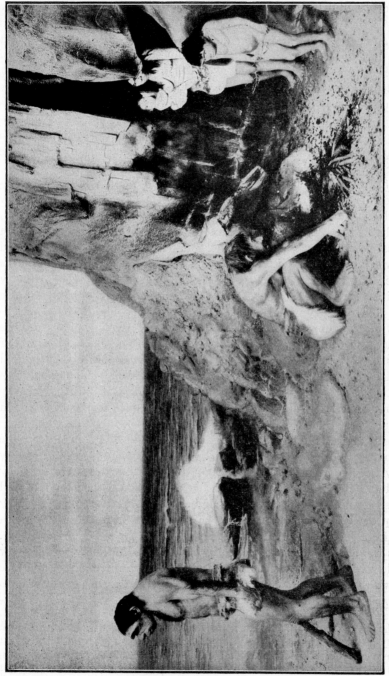

Fig. 30.10. Restoration of a Neanderthal family in the rock shelter of Gibraltar during the Fourth Glacial Age. (*Courtesy Chicago Natural History Museum.*)

was discovered but in late instead of early Pleistocene deposits. Like Neanderthal skulls these had a low forehead and heavy brow ridges and held an even smaller brain; but the shape of the head is rounder, so that some authorities have regarded Solo man as a very primitive form of *Homo sapiens.* The enigmatic *Rhodesian man* poses an even more difficult problem. The single known skull from Broken Hill cave, Rhodesia, is much more bestial in appearance than other Neanderthaloids. The bones are very thick, the brow ridges are even larger than in Java man, the face and palate are enormously developed, and the brain is small for so large a skull. In spite of these primitive features the brain case approaches the modern form, as does that of Solo man.

Piltdown man. The "dawn man," *Eoanthropus dawsoni,* was described by Smith-Woodward in 1913, from a cranium and lower jaw found in a gravel pit at Piltdown in Sussex, England. The brain case is clearly human and much more modern in appearance than those of typical paleanthropic men. It is well rounded, with broad, high forehead and weak brow ridges, and has a brain capacity well within the *sapiens* range. The enormous thickness of the cranial walls is its only really primitive feature. The jaw, on the other hand, is scarcely distinguishable from that of a chimpanzee. It is chinless, with apelike mode of attachment of the tongue muscles, and has massive tusklike lower canines projecting two-thirds of an inch beyond the rest of the tooth row. For years a controversy persisted as to whether the human brain case and apelike jaw could possibly be parts of one individual. Furthermore the question of age was unsettled, for in the same gravel bed occurred fossils of early, middle, and late Pleistocene animals, mixed together by stream action.

Discovery in 1915 of teeth and parts of a second skull 2 miles from the original locality gave strong support to the idea that the skull and jaw really belonged together; and in 1950, Oakley and Hoskins showed by the fluorine test[1] that the jaw and brain case are of the same age and almost certainly belonged to a single individual. Most surprisingly they also proved that Piltdown cannot be older than late Pleistocene; with the aid of geological data he can be assigned to the last interglacial age. Thus the original uncertainties have been cleared up, only to raise new problems. Here is a type of man, altogether human in cranium and face but with tusked, apelike jaw, living in England at a period when *Homo sapiens* and Neanderthalers were present in Europe. What was the rela-

---

[1] The fluorine content of buried bones and teeth increases with time, and at a given locality all fossils of the same age have about the same percentage of fluorine. At Piltdown the early Pleistocene fossils had 2 to 3 %; the middle Pleistocene fossils, about 1 %; and Eoanthropus and other upper Pleistocene fossils, from 0.1 to 0.4 % of fluorine.

tion of Piltdown man to other branches of the human stock? Far from being an early, primitive type as has long been supposed, the so-called "dawn man" seems to have been a late, specialized form. He was probably evolved in relative isolation, and apparently had nothing to do with the origin of the Neanderthaloids or of modern man.

The antiquity of "modern" man. All people now living belong to the single species *Homo sapiens*. This species was long believed to have appeared late in the Pleistocene, about the time the Neanderthalers vanished from Europe. But this view is no longer tenable. Men of our own kind are now known to have existed at least since the close of the great interglacial age and perhaps far longer.

Swanscombe man is the well-authenticated basis for this statement. In 1935 to 1936, parts of a long-headed, thin-boned skull of modern type were found at Swanscombe in the Thames Valley of England. They lay at a depth of 24 feet in terrace gravels of the great interglacial age, associated with flint "hand axes" and flake tools. The dating was confirmed by Oakley and Ashley Montagu in 1949, using the fluorine test.[1] This discovery carried the known antiquity of *Homo sapiens* back to a time antedating Piltdown man and all of the Neanderthaloids except Heidelberg man!

The long gap in the record of *Homo sapiens* from Swanscombe man to the Cro-Magnons has been partially bridged by later discoveries. Two fragmentary skulls of modern type were found in 1948 in the basal layers of the Fontechevade cave in central France. Associated animal remains show that they date from the last interglacial age. The flint tools that occurred with them are of flake type—a fact of interest because it used to be supposed that only Neanderthalers made tools of this sort. Three *Homo sapiens* skeletons were found by Coon in 1951, in the cave of Ghar Hotu in northern Iran, on an old shoreline of the Caspian Sea. Killed by a fall of the cavern roof, these men apparently had lived early in the fourth glacial age, at a time when Neanderthalers dominated Europe. They were heavy-set, about 5 feet 8 inches tall, with low-placed eyes, long teeth, and prominent chins, and differed from moderns chiefly in their lesser brain capacity.

Modern man. Completely modern skeletons begin turning up in fair numbers in European cave layers dating from the first interstadial of the fourth glacial age—a time variously estimated as 50,000 to 80,000 years ago. These ancient Europeans were very like some people we see today. They varied individually and from group to group, but not as much as do the modern inhabitants of the region. Most of them belonged to a big-

---

[1] At the same time, these workers showed that another reputedly ancient example of *Homo sapiens*, the Galley Hill skeleton, was in fact a relatively recent (postglacial) burial.

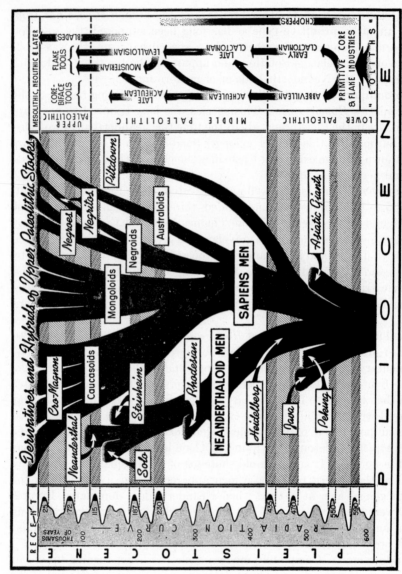

Fig. 30.11. A chart of the Pleistocene epoch showing the evolution of man and his cultures. The glacial ages are shaded, with the postulated milder interstadials a lighter gray. At the left is the Milankovitch radiation curve with its hypo-

headed, narrow-skulled, tall, large-boned type of man which in a broad sense is called Cro-Magnon. But they fall into distinguishable groups.

The *Cro-Magnons* proper (Fig. 31.17) lived chiefly in Spain and France. They were tall and robust. Many of the men were over 6 feet in height. As a whole they were long-headed, but some showed a tendency to round-headedness. The Cro-Magnon face was short and wide, with wide jaw and heavy chin, large coarse features, and eye orbits that were both wide and low. Many present-day Scandinavians show a similar combination of traits. In northwest Africa lived similar people, the *Alfalou*, also tall and big-headed, but with broader skulls, wider noses, and heavier brow ridges. From France eastward through central Europe to the Caspian Sea the Cro-Magnon type was represented by the *Combe-Capelle-Brünn* race—a shorter people, with narrower heads and faces, less prominent chins, heavier brow ridges, and rounder eye orbits. People of Brünn type can be seen today in parts of Ireland and Scandinavia. All of these Cro-Magnon peoples seem to have been parts of the basic "White," or *Caucasoid*, stock. Coon, a leading authority, attributes some of their characteristics to hybridization with Neanderthalers, but others question this interpretation.

The early history of the "Black," or *Negroid*, race is still very obscure. Its oldest examples were found not in Africa, but in a cave at Grimaldi on the Italian Riviera. Here the skeletons of an old woman and a 16-year-old boy were found buried close together. They apparently date from the first interstadial of the fourth glacial age. The *Grimaldians* were small, delicate-boned people, with long heads, broad noses, large protrusive teeth, and notably long forearms and shin bones. These are features most often found in Negroids, and the consensus of experts seems to be that if the Grimaldians were not "Blacks," they at least show evidence of Negroid admixture. They were unlike their European contemporaries and would seem to have been strangers in a strange land.

---

thetical dates for the glacial maxima and a 600,000-year time scale for the Pleistocene; many authorities believe this epoch endured a million years.

The evolution of stone tool types is diagramed at the right. The oldest implements are the scarcely recognizable "eoliths" of the late Pliocene and earliest Pleistocene. In later cultural assemblages four basic tool types made by different techniques can be recognized. One is the *core-biface* or "hand ax," a nodule of flint chipped on both faces to form an edge all around. Tools of this tradition evolved from the crude Abbevillean to the finely worked Late Acheulian implements. A second type is the *flake tool*, made from a flake struck from a flint core. This also evolved, from the crude Clactonian to the large, thin, well-made Levalloisian implement. Some groups of people seem to have used chiefly the "hand ax," others chiefly the flake, but mixtures of the two techniques are found in many cultural assemblages, as indicated by the connecting arrows. The stone tools of the Mousterian assemblages found with Neanderthal man show such a mingling of techniques. *Chopper tools* are a third basic type, unknown in Europe but characteristic of early cultural assemblages in the Far East, and associated with Peking man. The fourth basic type is the *blade tool* (Fig. 31.18), a long parallel-sided flake struck from a flint core at a single blow and then worked into a variety of forms. Blades appeared late in Paleolithic times, and spread into Europe with *Homo sapiens* during the Fourth Glacial Age.

Bones of *Homo sapiens* have been found in late Pleistocene deposits in many regions outside of Europe. Among the better known fossils are the "proto-Australoid" *Wadjak* skulls from Java, which resemble those of modern Australian natives except in their larger size; the *Boskop* and other South African skulls, like those of Bushmen but much larger; the *Chancelade* skull from France, in which some authorities see similarities to the Eskimo; and skulls of faintly Mongoloid aspect from a cave at Choukoutien, China, above that in which Peking Man was found. Post-

Fig. 30.12. Modern man at the close of the Paleolithic or Old Stone Age. A boar hunt in France. Half-wild dogs began to be used in hunting and as a protection for the camp during the transitional period (Mesolithic) that preceded the new Stone Age. (*Courtesy Chicago Natural History Museum.*)

glacial human fossils have been found in most parts of the world, including the Americas and Australia.

This, in brief review, is what we know about man's ancestry from the fossils. The gaps in the record are enormous, and interpretation of the evidence is not easy. Nevertheless some things do emerge clearly to view. It is now certain that men of our own species, *Homo sapiens*, have been in existence for at least ¼ million years. We also know that other species of men formerly existed and that some of them were present until late in the Pleistocene. The relationships of the various species of men to one another are still in large degree conjectural. We know that within our own species the three great stocks, "Whites," "Blacks," and "Yellows"—or at least the bony structures characteristic of these stocks—were already differentiated at least 35,000 years ago and probably very much earlier. The "Australoids" are often considered a fourth stock; they were here also. And finally, we know that these stocks were distributed in late Pleistocene times much as they are today. There were Caucasoids in Europe, Negroids in southern Europe and Africa, Australoids in the East Indies, New Guinea, and Australia, and Mongoloids in Asia and spreading into the New World.

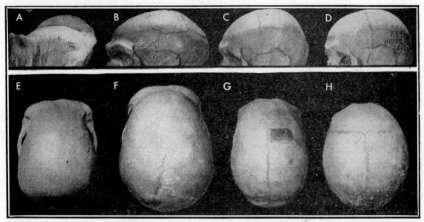

FIG. 30.13. Skulls of gorilla, old type men, and modern man, showing differences in proportions. Upper row: *A*, gorilla; *B*, Neanderthal man; *C*, Australian (*Homo sapiens*); *D*, European (*Homo sapiens*). Note modification of the brow ridges and increasing skull height. Lower row: *E*, Java man; *F*, Neanderthal man; *G*, Australian; *H*, European. Note the increasing breadth of the cranium relative to its length. (*Courtesy American Museum of Natural History*.)

Some hypotheses. The fossil record of man lends itself to varied interpretations. Weidenreich is the leader of a school which views human evolution as an essentially orthogenetic process. According to his hypothesis gigantic Asiatic ancestral types produced the smaller Java-Peking stock, which in turn gave rise to various populations in all of which similar changes occurred, leading through Neanderthaloid stages to modern man. Thus Java man begat Solo man who begat Wadjak man who begat the Proto-Australoids who begat the native Australian race; Peking man is regarded as ancestral to the Mongoloids; and from some ancestor like Java man came Heidelberg, from Heidelberg Neanderthal, and from Neanderthal the modern men of Europe. The Palestinian cave dwellers are thought to show the transition from the Neanderthaloid to the neanthropic level, as do Solo man and Rhodesian man. The rate of change is presumed to have varied in the different lines, but the general direction of change was the same in all. By this hypothesis Java-Peking, the Neanderthaloids, and *Homo sapiens* are merely three evolutionary levels in a universal human stock that was continuously evolving in the direction of modern man.

This is an attractive, neat hypothesis, but it seems to have serious objections. It requires acceptance of one or the other of two postulates rejected by most biologists—the existence of some orthogenetic directing factor in human evolution or of straight-line selection leading in the same direction in all branches of the human stock. Modern genetics lends no support to the concept of orthogenesis. As for the second alternative, selection is not observed to result in independent parallel changes in isolated populations living in different environments—conditions which were almost certainly characteristic of human populations through much of the Pleistocene. On the contrary, mutation, isolation, selection, and drift operate to produce divergence.

There is an alternative interpretation of the facts that seems in better accord with the evolutionary views of most biologists. This assumes that until very recently human evolution followed the general pattern seen in other mammals. Spreading accompanied by isolation and divergence led to the formation of various species and races of man. Most of the earlier ones eventually died out, but two more successful lines persisted. One, the more conservative, became Neanderthal man; the other, more progressive, gave rise to *Homo sapiens*. The latter prevailed in the end, and the Neanderthalers disappeared, though perhaps not without a certain amount of hybridization having occurred between the two. We call these two groups of people distinct species, but possibly it would be more correct to regard them as strongly differentiated subspecies.

Neither of these interpretations of man's evolutionary history is yet established or disproven; perhaps each contains an element of truth, as may be inferred from the discussions in Chaps. XXIV and XXXI. We have chosen the second upon which to base our diagrams of the relationships of fossil and living men.

CHAPTER XXXI

THE HUMAN SPECIES

We have considered man as a self-maintaining individual, as a member of a hereditary sequence, and as a product of evolution. Our account would be seriously incomplete if we failed to treat of mankind as an existing species, variable, racially diverse, and unusual in many respects.

To begin with, man *is* a single species, *Homo sapiens*. This species is complex both in origin and in composition and is unique among organisms in possessing a social heritage called *culture*. Culture, a product of the human mind, has evolved independently of man's biological evolution and at a rate which has lately become very rapid. It now so permeates the human environment and so modifies the behavior and appearance of individuals and groups that we find it hard to distinguish differences due to heredity from those produced by culture.

The human species comprises more than two billion individuals and is rapidly increasing. It occupies and dominates the earth to an extent never remotely approached by any other animal. Man's dominance and abundance are, however, of recent date and constitute an unprecedented situation to which he is far from adjusted. The sudden rise of *Homo sapiens* has profoundly affected not only the world environment, but even the trends of physical and cultural evolution within our species.

THE UNITY OF MANKIND

We have seen that the family Hominidae split off from the other primates during or before the Pliocene and that several different kinds of men existed during the first half of the Pleistocene epoch. It is now quite generally agreed that all these men are properly referable to the genus Homo, to which we also belong, though we continue to call them by such time-honored names as *Pithecanthropus erectus* and *Sinanthropus pekinensis*. It is also agreed that from one or more of the branches of the Java-Peking stock came the various types of Neanderthaloid men, specifically or subspecifically distinct from one another. Some of these persisted with but slight change until late in the Pleistocene. One group of Neanderthaloids must have changed more rapidly, for by mid-Pleistocene it had evolved into *Homo sapiens*. Whether or not it absorbed some of the less progressive groups, it is certain that by the end of the fourth glacial age this was the sole remaining species of man.

We can be sure that mankind constitutes a single species, for all groups of people living today are interfertile, and there are no morphological distinctions by which we may sharply divide them. If all living people, without exception, belong to the same species, one simple, clear fact emerges: all peoples of earth are infinitely more alike than they are different. Krogman has put this dramatically by saying that, ignoring cultural differences, we are 99.44 per cent alike and only 0.56 per cent different. Whether the actual ratio of identities to differences be 98:2 or 95:5 or even 90:10, the identities overwhelmingly preponderate. In terms of genetics, the genes which make us *Homo sapiens* far outnumber and outweigh the genes which make us different kinds of people.

THE DIVERSITY OF MANKIND

Although people are basically all alike, they are also all different. Except for monovular twins, it is probable that no two individuals in the world have exactly the same set of genes. We recognize particular persons by their individual peculiarities, and we are aware that large groups of people resemble one another more closely than they do members of other groups. In common parlance these distinguishable groups are called *races*, though the physical anthropologist tends to restrict this term to the subdivisions of the major groups.

The meaning of "race." At this point we are certain to encounter emotional reactions to the word "race" in many persons to whom this has become a "bad word" that ought never to be mentioned. Such connotations arise from the tensions that exist between certain groups of people; most of all they come from the pseudoscientific "raciology" of the late Nazi regime, in the name of which great crimes were committed. Perhaps it would be better if there were some other term we could use to designate the physically distinguishable groups of mankind, which do exist and of which we must take account. Since *race* is the term in use, we shall have to accept it, define what it means in science, and say what it does *not* mean.

The Biological Definition of Race. To the biologist race is a genetic and anatomical concept. It has nothing to do with cultural differences—with such things as language, religion, nationality, or social habits. We may define it in genetic terms, as does Boyd: "*A human race is a population which differs significantly from other populations in regard to the frequency of one or more of the genes it possesses.*" Or, since we do not know very much about the genetics of man, we may use morphological (phenotypic) differences for the recognition of races and say with Hooton that *a biological race is a great division of mankind, the members of which,*

though varying individually, are distinguished as a group by a certain combination of bodily characteristics which they owe to their common descent."
The criteria of race, so defined, are such things as the distribution of the blood group genes, or phenotypic differences in hair, skin, nose, eyes, stature, and body proportions.

"Sociological" Races. To the average person, in contrast, "race" is an undefined complex of bodily traits, cultural phenomena, language, nationality, religion, and geographic location, overlaid with subjective judgments as to mental or moral qualities. The same person may use "race" in various non-comparable and often conflicting senses, with first one and then another of these elements uppermost in mind. Thus we hear of the "White race," the "Jewish race," the "Latin race," or the "Irish race." The first assumes skin color as the basis of differentiation, the second religion, the third language, and the fourth either geographic location or a supposed peculiarity of temperament. Such confusion vitiates most arguments about "race," especially when charged with emotion and prejudice.

The Nordic "master race" of the Nazi zealots is a myth. True, there is a group of northern European peoples in whom long heads, blue eyes, and fair hair are prevalent and who constitute a Nordic race in the biological sense. But they are no more mysterious in origin, more gifted, or more heroic than other peoples. Only some of them are Germans, and most Germans are not Nordic. Similarly mythical is the "Jewish race" as a distinctive biological entity. There are Jews, and they have had a special history. Some Jews have a recognizable facial conformation, but more do not. The separateness of the Jews is primarily a cultural phenomenon which has entailed a partial reproductive isolation of certain Jewish groups.

Although the dominant Nordic, the scheming Jew, the fighting Irish, the inscrutable Oriental, and the brutish Negro do not exist in the biological world, they do exist in the minds of men. They are cultural, not biological phenomena and may be called *"sociological races."* As Braidwood says, "When enough people decide to think there is such a thing as a race, then there is such a thing as that race—for the people who think it. Habits, customs, choice of clothes, ways of fixing food, and even odder things get mixed into the idea of race. It is this sort of race on which race prejudice gets built. One of the problems of the biologist is to know how to fight it. You can't convince a crazy man that he is not Napoleon by showing him scientifically that this is not 1812, that he doesn't speak French, and that his wife's name is not Josephine. So far, science has not been much more effective in reeducating the people with race prejudice."

The Importance of Race Study. From the standpoint of science we need to know in what ways and to what degree people differ before we can investigate the reasons for their differences. We must also learn to distinguish differences due to culture from those due to heredity. And always we are led by the desire to learn more of the history of our species —man's origins and wanderings, the stages of his biological and cultural evolution, and the factors that have molded his development. Furthermore race classification is useful in a purely descriptive way, since it enables us to become familiar with the superficial characteristics of more than 2 billion people in a reasonably short time.

It should be obvious that there is another compelling reason for studying and teaching about races. Knowledge is the only antidote for ignorance and prejudice. The more about race people know, the less room there will be for baseless antagonisms and unfounded notions of racial superiority. And here let it be said that *no tests yet devised have revealed any inherent mental differences between the races of men.* There are certainly superior individuals in all races. There may also be superior cultures and superior environments, but that is another matter.

Genetics and the Races of Man.   In 1950, Boyd published an important book under the above title, in which he summarized our present knowledge of human genetics as it bears upon race classification and the genetic structure of human populations. As restated by Dobzhansky, Boyd's thesis is as follows: Every human being is a member of a biological community within which marriages take place. Such a community, termed a *Mendelian population* or *isolate*, possesses a gene pool, from which the genes of the individuals are drawn and to which some of them are returned unless the individual dies childless. Mankind, the human species, is the most inclusive Mendelian population. It is, however, a very complex system of isolates, kept apart by geography or by social forces. It happens that these subordinate populations often differ in the relative frequencies of genes for various traits in their gene pools. Boyd defines such different populations as races; his definition was quoted above. He points out that which and how many groups of allelic genes we choose to consider as differential criteria of race is an arbitrary matter.

The way to describe races, then, should be to determine the frequencies of particular allelic genes in human populations. However, only a few traits are as yet sufficiently well understood genetically so that such analysis can be made. The most important of these are the inherited variations in some components of the blood—the blood groups. Because of their medical importance and ease of determination certain blood groups have been investigated in populations all over the world. Boyd's analysis of the data is too complicated to be outlined here, but the following will illustrate the method and its results.

Of the various blood groups the best known and most widely tested is the O, A, B, AB series so important in relation to blood transfusion. The blood of every person in the world belongs to one of these four types. They are the phenotypic expressions of three allelic genes—*A*, *B*, and *O*, the latter recessive to both *A* and *B*. Blood group O has the genotype *OO*; blood group A may be the expression of either *OA* or *AA*; blood group B may similarly be either *OB* or *BB*; and blood group AB has the genotype *AB*. From these data the frequencies of the genes *O*, *A*, and *B* can be calculated for any population in which the phenotypic frequencies are known.

It turns out that gene *B* is high in the populations of interior and southwestern Asia and declines in all directions away from that center, being low in Europe and apparently absent in Australian natives and American Indians. Gene *A*, on the contrary, occurs all over the world, varying sharply from region to region and sometimes from tribe to tribe. The recessive gene *O* is, of course, everywhere present in inverse ratio to the combined proportion of *A* and *B*. Boyd analyzed in similar fashion the distribution of gene frequencies for the subgroups of gene *A*, and for the *MN* and *Rh* series of alleles.

On the basis of the blood-group genes, bolstered by what little is known of the genetics of other traits, Boyd divides mankind into six great races: (1) Hypothetical Early European; (2) European or Caucasoid; (3) African or Negroid; (4) Asiatic or Mongoloid; (5) American Indian; and (6) Australian. Considering his devastating and sometimes caustic critique of the older morphological approach to race study, it is interesting to see how closely his racial divisions conform to those of earlier classifications.

Phenotypic traits and measurements.   It will probably be a long time before we know enough about human genetics to be able to discuss racial classification solely in terms of gene frequencies. In the meantime we have the evidence of our eyes and of our measuring instruments to guide us. The traits in which men differ are the phenotypic expressions of genetic factors. This means that many traits must include a variable and undetermined environmental response, that we may often confuse similar phenotypic effects of different genes, and that we can deal only with differences that are visible or measurable. In spite of these limitations it seems evident that heredity must be the preponderant factor responsible for the observable differences between men; the agreement between genetically based and morphologically based classifications supports this conclusion.

The traits with which we deal are relatively trivial differences, relating to the skin and its appendages and to the proportions of the body and its parts. Such things as hair form, coloration, variations in facial features, and stature are apparent to the eye and together with cultural characteristics are the basis for the easy judgements we all tend to make about the race of individuals we encounter. (It would not be so easy if we saw these same people naked and clean-shaven.) Other traits are best revealed by measurement of various body parts, especially those of the head or skull. From these may be obtained indices expressing ratios, such as width to length of head, length of forearm to that of arm, and the like. By observation and measurement of numerically large samples of populations we can determine the mean values, range of variation, and incidence of particular phenotypic traits in each population. This is a method roughly comparable to but far less precise than the determination of gene frequencies in populations.

One thing we must always remember in racial analysis is that we are dealing with groups of people—with *populations*—and not with individuals. In the past it was often the practice to set up an ideal racial type

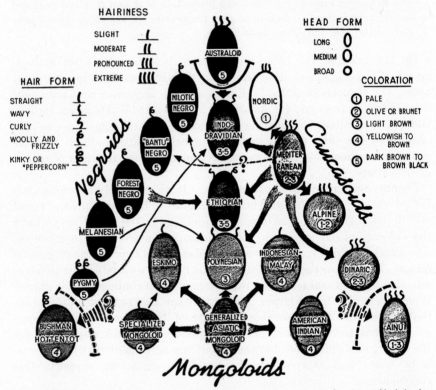

Fig. 31.1. Diagram to show head form, pigmentation, and amount and texture of hair in the principal groups and races of mankind, with the probable derivation of some of the races.

and to determine the race of individuals by comparison with a series of such types. Now we recognize that *the most aberrant individual is as much a member of his population as is the most typical;* that the characteristics of a population are the sum of those of the individuals composing it.

Without going into unnecessary detail, let us review some of the more important traits used in the morphological classification of races. *Hair* may be straight, wavy, woolly, or kinky ("peppercorn"); the differences seem to be strictly gene-controlled (Fig. 22.1). *Hairiness* is another important trait. Amount of beard, distribution and amount of axillary and pubic hair, and downiness of the body surface are its chief manifestations. *Skin color* depends upon the number of pigment cells present in the skin. Pigment cells are always present but may be so few that the skin appears white, so numerous that the skin is brownish black, or any shade between. *Hair color* results from varying amounts of two pigments, one reddish and the other the same brown-black that appears in the skin. *Eye color* is more complex but depends in part on the amount of brown-black pigment present. In blue eyes this pigment is lacking. *Head form* furnishes several usable traits, among them the height of the dome, the slant of the face, the breadth across the cheek bones, the prominence of the brow ridges, and especially the *cephalic index*, or ratio of breadth to length of the cranium. Heads are long when the ratio is less than 0.75, medium when it is 0.75 to 0.80, and broad when it is over 0.80. Actually the average for mankind is close to 0.79, and often only two categories are distinguished—long when the ratio is less than this figure, and broad or round when it is more. Many other traits are also taken into account, among them the shape of the nose (Fig. 22.3), lips, eyelid folds (Fig. 31.4), and external ear, the proportions of the jaws and palate, and the characteristics of the teeth. Stature and body build must be used with caution because of their responsiveness to differences in nutrition.

Older and newer traits.   With regard to any trait, we can often distinguish between an older, more primitive condition and a newer, more advanced condition. We may designate these respectively as *generalized* and *specialized*. To cite some examples, with the generalized condition in each case given first, we have heavy vs. reduced brow ridges, large protruding vs. small straight face, receding vs. prominent chin, broad and low-bridged vs. narrow and high-bridged nose, normal vs. shovel-shaped incisor teeth, five-cusped vs. four-cusped molar teeth, low-domed vs. high-domed skull, long and narrow vs. short and broad skull, abundant vs. scanty hair, straight vs. wavy or curly or woolly or kinky hair, and probably brown vs. either white or blackish skin. In each case the test is degree of resemblance to the ancestral condition as found among fossil men or among the higher living anthropoids. No subspecies or race of man has a monopoly on old or new traits, though the Australoids have more of the former than any other group.

THE RACES OF MAN

When one compares recent systems of race classification, his first impression is that they differ greatly. Thus Hooton (1947) defines 20 "subraces" in 3 "primary races" and a category of "composites"; Kroeber (1948) lists 14 races under 3 "primary stocks" and a group of "doubtfuls"; Krogman (1948) divides man into 3 or possibly 4 "subspecies" each with various races; Howells (1949) treats about 13 races and many lesser groups and mixtures under 4 major divisions; Coon, Garn and Birdsell (1950) recognize 30 human races as subdivisions of 6 "putative stocks"; and Boyd (1950) is content with 6 races, 1 of which survives as a mere remnant.

Closer inspection of these classifications, however, shows that the differences between them are more apparent than real and that the same groups tend to be recognized in all. Some of the seeming differences are merely those of terminology; the primary divisions of *Homo sapiens*, for example, are variously termed "subspecies," "great groups," "primary races," or "stocks," and a single race may go under several names. Sometimes there are differences in opinion as to the origin and status and consequently the proper position and "rank" of a group of people that is nevertheless recognized by all systems. When we consider that the human species is composed of numerous subordinate Mendelian populations, forming a hierarchy that begins with clans, tribes, and various economic and cultural isolates, continues on up through races and major groups, and finally culminates in the species *Homo sapiens*, it becomes clear that just how many and what races we recognize *by giving them names* is purely a matter of convenience. The groups and subgroups and sub-subgroups exist, regardless of how we classify them. It follows that there is no one "true" or "best" classification but only more useful and less useful ones, in so far as they do no violence to the facts.

The great groups of mankind.   Three major divisions of the human species are recognized in practically all classifications: *European* (Caucasoid, "White"), *African* (Negroid, "Black"), and *Asiatic* (Mongoloid, "Yellow"). Taxonomically these should be called subspecies, but it will be more convenient to speak of them as great groups, and of their subdivisions as races. Together these three account for some 90 per cent of all nations and tribes and for an even larger proportion of all living people.

In addition there are a few much smaller groups, well differentiated and accepted in all classifications, the rank of which is more doubtful. Thus, in the classifications mentioned, the *Australians* are placed as a fourth great group by Howells, Coon, and Boyd but are treated as a "composite race" by Hooton and are tentatively assigned to the Negroids by Krogman. Others regard them as a very primitive, black race of the "White" stock. The *American Indians* are often included among the more generalized Mongoloids but are made a primary group by Boyd and Coon. The *Polynesians*, usually treated as a composite race, are left unplaced by Boyd and are given primary rank by Coon. Finally we have the puzzling South African *Bushmen*, dismissed as an unsolved enigma by many anthropologists and by others forced into the Negroid group for want of a better place to put them.

We shall be on the conservative side in recognizing four great groups (subspecies) of man: European, African, Asiatic, and Australian. The characteristics and some of the racial subdivisions of these will be outlined below.[1]

---

[1] For those who desire further information on the topics covered in this chapter we recommend the following books, from all of which we have drawn freely: Hooton, *Up from the Ape*, The Macmillan Company, New York, 1947; Kroeber, *Anthropology*,

The great European or Caucasoid group.   The principal differential features of this branch of mankind are: *skin color* light brown (olive) varying to pale white, pink, or ruddy; *hair color* rarely dead black but of all lighter shades; *eye color* never black but of all lighter shades; *hair form* never woolly, usually wavy or straight, sometimes loosely curled. Other characteristics include: *nose form* usually high-bridged and narrow, sometimes medium, nasal openings usually anteroposteriorly oval, or narrow, nasal "*wings*" narrow to moderate, recurved in Armenoids: *beard* and *body hair* moderate to abundant; *face* usually straight; *lips* medium to thin, little everted; *chin prominence* pronounced to medium; *hair texture* medium to fine, rarely very coarse; *pelvis* broad and shallow in both sexes; *breast form* usually hemispherical and *buttocks* usually prominent in female. In terms of blood group genes Boyd defines this group as very high in *rh* and relatively high in Rh_1 and A_2, the other genes in moderate frequencies, M and N in normal ratio.

Judging from fossil evidence this seems to be the oldest of the great groups of mankind.[1] Perhaps this accounts for the fact that there are more races distinguished in it than in the others; but we should remember that the "Whites" have been more intensively studied than have the Mongoloids and Negroids. The Caucasoids are primitive in hair form and in hairiness of body but are the most advanced of all in degree of facial reduction.

There are five principal races of the "White" group upon which nearly everyone agrees; some anthropologists would add more.

The *Mediterranean race* surrounds the Mediterranean Sea and stretches east toward India.[2] This is the fundamental "White" race—ancient, rather generalized, and varied. Mediterraneans are prevailingly long-headed, with narrow and usually straight noses, olive skins, dark eyes, and hair that is dark and usually wavy. Two subtypes are often distinguished. One, the *classic Mediterranean*, is rather short and slender, with delicate features and smaller bones; many Arabs, most Egyptians and coastal peoples of North Africa, and some southern Italians

---

Harcourt, Brace and Company, Inc., New York, 1948; Howells, *Mankind So Far*, Doubleday & Company, Inc., New York, 1949; Coon, *The Races of Europe*, The Macmillan Company, New York, 1939; and Boyd, *Genetics and the Races of Man*, Little, Brown & Company, Boston, 1950.

[1] Swanscombe man and the Cro-Magnons seem to have been members of a still older proto-European stock (Boyd's *Hypothetical Early European*) ancestral to the modern Caucasoids. This very ancient group almost certainly had light brown skin and dark hair and eyes. Such coloration prevails among modern "Whites"; only those of northern Europe have the bleached coloration we erroneously think of as typical. Boyd thinks that the Basques may be relatively unchanged survivors of the proto-European stock.

[2] Unless otherwise stated, the distribution of races is here given as it was in 1492, before Europeans had spread all over the world to further complicate matters.

are of this sort. The other subtype, *Atlanto-Mediterranean*, is taller, more robust, and larger headed with coarser features; it is frequent among the Berbers and the Spanish and Portuguese. The Mediterranean race apparently originated in southwestern Asia. In Neolithic times it spread from the Near East over much of Europe and North Africa and is the basic stock from which the Nordics and Alpines were formed. South of the Sahara it blends with the Negroid race; and the inhabitants of India seem to be Mediterraneans mixed with an increasing proportion of dark-skinned, non-Negroid peoples toward the south. In southwest-

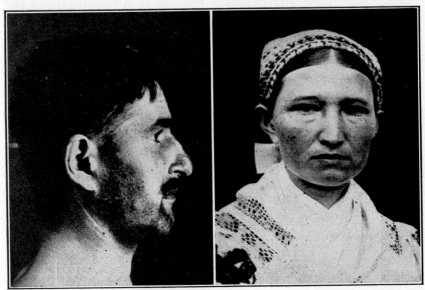

FIG. 31.2. Left, an Armenoid Dinaric from Tiflis; right, a Czech woman of Alpine type (*Courtesy Chicago Natural History Museum.*)

ern and central Asia many populations exhibit a transition from Mediterranean to Mongoloid.

The *Nordic race* is the one prevailing in northern Europe. It is essentially a bleached-out version of the more ancient Atlanto-Mediterranean type. The head averages long, with long, narrow, and deep-chinned face and a nose which is commonly long, high, narrow and thin-tipped; the mouth tends to be thin-lipped, the upper lip unusually long. The skin is pale or ruddy, the eyes blue or gray, the hair generally blond and straight or wavy; baldness is prevalent among the men. Nordic men tend to be robust, tall, slender, with sloping shoulders, shallow chest, a rather long and narrow trunk, and long legs. Many upland Swedes and Norwegians, north Germans, and some English, Scotch and Russians are of Nordic ancestry. In the United States, according to Hooton, about 23 per cent of the population consists of a Nordic-Alpine and 25 per cent of a Nordic-Mediterranean mixture, both partially stabilized. The *East Baltic* subrace or race has the Nordic coloration but a squarer head and a shorter, stockier build. It occurs along the shores of the Baltic, mostly among Finns, Esthonians, Lithuanians, and Baltic Russians.

The *Alpine race* is the most recent of the "White" races. It apparently arose by change of long-headed populations of Mediterranean ancestry to round-headed ones, over an area stretching from central Europe far into interior Asia. The causes of the change are still unknown, but its occurrence seems amply demonstrated. Among Alpine peoples the head averages short, approaching a globular form, and the face tends to be broad, short, and rounded, with slightly infantile features. The forehead and nose are usually rather broad, the jaw often squarish. The skin is blond to brunet and commonly intermediate in shade; the eyes are usually brown; the hair is dark and abundant, oftener straight than wavy, and the beard is heavy. Most Alpines are short or of medium height, thickset, with heavy neck, broad shoulders, deep chest, thick waist, and short thick arms and legs. This race dominates the highland and forest regions of the central core of Europe and in-

fluences the adjacent lowland populations. It includes most Bavarians and
Frenchmen, many Swiss, Czechs,
northern Italians, southern Slavs and
Russians, and most Turks. Eastward it
intergrades with Mongoloid peoples in
central Asia.

The *Dinaric race* may, like the
Alpine, have arisen through change
of long-headed to short-headed populations, as Howells thinks, or it may
have resulted from mixture of Alpines
and Mediterraneans, as postulated by
Coon and Hooton. At any rate the
Dinaric race differs from the short-
headed Alpine race in various respects.
The head is short but very flat behind
and the forehead slants up to a short,
high, posteriorly situated crown. The
foramen magnum and ears tend to

FIG. 31.3. An Ainu from Hokkaido, Japan.
(*Courtesy Chicago Natural History Museum.*)

be placed farther back than usual. The face averages large and long with rather prominent cheek bones, full lips of which the lower is often everted, and a large, narrow, high-bridged nose that is high at the root. The skin color is olive to brunet, the eyes are usually brown, and the hair is dark, abundant, and generally wavy but sometimes straight or curly. The *typical Dinarics* who live in the Balkans and around the Adriatic Sea are rather tall, heavy-jawed, and straight-nosed, and sometimes have blue eyes. From Asia Minor to northern Iran occurs the *Armenoid subrace*, a shorter people many of whom have a more specialized nose, convex in profile, the tip thick and depressed, the "wings" characteristically recurved, and often without any notch at the junction with the forehead. Such noses were characteristic of the ancient Hittites, as shown in contemporary sculpture.

The *Ainu race* appears to be an isolated branch of the "White" stock which once occupied all of Japan but was driven into the northern islands by the invading Japanese. How these "Whites" got so far from their relatives is a mystery which some seek to resolve by denying their relationship to other Caucasoids.

Thus Krogman thinks the Ainu may be generalized Mongoloids that have taken on some resemblance to "Whites," but this hypothesis is not widely held. These people are stocky brunets, medium-headed, and somewhat Alpinelike. They are generalized but not particularly primitive. Their most notable characteristic is extreme hairiness of head, face, and body.

The great Asiatic or Mongoloid group.

The chief recognition characters of this group of peoples are: *hair* straight and black, its texture coarse; *skin color* yellow or yellow-brown; *eye color* medium to dark brown; *eye form* varying from ordinary to specialized, the latter with slitlike

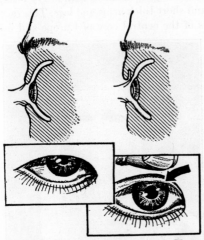

FIG. 31.4. The mongoloid eye fold. Upper left, section of eye of Negroid or Caucasoid, upper lid without fold. Upper right, section of eye of "specialized" Mongoloid, upper lid with overhanging fold. Lower left, eye with mongoloid fold concealing edge of lid; lower right, same with fold retracted by finger to expose edge of lid. (*Redrawn from Wilder, The Pedigree of the Human Race, by permission Henry Holt and Company, Inc.*)

slanting opening caused by a fold of the upper lid, which, when the eye is open, conceals the edge of the lid along its whole extent or on the side toward the nose; *nose form* generally infantile, of medium breadth, with low root and bridge, short somewhat thick tip, and moderate "wings," usually concave or straight in profile; *cheek bones* prominent, usually covered by a fatty pad; *hairiness* of face and body the least of any of the great groups. Other characteristics include: *build* variable, commonly with broad shoulders, long trunk, and short arms and legs; *stature* variable, in males usually averaging under 5 feet 7 inches; *incisor teeth* usually shovel-shaped; a *sacral pigmented area* (Mongoloid spot) often visible in early life. Excluding the American Indians (placed as a primary group), Boyd defines the Mongoloids in terms of blood-group genes as being high in A_1 and B, highest of all in the rare gene Rh^z, having little if any A_2 and rh, and normal frequencies of M and N.

The *classic Mongoloid race*, in which these traits find their fullest expression, occurs from northeastern Siberia to northern China, and includes some Tibetan and Mongolian groups. The head is round, with a cephalic index generally over 0.80 and averaging 0.85. The face tends to be unusually flat and "moonlike," partly from its breadth, low nose, and flat forehead, and partly because the hollow from eye sockets to cheek bone is filled flush with fatty tissue. "Slant eyes" are commonest and most pronounced in these populations, but the trait varies individually and from region to region. Howells calls these people the "specialized Mongoloids," and thinks they are a recent regional modification comparable in origin to the Alpines. Hooton vigorously dissents from this view. He considers them an old, strongly differentiated race which has produced most of the less distinctive Mongoloid races by hybridization with other groups of people.

The *arctic Mongoloid race* differs from the classic Mongoloid in being long-headed, with a somewhat roof-shaped cranium, very broad and very long face with exaggeratedly jutting cheek bones and a rather narrow nose, and much less frequent development of the complete Mongoloid eyelid fold. This race, also called the *Eskimoid*, includes the Eskimo of North America and various tribes of extreme northeastern Siberia.

All other Mongoloids lack the extreme "specializations" just described, and are generalized by contrast. This does not mean that they are all alike. Some

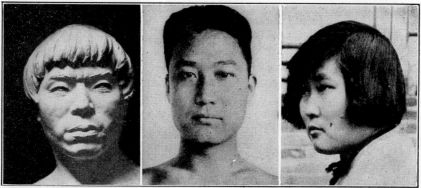

FIG. 31.5. "Specialized" Mongoloid types. Left to right: an Eskimo man, modeled by Malvina Hoffman; a Manchu from Peking, China; a Buriat Mongol woman from eastern Siberia. (*Courtesy Chicago Natural History Museum.*)

groups are round-headed, some long-headed; some are tall and robust, others small and delicate; skin color varies from yellowish to yellow-brown. Before taking up the populations that constitute distinguishable races, let us pay our respects to the Japanese and Chinese, who together make up a large fraction of mankind and yet about whom we actually know very little.

The *Chinese* are a mixture of Mongoloid races. They vary tremendously in type, from tall to short, and from long-headed to round-headed. Not much can be said about them that would apply to all. The classic Mongoloid type is common in the north and becomes less numerous southward. A southward diminution in average size also is notable. Many southern Chinese are small and delicately built, with less flattened faces and "finer" features than the northerners. In these respects they show an approach to the Indonesian-Malay race that occurs still farther south.

The *Japanese* came to their islands as invaders from Korea not long before the Christian era, and drove the aboriginal Ainus northward. The newcomers seem to have included both classic and other Mongoloid types, and many modern Japanese are indistinguishable from mainland people. Other Japanese, however, have beards, wavy hair, and chiseled features that suggest a mixture with Mediterranean "White," and some have traits reminiscent of Indonesians. The significance of these facts is wholly unknown.

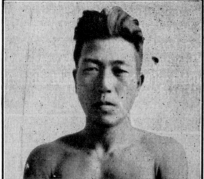

FIG. 31.6. One sort of Japanese. (*Courtesy Chicago Natural History Museum.*)

Three great arms of predominantly Mongoloid populations stretch out away from the East Asian center—one into western Asia, one southeast into Indonesia, and one into America. Each constitutes a different racial group.

The *Mongol race* includes the peoples of northern and central Siberia. They are yellow-skinned, mostly round-headed, and strongly built though not tall. In the north are the reindeer nomads, whose outposts reach northernmost Europe. On the steppes and mountain slopes from Mongolia to the Caspian and Black Seas live the horse nomads, and most of the people of Tibet belong to this race. Many Mongols have skulls almost indistinguishable from those of Alpines, and some have heads as large as any in the world.

FIG. 31.7. Left, an Indonesian Igorot from northern Luzon, Philippine Islands, modeled by Malvina Hoffman. Right, a Malay (Moro) from Mindanao, Philippine Islands. (*Courtesy Chicago Natural History Museum and American Museum of Natural History, respectively.*)

The *Indonesian-Malay race* occupies the islands of Indonesia—Sumatra, Java, Borneo, Celebes, and the Philippines. Southeastward in Asia and through the Malay Peninsula there is a gradual transition toward this race. The peoples of this group are smaller and slighter than the Mongols, brown-skinned, and of variable head form. Two subraces can be distinguished, evidently representing two migration waves. The older *Indonesians* are less strongly Mongoloid and have longer heads, narrower noses, and slightly wavy hair. They probably contain Mediterranean and some Negrito genetic elements. This subrace includes relict groups in southeastern Asia, and tribes in the mountainous interiors of the islands. Everywhere in Indonesia the older peoples have retreated before the *Malays*, a broad-headed, straight-haired, flat-nosed, yellower-skinned group of much more Mongoloid appearance, which occupies the coasts and fertile lowlands.

The *American Indian race*, the third great arm of Mongoloid populations, stretches, via Bering Straits, to America, and includes all the aboriginal peoples of the New World. The American Indians (who despite popular legend are not "redskins") all have dark hair and eyes, medium brown skins, little or no hair on face and body, and straight or rarely wavy hair on the head. All have large, broad faces with high cheek bones. These are Mongoloid traits which give the Indians a deceptive appearance of uniformity. Actually there is as much variation as among the "Whites"—in stature, head form, shape of nose, and other characteristics. Almost every American Indian type has a close counterpart somewhere among the Mongols or Indonesians.

Howells places the American Indians among his "generalized" Mongoloids. Hooton regards them as a composite race, predominantly Mongoloid but with "White" and Australoid and possibly a trace of Negrito in the mixture. But Boyd and Coon rank them as one of the primary groups, largely on the basis of the blood-group genes. Boyd defines this group as possessing varying (sometimes high, sometimes zero) incidence of A_1, no A_2, probably no B or rh, low N, and Rh^z present.

The eastern woodland Indians of North America were tall, with long, high skulls and narrow, straight noses—in appearance quite like some of the darker skinned Europeans. The Plains Indians were more varied but on the whole were tall, with wide cheek bones and narrow, high, hawklike noses. The many tribes of western North America including Mexico were more nondescript but prevailingly short and round-headed, with variously shaped but never high-bridged noses. Such people form the bulk of the Mexican and Guatemalan populations today. The Mayas of Central America are quite different, with a large, long face, high convex nose, prominent upper lip, and large heavy-lidded eyes. In South America the Indians of the Andes and West Coast are again mostly round-headed and nondescript in type. Those of the Amazon Basin are more varied, some being short people with flat faces and frequent Mongoloid folds, while others are longer-headed and more like the eastern long-heads of North America, with wavy hair and features resembling those of Europeans.

The antiquity of man in America has long been a moot question. In the absence of clear evidence it used to be assumed that he first arrived only a few thousand years ago. Most anthropologists were dissatisfied with this conclusion, since it required them to believe either that the American Indians had differentiated with extraordinary rapidity in their new home, or that a succession of already different racial groups had found their way here. An increasing body of archeological evidence supporting a greater antiquity has been greatly strengthened by C_{14}

datings published since 1950. Objects of human manufacture (sandals) which
are 9,100 years old have been found in an Oregon cave; and bones of man associated with those of ground sloth and guanaco from southern Chile prove to
be 8,800 years old, giving the latest possible time of man's arrival at the southern
tip of the Americas. Weapons and other traces of man found in a New Mexican
cave have been geologically dated as of fourth glacial age; and in Minnesota the

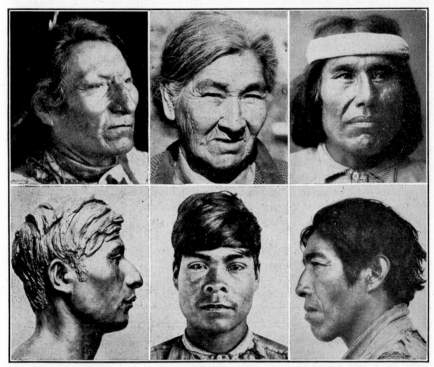

FIG. 31.8. American Indians. Upper row, left to right: Muiconju Sioux, a North American
Great Plains type; Ottawa or Pottawatomie, an eastern North American Algonquian type;
Patagonian from southernmost South America. Lower row, left to right: Maya from Yuca-
tán, modeled by Malvina Hoffman; Tarascan from Michoacán, Mexico; Cayuá from Matto
Grosso, Brazil. (*All courtesy Chicago Natural History Museum, except Sioux, American
Museum of Natural History, and Algonquian, photo by Prof. Emerson F. Greenman.*)

skeleton of an Indian woman was found in presumably undisturbed deposits of a
glacier-margin lake that existed some 10,000 to 15,000 years ago. The earliest
well-established radio-carbon date for the occurrence of man in America is 10,455
years ago.This age determination was made on dried dung of the extinct giant
ground sloth found with associated human artifacts in Gypsum Cave near Las
Vegas, Nev.[1] Man had certainly reached the New World by the end of the last
glaciation and may well have come during the preceding interglacial.

[1] For this and other radio-carbon dates see W. F. Libby, *Radiocarbon Dating*,
University of Chicago Press, Chicago, 1952.

The great African or Negroid group. The Negroid peoples are distinguished chiefly by the following traits: *hair form* woolly or frizzly; *skin color* dark brown to black; *eyes* dark brown to black; *nose opening* in skull broad. Other traits include: *nose* with bridge and root usually low, profile concave or straight, rarely convex, tip thick and usually elevated, "wings" thick and flaring; *lips* thick, the upper convex, membranous lining much everted; *lower face* often protrusive; *head form* medium to long, brow ridges small and forehead rounded; *hair* almost absent on body and scant on face, generally short on head; *arms* and *legs* with long distal segments; *pelvis* relatively narrow; *female breast form* usually conical and *buttocks* usually less projecting than in "Whites." Excluding the Melanesians, Boyd defines the African group in terms of blood genes as being tremendously high in *Rhº*, moderate in *rh*, relatively high in A_2 and the rare intermediate A (A_{1-2}, etc.) and *Rh* genes, rather high in *B*, and probably with normal *M* and *N* frequencies.

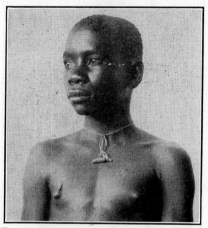

FIG. 31.9. A Negro youth from the Congo Basin in Africa. (*Courtesy American Museum of Natural History.*)

The *African Negro race* includes most of the native African populations south of the Sahara. In all these people there is a high incidence of the traits just listed but great variation in other respects. In different groups stature may be short to tall, body build medium to robust, legs short to long. The many tribes occupy the tropical forests of West Africa and the Congo Basin, and the more open parkland and savanna regions of the Sudan, East Africa, and South Africa, except where the Nilotes occur. The large New World populations of African Negroes are concentrated in the eastern United States, around the Caribbean, and in Brazil; they are everywhere mixed with "Whites" and American Indians in varying combinations.

The *Nilotic Negroes* are a distinctive subrace found about the headwaters of the Nile and in the lake region of Africa. Straighter-faced, narrower-nosed, and longer-headed than other Negroes, they are excessively tall and slender, and include the tallest people in the world. There are whole tribes in which the men *average* 6 feet in height, with 6 feet 8 inches as common a variation as 5 feet 4 inches. There may be some Mediterranean in the Nilotes, but this cannot account for their tallness.

The *Melanesian Negro race*, the second major division of the Negroids, is found far away from Africa in the great island group extending from New Guinea eastward through the Solomons and New Hebrides to Fiji. This island chain has always formed the central track of migration for peoples moving to the Pacific, and along it have passed Negritos, Australoids, and Polynesians. But the basic population is Negro. Such differences as the Melanesians show from African Negroes are apparently the results of mixture—chiefly with Australoids and Negritos.

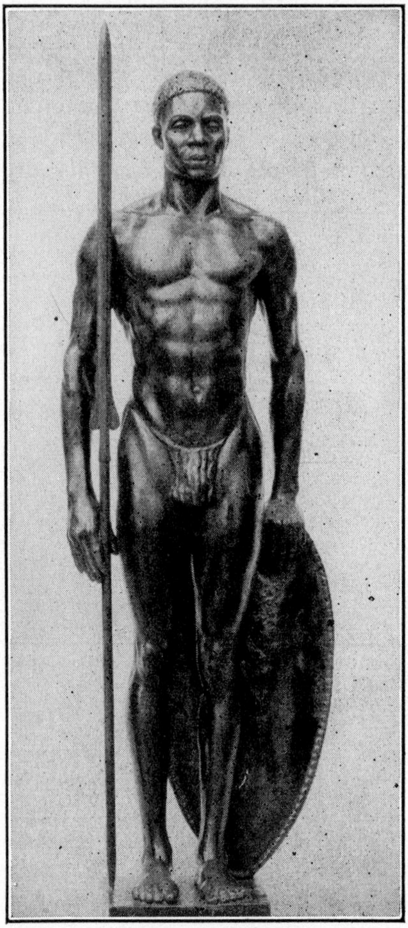

Along the north coast of New Guinea and on many of the smaller islands are people who speak Melanesian tongues (Fig. 31.11, left). They have hair that is usually frizzled into a mop, much more beard and body hair than in African Negroes, and a nose that is deeply depressed at the root and broad, with low bridge, thick elevated tip, and circular nostrils directed forward. In the rest of coastal and interior New Guinea and in a few of the smaller islands the people speak Papuan tongues. They show a strong admixture of Negrito and Australoid (Fig. 31.11, right), the product often being what Howells describes as "a stumpy, heavy-nosed, broad-mouthed, beetle-browed form of incredible ugliness." The nose is often aquiline and sometimes hook-tipped, suggesting the Armenoid type except for its greater width and depressed root.

The *Negritos or Pygmy Negroids* are the smallest of men. In some tribes males average only 4 feet 8 inches in height. Negritos are in no sense mal-formed dwarfs, but simply small, well-proportioned people. In most ways they resemble Negroes, from whom they were almost certainly derived. Some of their traits suggest infantilism (preco-cious maturity). These include narrow shoulders, short legs, bulbous fore-

FIG. 31.10. A Negro warrior from central Africa, modeled by Malvina Hoffman. (*Courtesy Chicago Natural History Museum.*)

heads, and infantile features, the nose being broader than it is long. This race has only a few surviving remnants with widely discontinuous distribu-tion. It occurs in the Congo Basin of Africa, the Andaman Islands in the Indian Ocean, the Malay Peninsula, the Philippines, and New Guinea. All the Negritos are forest-dwelling hunters without fixed habitations; they have been forced by peoples with higher cultures to live in the most inaccessible and least desirable environments.

The racial enigmas.   There are many groups of people who do not fit well into any scheme of racial classification. Most of these are transitional populations in the zones between the regions occupied by the European, Asiatic and African races, or populations produced by recent racial mixture. A few constitute veritable puzzles for the anthropologist. Chief among these are the Australoids, the Bushmen, the Polynesians, the Basques, and the Ainus; the last group has already been discussed in treating the "Whites."

Fig. 31.11. Melanesian Negroes. Left, a young man of Malaita, Solomon Islands, showing strongly Negroid traits somewhat modified by Micronesian influence, as is common among the coastal Melanesians. (*Photo by Dr. Justin W. Leonard.*) Right, a Papuan from Mount Hagen in eastern interior New Guinea, showing mixture of Australoid and Negritoid traits. (*Photo by M. J. Leahy, courtesy American Museum of Natural History.*)

The *Australoids*, the aborigines of Australia, resemble Negroes in their dark brown skin and broad noses, and are like "Whites" in having hair that is straight to curly and abundant on face and body. In other respects they are unique. The skull is long, narrow, low-crowned, and thick-walled, with small brain capacity. The forehead recedes strongly, the brow ridges are heavy, and the nose is deeply notched at the root. The lower face is protrusive, with large teeth and lips that are full but thinner than in Negroids. No other race shows so many primitive traits.

The Australoids are sometimes classified with the Negroids, sometimes with the Caucasoids and often are left unplaced. There is a growing tendency to accord them primary rank, as is done by Howells, Coon, and Boyd. They are nevertheless so primitive that they might almost have been ancestral to the other major groups. The Australoids have certainly had a long independent history and did not originate in Australia. The Pleistocene Wadjak skulls from Java are Australoid in all but their greater size; the mixed peoples of southern India appear to contain a considerable Australoid element. In blood-group gene frequencies the Australoids are set off from all other major groups by having high A_1, no A_2, no rh, high N, and Rh^z present.

The *South African Bushmen*—a dwarfish people, but not so small as Negritos— live in the Kalahari Desert of southwest Africa. They show an extraordinary combination of Negroid with apparently Mongoloid traits. In their black hair growing in tiny spirals ("peppercorns"), broad noses, and full, everted lips they resemble Negroids; in their yellow skin, slitlike slanted eyes, bridgeless nose and projecting, fat-covered cheek bones they resemble Mongoloids. But they are

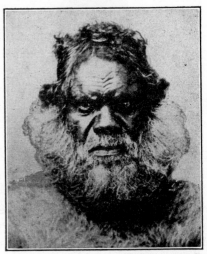

FIG. 31.12. African Pygmies of the Ituri Forest in the Congo Basin, contrasted with a tall European. (*Courtesy Chicago Natural History Museum.*)

FIG. 31.13. A native Australian. (*Courtesy Chicago Natural History Museum.*)

unique in the enormous development of steatopygia (fat accumulation on but-tocks and thighs), especially in the women, and in certain peculiarities of the male and female external genitalia.

Some authorities derive the Bushmen from an ancient cross between Negritos and Mongoloids; many believe they are a relict group descended from the late Pleistocene Boskop people of Africa; still others think they are a specialized offshoot of the Negroid stock that has taken on a wholly accidental resemblance to the Mongoloids. No really acceptable theory of their origin and relationships has yet been proposed. Bushmen or similar peoples seem once to have occupied much of East Africa and to have been forced into their present inhospital home-land by pressure from invading Negro groups. The Hottentot tribes that now surround them share some of the Bushman traits and seem to represent hybrid populations in the zone of contact with the Bantu tribes of Negroes.

The *Polynesians*, Pacific islanders living within the great triangle formed by New Zealand, Hawaii, and Easter Island, are tall, large-boned, large-featured, and light brown in color. There is some variation from group to group, but morphologically the Polynesian race is remarkably uniform. Coon makes it a primary group, but in nearly all other classifications it is considered a well-blended composite race. Boyd says that their blood-group gene frequencies are not constant enough to permit the Polynesians to be placed with any other race or defined genetically as a race by themselves. They seem to contain an evident "White" element, manifest in the general build, facial traits, wavy hair and beards. A Mongoloid strain is also present and probably as important as the "White," though harder to detect and affecting chiefly the size and form of the face. In some populations there is a trace of Negroid—not enough to darken the skin, but bringing in genes that broaden the nose and make the hair frizzy.

The origin of the Polynesians is another racial mystery. Their legends and genealogies agree that they came from the west in a great migration that began after the time of Christ. We can deduce that they came from somewhere in Indonesia; but they left no traces.[1] They could have acquired their Mongoloid element in Indonesia, but where did the "White" (Mediterranean?) component come from? The Negroid strain was doubtless added during their passage through

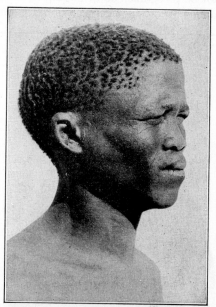

FIG. 31.14. A Bushman of the Kalahari Desert, South Africa. (*Courtesy Chicago Natural History Museum.*)

Melanesia but is so slight that the migrant peoples must have hurried through or largely by-passed that region.

The *Basques* are an interesting people who live at the western end of the Pyrenees in France and Spain. They are linked together by a most remarkable language, which is utterly unlike any other in Europe and is thought to be a survivor of the tongues spoken in that region before the spread of the so-called "Aryan" languages. Most racial classifications ignore the Basques as a biological group, dividing them among Alpines and Mediterraneans. Boyd, however, finds them distinctive in blood-group gene frequencies. They have the highest incidence of *rh* of any tested group, probably no *B*, relatively high *Rh*₁ and *A*₂, and appar-

[1] The theory that the Polynesians came from Peru on balsa rafts has been persuasively presented by Thor Heyerdahl in his book *Kon-Tiki*, and he and his companions have demonstrated that such voyages could have been and perhaps were made. Anthropologists, however, feel that the evidence for an Asiatic origin of these peoples is overwhelmingly strong.

ently more *N* than other Europeans. Boyd thinks that the Basques are a relict population descended from the earlier inhabitants of Europe, and on these grounds he erects a hypothetical sixth great group, the *Early European*, which presumably included the Cro-Magnons and other proto-European peoples.

In concluding this brief survey of human races, let us emphasize once more that (1) none of these races exists save as a variable population, (2) each such population contains many people who as individuals could not be recognized as belonging to that race, (3) all existing races are connected to others by transitional populations, and (4) the races conven-

Fig. 31.15. Polynesians. Left, a Samoan; right, a Hawaiian, modeled by Malvina Hoffman. (*Courtesy Chicago Natural History Museum.*)

tionally recognized and named represent only a small fraction of the genetically different "isolates" that exist at various levels within the species.

CULTURAL LEVELS AND EVOLUTIONARY TRENDS

Man's evolutionary history divides itself into two very unequal periods characterized by quite different evolutionary trends. The first comprised all of human existence up to perhaps 8,000 years ago; the second includes subsequent time. Since the factors responsible for the change were cultural, let us briefly consider the role of culture in human evolution.

What culture is.   Culture is the whole body of knowledge and belief, custom and practice by which a group of people lives, and all the things these people make and do in consequence. Transmitted from generation to generation by teaching and example, it is cumulative in content and endures as long as does the group. It changes, for the most part slowly but sometimes rapidly; and it lives in the minds of men.

Man became MAN when he gained the rudiments of culture, sometime about the beginning of the Pleistocene. Before that he had been only one among the beasts, dependent for adaptation upon slow evolutionary changes in his body; but with the acquisition of tools, fire, and speech it was as though he had emerged onto a new and freer evolutionary plane. Now he could create extracorporeal organs at need—stone weapons more deadly than teeth or claws, a hairy coat to warm his naked body, or a pry pole to give him giant strength. He could even somewhat change his environment; with fire he could cook and eat previously unusable foods, ward off fierce predators, and survive the glacial winters. Speech allowed him to exchange ideas, act in concert with his fellows, and even more important, pass on his accumulated lore to his children. Tools, fire and speech marked the beginning of culture, and the *Emergence of Man.*

Since that beginning no group of people has existed without some form of culture, however primitive. So long as men lived in small, relatively isolated groups or tribes, each such group had its own culture with its own local peculiarities. Changes came chiefly from within, and were naturally very slow. But cultural elements—ideas and techniques—are readily transmitted from one group of people to another through both peaceful and warlike contact. By late Pleistocene times people had become more numerous and the contacts between them multiplied, so that diffusion of cultural elements became more rapid. Since human populations began their rapid growth some 7 millenniums ago, there has been a continued acceleration in the tempo of cultural change. The spread of a new idea or invention in modern societies has become almost instantaneous in contrast to the slow diffusion of earlier times. All the advanced cultures have borrowed widely from each other, so that they have become more and more alike at the same time that they were coming to include more and more people. The many originally separate cultural streams are flowing into a few great rivers.

Culture has obviously been effective in adapting man to environment and environment to man. It has also been potent in shaping man's heredity. Cultural differences between groups often act as isolating factors that hinder extensive interbreeding. They may affect birth and death rates and hence the rate of growth of populations and the distribution of age classes within them. Culture partially shelters the individual from the direct influence of the environment; selection therefore comes to operate more at the group level, so that peoples with more effective cultures increase at the expense of peoples with less effective ones. Above all else, it was cultural advances that ultimately led to the tremendous

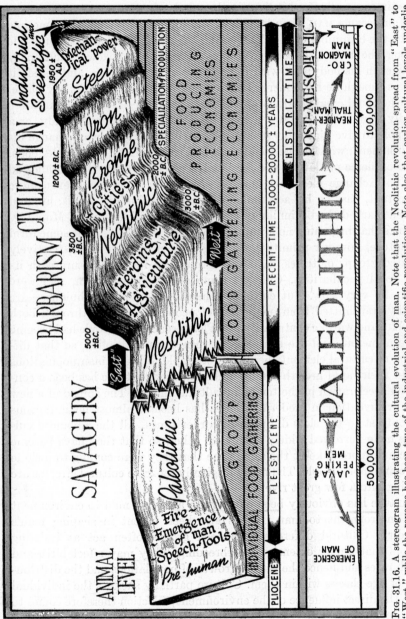

Fig. 31.16. A stereogram illustrating the cultural evolution of man. Note that the Neolithic revolution spread from "East" to "West," while the reverse has been true of the industrial and scientific revolutions. Note also that earlier cultural levels underlie all later ones, their activities being incorporated in the higher cultures. The complete time scale of the Pleistocene is given below to show the enormous duration of the Paleolithic cultural era in contrast to the brevity of post-Paleolithic time.

growth in certain populations, which resulted in profound modification of the earlier evolutionary trends in man.

Pre-Neolithic cultures and evolutionary trends.   All cultures can be grouped into a few great levels, each characterized by a certain way of existence, or *basic economy*. Each level is separated from the succeeding one by some epochal cultural advance that wrought great changes in the life of the people who shared it. There have been only a few such cultural revolutions in the history of mankind, and of these the *Neolithic Revolu-*

Fig. 31.17. A late Paleolithic scene in a cave in France. A Cro-Magnon artist is making an outline of his left hand, pressed against the cave wall, by blowing powdered red ocher through a bone tube around it. Many such "hands" have been found; presumably they had some magic significance. Inset: Head of a stag in the Grotte de Lascaux, Montignac-sur-Vézère, Dordogne, France, representative of the simpler Cro-Magnon cave art. (*Courtesy Chicago Natural History Museum and the Service Commercial, Monuments Historiques, Paris, respectively.*)

tion, caused by the discovery of food production, was perhaps the most significant. It marked the beginning of man's period of dominance and abundance and the turning point in human evolutionary trends.

Throughout the million years or so of the *Paleolithic* cultural era, or *Old Stone Age,* men remained savages. That is only another way of saying that they lived at the lowest economic level, in a *food-gathering economy*. They existed by hunting and fishing and gathering wild foods. Cultural evolution was almost unbelievably slow—how slow may be appreciated by comparing the earliest known culture with that of the Cro-Magnons.

Half a million years ago Peking man lived in caves in China. He hunted large animals and cooked their meat over his campfires, split their bones for marrow, and collected hackberry fruits and other wild plant foods. He fashioned crude chopping tools from stone and also used split bones as implements. He was, incidentally, a cannibal; the human bones found in his cave dwelling were charred, split, and scattered, and all the skulls had been opened to get at the brain.

More than 400,000 years later, we find *Homo sapiens* leading much the same sort of existence in Europe. Cro-Magnon man, like Peking man, lived in caves, hunted large animals, cooked their meat over his camp-

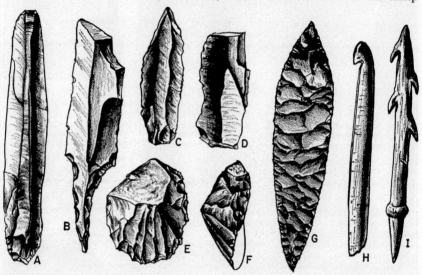

Fig. 31.18. Upper Paleolithic blade tools and bone implements. *A*, plain blade. *B*, an awl or borer. *C*, a pointed burin or graver. *D*, a square-angled burin. *E* and *F*, two views of a keeled round scraper. *G*, a laurel-leaf point. *H*, a part of a spear thrower made from antler. *I*, a bone harpoon point. (*Redrawn from Braidwood, Prehistoric Men, by permission Chicago Natural History Museum.*)

fires, and collected wild plant foods. He still used stone weapons and tools but made them in greater variety and with far more skill; he also used objects carved from bone and antler by means of flint burins. He dressed in skin clothing sewn with sinew by means of bone needles. He doubtless had a rich lore of legend and fable, and certainly he practiced magic to insure successful hunting. To this end he had created the first great artistic tradition in the form of carved images and especially of animal paintings on cave walls, many of which are still preserved. Withall he was still a savage food collector.

We can be sure that all Paleolithic peoples lived in small scattered groups, for the food-collecting economy cannot support large populations. The archeological record confirms this deduction. Furthermore, all movement had to be on foot; mountains and rivers, swamps and deserts formed effective barriers to contact between populations, to say nothing of the oceans. We may therefore conclude that throughout the Paleolithic cultural era evolutionary trends in man were determined by low population densities, the existence of many small and more or less isolated breeding groups, little environmental control by man and hence effective selection on both individual and group levels, and a totality of conditions favorable for the occurrence of genetic drift. In other words things were much the same from the evolutionary standpoint as they had been before man acquired the basic elements of culture.

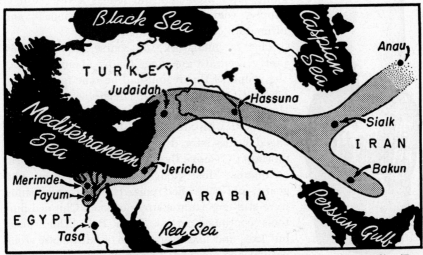

FIG. 31.19. The "Fertile Crescent" (shaded) as extended in the light of modern studies. Here agriculture was born and the Neolithic revolution began. The location of the oldest known farm villages is shown. (*Redrawn from Braidwood, Prehistoric Men, by permission Chicago Natural History Museum.*)

Under such conditions we should expect increasing divergence between isolates in the human population. According to the geological record that is what actually occurred. Various species of men developed prior to or during the Pleistocene, among them *Homo sapiens*. Long before the close of the epoch our own species had differentiated into at least three or four great groups or subspecies, each with several or many geographically separated races. We may be sure that none of these were ever "pure" races in the sense that their individuals were all alike genetically or morphologically; but there was probably less variation within them than there is in most groups today, simply because there was less chance for gene interchange between different groups.

Post-Neolithic cultures and evolutionary trends. Sometime between 8000 and 5000 B.C., or let us say about 8 milleniums ago, agriculture and herding were discovered by certain people of the Mediterranean race. This apparently occurred in the hilly flanks of the region called the "Fertile Crescent" that extends from Egypt to Iran. How it happened is unknown, though it is plausibly supposed that with increasing aridity in postglacial times men began to seek new plant foods to replace the vanishing game. From collecting the heads of wild wheat and barley they came to grow these grasses nearer home, and eventually to cultivate them as crops. Driven by scarcity of natural pasture, wild cattle, pigs, sheep

Fig. 31.20. A Neolithic celt, or polished stone ax, from the Swiss lake villages. The stone head was set in an antler base dressed to fit into a slot in a wooden helve.

and goats may have come to feed in the stubble fields, where they might be first tolerated as easy game, later protected and fed as a reserve food supply, continually selected for tameness, and ultimately completely domesticated.

This is guesswork, of course, but probably pretty accurate guessing, for by about 5000 B.C. the people of this region had become farmers and herdsmen, living in small villages scattered from the Nile valley to northern Iran. The grain was cultivated with stone hoes, harvested with flint-edged sickles, stored in bins and pits, pounded in mortars to remove the chaff, and ground into meal on querns. Most villages had cattle, sheep, and goats, and some had pigs. Hunting and fishing were still important sources of food. Chipped flint tools continued in use from Paleolithic times, but axes and hoes were made of hard dense stone ground and polished. The ground stone ax, or *celt*, was to the older archeologists the distinguishing sign of the Neolithic or New Stone Age. By 5000 B.C. pottery made from baked clay was in general use, and cloth was being woven along the margins of the "Crescent."

The new abundance of food brought an immediate increase in population. Villages multiplied in the rich river valleys, and agriculture spread into the uplands. The Neolithic economy expanded rapidly into Greece, southern Russia, and along the Danube valley into Europe. It also followed the shores of the Mediterranean and the Atlantic Coast to Britain and the Baltic area, showing that coastal trade in small boats had begun. In England Neolithic cultures were replacing Paleolithic ones by 3000 B.C., and in the Baltic 500 years later.

Although food production was first discovered in the Near and the Middle East, it was developed independently in various other parts of the world. A series of separate cultures at the Neolithic level thus came into existence—one in the Orient, based upon rice; one in America, based upon maize, beans, squash, and (in Peru) the white potato; and others in various regions where such plants as yam, banana, taro, breadfruit, and coconut came to support food-producing economies.

Subsequent cultural progress was extremely rapid compared with what had gone before, and its graph forms an ever-steepening upward curve. Especially in the regions affected by the earliest of the Neolithic cultures did discoveries, inventions, and social changes come crowding close upon one another—urbanization, specialization of occupations,

Fig. 31.21. Swiss lake swellers of the late Neolithic haul in their seine at Neuchâtel, Switzerland. A part of their village, built on piles over the lake, is seen at the right. Whatever was dropped sank into the mud of the lake floor and was preserved Among the things found in the mud are many kinds of stone tools and wooden implements, cloth woven from flax fibers, fishing nets and floats, and even the remains of grain, vegetables, fruits, and small loaves of bread baked without yeast. (*Courtesy Chicago Natural History Museum.*)

writing, money, bronze, iron, steel, and a multitude of other innovations, not necessarily in the order named. Each major development wrought changes in economy, and it is not easy to decide what and how many cultural revolutions can be distinguished, even if we consider only the history of Western civilization. Thus by some the rise of cities is ranked as the *urban revolution*, while to others it seems no more than a logical outcome of the Neolithic economy. All can agree on the *industrial revolution*, in which power-driven machines came into use for the production and transport of goods, and on the *scientific-technologic revolution* now in progress, in which man is beginning to apply the results of science to transform the world and his way of life.

Prior to the discovery of food production man's numbers had always been automatically kept in delicate balance with those of his wild food organisms, and he could never become abundant. By one estimate there were never more than 7 million people in the whole world in Paleolithic times. Agriculture released man from the control of natural food chains. Labor could make more food, and "with every mouth God sends a pair of hands to feed it." The Neolithic peoples began to multiply (Fig. 34.1) and spread, pushing some of the Paleolithic people ahead of them, mixing with others, and transmitting the new economy to friend and foe so that they also became a part of the Neolithic populations.

Thus began the great change in man's evolutionary trends. In place of isolation and increasing differentiation, now movement of populations and racial mixture became dominant processes over most of Eurasia. Mediterraneans spread over much of Europe and into India and central Asia; Mongols came out of Asia into Europe; the Nordic wanderings are a matter of record. Much later the "Whites" erupted out of Europe into the Americas, Australia and South Africa, exterminating or mixing with the native populations. Large numbers of African Negroes were brought as slaves to the Americas. Their descendants now dominate many of the West Indian islands, are thoroughly mixed with "Whites" and American Indians in Brazil, and are in process of being amalgamated with "Whites" in North America. In Mexico, Central America, and much of South America the populations are still predominantly Indian but contain a variably large "White" admixture and in some countries considerable Negroid. All over the world this mixing process has been going on to a greater or lesser degree, and it will doubtless continue. Races are merging and becoming less distinct than ever, but this does not mean that men will all eventually be alike. As the world fills up with people, mass migrations and large scale mixing will probably diminish in importance, and the various racial mixtures may have a chance to become stabilized in new patterns. Individual differences within populations will probably increase, since the common gene pool from which each individual draws will contain a greater variety of variable genes.

THE ZOOGEOGRAPHY OF MAN

Everything points to Asia as the region where the great groups or subspecies of man arose. Broadly viewed, we see them arranged radially, in sectors extending out from the Asiatic mountain mass. The "Whites" are to the west, in southwestern Asia and on both sides of the Mediterranean. The Mongoloids are on the north and east, and surround the Pacific. The Negroids lie to the south on both sides of the Indian Ocean, interrupted in southern Asia.

Now let us look more closely at the continental radii. In the European peninsula remnants of the old Paleolithic or proto-European people lie out on the margins, in Scandinavia, Britain, and France. In Africa the oldest race, the Bushmen, are crowded into an inhospitable desert near the tip. The Australoids are out at another dead end. Even America, the most recently occupied part of the world, contains people of Mongoloid ancestry who seem more primitive than the Mongoloids now living in eastern Asia.

We know that Neanderthaloids once held all Europe and northern Africa, that they were replaced by Paleolithic "Whites" apparently coming from the east, and that these in turn were displaced by the Neolithic Mediterraneans. We also believe that Bushmen once occurred over most of East and South Africa, and that Australoids were in India and Java and doubtless all through southern Asia. Everywhere the picture is the same. Older peoples, more primitive in culture and often in physical type, have been displaced toward the peripheries by later peoples, spreading from the general direction of Asia.

This is the basic pattern of human distribution. The great migration waves that followed the Neolithic and industrial revolutions have modified but not erased it. The Neolithic peoples spread over the lands, forcing the earlier peoples back when they did not absorb them. They also had boats, and so were able to move rapidly along coast lines and to islands, thus leapfrogging beyond the older peoples. The industrial revolution made Europe the center of culture and population growth, and from this center the "Whites" have spread out to all parts of the world during the past 500 years. As we have seen, they went especially to the peripheral regions, thinly held by peoples with Neolithic or more primitive cultures. Lesser but significant transplantations of Negroids and Mongoloids have also occurred.

Turning now to the individual groups, the *Caucasoids* or "Whites" apparently became differentiated in southwestern Asia at a time when Neanderthalers held all the lands to the north and west. By mid-Pleistocene times some of the "Whites" had penetrated into Europe and North Africa, and during the fourth glacial stage they took over those lands completely. They also spread into central Asia and China (perhaps explaining the Ainus and Polynesians), and into India to mix with the earlier dark-skinned inhabitants.

The *Mongoloids* seem to have formed east of the "Whites" and north of the Asiatic highlands. Northern Asia was probably full of generalized Mongoloids at the time when some of them crossed to America, and the marginal types of American Indians may show fairly well what these early Mongoloids were like. Their resemblance to the older "White" long heads suggests a common origin and a time when there were no Caucasoids and Mongoloids but only a lighter skinned group of people in the north, distinct from darker skinned peoples in the south.

We have already discussed the *Bushmen* and *Australoids*, including the possibility that both may be remnants of ancient major stocks. The Bushmen cannot be traced; but the Australoids surely came from Asia. It is uncertain when they reached Australia; but if they used boats, as seems likely, it could not have been much more than 10,000 years ago.

The distribution of the *Negroids* is the hardest to account for. Both the Negroes and the Negritos show similarly discontinuous distribution on opposite sides of the Indian Ocean. By all zoogeographic analogy we should look for their origin in adjacent but separate parts of southern Asia. It is quite impossible to suppose that they independently found their way from the Congo to Melanesia, or vice versa. An Asiatic origin for the Negritos is not hard to accept, for some of them still survive in the Malay Peninsula, and they have left traces in the populations of Ceylon and southern India. But—and this is a serious objection—there is nothing at all to show that Negroes were ever anywhere in Asia. Boyd, on the basis of blood-group genes, tries to avoid this dilemma by saying that the Melanesians are not really Negroes at all, but only look like Negroes; no other anthropologist apparently holds this view.

Both Negroes and Negritos used boats to get to the islands where we find them. This is certain, for the Negritos were the only people to reach the Andamans, far out in the Indian Ocean, and the Negroes have Neolithic cultures, which included knowledge of boats. We also know that the Negritos went first, for everywhere they are enclosed by more advanced peoples, who in Melanesia and Africa are Negroes. So much is clear, but nothing else. How did Negritos in the first place, and later on Negroes, reach the Congo Basin in West Africa, when the whole eastern part of Africa fronting the Indian Ocean was held by Mediterraneans and Bushmen? If the Grimaldi Negroids are really Negroids, how did they come to be in Europe during the fourth glacial age? And if the Negroes really came from southern Asia, why have they left no trace of their presence?

As yet there are no answers to these questions. Howells suggests that the mystery of the Polynesians may furnish a clue to the last, however. The Polynesians migrated by boat to the Pacific in fairly recent times. We are quite sure they came from Indonesia, and yet they left no traces behind them, either. Did the Negroes, like the Polynesians, sail away *en masse* from their Asiatic homeland at a still earlier date? And while some went east to Melanesia, did others follow the African coast around the Horn and northward to the mouth of the Congo? If so, they had been preceded by the Negritos. If this hypothesis seems improbable, as it does, no one has yet suggested one more likely. The Negroes and Negritos remain the greatest of all the racial enigmas.

Part IV: THE ECONOMIC AND SOCIAL
INTERRELATIONSHIPS OF ORGANISMS

CHAPTER XXXII

THE PHYSICAL ENVIRONMENT OF ORGANISMS

We have seen that all organisms share a kinship based upon descent from a common ancestry far back in geologic time. In this kinship we have the clue to the essential similarity of protoplasmic composition and cell structure throughout the living world, as well as to the more detailed resemblances that are shown by organisms with a less remote common ancestor.

There is another sense in which all forms of life are related. This relationship consists in the intricately interwoven dependencies, competitions, and exploitations that exist among all forms of life, through their necessity of maintaining themselves by the capture and expenditure of energy. Here the relationship is primarily an *economic* one, far too complex to be known in full detail, yet clear enough in at least two respects to be undoubtable. Part of our knowledge of this relationship comes from a consideration of the "energy cycle," in which we can trace the maintenance of all life to utilization of energy that is ultimately derived from the sun. Another part comes from the incomplete but considerable portion of the economic and social interplay among organisms that biologists have been able to trace and to some extent to measure.

THE ENERGY CYCLE IN THE ORGANIC WORLD

All being alive involves a constant expenditure of energy, and precisely as in any engine, a part of this energy is never again available for any life processes. With no significant exception, all this energy upon which life depends comes from the sun. Until it is finally dissipated beyond the use of any protoplasmic device, it goes through a series of transformations and interchanges that support the entire organic world. In the sense that the energy from the sun is gradually lost and must be continuously replaced, the process is noncyclic; but in its turnover and reutilization of raw materials and in the often long series of transferences of energy from one organism to another—always with some loss of total usable energy—a cyclic relationship is well marked.

The original capture of energy. Roughly, about one-millionth of the sun's constant output of energy falls upon the earth in the form of radiation, and this condition has existed since the origin of the earth. Of this energy, some 0.3 to 3 per cent is conserved and utilized in the building up of protoplasm and the maintenance of life. The ability to capture and transform this energy is confined to the green plants and is due to the peculiar properties of chlorophyll, which is able to transform light energy into chemical energy and store it in the form of chemical compounds.

The raw materials involved.   Protoplasm and cell products are composed chiefly of carbon, oxygen, hydrogen, and nitrogen, together with smaller quantities of calcium, phosphorus, sodium, potassium, sulfur, magnesium, iodine, copper, iron, zinc, and a few other elements. These are distributed more or less generally over the earth, either as elements or as simple compounds, and, as such, contain no energy that is available to living organisms.

The storage of energy; food synthesis.   The building of organic molecules out of the simpler inorganic molecules and elements requires an expenditure of energy. Once synthesized, the complex organic molecules contain not only the original raw materials (atoms and simple combinations of atoms) but also the energy that was necessary for their construction. We have seen earlier that the complex molecules from which protoplasm is built include proteins or their component amino acids, carbohydrates, and fats, and that these same substances are the foods on which organisms depend for growth and all catabolic processes. Only plants have the ability to synthesize these substances from simple inorganic material, and only the green plants can perform the basic photosynthesis in which light is captured and stored as chemical energy. Once this synthesis has taken place and sugar is available, other plant tissues can utilize the energy in the sugar (or its derivatives) by oxidation, to build simple nitrogen compounds into amino acids and proteins, and simple carbohydrates into fats.

The green plant takes in carbon in the form of carbon dioxide from the air or in solution in water and takes in water from the soil. Carbon dioxide and water are combined by photosynthesis to form sugar, with the giving off of oxygen as a by-product. Nitrogen is obtained in the form of ammonia or nitrate salts in solution in the soil water, as are the necessary supplies of calcium, phosphorus, potassium, sulfur, etc. From these raw materials are synthesized all the food substances needed for building more protoplasm (growth and reproduction), for expenditure in maintaining life, and for storage against future needs. The energy of the sun is thus stored in the form of the complex molecules of protoplasm and plant products. Altogether this amounts to billions of tons of synthesized carbon compounds in existence on the earth.

The release of stored energy.   Free oxygen is not a necessity in any of these building-up processes and is, in fact, a waste or by-product of photosynthesis; but it is required for the utilization of the energy stored in food. All utilization of this energy is by means of oxidation, and oxygen is thus the key that unlocks the stored energy for use. As a consequence, all living things require a supply of oxygen and, except for some bacteria

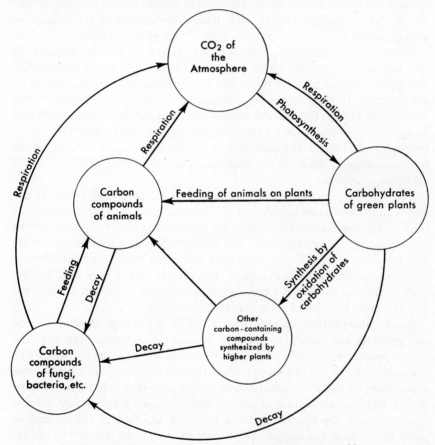

FIG. 32.1. Diagram of the carbon cycle in the organic world.

and a few fungi, algae, and parasitic animals, are dependent upon un-combined oxygen, which they acquire by respiration.[1]

The transference of stored energy. Once the plant has built up the higher carbon and nitrogen compounds, all other forms of life crowd in to share the product. Colorless plants, unable to utilize the sunlight, and animals, unable to synthesize any basic food substance, must exist

[1] The role of green plants in maintaining a supply of oxygen in the atmosphere was discussed on p. 171.

upon what they can secure directly or indirectly from the green plants. Many elaborate "food chains" have been developed, in some of which the last and most powerful animal, or the last and most remote parasite, obtains its food at fourth, fifth, sixth, or seventh hand after its original synthesis by the plant. The synthesized molecules may circulate so long as they never are broken below the level of simple sugars or amino acids; but in each organism and at each transference some of them must be broken below this level to provide animal and plant energy.

Moreover, not all protoplasm is eaten. Many plants and animals die and fall to the ground, where their dead substance would accumulate and remain locked up were it not for the processes of *decay* carried on by soil bacteria. In these processes the organic substances are broken down, with loss of heat to the soil and atmosphere, and the original elements and inorganic compounds are returned to the air and soil, where they again become available for the carbon and nitrogen cycles. A similar return is also constantly made by the respiration and the nitrogen catabolism of all living organisms.

The *soil* thus plays a very important part in the energy cycle. It not only maintains a huge population of bacteria, fungi, and other organisms that slowly but constantly oxidize the compounds that have escaped the catabolism of higher organisms, but it also serves as a storehouse for the end products of this decay until they are again taken up by the green plants to enter the synthesis part of the cycle. In fact, a very considerable part of the soil is formed by the decay-producing organisms themselves and the end products of their oxidative processes.

Some quantitative considerations. The preceding account of the energy cycle has been given largely in qualitative terms. Actually, the whole process is capable of being treated in a quantitative way. The utilization of the radiant energy from the sun to propel all life processes is governed by the same quantitative energy laws that hold for any engine or any physical utilization of power, and the same total energy is freed whether foods are burned under a boiler or oxidized in the animal or plant body. As in the engine, only a part of the energy released by oxidation within the organism is convertible into useful work, and the rest is lost as heat. The efficiency of the conversion in human muscle, some 20 to 33 per cent of the total energy available for work, compares favorably with that of the best existing steam engines.

SOME QUANTITATIVE VALUES

1 gram of sugar	by oxidation yields	4.1 Calories
1 gram of fat	by oxidation yields	9.4 Calories
1 gram of protein	by oxidation yields	5.6 Calories
1 gram of carbon	by oxidation yields	8.0 Calories
1 gram of hydrogen	by oxidation yields	34.5 Calories

One Calorie is the quantity of heat necessary to raise the temperature of 1 kilogram of water 1°C.[1]

One pound of bread will give approximately 1200 Calories.

Man needs 1500 to 5000 Calories per day.

One acre produces from 1 to 4 tons of carbohydrates per year.

One square meter of green-leaf surface synthesizes 1 to 2 grams of sugar per hour.

Bread contains 53.3 per cent carbohydrate, 9.1 per cent protein, 1.6 per cent fat, 35.0 per cent water (from which no energy is obtainable).

THE PHYSICAL ENVIRONMENTS IN WHICH ORGANISMS LIVE

In considering the various interrelationships that bind all the organic world into a huge economic and social complex, it is necessary to see something of the problems and needs imposed upon organisms by the conditions of the physical world in which they live. For purposes of analysis, we may subdivide the influences of physical environment into those of the *medium* in which the organisms live, and those of the *physical* (and *chemical*) *factors* that condition the medium and determine the reactions and metabolic processes of the organisms within it.

The Media in Which Organisms Live

All life of which we have any knowledge is confined to a shallow zone at the surface of our earth, where *soil*, *water*, and *air* meet and intermingle to a slight depth. Thus any organism must live in water or air or soil or in some combination of the three. These three media differ markedly in many physical properties, and each presents its own special problems to the organisms that live within it. The requirements for mechanical support and the problems of locomotion, adjustment to temperature changes, respiration, food gathering, and reproduction in aquatic, aerial, and terrestrial media are so unlike that they impose many structural adaptions upon organisms. Ordinarily we can determine from morphological inspection whether a given organism is fitted for life in water, on the land, in the soil, or for borderline or alternate existence in two (or more) of these media.

The medium and mechanical support. Because of the great buoying power of water, aquatic organisms can attain much greater size and weight and a much greater expanse of surface with a given amount of skeletal or supporting tissue than can land animals. This buoyancy of water is utilized in two quite different ways. On the one hand it has permitted the skeletonless development of such large marine organisms as the jellyfish and the octopus among animals and the giant kelps and

[1] More exactly, the amount of heat required to raise the temperature of 1 kilogram of water at 15°C. to 16°C.

other huge algae among the plants; on the other it has permitted the development of heavy armor and protective coverings, as in the starfishes and shelled mollusks, without the necessity for powerful locomotor organs. On land, the common earthworm and slug represent something like the upper limits in size for a skeletonless, motile organism; in the sea, animals with as little mechanical support may attain a weight of a ton or more.

Fig. 32.2. Support and locomotion in water. Marine life around the wharf piles at Vineyard Haven, Mass. Large organisms such as the jellyfish can exist without skeletal structures because of the buoyancy of water. The density of water makes streamlining a necessity for rapid motion, as illustrated by the fish and the squid. (*Courtesy American Museum of Natural History.*)

The Medium and Locomotion. Differences in the problems of locomotion in water, on land, and in air are even more marked than those of mechanical support. The motile aquatic animal has something of the same problems as the lighter-than-air dirigible. Although not lighter than the water (or very little lighter), its weight is supported by the medium and its locomotor organs have only to propel it through the water. Since, however, water is comparatively dense, movement through it meets with great resistance unless the force required to displace the water is largely balanced by the push gained when the water in turn displaces the moving object. As a consequence "streamlining" is highly important. All motile aquatic organisms, except those that simply drift and others that crawl slowly (Fig. 32.3) are distinguished by some type of streamlined form.

In terrestrial animals, on the other hand, locomotion involves not only propulsion but the support of the body in a medium that supports less than one-thirtieth of the body weight. Locomotor movements must involve either the overcoming of a relatively great friction with the earth (and this becomes increasingly difficult with each increment of size and weight) or the lifting of the body and the maintaining of its equilibrium as it is moved forward. All the larger and more motile terrestrial animals have the greater part of the body weight accounted for in *supporting and locomotor appendages.* Here streamlining is generally less important, although it becomes a factor in the adaptation of certain terrestrial animals to high rates of speed. Flight through the air demands still other highly specialized adaptations, notably the development of great skeletal rigidity with light weight, streamlining, and the acquisition of powerful flight muscles with skeletal modifications for their efficient origin and insertion.

The medium and fluctuations in temperature. The temperature relationships of water differ markedly from those of air or land. The most important of these differences are due to the specific heat of water and its latent heats of freezing and of evaporation. By the *specific heat* of water is meant the amount of heat (calories) required to raise the temperature of 1 gram of water 1°C. We have already seen that this amount is 1 calorie.[1] Water, with a specific heat of 1.0, may be compared with some other substances: lead, 0.012; mercury, 0.0334; carbon, 0.16; sand, 0.15; alcohol, 0.535. Only ammonia exceeds water in specific heat, and nearly all other substances have a markedly smaller value than water.

By *latent heat* is meant the amount of heat required to change water from its solid state to a fluid state and from a fluid state to a gaseous state without a change in temperature. To change 1 gram of ice to water (with the temperature kept at 0°C.) requires 80 calories, and when 1 gram of water freezes, it gives up 80 calories to the surrounding medium. The latent heat of evaporation is even greater. To change 1 gram of water to 1 gram of water vapor without a change of temperature requires

Fig. 32.3. A naked marine snail, *Dendronotus arborescens*, with large branched gills. This slow-moving creature has no need for streamlining. (*Courtesy American Museum of Natural History.*)

from 590 to 540 calories (depending upon the temperature), and this amount of heat is given up when the water vapor condenses. In this respect water is hardly approached by any other substance.

As a consequence of these properties the temperatures of bodies of water tend to be very stable and to change relatively slowly. In a locality where air and soil surface temperatures not infrequently change as much as 30°C. in 24 hours, the ponds and streams will in the same period show

[1] One-thousandth of a great Calorie—see footnote, p. 63.

very small changes in temperature, hardly more than 5°C. at most. In most parts of the United States the annual temperature range in lakes and deep ponds is only 15 to 30°C.

The medium and respiration. All organisms, irrespective of the medium in which they live, must be able to secure oxygen and excrete carbon dioxide. Except for a few protozoa, a few algae, and a number of bacteria, which are able to liberate combined oxygen from various of its compounds, all organisms depend upon a gaseous interchange with the medium that surrounds them to meet this need.

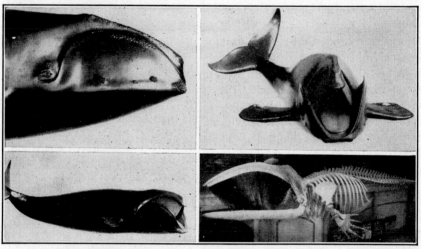

Fig. 32.4. One of the largest food strainers. The right whale (*Balaena bisayensis*) has "whalebone" (baleen) strainers hanging from the upper jaw. A mouthful of seawater is strained out through these, leaving the food organisms inside the mouth. The chief food of the whalebone whales is small shrimplike crustaceans which are often enormously abundant in ocean plankton. (*Courtesy American Museum of Natural History.*)

For terrestrial animals living in an atmosphere that is one-fifth oxygen and much less than 1 per cent carbon dioxide, the chief problems of respiration are to provide a sufficiently extensive respiratory surface for gaseous interchange and to protect such a surface from too great a water loss. (All membranes permeable to oxygen and carbon dioxide are also freely permeable to water vapor.) Many small terrestrial animals solve this problem by utilizing the body surface for respiration and avoid desiccation by remaining within permanently damp situations. A much more successful and less restricted terrestrial existence has been achieved in other animals by the development of special, *internal* respiratory surfaces that are protected from evaporation and must be aerated by special breathing movements. Such structures are the lungs of the vertebrates, the tracheae of insects, and the modified internal gills of arachnids ("book lungs") and of terrestrial mollusks.

For aquatic organisms, the interchange is between the gases of the tissues and the gases dissolved in the water. Since there is no evaporation problem and since mechanical support by the water permits a comparatively large development of surface area, the utilization of the body surface is much more practicable for aquatic than for terrestrial creatures. But even among aquatic organisms there are a number of factors that limit the usefulness of the body surface for respiration. Increasing size

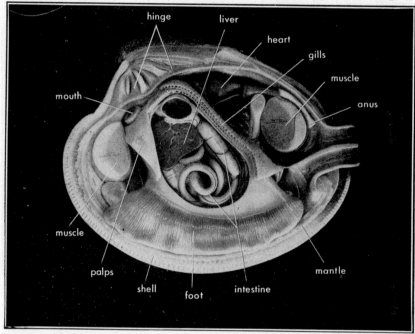

FIG. 32.5. A sedentary food strainer of shallow marine waters. A model of the hard-shell clam, *Venus mercenaria*, with the gills of the exposed side cut away to show the remaining structures. Beating of the cilia which cover the surfaces of the gills and mantle causes plankton-bearing water to flow into the spaces around the body and between the gills. The water enters pores in the gills and is carried by canals to the excurrent opening; the food particles remain on the surfaces of the gills and are swept forward into the mouth. (*Courtesy American Museum of Natural History.*)

or metabolic rate may finally make the surface area of the body inadequate for a sufficient gaseous exchange; motile or burrowing habits may require an integument too thick and tough to serve as a respiratory membrane; and the necessity for streamlining limits the amount of surface area that can be utilized for respiration. Under these conditions, the aquatic organism has to provide some special respiratory device, nearly always areas of thin tissue through which rapid gaseous interchange can be carried on between the body fluids and the water. These aquatic respiratory organs, or *gills*, are of many types. In fast-swimming or bottom-dwelling forms gills are usually enclosed in some protected chamber and aerated by special breathing movements.

Among the plants a somewhat comparable contrast between adaptations for terrestrial and aquatic life occurs. The necessity for respiration under drying conditions is met in terrestrial plants by a water- and respiration-proof *cuticle* and the development of *stomata*, which permit respiration and yet prevent undue water loss. In normally submerged plants the cuticle and stomata are absent. In many amphibious plants that are often partially submerged beneath oxygenless water, special air ducts are developed to carry atmospheric air to the submerged parts.

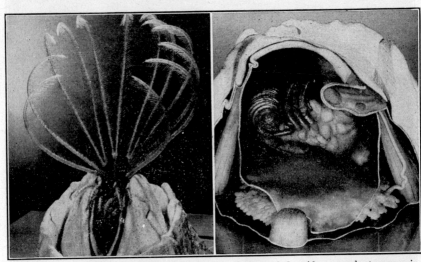

Fɪɢ. 32.6. The common rock or acorn barnacle, *Balanus balanoides*—a sedentary marine crustacean that casts a net to catch plankton. The greatly reduced body is attached by the head and enclosed in a shell of calcified plates, with a ventral door through which the feathery feet can be extended. The feet flicker in and out almost too fast to be seen, each time straining out of the water whatever plankton organisms happen to be there. On the left the barnacle is seen with feet extended, on the right with them coiled inside the closed shell. (*Courtesy American Museum of Natural History.*)

The medium and food manufacture in plants. The problems of obtaining the raw materials and energy for food manufacture are not greatly different for terrestrial and aquatic plants. The penetration of light into the water permits some photosynthesis to a depth of perhaps 100 meters or more, although the great majority of aquatic green plants are confined to the upper 10 to 20 meters. Carbon dioxide is present in solution in nearly all natural waters and is constantly being supplied by the respiration of living aquatic organisms and the decay of dead ones. The other requisites for food manufacture are also in solution and are available by diffusion through the permeable surface membranes of aquatic plants.

The medium and food capture by animals. Both terrestrial and aquatic animals show a wide variety in the kinds of foods they seek and in the methods employed to secure it. Aside from the associated problems of locomotion, one of the main differences between the water and the land is the relatively huge amount of food material that is dispersed in the upper layers of nearly all aquatic situations. This food is chiefly in the form of small living plants and animals, together with a considerable quantity of nonliving food—dead organisms or fragments of them. The minute drifting plant and animal life is collectively called the *plankton*. Existence of this abundant and constant food supply has permitted the development of an important aquatic fauna that feeds upon it. The members of the fauna include:

Motile Food Strainers. Among these are many fishes, some of the whales (Fig. 32.4), and a number of both small and medium-sized invertebrates. All are equipped with some type of *sieve* (frayed whalebone, gill rakers, or mouth or foot bristles), through which quantities of water are strained while the animals swim through the suspended food particles. These animals do not pursue individual prey but simply strain a sufficient quantity of water to yield the requisite food.

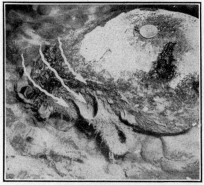

FIG. 32.7. A food strainer of swift streams. The curved, trumpetlike silken funnel of the caddis worm Neureclipsis, attached to a rock in a mountain brook in Pennsylvania. The larva lives in the narrow end of the funnel and feeds upon the food particles strained from the flowing water. (*Photo by Dr. Leonard N. Allison.*)

Nonmotile Food Strainers of Quiet Waters. These are sedentary forms, such as the sponges (Figs. 13.4 and B.3), oysters and clams (Fig. 32.5), protochordates (Figs. 27.5 and B.26) and others, that by means of cilia or flagella cause a slow, steady stream of water to flow through body passages that are equipped to retain the food particles carried in with the water current. Most of these organisms utilize the same water currents to bathe their respiratory surfaces and so combine breathing with food gathering.

Nonmotile Food Strainers of Flowing Waters. This is a smaller group very characteristic of riffles and gentle rapids in brooks and rivers. It is largely composed of aquatic insect larvae that either spin silken nets (Fig. 32.7) or, clinging to some stable support, hold sievelike body parts (bristly fringed forelegs or mouth parts) out into the current and wait for food particles that are brought to them.

Food Trappers or Stingers. The most conspicuous of these are the jellyfishes and other coelenterates, which, floating near the surface, trail tentacles armed with stinging cells through the densely populated subsurface waters and rely on chance to bring their food organisms into contact with the triggers that discharge poisoned stings. For the smaller jellyfishes the food organisms are members of the great floating assemblage of minute, rapidly reproducing plankton animals; for the larger coelenterates it is likely to be some of the host of smaller motile food strainers that feed in the subsurface waters.

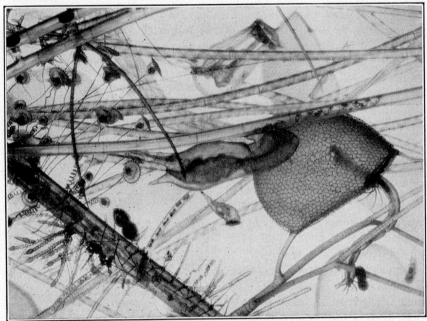

FIG. 32.8. Microscopic pond life—a community of interdependent plants and animals. The long cylinders are parts of filamentous green algae, mostly Spirogyra. The large object on the right is one of the trap-bladders of the bladderwort Utricularia, an aquatic flowering plant, with a captured insect larva. In the center a large rotifer sucks out the contents of a Spirogyra filament, cell by cell. Desmids, diatoms, and other small algae are attached to the larger objects, and at the left are stalked food-straining protozoa (Vorticella)—some extended, with beating cilia, and others with stalks contracted like coiled springs and with their cilia pulled in. (*Courtesy American Museum of Natural History.*)

Most of these aquatic schemes of food capture have counterparts among terrestrial and aerial animals, but proportionately they are far more important and support a far larger fauna than on land, where the pursuit and capture of individual prey is more generally the rule.

The medium and reproduction. We have already seen that external fertilization is essentially an aquatic adaptation and that all self-motile gametes are swimmers. We have also seen—in the vertebrates, at least— that the original oviparous habit involved water as a medium to protect the eggs from shock and dessication.

 Terrestrial life has either necessitated a return to the water for reproduction, the dependence upon permanent or recurrent water films in the terrestrial habitat (zygote formation in the mosses and ferns), or the development of special terrestrial adaptations. Among animals, the latter have been chiefly the habit of internal fertilization and the development of either shelled eggs or a viviparous habit. In addition, the terrestrial vertebrates have acquired special extraembryonic membranes (allantois and amnion) and the amniotic fluid, as reproductive adaptations for terrestrial existence. In plants ter-restrial adaptations for reproduc-tion have been associated with the emphasis placed upon the sporo-phyte generation and involve the development of spores or pollen grains that are passively carried by wind, water, or insects.

The Physical Factors That Affect Organisms

In whatever medium or media the organism lives, it is subjected to a number of physical conditions and energies that not only modify and condition the medium but also govern and limit the activities of the organism. Among these factors are temperature, quantity and intensity of light, humidity, currents in the medium, the pull of gravity, the pressure of the medium, and the presence and concentrations of various chemical substances.

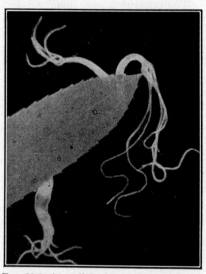

FIG. 32.9. A small fresh-water food stinger. Hydra extends its tentacles and waves them gently through the water. Small plankton organisms that touch them are stung by the poisonous nematocysts imbedded in some of the ectodermal cells, and are held to the tentacles by the nematocyst threads while the arms are contracting and the prey is being pushed into the mouth. (*Courtesy General Biological Supply House, Inc.*)

Temperature. Measured temperatures within our universe range from close to absolute zero ($-263°$C.) to more than $6000°$C., the approximate surface temperature of the sun. Active life processes, how-ever, are limited to a range between a few degrees below $0°$C. and some 60 or 70° above. Quiescent states, in which an organism may survive for a time with a nearly complete cessation of metabolic processes, would extend these limits perhaps a score or more degrees in each direction. For any one kind of organism, the *limits of toleration* for temperature extremes are narrower, usually very much narrower, than those indicated above, and somewhere within its own specific limits of toleration each organism has an *optimum* temperature most advantageous for its needs.

The limits of toleration and the optima of different species vary widely. Some species have wide limits; others have very narrow ones; for some the limits of toleration lie within the range of temperatures characteristic of the tropics, while for others the limits are within the temperature ranges of the temperate or boreal climates. Here we find a part of the explanation of the geographic distribution of numerous organisms, both plants and animals.

Temperatures also play an important part in governing the daily activities and habitat selections of organisms. This is shown if we watch a wandering animal when it encounters a difference in the temperature of its medium. If the new temperature is farther from the optimum than the old, the animal will ordinarily show an avoiding reaction and turn back or away from it; if it is nearer the optimum than the old, the animal ordinarily moves into the new situation.

Such reactions or turnings in response to temperature are typical of a large number of more or less fixed and automatic responses that organisms make to stimuli from their environment. All these automatic responses are termed *taxes*,[1] or *tropisms* (Greek, *trop*, "a turning"), and the particular turnings in response to temperature are termed *thermotropisms*—*negative thermotropism* when the organism turns away from a given temperature, *positive thermotropism* when it turns toward a given temperature. Thus *Epiphragma solatrix*, a crane fly found in Florida, if in a temperature of 15°C., is ordinarily negatively thermotropic to a temperature of 10°C. but positively thermotropic to a temperature of 20°C.

Humidity. Another environmental factor of much importance to many terrestrial organisms is the amount of moisture in the air. All the space occupied by air has a capacity for water vapor. Since the molecules both of the air and of the water vapor are widely dispersed, a given cubic space, at a given temperature and pressure, has a water capacity that is independent of the air present. When an air space contains less than its capacity of water vapor, it tends to take up water by *evaporation* from all available sources. Among such sources is the water contained in living organisms. Organisms have very different degrees of protection against water loss, and we find that they have very different limits of toleration for the water capacity of the air space about them.

One of the most useful measurements of the amount of water vapor in the air is the *relative humidity*—the percentage of saturation with water vapor that exists for a given situation at a given time. The lower the relative humidity the more rapidly and the more powerfully will evaporation go on; the greater the relative humidity the less difficulty will an organism have in retaining its water content. At midday during May, various types of natural situations in northern Florida vary from

[1] Pronounced *tax'ees;* singular, *taxis.*

a relative humidity of 15 to 25 per cent (open sand-scrub and blackjack oak habitats) to 85 to 95 per cent (below the shrubs and herbage of deep woods and swamps). The lower humidities are far beyond the limits of toleration for amphibians and many insects, and these animals show a type of *hydrotropism* that keeps them within areas of relative humidity as near as possible to their optima. Some of the lizards and insects of this region, on the other hand, are well adapted against water loss and move freely into or live only in the xeric sand-scrub areas.

Humidity and temperature together. So far we have considered temperature and humidity separately. If one wished to make the simplest and clearest experiments concerning their effects on the behavior of organisms, he would attempt to hold the one constant while he varied the other in his experimental setups. But in nature conditions are generally not simple. When both temperature and humidity are varying, it is often impossible to be certain which is the more stimulating or limiting factor. Moreover, for a given organism the limits of toleration and the optimum for temperature change with changes in humidity, and vice versa. Man, for instance, at a humidity of 20 to 30 per cent, can tolerate for several hours temperatures that would be quickly fatal at a humidity of 80 per cent or more. Air-conditioning engineers have found that for each temperature there is a certain optimum humidity within which man is most comfortable and works with greatest efficiency. For each temperature this optimum humidity lies at a different point on the scale of percentage of saturation.

Light. Aside from furnishing all the energy for photosynthesis, light has many important effects on the reactions and behavior of organisms. Many organisms have limits of toleration and optima for its various intensities, and much of the behavior of both plants and animals can be traced to *positive* or *negative phototropisms* to certain of these intensities. The positive phototropism of moths, beetles, and flies to lights at night is particularly interesting in view of the fact that nearly all these same insects show a marked negative phototropism to all but the weakest intensities of daylight. Practically all green plants show a marked positive phototropism in the direction of growth of their green parts. This is often strikingly conspicuous in plants grown indoors, and in the differences of shape that develop in two trees of the same kind when one grows in a forest and the other in an open field.

The behavior of many organisms is also influenced by the proportion of light and lightless hours in the day. This is most conspicuous in those regions of the earth where marked differences in length of day are a part of the change in the seasons. Changes from summer parthenogenesis to autumnal bisexual reproduction in certain insects and the migratory behavior of certain birds have been found to be largely regulated by changes in the relative amounts of daylight and darkness in each 24 hours.

Other factors of the physical environment. Some of the ways in which temperature, humidity, and light modify the environment and influence the behavior and distribution of organisms have been briefly described. With these for examples, some of the other important factors may be even more briefly mentioned. All these (except gravity and perhaps contact) exhibit a wide range of intensities, for which organisms have various limits of toleration and optima and to which many organisms respond by positive or negative tropisms.

Pressure of the medium is of most importance to the organisms that live in the sea or in deep lakes, where some species are limited to the surface waters and others to various levels in the greater depths. Some of the whales appear to show the widest limits of toleration to pressure, and range from the surface to depths of several hundred fathoms. There is little evidence that air pressure, as such, is very important in setting limits of toleration for terrestrial animals, but tropistic behaviors toward varying intensities of pressure are shown by a number of forms. Reactions to pressure of the medium are termed *barotropisms*.

Currents in the medium are most important for aquatic organisms, although a considerable number of insects show reactions to air currents. Nearly all fish automatically head into a current, changing their positions promptly with each change in its direction. This is easily demonstrated by placing a number of small fish in a pan of water and then stirring the water so that it whirls. If the pan contains both stream and pond fishes, the former usually show a much more delicate and precise reaction. Reactions to the current in the medium are termed *rheotropisms*—positive if the organism faces or moves against the current; negative if it avoids or attempts to escape from it.

Various *chemicals* that are dissolved or diffused in the medium are important factors, both because reactions (*chemotropisms*) on the part of organisms are produced, and because many of these substances may exist in concentrations above or below the limits of toleration of some or all organisms. Among the very important substances in solution in water are oxygen, carbon dioxide, various calcium salts, and hydrogen and hydroxyl ions. Less generally important, but of particular interest from the standpoint of conservation, are the vast quantities of sewage and of poisonous mine and factory wastes that, through thousands of miles of the streams of the United States, have come to exceed the limits of toleration of nearly all forms of life.

Contact. Numerous animals exhibit a positive reaction to contact with some comparatively stable surface. This reaction (positive *thigmotropism*) tends to keep a considerable number of invertebrates and perhaps some of the smaller vertebrates hidden in crevices or beneath protecting rocks and leaves when they are not in search of food. Nearly all the crayfishes and lobsters furnish very good examples of this type of reaction.

An interesting and characteristic society of small animals that live at the surface of quiet waters (marsh pools and small ponds) is partially to be accounted for by the positive thigmotropism of many of its members to the air-water surface film. This film is sufficiently stable to serve as a "ceiling," where small aquatic animals may cling or move about, and to serve as a floor for a rather diverse population of small arthropods.

Gravity. Many plants exhibit very clear-cut reactions to gravity. The embryonic root at germination always exhibits a very strong *positive geotropism* and "insists" on growing downward, even though the young plant is turned upside down after growth has begun. The embryonic leaf shoot, on the other hand, shows a definitely *negative geotropism* and grows upward, even if this necessitates overcoming considerable interference. The bending of the root or stem results from unequal rates of growth on its opposite sides. Such differential growth is caused by localization, under the influence of gravity or light, of definite growth-stimulating substances—hormones called *auxins*. In general, geotropism is more characteristic of plants than of animals, but a number of animals show a definite geotropism.

The Soil as an Environmental Complex

Soil may be defined as the layer of mixed mineral and organic material, penetrated by plant roots, that covers at least 95 per cent of the land surface. It lies at the contact of the atmosphere with the lithosphere, and is subject to repeated wetting and partial drying, to leaching in its upper layers and cementation in its middle and lower layers, to changes of temperature, and to the influences of the plants and animals that live upon and within the soil.

It would appear logical to consider the soil as one of the media in or upon which organisms live, but, unlike air or water, the soil is so complex and varies so widely from place to place that in its relationships to the organism it combines the roles of medium and modifying factors. We have already seen that the soil is the storehouse for a large list of necessities for organic life and that its characteristic biota of bacteria, fungi, and animal life has a very important part to play in the energy cycle. Just as temperature, light, and humidity may vary widely in intensity and quantity and thus produce widely different environmental conditions, the variations in soil are likewise of great importance in governing both the geographic and local distribution of organisms.

In order to appreciate the complexity of the soil and its great variability it is necessary to know something of the parent materials and the processes

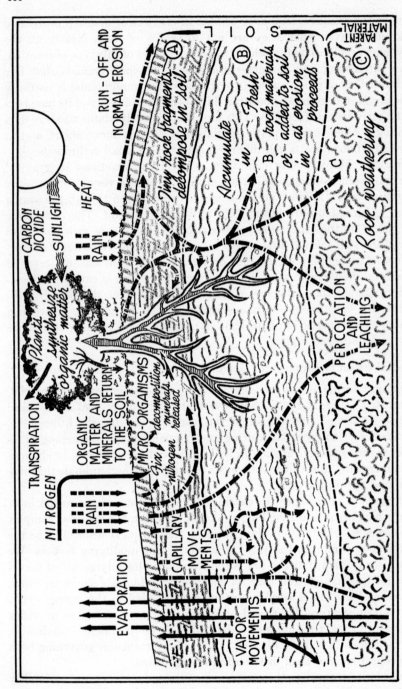

Fig. 32.10. The principal dynamic processes in a soil, much simplified. (Redrawn from *Climate and Man, Yearbook of the U.S. Department of Agriculture for* 1941.)

and agents that produce and modify it. The most important of these are
(1) the *kind of rock* from which it is largely derived; (2) the *kind of climate*
(temperature, rainfall, etc.) in which it has been formed; (3) the *type of
vegetation* that has grown upon it; (4) the *length of time* the weathering
processes have continued; (5) its *texture* (kinds and sizes of particles);
(6) *aeration and drainage;* (7) the *predominating processes* that have
operated and the order in which they have occurred. We shall consider
only a few of these very briefly, to illustrate something of the possibilities
for variation in the resulting types of soils and to point out some of the
factors that result in the belts and zones of soil groups illustrated in
Fig. 32.11.

When the surface of the land is first exposed to weathering processes,
it consists either of bedrock or (very locally) of unconsolidated marine
or fresh-water deposits. Under the action of wind, water, gravity, changes
in temperature, and chemical solution, the rock disintegrates and crum-
bles into various-sized particles that may be roughly classed as gravel,
sand, silt, and clay.

Gravel particles are more than 1.0 mm. in diameter.

Sand particles range in diameter from 1.0 to 0.05 mm.

Silt particles range in diameter from 0.05 to 0.005 mm.

Clay particles are less than 0.005 mm. in diameter.

As these particles accumulate, they are subjected to the action of
soil water. If rainfall is distinctly greater than evaporation, the soluble
salts of calcium, magnesium, potassium, etc., will tend to be carried
down beyond the reach of plant roots and thus lessen the productivity
of the soil. On the other hand, if the rainfall is distinctly less than evaporation, the soil water will move *upward,* and the soluble salts will accumulate on the surface, producing alkali soils that are unproductive
because of the too great concentration of salts and the too low moisture
content. In regions where rainfall and evaporation rates are more nearly
balanced, the soluble salts produced by weathering tend to remain in
the soil and form a storehouse from which plants may freely draw. Here
plant life, and consequently animal life, is abundant, and the organic
accumulations from the dead bodies and the catabolic wastes of plants
and animals are added to and retained by the soil.

Soil types and soil groups. Since the type of soil is largely determined by the climate, we find that different types of soils are characteristic of different climatic belts and zones. This is illustrated by Fig.
32.11. Such a map can show only the very broad and generalized regions
of different soil types. Since there are many local peculiarities of climate
and even more local variations in rate and sequence of soil-forming
processes (because of drainage, local geological history, etc.), each of the
soil areas shown on the map may, and usually does, contain numerous

patches and streaks of soils that have not yet reached the typical end condition for that climate.

In general the soils east of the Mississippi River have a low content of soluble salts, because precipitation is greater than evaporation. West of the Mississippi evaporation becomes greater than rainfall (except for restricted areas in the mountains and along the Pacific Coast). In the humid regions east of the Mississippi the soils generally contain less of

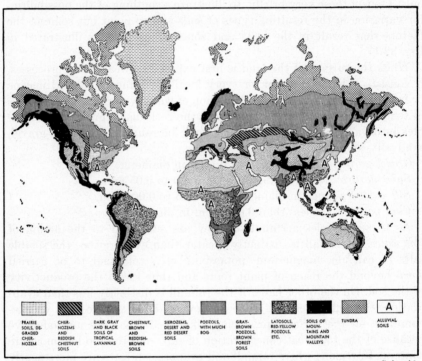

FIG. 32.11. The great soil groups of the world. (*From Charles E. Kellogg, courtesy Scientific American.*)

the soluble calcium and magnesium salts than did the parent materials, and since iron and aluminum compounds are less soluble than the calcium salts, the soil is chiefly composed of aluminum and iron compounds. In the less humid areas west of the Mississippi, on the other hand, the soluble calcium and magnesium tend to accumulate near the surface, and the soils contain a higher concentration of calcium and magnesium salts and a somewhat lower proportion of aluminum and iron compounds than the parent material.

The Chernozem, Chestnut, Brown, and Sierozem soils are all examples of the calcium-rich groups (*pedocals*); the Podsol, Gray-brown Forest, Prairie, and Red and Yellow soils are examples of the calcium-poor group (*pedalfers*). The warm and humid climate of the tropics produces zonal (climatic) soils known as *laterites*, or *latosols*, which are particularly high in iron and aluminum.

It will be noted that there are a number of *soil groups* in both the calcium-rich and the calcium-poor classifications. This is due largely to the various kinds of ratios between rainfall and evaporation. At the one extreme, evaporation is greatly in excess of rainfall; at the other, rainfall is greatly in excess of evaporation. Moreover, some other factors enter in. The physically active parts of the soil are the humus (derived from organic materials) and clay particles. Altogether, these have an enormous surface area and usually possess electronegative charges. Consequently, they tend to hold the positively charged molecules of calcium and magnesium against the leaching effect of heavy rainfall and so keep them available for the plants. Thus it is possible for certain types of soils to be subjected to heavy rainfall and still produce a luxuriant growth of vegetation year after year. The more productive soils may be thought of as composed of relatively insoluble mineral particles coated with gelatinous organic and inorganic colloidal films to which enormous numbers of soil organisms cling.

The Prairie, Chernozem, Gray-brown, and Savanna soils are generally rich in soluble raw materials for food manufacture, and because of their generally favorable moisture conditions plants growing upon them are able to utilize great amounts of the sun's energy. The areas of these soils (Fig. 32.11) represent the greatest *energy-capturing zones*, and it is here that we find the great grain, grass, and cattle-producing regions of the United States. The fertile lands of Russia, Argentina, and Africa lie in belts of very similar climate and soils. The once vast bison herds of North America, the huge cattle production of the Argentine, and the tremendous animal life of Africa were (or are) possible because of the luxuriant grass production in regions where abundant materials for photosynthesis coincide with an adequate supply of soil moisture.

CHAPTER XXXIII

THE BIOTIC ENVIRONMENT OF ORGANISMS

We have seen something of the diverse physical media and factors that the organism encounters, and by which much of its activity and existence is controlled. However, no organism "liveth unto itself." It has a variety of inescapable relationships with the other organisms about it, which involve various types of feeding-upon, being-fed-upon-by, competition-with, and cooperation-with activities, as well as many less obvious and less direct interdependencies. The "other organisms" include individuals both of its own species and of other species that may belong to different genera, families, orders, or phyla and often to the other organic kingdom. Some of the more conspicuous of these biotic relationships are outlined below.

The biotic potential. One of the very important considerations in fixing the organism's role in the plant and animal society in which it lives is its own *potential reproductive rate*, or *biotic potential*, which is, theoretically at least, a constant for a given species, dependent upon that species' inherited *sex ratio, number of young per female*, and *number of generations per unit of time*. It may be stated as a formula:

$$PZ^n(R^{n-1}) = \text{biotic potential (for a given unit of time)}$$

where P = number of females started with.

$\quad n$ = number of generations in a given unit of time.

$\quad R$ = proportion of females in each generation ($= 0.5$ when sexes are equal; 1 when all females reproduce by parthenogenesis).

$\quad Z$ = number of young produced by each female.

Since n and Z are theoretical maxima, they could obtain only under optimum conditions for all the factors that affect the species in question and are, at best, difficult to determine. However, sufficiently accurate approximations can be obtained to show the almost incredibly great potential reproductive ability of even slow-breeding organisms and the tremendous differences of biotic potential that exist among different kinds and groups of organisms.

Biotic potential versus environmental resistance. When one calculates some of the approximate values for biotic potential for various organisms, it is at once obvious that no organism ever does approach its potential reproductive rate. L. O. Howard, of the U.S. Bureau of Entomology, determined the biotic potential of the common house fly living under optimum conditions in a laboratory in Washington, D.C. He used experimentally determined values for n, R, and Z: $n = 7$ generations per year; $R = 0.5$; and $Z = 120$ eggs per female. With these values, a pair of flies should be potentially able to produce $1 \times 120^7 \times 0.5^6 = 5{,}598{,}-860{,}000{,}000$ progeny in the course of a year.

Actually, of course, nothing like this could happen, not because the values or calculations are false, but because optimum conditions could not be maintained. Even if temperature, humidity, light, and other physical factors should stay at optimum, limits to food and space would soon produce such an intense competition that only a portion of each generation (beyond the first few) could possibly survive. Moreover, there are many organisms that feed upon flies, and not only would their toll on the population greatly cut down the number of flies that would live to produce offspring but the population of fly-eating organisms would tend to increase rapidly as the fly population increased.

Population Size. Even though the biotic potential of any organism is never attained, the concept and the actual or approximate values for a given species have a much greater use than as mere exercises in arithmetic. Since the biotic potential (as an inherent maximal reproductive rate) is a constant for each species, we can use it to gain an idea of the toll that the total environment levies on that species. This is because the existing population of any species of organism—the number of bass in a given lake, for instance—is a quotient of its biotic potential and the resistance it encounters from all adverse environmental factors. It may be stated as

$$\frac{\text{Biotic potential}}{\text{Environmental resistance}} = \text{existing population}$$

Since the biotic potential may be determined (at least approximately) by experiment and observation and the existing population may be counted or estimated, we can thus obtain a quantitative measure of the total resistance of all environmental factors.

When the English sparrow was first introduced into this country, it was freed from its native European competitors and enemies, and for a time it multiplied at a tremendous rate. In 1889, when agriculturists and others were alarmed by its rapid increase and spread across the country, it was estimated that a single pair of English sparrows could in 10 years give rise to 275,716,983,698 descendants. Gradually this species met a stronger environmental resistance. This was partly due to the development of sparrow-eating habits by a number of our hawks, owls, and shrikes; partly to decreasing food supply brought about by changed agricultural practices and the decrease of the horse population in towns and cities; and partly (once all suitable physical environments had been occupied) to the great competition for food and nesting sites that developed within the sparrow population.

From 1916 through 1920, the U.S. Biological Survey carried on a detailed bird census. They found that in the North Central states there was an average English sparrow population of 11 nesting pairs to 100 acres; and within this 5-year period the population fluctuated between 9 and 13 pairs per 100 acres. According to the estimate made in 1889, each 100 acres should have produced 575 sparrows each year, but in the period studied they were just holding their own. In the Northeastern states the environmental resistance was greater, for there the nesting pairs averaged but 5, with a fluctuation between 3 and 7 pairs per 100 acres during this same 5-year period.

Numerous examples are on record of some imported insect that, freed from its native parasites and predators, in the presence of an abundant food supply, increased at a rate that seemed comparable to the calculated biotic potential, but when its native enemies had been imported, became reduced to a small, stable population.

Population Fluctuations. Another illustration of the relationship between biotic potential and environmental resistance is found in the sporadic outbursts of tremendous numbers of certain animals from their normal habitats and geographic boundaries, to occupy and often to become great pests in adjoining territories. Plagues of rats, field mice, and locusts that arrive in countless hordes, eat the country bare of standing crops, and then move on or soon die off are well known. They illustrate the tremendous potential reproductive power that can quickly produce a thousandfold increase in a normal population whenever the environmental resistance is reduced by a few seasons of unusually favorable conditions. On a small local scale such rapid fluctuations in the numbers of various (often nonpest) species are common and may be seen in most years in nearly any region.

Some Biotic Factors of the Environmental Resistance

We have already seen, at least by implication, that a part of the environmental resistance is due to the physical environment. Any departure from the optimum conditions of temperature, humidity, light, etc., operates to increase the time required to produce another generation and to decrease the number of offspring. We have also referred to the competition for food and nesting sites and the mortality that is caused by parasites and predators. These last are examples of biotic factors of environmental resistance that are discussed in more detail below.

The resistance produced by the organisms that form a part of the individual's environment is in part direct and more or less evident, and in part indirect and difficult to discover or evaluate. The more direct restraints placed upon an organism by the other forms of life about it are those of the *predators* that prey upon it, the *parasites* that live at its expense, and the *competitors* that vie with it for various limited necessities for existence and reproduction.

Predators and parasites. By a *predator*, we mean an animal that catches and kills another animal: wolves, foxes, weasels, spiders, and snakes are familiar examples. The food strainers and trappers referred to on pages 551 and 552, and a few plants such as the bladderworts, sundews, and pitcher plants that trap animals for food are hardly predators in the restricted sense but may also be classified here. By a *parasite*, we mean an organism that lives on or in the tissues of another organism, the *host*, feeding on the host's tissues, its digested food, or the products of its metabolism. Parasitic habits and adaptations are more varied than predatory habits; parasites include both *ectoparasites*, such as fleas and lice, and *endoparasites*, such as tapeworms, hookworms, the plasmodium of malaria, and literally thousands of other animal and plant organisms.

Fig. 33.1. *Cordyceps dipterigena*, a parasitic fungus that attacks only flies. (*Photo by Prof. E. B. Mains.*)

The plant and animal kingdoms furnish innumerable examples of parasites and of host organisms. Plants parasitizing plants, plants parasitizing animals, animals parasitizing plants, and animals parasitizing animals are all common and well-known phenomena. Both predators and parasites take a tremendous toll of the organisms that they feed upon and tend to increase their proportionate toll whenever circumstances permit the abundance of their prey or their hosts to increase.

Competitors. Many of the necessities that any organism requires for continued existence are limited in quantity and distribution. Suitable food or raw materials for food manufacture, nesting sites, areas in which physical factors do not exceed the limits of toleration, and refuges in which animals may escape their predators are all limited in amount or in extent. In any situation some of the necessities for existence may be much less restricted than others. The necessary oxygen for respiratory needs is practically unlimited, at least in terrestrial situations, and the space in a field suitable for ant nests or gopher burrows is not badly crowded. Similarly, we find that there is much unoccupied space for grasses and herbage on the floor of a well-shaded forest, however crowded the individual grass plants may be on a lawn.

Here we see a principle in operation that is often termed *Leibig's law of the minimum*. Every organism has a rather long list of necessities, and it is *that necessity that exists in minimal quantity* that produces the most stringent competition and limits the size of population. The ant population in a field is probably limited by the food supply; and the

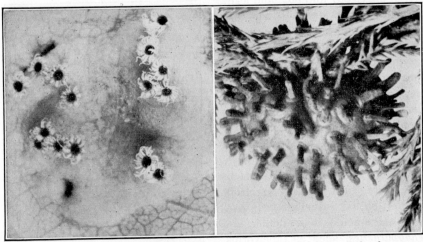

Fig. 33.2. A parasitic fungus. Gymnosporangium, that has two hosts. Left, cluster-cup (aecial) stage on apple. Spores from this stage infect juniper, producing the peculiar object at the right—the teliospore stage. Spores from this stage again infect the apple. (*Photo by Prof. E. B. Mains.*)

severe physical conditions and low supply of raw materials for food manufacture limit the grass and herb population of an oak scrub. On the forest floor, the minimal necessity is probably light, although grasses are poorly equipped in several ways to compete with the typical forest plants.

Competition occurs both between the individuals of the same species and between individuals of different species. Because the requirements of all members of the same species are alike in practically all respects, *intraspecific* competition is particularly severe, as it is between different species that have very similar total requirements. *Interspecific* competition in most instances, however, is only partial, and each species can usually find at least restricted areas or habitats where conditions are nearer to its own optima than to those of its rivals and in which it therefore has some advantage over the latter.

Some indirect restraints.   The indirect restraints that may be placed upon an organism by its biotic environment are variable and fluctuating but nonetheless important. Ordinarily, for instance, the martin of the Canadian coniferous forests is not molested to any important extent by the Canada lynx that feeds extensively upon the varying hare of this region. But the hare population is subject to periodic epidemics that tremendously reduce its numbers, and at these times the martin not only finds severe competition from the lynx but is actually preyed upon by it.

Another example is the relationship that appears to exist between the bobwhite quail and the cotton rat of our southeastern coastal plain. Here the rats, when they are very numerous, may become an enemy of the quail through feeding upon the latter's eggs and young. The rats are the usual and preferred food of a number of hawks and owls that do not ordinarily molest the quail to any appreciable extent. When, however, the rat population is for any reason markedly reduced, the hawks and owls that had depended upon them for a food supply turn to the quail and may become an important check upon the quail population. It would thus appear that the rat population, if it is either too great or too small, affects the quail adversely; but in some intermediate and average size it is beneficial in forming a "buffer population" that protects the quail from injurious predation by the hawks and owls. If this relationship is real—and there is much evidence to substantiate it—the various parasites that live upon the cotton rats and those that live upon the hawks and owls must also play an indirect but often an actual part in the quail's environment.

Highly probable or partly substantiated instances of such indirect relationships are very common, and there is little doubt that any form of wildlife, if it were sufficiently studied, would show the same sorts of indirect dependencies upon other organisms. The complexity of these relationships, however, and the continual fluctuations in their intensity make them exceedingly difficult to demonstrate or to evaluate quantitatively.

One of the important features of all biotic resistance is that it is very variable and that it tends to become increasingly severe whenever the organism's reproductive potential is temporarily freed from restraints that ordinarily hold it in check. If, for instance, any species encounters a period of particularly favorable physical conditions, the resultant drop in environmental resistance permits a prompt increase in population size. Sooner or later average or adverse physical conditions will return, but not because of any influence exerted by the rise in population. The biotic resistance, on the other hand, tends to increase with and as a consequence of the increase in the organism's population size. For this increase intensifies intraspecific competion, and favors an increase in the populations of predators and parasites that feed upon the organism.

This tendency of the biotic resistance to hold an organism's population size in check when the physical resistance decreases leads to some rather paradoxical relationships that appear to be well substantiated by field observations. There is evidence, for instance, that an extreme reduction in the numbers of an organism's normal predators may be actually harmful for that organism. In an environment in which food and physical factors show a wide seasonal (or other periodic) fluctuation, an organism, if freed from nearly all biotic resistance, will tend to build up so large a population size in good times that it will completely exhaust all food supplies before the next adverse season has ended.

Something very like this was shown some years ago by the elk herd at Jackson Hole, Wyo. Here the abnormally large summer increase in the protected elk population, freed from the normal predation of mountain lions and bears, resulted in such a large winter herd that they quickly exhausted the limited winter forage and were faced with wholesale starvation. Fortunately, in this case, the local forest rangers met the emergency by the importation of enough hay to tide the elk over until the reappearance of the next spring's abundant natural forage.

COOPERATIVE RELATIONS AMONG ORGANISMS

By no means all of an organism's relationships to the other forms of life about it are adverse or inimical. Many types of interdependency involve cooperation and mutual aid. Some of these cooperative relationships are among individuals of widely different species, or of different orders, classes, phyla, or even kingdoms. Others are shown by the many kinds and degrees of social behavior that exist among individuals of the same species—the herds, coveys, schools, flocks, packs, and unnamed family groups that confer various sorts of mutual advantage to some or all of their members.

Cooperation among widely different forms of life shows almost every gradation from close, often obligate, partnerships in which the benefit received by each of the participants is clear-cut and unmistakable, to cases that are difficult to distinguish from true parasitism. An example of the truly mutual relationship termed *symbiosis* (Greek, "a living together") is shown by the lichens, a widespread group of lower plants in which each "individual" plant comprises an alga intimately associated with a fungus. The chlorophyll of the algal cells carries on photosynthesis, and the tissues of the fungus protect the delicate algal cells and collect and store water and minerals for their needs. Both the alga and the fungus are maintained by the anabolic profits of the partnership. A somewhat similar example is shown in the relationship between many of the legumes, such as clover, alfalfa, and peas, and the nitrogen-fixing bacteria that live within their root nodules. The legumes provide protection and the requisite food supplies for the bacteria and receive, in return, a rich supply of available nitrogen for their own growth.

Comparable examples are also common among animals. The termites (Fig. B.21G), notorious devourers of wood, are unable to digest the

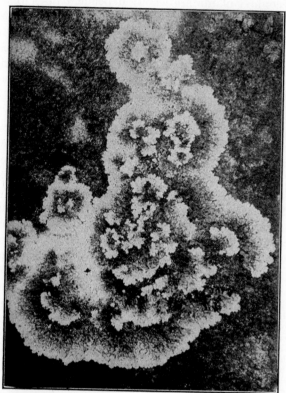

Fig. 33.3. An encrusting lichen, Parnelia species, growing on rock in Chester County, Pa. Lichens are made up of two simple plants, one a green alga and the other a fungus, growing intermingled in close symbiotic relation with each other. Encrusting lichens are characteristic pioneer plants on exposed rock surfaces; by their aid to the weathering process they help to make soil and to produce conditions suitable for other organisms. (*Photo by Prof. A. M. Laessle.*)

woody tissues that they chew and ingest. Instead, they are dependent upon the unicellular organisms that inhabit their intestines for the enzymes that will make the woody pulp available for their own tissues. A termite deprived of its intestinal symbionts will starve in spite of a plentiful supply of wood, whereas the unicellular organisms that provide the enzymes depend upon the termite for protection, moisture, and a continuous supply of wood in the proper physical condition for digestion.

Only slightly less intimate relationships exist between many species of plants and of insects. The *insect visitors to flowers* are rewarded by nectar or pollen that in many instances forms the insects' staple, or even sole, food supply. In return, the insect, in its journey from blossom to blossom, carries pollen from anthers to pistils and so effects the fertilization of the plant's ova. So close is this relationship that a great many species of both insects and plants are wholly dependent upon this mutual ex- change for their continued existence. Many of the specific structural characters of both insects and flowers and many of the specific psychological behaviors of insects are special adaptations to some particular insect-flower interdependency.

Various intermediate relationships also occur, in which one member receives much more than 50 per cent of the total benefit. Nearly every ant and termite nest houses a number of so-called "guests"—other species of arthropods that live in the nest, and that vary in role from more or less innocuous scavengers to definite social parasites living on the food gath- ered by the ants for their own use, much as rats, mice, and roaches live at the expense of man. Such social parasitism, *commensalism*, may be combined with other, and symbiotic, relationships, and it is not always possible to distinguish between the two.

Another rather special type of interspecific relation- ship is exemplified by the *"slave-making" habits* of certain ants. These slave makers raid the nests of certain other ant species, kill or drive off the adult ants, and carry back to their own nests the young (pupae) of their victims. These young, when they mature, become a part of the social organization in the nests of their captors and perform a number of essential duties for the maintenance of the group.

FIG. 33.4. The root system of a young bean plant, with nu- merous tubercles or nodules in which ni- trogen-fixing bacteria live symbiotically with the green plant. (*From Haupt, An In- troduction to Botany.*)

Although cooperative relationships among individuals of the same species reach their highest development among ants, termites and men, representatives from nearly every order of the vertebrates and arthropods show at least some degree of *social behavior*. In many instances such intraspecific cooperation is seasonal, as in the hibernating assemblages that are formed in various species of insects, amphibians, and reptiles, the winter herds of deer that band together for protection, and the wolf packs that gather for winter hunting. Other groups appear to be nearly or wholly permanent, as the beaver colonies that build and maintain dams, houses, and canals, and the prairie dog "towns" of hundreds or even thousands of individuals. Many or most of these groups are primarily family aggregations, resulting from the long-continued association of parents and offspring. Others have their nucleus in a family group that has been joined by unattached individuals or smaller groups in the same

FIG. 33.5. A small swift trout stream in northern Michigan, showing a pool in the foreground and a riffle just above the bend in the stream. (*Photo by Dr. Justin W. Leonard.*)

area. In all instances the group tends to confer some type of advantage on its members that is not equally available to the isolated individual.

BIOTIC COMMUNITIES AND THEIR SUCCESSIONS

As a result of the many sorts of interrelationships that obtain between organisms and their physical and biotic environments, the plants and animals of any region tend to group themselves into a series of "biotic communities."

The simplest of these are the large number of *primary communities* that are based upon the similarity of responses shown by their members to certain intensities of various physical factors. For instance, in most creeks the processes of stream erosion and the nature of the eroded material have resulted in an almost invariable sequence of swift, shallow riffles and deep, quiet pools (Fig. 33.5). In the former, the water is well aerated and flows over a clean pebble and coarse sand bottom; in the latter, the water moves slowly past silty margins and over a mud- and silt-covered bottom.

NATURE'S HOUSE THAT JACK BUILT

this is the
HAWK

that eats the

SNAKES
that eat the

FROGS
that eat the

HOPPERS
that eat the

GRASS
that grows in the

EARTH
about us

FIG. 33.6. The "pyramid of numbers"—a graphic representation of food-chain relationships among organisms. (*Based on an exhibit in the Royal Ontario Museum, Toronto, Canada.*)

In every *riffle*, we find a definite assemblage of organisms that are adapted—by their needs and reactions to current, hard surfaces and oxygen concentration—to live in riffles, and by these same factors are prevented from establishing themselves in pools. All the species in these communities have reactions to physical factors that are sufficiently similar to keep them confined to riffles, but they do not all have closely similar biotic relationships. Some of the members of the riffle community are various species of algae that are carrying on photosynthesis; some are

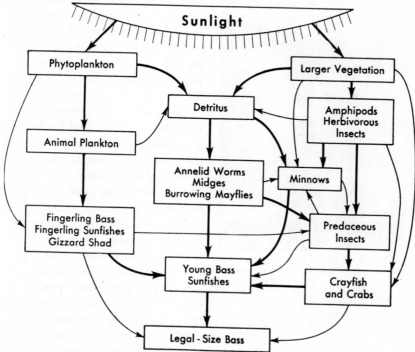

Fig. 33.7. Diagram of certain food-chain relationships in the St. Johns River, Fla.

animals that feed upon the algae; others are food strainers; and still others are somewhat larger animals (chiefly insect larvae) that feed upon the algae eaters and the food strainers.

Other primary communities occupy the pools; and in like manner all types of aquatic and terrestrial situations—roadside ditches, the shores, margins, bottoms, and open waters of lakes, the soil, leaf-mold and surface strata of forests, swamps, and grasslands—have their characteristic primary communities. These, in turn, are interrelated to form larger and more complex communities. We can recognize *stream communities*, composed of the members of pool and riffle communities and of some additional organisms that are not restricted to either pool or riffle but visit and feed in both of them. In the same way, the primary soil, leaf-mold, floor, herbage, shrub, and tree-inhabiting communities of the hardwood forests combine to form a larger *hardwood forest community*, to which animals like the gray squirrel and raccoon (at least partly) belong, although these animals are not confined to any of the primary communities of the forest.

Food chains. Many of the internal relationships of biotic communities are due to specific sequences of various organisms in the energy cycle. Although all animal food is dependent upon the anabolism of plants, not all kinds of animals can eat plant food. In fact, most of the plant-eating animals are adapted to feed on only a few species or types of plants, and most flesh eaters are limited to a very small list of suitable prey. Most organisms are specialists in their food habits and are confined to particular kinds and sizes of food. This results in a wide variety of food chains.

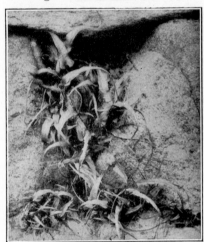

FIG. 33.8. The walking fern, *Camptosaurus rhizophilus*, growing in a rock crevice, Chester County, Pa. This pioneer plant is able to endure the severe environmental conditions provided by rocky cliffs and outcrops which are more or less moist and partly shaded. (*Photo by Prof. A. M. Laessle.*)

All food chains have their basis in some dependable supply of a definite type of food, either (primarily) in some continuously renewed supply of plant protoplasm or (secondarily) in some constantly accumulating supply of organic detritus such as occurs in the soil or on the bottoms of lakes, ponds, and pools. Given such a food supply, the resulting food chain is somewhat as follows:

First Link. The constantly renewed supply of plant protoplasm or the steady accumulation of detritus.

Second Link. One of a few different species of "base-industry" animals that feed upon the plant protoplasm or detritus and convert it into animal protoplasm. All base-industry animals exist in large populations and have a high biotic potential. Example: the "midges" (Chironomus) that feed on lake-bottom detritus and occur in tremendous numbers.

Third Link. Larger and stronger animals that feed upon the base-industry population. They are much less numerous and have a smaller biotic potential than the base-industry animals. Examples: the spiders, dragonflies, and robber flies that feed on midges.

Fourth Link. Still larger and stronger animals that feed upon the third link. Their size makes it unprofitable for them to hunt and eat the small midges, and they depend upon the "third link" organisms to concentrate their food into larger packages. They exist in still smaller numbers than the "third-link" organisms and have a still smaller biotic potential. Examples: frogs and fish that feed upon spiders, dragonflies, and robber flies.

Fifth Link. Still larger and stronger forms with still smaller population and biotic potential. Examples: the herons and other large wading birds that live largely on frogs and shallow-water fishes.

Sooner or later, a given food chain reaches its end in animals too large and too powerful to be fed upon by other predators. They are also too few and too slow-breeding to support another link. The number of links will vary but in most instances will not exceed five or six. The tracing of actual food chains is greatly complicated by the existence of alternative possibilities and by the large number of possible short circuits and crossings over with other chains. Thus a fox may finally reap the benefit of photosynthesis via grass and rabbits; via grass, grasshoppers, and quail; or

FIG. 33.9. The red mangrove, *Rhizophora mangle*, growing on the shore of Biscayne Bay near Miami, Fla. This is the dominant plant of a pioneer community characteristic of shallow, muddy seashores in tropical and subtropical America. The tangled mass of roots breaks the force of the waves and holds silt, building the shore outward. The spikelike seedlings, dropping from the overhanging branches, root first into the mud, plant themselves and extend the seaward margin of the thicket. (*Photo by Prof. A. M. Laessle.*)

via plant sap, sap-sucking insects (plant lice and leaf hoppers), lady beetles, spiders, tree frogs, and snakes.

The accompanying diagram (Fig. 33.7) shows some staple food relations among various common groups of animals and plants in the Saint Johns River in northern Florida. The energy from the sun is captured by the photosynthesis of two great groups of plants: the *phytoplankton*, minute but immensely abundant microscopic algae that drift submerged through the open, sunlit waters of the river and its lakes; and the larger rooted or drifting plants of the shallow margins, bays, and inlets. The latter comprise both a luxuriant growth of submerged and emergent rooted plants and huge drifting "rafts" of water hyacinths and water lettuce. Both the phytoplankton and the larger vegetation support large populations of "base-industry" animals and contribute large quantities of dead plant tissues to the detritus on the bottom. The latter supports a tremendous biota of bacteria, fungi, algae, protozoa, and minute crustacea; these organisms add one or two links, not indicated in the diagram, to the "detritus food chain." The arrows lead from supply to user and

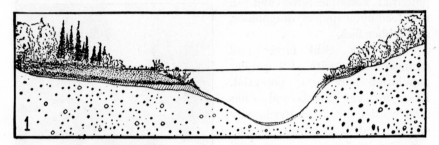

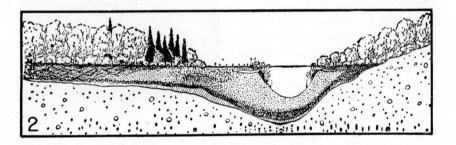

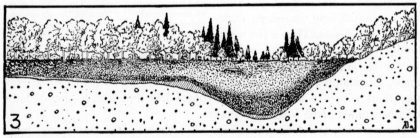

FIG. 33.10. The filling of a lake with peat deposits, and the succession of land plants on its margins. (*From Shull, Principles of Animal Biology.*)

indicate by the various thicknesses of line the approximate importance of the relation.

Another type of food chain is found in *host-parasite relationships*. Here the progression from link to link in size, numbers, and biotic potential is just the reverse of that shown in prey and predator relationships. The parasites of the fox are smaller, more numerous, and have a higher biotic potential than the fox, and they, in turn, are hosts for still smaller, more

FIG. 33.11. A stage in the extinction of a small glacial lake in Michigan. The lake, which formerly occupied the entire basin, has been almost filled by the accumulation of plant debris and soil washed down the surrounding slopes. At the edge of the open water is a zone of rooted aquatic plants with emergent leaves—a typical pioneer aquatic community. Later successional stages are represented by the dense semifloating mat of sedges, herbage, and low shrubbery outside the zone of aquatics, and by the bog forest of tamarack, poison sumac, and other woody plants seen in the background. Eventually the entire lake basin will be covered by such a forest. This, in turn, will be replaced by other types of forest spreading in from the margins of the swamp, until in theory the area should eventually attain the beech-maple climax stage. (*Photo taken on the E. S. George Reserve, Livingston County, Mich., by J. Speed Rogers.*)

FIG. 33.12. A "wet prairie" in northern Florida, densely occupied by pioneer communities of floating and of rooted emergent plants. In the background can be seen a live-oak hammock community. (*Photo taken near Gainesville, Fla., by J. Speed Rogers.*)

numerous, and more rapidly reproducing parasites. Some of these relationships are just beginning to be understood, but instances of host-parasite chains of three and four links are known.

Succession. Another phenomenon that complicates the ecological relations of organisms is that known as *succession*. This is the more or less orderly progression of different types and kinds of communities that, in the course of time, come to occupy any given local area. Generally speaking, succession is brought about by two main sets of inter-related causes: local geological processes[1] and the changes in soil, water level, light, humidity, etc., that are produced by the activities of the organisms themselves.

FIG. 33.13. A longleaf pine flatwoods in northern Florida. This is a persistent sub-climax community maintained by recurrent fires. It is characteristically developed on Leon soils, in which there is a hardpan at shallow depth; the soil above this layer fluctuates from saturated, in rainy periods, to very dry in times of drought. The herbage and shrubs of the flatwoods comprise only species able to survive in this rigorous environment marked by extreme variation in water supply. The pine roots, however, penetrate the hardpan and reach permanent moisture. If fire is kept out these flatwoods undergo succession toward the regional climax, which is a broad-leaved evergreen "hammock"; but fire is a normal and frequent ecological factor in this type of environment. (*Photo taken in Dixie County, Fla., by J. Speed Rogers.*)

When an area is first accessible to terrestrial or to aquatic life, it usually presents a rigorous and difficult environment, with meager food supplies and severe physical resistance. Thus the sand dunes that form on the leeward sides of many sandy lake and ocean shores are at first mere sand ridges, lacking in many of the soil substances required by most rooted plants, subject to extreme fluctuations in temperature, often desertlike in the lack of available moisture, and still liable to "blowouts" that expose roots at one point and bury entire plants at another. Very few organisms can endure such violent factors, but certain drought, heat, and wind-tolerant species are able to form a "pioneer community" here, where they are free from the biotic resistance of less hardy competitors. In time, however, as the pioneer community establishes itself, it begins to effect changes in its environment. Organic material accumulates in

[1] Stream erosion with the production of new-made bars, banks, cliffs, and changes in gradient; the shore deposits of lakes and oceans—bars, spits, dunes, and coastal flats; the formation and the extinction of lakes, etc.

the soil and thus provides more soil nutrients and retains more soil moisture. Shade is provided, and the extremes of light and heat are thereby
reduced. The sand becomes anchored by the roots of the pioneers and
ceases to drift with the wind. Now other plants and animals can invade
the area; they were unfitted to exist under the extreme pioneer conditions
but once they can find a foothold are better adapted to the increasing

Fig. 33.14. The climax association of northern Florida. A broad-leaved, evergreen hammock dominated by magnolia, holly, red bay, and laurel oak. (*Photo taken near Gainesville,
Fla., by J. Speed Rogers.*)

biotic competition. In time the newcomers will replace the members
of the pioneer community and, as they continue to occupy the area, produce a deeper, more organic, and moister soil, a denser shade and more
humid atmosphere. They, in turn, will be supplanted by another complex
of organisms still better fitted to survive and reproduce in the increasingly intense biotic competition of the ameliorated physical environment.

These successive changes are not unending. In time the area will become suitable for invasion by a group of plants and animals that, although

they may continue to effect some changes in soil, shade, humidity, and other conditions, are fitted to maintain themselves in the environment they produce. Such a community is termed a *climax* and is stable and self-maintaining so long as the general climatic conditions of the region— the average seasonal rainfall and average seasonal temperatures—do not

Fig. 33.15. The climax association of southernmost Florida. A tropical Everglades hammock, showing the abundance of air plants (epiphytes), trailing vines (lianas), and palms. (*Courtesy Carnegie Museum, Pittsburgh.*)

change. In the region that surrounds the southern half of Lake Michigan, for example, the climax community is a deciduous forest dominated by beech and sugar maple.[1] By no means all of this region had developed beech-maple forests or had reached this stage before modern civilization

[1] Actually this community comprises a considerable number of characteristic plants and animals, but the beeches and maples and a few other trees largely determine the peculiar complex of physical and biotic factors to which all the members of this community are adapted.

Fɪɢ. 33.16. The montane cloud forest of Honduras. This climax association develops at elevations of 6,500 to 7,000 feet where the mountain summits rise into the trade wind clouds. The slopes below are occupied by pine forests, and the valleys, by grassland and thorny scrub; but "la montana llorona" (the weeping forest) of the peaks is always dripping wet from rain or mist. This vapor forest is similar in appearance to the most luxuriant tropical rain forest, though very different in details of composition. Many of its trees are immense; every tree is loaded to capacity with epiphytes, and every exposed bark surface is covered with a wet sponge of filmy ferns, mosses, and leafy liverworts. The tree canopy is continuous; below it are tree ferns, shrubs of the melastome family, and a multitude of other plants. In spite of the lavishness of the plant life, animals are relatively few. This is the home of the quetzal, sacred bird of the Aztecs and Mayas, and of various other interesting species; but in abundance and variety of vertebrate and invertebrate life it does not compare with the tropical lowland forests. (*Photo taken on Cerro Uyuca, Honduras, by Prof. Archie F. Carr, Jr.*)

had destroyed most of the forests. The time required for the completion of successional changes within a stable climate probably ranges from several hundred to many thousands of years, depending upon the kinds of areas that were originally available to the various types of pioneer communities, the length of the growing season, and the nature and rate of local geological processes. We know that the present climate of the region about the southern half of Lake Michigan is geologically very recent, perhaps too recent to have permitted the slower successional sequences to have developed to a climax community. Moreover, local geological processes are continuously providing new situations for pioneer communities or are retarding or setting back the potential successional sequence.

Fig. 33.17. Mountain meadows and coniferous forests on Mount Rainier, Wash., at about 5,000 feet altitude. In early summer this is a veritable subalpine flower garden, with heathers, daisies, anemones, columbines, larkspurs, pasqueflowers, lupines and many other flowers blooming in profusion. The summer season is short, and only plants which can mature their seeds rapidly and endure long, cold winters can survive. This environment is much the same and has many of the same species as the arctic meadows that lie near sea level in Alaska. It is the home of marmots, pikas, bighorn sheep, and Rocky Mountain goats. (*Courtesy Carnegie Museum, Pittsburgh.*)

New sand dunes, for instance, continue to form along the southern and southeastern shores of the lake and as they gradually move inland, until stabilized by the sand-dune pioneers, destroy areas of late-stage succession on parts of the earlier dunes and produce new ponds and marshes by damming the former drainage. Elsewhere, stream erosion is producing new sand bars and mud flats or exposing new clay banks or rocky cliffs. The dwindling lakes of a former geological period still present shore lines and shallow basins for occupancy by the pioneer communities of a successional sequence that will finally cover even the lake basins with a beech-maple forest. Every type of area newly available for terrestrial life has its own special group of pioneer organisms, and the successive stages in each sequence, or *sere*, are more or less specialized and predictable. The pioneers and subsequent sequence of communities that change a dry, wind-swept, sandy ridge into a moist, densely shaded forest are, of course, very different from those that, change a lake or pond into

Fig. 33.18. An Arizona desert. Here the plants are all xerophytes, adapted for survival under arid conditions. Leaves are generally small or absent, root systems are extensive, and the plants may have water-storing stems or heavily cutinized surfaces or an abundance of hairs or other adaptations against drought. Many are also protected against browsing mammals by a formidable armor of thorns or spines. (*Courtesy Carnegie Museum, Pittsburgh.*)

the same sort of beech-maple climax, and both of these differ from the sequences that lead to the climax from a rocky cliff or from the bare, muddy margins of a stream.

We have used the ecologically classical "Chicago region" as a basis for our brief discussion of succession,[1] but in a region as large and varied

[1] Because of the early and important work of Prof. Cowles and his students, of Dr. Shelford and others, and partly because the exceptionally fine sequence of very young to old dunes in northern Indiana and southwestern Michigan so clearly shows all the stages of sand-dune succession.

as the United States, with so many types of climates, scores of different regional climaxes exist. Each has its own more or less typical successional stages, which lead from the various pioneer situations to the local climax. Westward from the Chicago region, as changes in the amount and seasonal distribution of rainfall are encountered, the climax community becomes an association of prairie grasses; and still farther west, it is an association of Great Plains bunch grasses. Southward, in the Eastern states, other hardwood trees replace the beeches and maples as dominants of the climax deciduous forest, and in northern Florida the climax association is a broad-leaved, evergreen "hammock," dominated by magnolia, holly, red bay, and laurel oak.

Succession in northern Florida provides a good illustration of the not uncommon circumstance in which, because of special conditions, some preclimax community attains a semipermanence or permanence and, in effect, becomes the actual climax. Such a conditional permanence appears to hold for the longleaf pine forests so long as they are periodically subject to fires. The latter are typically ground fires that destroy the invading underbrush, the forerunners of the hammock community, and so maintain the open, wind-swept, sunny forest floor that the pine requires for the growth of its seedlings. Throughout historic times, the frequent burning (at least once in every few years) of the pinewoods to provide better pasture has been a standard and well-nigh universal practice; and there is reason to believe that such periodic burning, both by prehistoric Indians and as a result of lightning, has long operated to maintain the pine-dominated communities. Today it is known that the elimination of fire allows the pine forests to be replaced by hardwood hammocks, and it seems evident that existing hammocks either owe their development to some natural barriers that protected them from fires or were developed from such preceding communities as swamps and seepage thickets.

Some special phases of succession are so rapid that one may actually follow them in detail. An infusion of dried grasses in water quickly develops a huge population of bacteria, and within a few days, one or more species of protozoa (introduced with the dried grasses or air-borne with dust particles) appear, feed upon the bacteria, and multiply at a prodigious rate. Then, within a few more days, other species of protozoa appear, and the earlier species wane. This process may continue, each form producing biotic, chemical, or physical changes in its environment that pave the way for some succeeding form, until a sequence of perhaps a dozen species will occur within the space of a few weeks. A similar but somewhat slower succession can be seen in the stages of decay of a fallen tree. Within a few years—the number depending upon the kind and size of tree and the place where it falls—it will have changed from sound wood to a moldering heap of humus and in the process will have formed the habitat of a number of successive microcommunities, each dependent upon some particular stage in the decay of the log and each tending to destroy its own environment and make conditions favorable for its successors.

Fig. 33.19. An undersea community. Portion of a Bermuda coral reef. Here most of the food chains start with the floating plankton, which is the food of the sponges (bottom and right rear), of the stony corals, the fingerlike horny corals and sea fans (all coelenterates), and of the simple chordates called "sea squirts" or tunicates, of which two groups can be seen attached to dead coral branches. Coral snails and small fishes form other links in the chain, and these are in turn fed upon by larger vertebrates such as the fierce moray (shown with head projecting from a crevice). (*Courtesy University of Michigan Museums.*)

Since all succession is the result of the dynamic relations among populations and many kinds of intricately interrelated organisms, it exhibits many details, modifications, and local variations that cannot be considered here. It should be apparent, however, that the activities of civilized man, with his crop plants and his herds, his abandoned fields, cutover forests and roadsides, his drainage and irrigation projects, and his damming and pollution of streams, intrude on a huge scale into natural successional sequences. These intrusions do not eliminate succession, but they do profoundly modify it, introduce new stages and new communities, set back or advance the progress of natural stages, and even change the local type of climax toward which the region trends. Not a few of man's modifications have proved unfortunate for his own long-run and even comparatively immediate needs, and it is becoming increasingly clear that a knowledge of the interdependencies of organisms and communities and of their successional relations is highly necessary for any rational and efficient maintenance and long-continued use of the world's natural biotic resources.

CHAPTER XXXIV

MAN AND THE BIOLOGICAL WORLD

We began our account with the idea that we could best present man as a part of the organic world by a sequence of viewpoints: the individual as a functioning machine, as a unit in a hereditary sequence of generations, as the product of continued change and adaptation through geological ages, and as a member of an interdependent society bound by social and economic ties. It has not always been possible or desirable to adhere strictly to such a scheme. The individual plays all these roles at once. An appreciation of the functioning machine, for example, must take into account the operations it must perform in competition or cooperation with other forms of life and the conditions imposed upon it by a germ plasm that bears the imprint of countless and ever-changing adaptations to past environments.

We have considered man's position in this world of life as one of the million or so kinds of existing organisms that represent the current stage of evolutionary development. This is in no sense to deny or ignore the many attainments that set man apart from other organisms, but to emphasize that his peculiarly human culture does not cancel his kinship with other living things, nor truly free him from the laws that govern their existence.

It might be well, in view of the foregoing statement, to review man's place in the organic world. His kinship with other organisms can be too strongly stressed as well as too much ignored. He is at once an animal, a vertebrate, a mammal, a primate, a member of the family Hominidae, of the genus Homo, and of the species *Homo sapiens*. As an organism he shares a complex of important and fundamental characteristics with all other forms of life. As an animal he fails to share in the peculiar features of the less closely related plants, but he does show in common with all animals other qualities not found in plants. It is the same for each succeeding taxonomic category, until as *Homo sapiens* (the sole living species of the genus) he exhibits qualities peculiarly his own. Because of these qualities he has been able to develop speech, conscious thought, and the evolving cultures of modern man. When we recognize man as an organism, an animal, a vertebrate, or a mammal, we are focusing attention on those qualities he has in common with the group in question. Conversely, such a recognition of kinship does not imply the occurrence of peculiarly human qualities in nonhuman kin.

This organic kinship and subjection to biological law are far more obvious in some of man's roles than in others. The acceptance of kinship is implied and unchallenged in all of our concepts of man as a functioning machine. Here our considerable modern knowledge of both function and malfunction largely ignores the boundary between man and other mammals and could not have been gained were not the results of animal experimentation applicable to man.

When we turn to the human individual as a link in a sequence of generations or as the product of evolution, it is somewhat less obvious that he is subject to the same biological principles that apply to other organisms. Here we must often deal with less concrete and immediate evidence. There is not nearly so much room for difference of opinion about the structure of a heart or a brain or about the chemical identity of two well-analyzed physiological reactions as there is about the chain of cause and effect that connects an individual genotype and its phenotypic expression or the conclusion that the pineal body of the mammalian brain is a heritage from a Carboniferous reptilian ancestor. Some aspects of kinship remain obvious even in the sequence of generations; the processes of germ cell formation, fertilization, and embryonic development can be directly observed and show the same unmistakable relationships that are exhibited by man as a functioning machine.

Beyond this point, however, we encounter viewpoints and interpretations of data that, based on the purely human phases of man's activities, are less concerned with his biological background. Anthropology, psychology, sociology, economics, and the interwoven fields of study we term the humanities are each concerned with peculiarly human aspects of man's activities and relationships. Each of these disciplines has collected and organized the data pertinent to its particular field and has built its own concepts and interpretations of man and his potentialities. When man is studied from these special viewpoints, his organic heritage and constitution are obscured by his cultural characteristics and attainments, and the assumption is often tacitly made that man, having become human, is somehow freed from the consequences of any former kinship.

Much of this ignoring of man's organic heritage comes from the complex interweaving of biological and cultural elements in all human activities and environments and much from the very specialization of study and viewpoint that makes increase of knowledge possible. Our proneness to extend analogies and implications far beyond the factual foundation on which they are based can result in useful hypotheses; it can also gloss over fatal inconsistencies in a supposed chain of cause and effect if untested by reference to relevant data. The biologist cannot pretend to more than a layman's knowledge of the social sciences or humanities. They are concerned with inquiries into special and uniquely human phases of man's behavior that lie mostly outside of his competence or concern. He does, however, retain the right to scrutinize the biological assumptions and implications that are inherent in these other points of view in the light of his own body of established fact and principle. Thus he can find no more than unsupported wishful thinking, or at most an appeal to now discredited biological hypotheses, to support belief in any form of biological inheritance of acquired characters. This statement holds not merely for morphological features but also for habits, emotions, attitudes, or any other qualities supposed to be impressed upon the germ plasm by experience or training.

Here, it seems to us, is the crux of the problem. We owe all of civilization to the invention and evolution of culture, and nearly all of the humanities, sciences, and arts to cultural inheritance. But it was a product of organic evolution that became capable of inventing and developing culture, and it is an organic germ plasm that must continue a stock capable of utilizing and maintaining it.

Our *ecological* ties with the organic world are also often forgotten or ignored. Civilization has given man increasing control over his environment and an ever-expanding power to exploit it, without supplying correspondingly evident indications of the consequences involved. Much that man does he does blindly. He has not freed himself from the "web of life," however much he may have lengthened some of the strands. A great deal of his apparent freedom comes from the social and economic division of labor that tends to conceal the interwoven strands; the city dweller is less conscious of ecological ties than is the farmer.

We depend upon agriculture to produce the many plants and animals required by man for food and clothing and for much of his shelter and industrial needs.[1] Nearly all of agriculture is applied biology and much of it applied ecology, and however much it may be controlled or modified by social or economic forces, it is still dependent upon the basic relationships of organic food chains. The farmer is faced with the problem of soil fertility and finds that this involves the activities of many soil organisms as well as those of his crops. He must also deal with weeds, with insect pests, and with diseases caused by viruses, bacteria, fungi, and animal parasites which are transmitted or harbored by still other animals and plants. Soils and crops, pests and competitors are all affected by the physical environment and its fluctuations, and so perpetuate another

[1] The increasing use of synthetic fibers, plastics, and the like is in large part simply an extension of the role of agriculture, since most of these products use plant tissues as raw materials.

bond by which man is tied indirectly but effectually to temperature, light, and moisture.

Medicine is another field of applied biology that must deal with man as an organism and with man's persistent ecological ties. Nearly all disease which is not mere malfunctioning of the machine is some form of host-parasite relationship, often complicated by other organisms that act as carriers, alternate hosts, or "reservoirs" of infection. Malaria, yellow fever, and typhus fever, for example, illustrate intricate interspecific dependencies that involve not only man as host and the parasite but the intervening roles of such "carriers" as mosquitoes, lice, and fleas, and of still other organisms that may be effectively concerned in

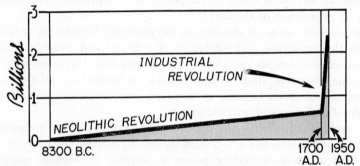

FIG. 34.1. The increase in world population from prehistoric times to the present. (*After Warren S. Thompson, courtesy Scientific American.*)

the relationship. Medicine, engineering, and sanitation have done much to reduce the toll taken by these and other diseases and have indeed made possible the huge population densities that are an essential condition of modern civilization; but few if any diseases have been eliminated. They are merely held in check or relegated to the more backward regions so long as civilization can empirically or rationally interrupt the ecological chains upon which they depend.

We have seen that man's cultural, intraspecific relations, because they involve phenomena and activities that are but primitively if at all exhibited by other organisms, are the special province of the social sciences and are largely outside of the biologist's professional concern. Even here, however, the concepts of biotic potential and environmental resistance appear to hold, but with the decreasing pressure of the physical and interspecific environment replaced by an ever-increasing intraspecific competition.

Man cannot afford to ignore his ecological relationships, for he has become an exceedingly powerful ecological agent. His tremendous increase in numbers and his cultural inventions (particularly his learning how to exploit the energy accumulated as coal and oil through many

millions of years of photosynthesis and organic cycles) have given him
the ability to dominate his environment to an extent never approached
by any other species. Thus far, however, he has been more powerful to
exploit than able to control or even to realize the consequences of his
exploitation. Much of agriculture, forestry, mining, and industry has had
consequences that were unforseen or ignored, until eroding farm lands,
dust bowls, dwindling forests, floods and droughts, and silted and polluted
streams—to say nothing of vanishing fish, game and other wildlife—
demonstrated that man is still bound by ecological laws and could con-
ceivably arrive at a condition analogous to that of many other animals
that, in a much more limited way, have been ecologically too successful
for their own long-time good.

APPENDIX: A SURVEY OF THE KINDS OF ORGANISMS

This book deals with those broad aspects of life that help us to understand man as an organism and to appreciate the various relationships that exist among all forms of life, including man. In attempting thus to treat of life in general, we have had to discuss many particular examples and kinds of organisms, for "life" as such is a mere abstraction. There is no life save in the form of real individuals that belong to particular species and genera and higher groupings and that exist as members of actual socioeconomic complexes. We are not especially concerned with the classification of animals and plants, except to the extent that this classification enables us to see where our chosen examples stand in relation to other forms of life. A survey such as that which follows does have another value, however, in that it furnishes a panoramic view of the results of organic evolution at its current stage.

The background for this survey is contained in the preceding sections of this book. In Part I we reviewed the major patterns of organization in structure and function; classification is based largely upon knowledge of comparative anatomy and physiology. In Part II we examined the concept of heredity, upon which any taxonomic scheme based upon relationship must rest. Part III showed how homologies in structure, origin and function give a basis for judging relationship; it also reviewed the geological evidence bearing on the evolution of plants and animals. In Chap. XXIV the principles of classification and the methods of naming organisms were discussed.

Here we shall survey many of the actual patterns into which living things have been molded by the process of evolution. The groups are arranged as far as possible in phylogenetic order; of course, no sequential treatment can fully express relationships. The most that can be done is to try to keep closely related groups together and to place the simpler and less specialized first, the more complex and more specialized later. These two aims are mutually inconsistent when we pass from one group to the next; we leave the highest forms of the first to take up the lowest forms of the next, and often this means going from more complex back to simpler organisms.

This appendix is designed primarily for reference but should not on that account be deemed unimportant. Knowledge of the principal groups of plants and animals and their major subdivisions is essential to an understanding of much of the general content of biology.

The accompanying chart is designed to show some of the more important phylogenetic relationships within the plant and animal kingdoms, and the structural levels of the various groups. It is necessarily very much generalized, but it will aid in placing the groups treated in preceding chapters and in the following pages.

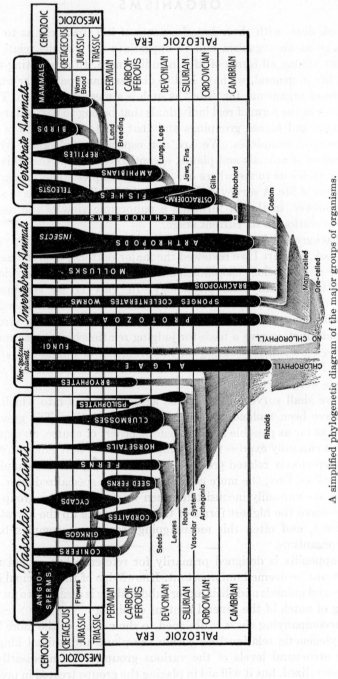

A simplified phylogenetic diagram of the major groups of organisms.

THE PLANT KINGDOM

In classifying plants according to degrees of relationship, certain features are more useful than others. The more important of these are briefly discussed below. It should be pointed out, however, that they are of unequal value, and that their applicability and usefulness vary from group to group.

1. *Cell Structure.* One of the simplest groups of plants (the blue-green algae) is made up of cells which with few exceptions have no nuclei. There is considerable reason to believe that they are rather closely related to the bacteria, which also lack definite nuclei. Other instances of likeness in cell structure are similarly interpreted as indicative of relationship.

2. *Arrangement of Cells.* In some of the very simple plants every cell division is followed by separation of the daughter cells, so that each plant consists of a single cell. In others the cells remain together in pairs; or larger numbers of cells form accumulations that may be arranged into filaments, sheets of cells, or three-dimensional cell groups of various shapes. Although all these types of cell arrangement are found in several rather distantly related groups of thallophytes, within each of these groups they often indicate relationship of species and genera.

3. *Presence or Absence of Particular Organs or Tissues.* Whole plant groups may be characterized by the presence or absence of some particular vegetative organ or tissue. Thus the presence of true roots in all modern pteridophytes is an indication that these plants are more closely related among themselves than are any of them to the mosses or other rootless plants; it likewise indicates a closer degree of relationship to the spermatophytes (which also have roots) than to the groups of plants in which roots are lacking. Again, the absence of tracheal tubes (vessels) from the wood of most gymnosperms indicates that these plants are more closely related among themselves than they are to the angiosperms, in which tracheal tubes occur.

4. *Similarity of Reproductive Structures.* Throughout the plant kingdom the reproductive mechanism, including the structure of the reproductive organs, affords one of the best and most used means of determining relationships. The vegetative structures are much more likely to show

adaptive modifications to unlike modes of life. Thus among the closely related oaks one species may be a large forest tree and another a spreading shrub with underground stem, but both have very similar flowers and fruit. The reproductive structures exhibit a wide variety of characteristics—such as differences in number and arrangement of flower parts—that are little affected by the environment and yet are so modified from group to group and from species to species that they afford excellent indications of relationship.

Older and newer systems of classification.   The conventional system of plant classification, which we have used throughout this book on account of its convenience and familiarity, divides the Plant Kingdom into four great groups, called *divisions*, as follows:

Division I. Thallophyta (algae and fungi).
Division II. Bryophyta (liverworts and mosses).
Division III. Pteridophyta (ferns and fern allies).
Division IV. Spermatophyta (seed plants).

For many purposes this scheme is still quite useful, but there has been a growing tendency to break away from it in favor of some classification that would more adequately represent plant relationships as they are now understood. Various more modern classifications have been proposed and some of these have gained wide acceptance. These new classifications scarcely affect the groups of ordinal, or lower, rank in the seed plants. The rearrangements have to do chiefly with the algae and fungi, and with the higher categories throughout. The classification given below largely follows the treatment in an excellent recent textbook,[1] except that we have adopted Trippo's proposal to use the same names for the major categories as have long been standard in zoology. These are, in descending rank: kingdom, subkingdom, phylum, subphylum, class, subclass, order, suborder, family, subfamily, genus, subgenus, species, and subspecies. The extents of the older divisions are indicated, and the names of extinct groups are starred.

---

[1] Hill, Overholts and Popp, *Botany: A Textbook for Colleges*, 2d ed., McGraw-Hill Book Company, Inc., 1950.

The Major Plant Groups and Some of Their Subdivisions

SUBKINGDOM I. THALLOPHYTA

The simplest plants. Body a thallus without true roots, stems or leaves. Mostly microscopic or small

PHYLUM I. THALLOPHYTA. Algae and Fungi.
  Subphylum I. **Algae.** (Containing chlorophyll.)
    Class 1. MYXOPHYCEAE. (Cyanophyceae.) The Blue-green Algae.
    Class 2. CHLOROPHYCEAE. The Green Algae.
    Class 3. BACILLARIOPHYCEAE. The Diatoms.
    Class 4. PHAEOPHYCEAE. The Brown Algae.
    Class 5. RHODOPHYCEAE. The Red Algae.
  Subphylum II. **Fungi.** (Without chlorophyll.)
    Class 1. SCHIZOMYCETES. The Bacteria.
    Class 2. MYXOMYCETES. The Slime Molds.
    Class 3. PHYCOMYCETES. The Algalike Fungi.
    Class 4. ASCOMYCETES. The Sac Fungi.   Eumycetes. True Fungi.
    Class 5. BASIDIOMYCETES. The Club Fungi.

> Algae
> Fungi
> THALLOPHYTA

SUBKINGDOM II. EMBRYOPHYTA

Developing an embryo from a zygote produced by fusion of gametes

Phylum II. BRYOPHYTA. Liverworts and Mosses.
  Class 1. HEPATICAE. The Liverworts.
  Class 2. MUSCI. The Mosses.

> BRYOPHYTA

PHYLUM III. TRACHEOPHYTA. The Vascular Plants.
  Subphylum I. **Psilopsida.** *Psilophytales. (Rhynia, etc.)
  Subphylum II. **Sphenopsida.** The Wedge-leafed Plants.
    Class 1. EQUISETINAE. The Horsetails. (*Calamites, Equisetum.)
  Subphylum III. **Lycopsida.** The Small-leaved Plants.
    Class 1. LYCOPODINAE. The Club Mosses and Allies. (*Lepidodendron, *Sigillaria, Lycopodium, Selaginella, Isoetes.)
  Subphylum IV. **Pteropsida.** The Large-leaved Plants.
    Class 1. FILICINAE. The Ferns.

> PTERIDOPHYTA

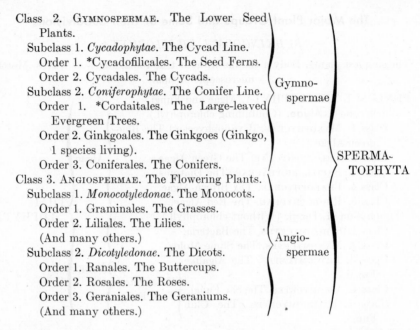

Class 2. GYMNOSPERMAE. The Lower Seed Plants.

Subclass 1. *Cycadophytae*. The Cycad Line.

Order 1. *Cycadofilicales. The Seed Ferns.

Order 2. Cycadales. The Cycads.

Subclass 2. *Coniferophytae*. The Conifer Line.

Order 1. *Cordaitales. The Large-leaved Evergreen Trees.

Order 2. Ginkgoales. The Ginkgoes (Ginkgo, 1 species living).

Order 3. Coniferales. The Conifers.

Class 3. ANGIOSPERMAE. The Flowering Plants.

Subclass 1. *Monocotyledonae*. The Monocots.

Order 1. Graminales. The Grasses.

Order 2. Liliales. The Lilies.

(And many others.)

Subclass 2. *Dicotyledonae*. The Dicots.

Order 1. Ranales. The Buttercups.

Order 2. Rosales. The Roses.

Order 3. Geraniales. The Geraniums.

(And many others.)

Gymno-spermae

Angio-spermae

SPERMA-TOPHYTA

The most important characteristics of the four great plant *divisions* have already been described and discussed in the section on the major patterns of plant life (Chap. XIII). Here these features will be recapitulated briefly, and our attention will be given more particularly to the principal subphyla, classes, and orders of plants.

Phylum I. THALLOPHYTA (tha lŏf' it a; Greek, *thallos*, "young shoot or frond," *phyton*, "plant").

The thallophytes (thal' o fīts) are the simplest plants—unicellular, or with a body composed of simple, relatively unspecialized cells that make up a thallus. Including the unicellular Protophyta (pro tŏf' it a), the phylum comprises some 84,000 species. These fall into two major groups—the *algae*, which possess chlorophyll and carry on photosynthesis, and the *fungi*, which lack chlorophyll and must obtain their food from other organisms (or rarely by means of chemosynthesis).

Subphylum I. **Algae** (al' jē). Seaweeds, pond scums, and a host of microscopic water plants make up the bulk of the 14,000 species of this group. A few are terrestrial; most of these live in moist situations, but some are symbiotic with fungi, forming lichens that often occur on bare rock and in other very dry places. Although most algae are small, some of the giant seaweeds called *kelps* attain a length of more than 100 feet. Five major groups are distinguished, and some authorities recognize additional ones.

The Blue-green Algae (Myxophyceae) consist of single cells or of colonies of similar cells surrounded and held together by a gelatinous sheath (Figs. 26.2 and A.1). The colonies may be spherical, platelike, or filamentous in form. The most distinctive feature of this group, shared only with the bacteria, is the absence of a definite nucleus in the cell; there is merely a clearer central portion of the protoplasm that seems to have some of the functions of a nucleus. The cells also lack plastids. In addition to chlorophyll the Myxophyceae contain a blue-green pigment (phycocyanin), and sometimes red, yellow, purple, or brown pigments. The Red Sea gets its name because of a red alga that is a member of the blue-green

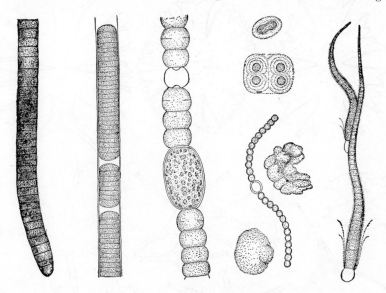

Fig. A.1. Blue-green algae. (*From Sinnott, Botany, 4th ed.*)

group. Cell division takes place by simple fission—a process rare among higher forms; sexual reproduction does not occur. There are no motile cells.

Considering their simple structure, simple mode of reproduction, and the fact that they store carbohydrates as glycogen (like animals) instead of as starch (like most plants), the blue-greens seem to be only distantly related to other kinds of green plants. It may be that they are the simplest, most primitive cellular organisms living today.[1] Yet they flourish alongside of more advanced types of plants, and often dominate the plankton flora of ponds, lakes, and the sea at certain times and places. Some species grow on the moist surfaces of soil, rocks, and tree trunks.

[1] The *bacteria* (a group of fungi) are even simpler in structure, but because they lack chlorophyll and, except for a few chemosynthetic species, are dependent upon other organisms for their food sources, most of them are probably of later origin and specialized by degeneration. Their similarities to the blue-greens suggest some sort of relationship, and they may be an offshoot from primitive blue-green algae.

The Green Algae (Chlorophyceae) include unicellular and colonial motile forms that swim by means of flagella or cilia, and also nonmotile types (Figs. 13.11 and 12, 26.4, 32.8 and A.2). The latter range from single cells of various forms to cell colonies that may be spherical, leaflike, or filamentous in form. Most of the green algae are actually greenish yellow in color, because of the presence of a yellow pigment in addition to chlorophyll. Some of the motile forms have a red or brown pigment spot that is sensitive to light, called the *eyespot*.

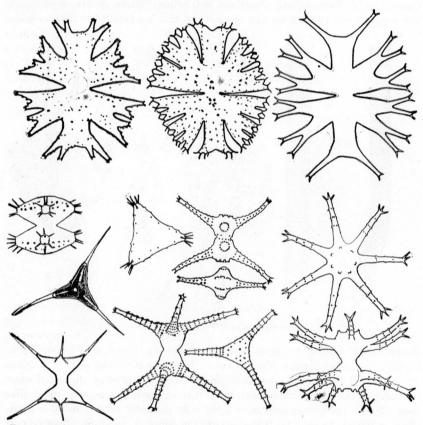

Fig. A.2. Various desmids (green algae). (*From Hill, Overholts and Popp, Botany, 2d ed.*)

The members of this group are largely inhabitants of fresh water, though some live in damp terrestrial situations. In many respects the green algae resemble the higher plants and differ from the blue-green algae. Among the characters that the green algae share with the higher plants are cells with distinct nuclei, chlorophyll that is apparently identical and similarly contained in chloroplasts, a cellulose cell wall that is structurally similar, and starch instead of glycogen produced as a food reserve.

The *Diatoms* (Bacillariophyceae) have already been discussed in some detail in Chap. XXVI. They are unicellular algae (Figs. 26.7 and A.3) with definite nucleus and plastids, containing chlorophyll and yellow and brown pigments, and storing their food as fats. Their most distinctive feature is the silicious shell which they secrete. It is made up of two valves that fit together like the halves of a pill box, with the edges overlapping, and the surfaces of the valves have a remarkable appearance of fine sculpturing or striation due to the presence of thick and thin places in the wall. Diatoms are abundant in salt and fresh waters, both in the free-floating plankton and attached to or resting on the surfaces of plants and other objects. They are preponderant in the plankton of flowing streams. In the ocean they are the most important of all the "base industry" organisms.

The Brown Algae (Phaeophyceae) are plants with cells containing definite nuclei and plastids, chlorophyll, and a yellowish-brown pigment that masks the green color; they store their foods as carbohydrates and complex alcohols. They are, with rare exceptions, marine and include the largest of all algae besides many

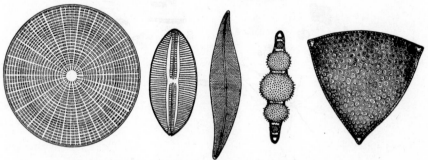

Fig. A.3. Representative diatoms. (*Courtesy General Biological Supply House, Inc.*)

small forms (Fig. 26.6). Most of them occur in the cold and temperate zones. They usually grow attached to rocks, with the long, limp thallus floating upward. The principal advance of this group over the green algae is that the thallus shows the beginnings of cell differentiation and division of labor. It is usually divided into a rootlike or disklike *holdfast* attached to some object, a *stem*, and leaflike or ribbon-like *blades*. These structures are only superficially like the roots, stem, and leaves of higher plants, and the blades consist of semi-independent cells, as in other algae. The gulf weed (Sargassum) is a drifting warm-water species of this group; other common types are bladder wrack, or rockweed (Fucus), devil's apron (Laminaria), and the large kelps of the Pacific Ocean, one of which (bladder kelp, Nereocystis) may attain a length of 150 feet. About 900 species of brown algae are known.

The Red Algae (Rhodophyceae) are, like the last group, principally marine. They occur for the most part in the temperate and tropical seas and are abundant in coral reefs, to the formation of which some of them contribute. Indeed, some of the red algae of the reefs are commonly mistaken for corals. The plants of this group (Fig. 26.5) have cells containing definite nuclei, chlorophyll, and red and blue pigments that mask the green of the chlorophyll; they store their food products as a special type of starch. About 2,500 species are known.

Subphylum II. **Fungi** (fun' jī). The fungi are set apart from other thallophytes and from nearly all higher plants in their lack of chlorophyll. Not all of the various groups of fungi are closely related. In all probability they originated at different times and from different groups of algae, so that phylogenetically the "fungi" do not form a natural group. Functionally they are sharply distinguished from all other plant groups by their inability to manufacture food by photosynthesis.

The Bacteria (Schizomycetes) are familiar by name to everybody. They are single-celled plants which, like the blue-green algae, lack a distinct nucleus.

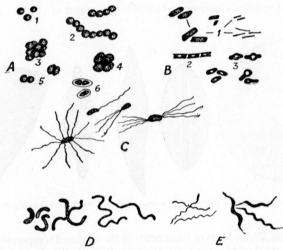

Fig. A.4. Types of bacteria. *A*, spherical forms; 1, coccus; 2, streptococcus; 3, staphylococcus; 4, Sarcina; 5, diplococcus; 6, encysted diplococci. *B*, bacilli without flagella; 1, various forms and groupings of bacilli; 2, 3, development of endospores in various positions. *C*, bacteria with flagella. *D*, forms of spirilla. *E*, spirochaetes. (*From Hill, Overholts and Popp, Botany, 2d ed.*)

According to the shapes of their cells, bacteria are spoken of as *cocci* (spherical), *bacilli* (rod-shaped), *spirillae* (spirals), etc. All are extremely minute.

Bacteria or their spores occur practically everywhere. The bacterial spore is not a reproductive cell, since a single bacterium produces but a single spore; instead it is an inactive, resistant stage adapted for dispersal and survival under conditions of dryness, heat, or cold, which would be fatal to the active phase of the cell.

We are prone to think of all bacteria as noxious, and it is true that many of them are parasites of animals and plants and that they include the causative agents of a large number of human diseases. Far more, however, are not injurious to other organisms, and a great many are beneficial, both from the standpoint of their usefulness to man and because of the indispensable part they play in organic cycles. We have already made mention of some of their more important roles in discussing the colorless plants in Chap. XIII, the geological history of plants in Chap. XXVI, and the biotic environment in Chap. XXXIII. We need no more than briefly recall some of the points there discussed.

The decay-causing, saprophytic bacteria destroy the dead bodies of animals and plants and thus make the compounds locked up in them available for reutilization by living things. The nitrifying and nitrogen-fixing bacteria add nitrates to the soil and make possible the synthesis of proteins by plants. Symbiotic bacteria in the intestines of herbivorous vertebrates and insects break down the otherwise indigestible cellulose of plants and make it available to the animals as a source of carbohydrate food. Man makes use of many kinds of bacteria in the preparation of food, in industrial processes, in sewage disposal, and in other ways.

The Slime Molds (Myxomycetes) are among the most primitive of the thallophytes, and, although we have included them among the fungi, they are so unlike other plants that they are sometimes given rank as a distinct phylum. In their vegetative state they consist of a mass of protoplasm, slimelike, usually dirty white or yellowish in color, containing many nuclei but not divided into cells. This multinucleate, noncellular mass of protoplasm—often as much as a cupful in a single slime mold—shows active creeping movements. It can spread out in a thin network and, amoebalike, move about over the surface of the material on which it grows. It avoids light and seeks moisture; rotting heaps of leaves and decaying logs are favorite habitats. A slime mold reproduces by transforming most of its mass into spores, borne on stalks; the spore masses and stalks are of various colors —brown, black, red, orange, etc. When the spores fall into water or upon moist surfaces, they germinate into small ameboid or flagellated single cells. These move about, feed, and grow; if they touch others of their kind, they fuse with them, and by such growth and amalgamation a new multinucleate slime mold is in time produced.

The True Fungi (Eumycetes) include a host of species showing the utmost diversity in form and mode of life. Among them are the yeasts, responsible for various types of fermentation, and used by man for raising bread, making beer, and for other purposes. The majority of the fungi are saprophytes, but many are parasites of animals (Fig. 33.1) or of plants (Fig. 33.2), and these are the cause of serious diseases and great economic loss.

About the same range in structural pattern occurs in the fungi as in the algae— from unicellular types, through loose cell aggregations, to types with a multicellular thallus in which the beginnings of cell differentiation and division of labor are shown. Many of the higher fungi have holdfasts and stalks comparable to those of the brown and red algae, but no fungus possesses anything that corresponds with the blades of these algae or with the leaves of higher plants. Frequently the thallus of the higher fungi forms a mass of fine, threadlike strands called *mycelia* (mī sēl′ i a); mushrooms, which we commonly think of when fungi are mentioned, are, in fact, only the fruiting bodies of a mycelial thallus, which ramifies through a mass of decaying leaves or other food source from which the mushroom appears to sprout. Peculiar modifications of the thallus occur in many parasitic fungi, related to special requirements of parasitic existence; thus in certain groups, some of the mycelial filaments form specialized organs called

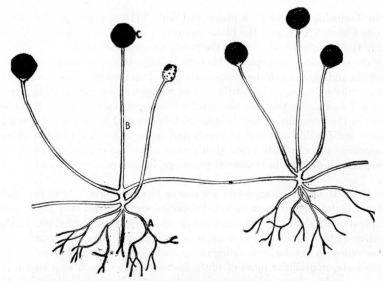

FIG. A.5. Black bread mold, *Rhizopus nigricans*, an algalike fungus (phycomycete). The mycelium (*A*), composed of much-branched filaments or hyphae, penetrates the substratum; it sends up stouter hyphae (*B*) on which are borne the sporangia (*C*). One sporangium has burst, shedding its spores. (*From Sinnott, Botany, 4th ed.*)

FIG. A.6. Sac fungi (ascomycetes). Upper left, the bird's-nest fungus, *Cyathus striatus;* the others are disk fungi. Upper right, *Ombrophila enterochroma;* lower left, *Peziza badia;* lower right, *Bulgaria rufa*. (*Photos by Prof. E. B. Mains.*)

haustoria (haw stor' i a), which can penetrate the living cells of the host and absorb water and food.

In a large number of plants, particularly those growing in forests, the function of the root hairs has been partly or completely taken over by fungus filaments

F IG. A.7. Sac fungi (ascomycetes). Upper left, the tar spot of maple, Rhytisma; upper right, the common morel found under hardwood trees, *Morchella esculenta;* below, a morel that grows under pines, *Helvella esculenta. (Photos by Prof. Alexander H. Smith.)*

called *mycorrhiza* (mī' kor rīz' a); these penetrate the tissues of the root, form a mycelial mat about its surface, and absorb water and dissolved substances from the soil. The relationship is evidently symbiotic, the green plant obtaining necessary substances through the agency of the fungus and the latter benefiting by having access to the foods elaborated by the green plant. Among the plants that are known to be partly or completely dependent upon mycorrhiza are many common forest trees such as oak, beech, and hornbeam, the famous heather of the Scotch Highlands, certain ferns, and nearly all orchids. In some instances the green plant may grow in the absence of the fungus, and vice versa; this is true of certain of the forest trees and the fungi normally associated with them.[1] In other

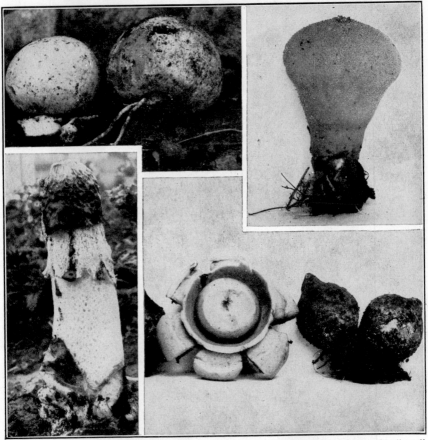

FIG. A.8. Higher fungi (basidiomycetes). Left, a stinkhorn, Dictyophora, the "egg" stage above and the mature mushroom below; upper right, a puffball, *Lycoperdon perlatum*; lower right, an earthstar, *Geastrum triplex*. All belong to the puffball group. (*Photos by Prof. Alexander H. Smith.*)

instances the symbiotic relationship has become obligatory, neither the green plant nor the fungus being able to exist alone. This is the case in many orchids, and until this relationship was known, floriculturists had great difficulty in raising these orchids in greenhouses.

[1] Among these fungi are many of the common forest mushrooms, such as Amanita (most of the species of which are highly poisonous), Boletus, and Russula. These mushrooms are the fruiting bodies of mycelial masses associated with tree roots.

The Lichens (lī′ kens) constitute a striking example of intimate symbiotic relations between two distantly related plants—one an alga and one a fungus— by means of which the former obtains the necessary raw materials for photo- synthesis and the latter receives a supply of manufactured food. Lichens com- monly form irregular patches on rocks (Fig. 33.3), the bark of trees, or the soil. These patches consist of a thallus, which may be thin and tightly applied to the substratum, or rough, scaly, fibrous, leaflike, or pendulous. The color of lichens is extremely varied, but gray-greens, browns, reds, and smoky colors predominate. Each lichen consists of a single-celled green alga mingled with a mass of fungus filaments; the two plants together form the thallus. The fungus filaments absorb

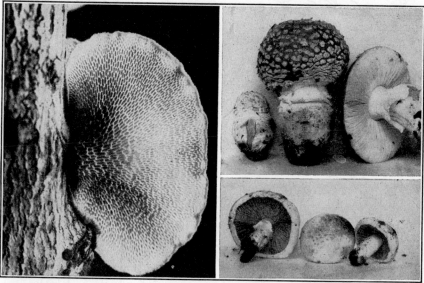

FIG. A.9. Higher fungi (basidiomycetes). Left, a bracket fungus saprophytic on dead trees; upper right, the poisonous *Amanita muscaria;* lower right, the edible meadow mushroom, *Agaricus campestris. (Left by Prof. E. B. Mains, the others by Prof. Alexander H. Smith.)*

water and dissolved substances from the substratum; the algal cells utilize these materials for photosynthesis; and both plants make use of the manufactured food. Alga and fungus reproduce independently of each other, and the lichen association may also be propagated by joint vegetative methods. The algae and some of the species of fungi that enter into these lichen associations may live apart from each other; but many others of the fungus species that form lichens cannot survive except in partnership with an alga.

Phylum II. BRYOPHYTA (bri of′ i ta), Greek, *bryon,* "moss"; *phyton,* "plant."

The bryophytes (brī′ o fīts) form the second great division of the plant kingdom, the group comprising about 17,000 existing species of liver- worts and mosses. They are the simplest land plants, undoubtedly derived from some group of green algae; but they differ from all thallophytes in their higher degree of structural organization, related to the requirements of life upon land, as we have already seen.

The Liverworts (Hepaticae) are mostly found in moist situations, such as the soil of seepage slopes, and rocks and tree trunks wet with spray or mist. A few are aquatic, floating on the surface of ponds (Fig. 13.13). About 9,000 species have been described; most of these are creeping thallus types, but some are upright

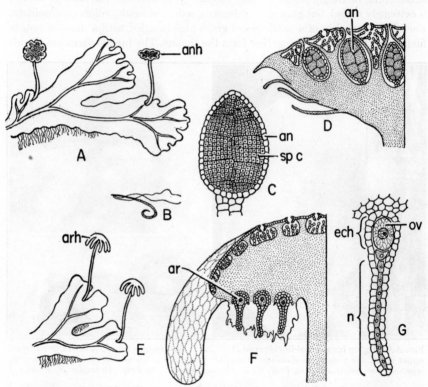

FIG. A.10. A thallus liverwort, Marchantia. *A*, gametophyte plant with antheridial heads. *B*, swimming sperm. *C*, section of antheridium. *D*, section of antheridial head with antheridia in place. *E*, gametophyte plant with archegonial heads. *F*, section of archegonial head with archegonia in place. *G*, archegonium containing mature egg. *an*, antheridium; *anh*, antheridial head; *ar*, archegonium; *arh*, archegonial head; *ech*, egg chamber; *n*, neck of archegonium; *ov*, ovum or egg; *spc*, sperm-forming cells. (*Modified from Turtox chart, courtesy General Biological Supply House, Inc*)

"leafy" forms. Marchantia is a common thallus liverwort often studied in the classroom. It has a flat, ribbonlike form; the under surface is furnished with simple rootlike filaments called *rhizoids* which serve for anchorage and absorption, while the upper surface is covered with a cuticle and has numerous stomata. The thallus is produced by cell division at an apical growing point (in a notch at the tip); from time to time this growing point divides, so that the thallus bifurcates. There is some differentiation among the cells but no vascular tissue.

The life cycle of Marchantia (Fig. A.10) is similar to that of the moss, described in Chap. XVII. Stalked organs, some bearing antheridia and others archegonia, are formed at certain times. The sperm produced in the antheridia are flagellate and motile; when the surface of the liverwort is wet, they can swim in the water film to reach and fertilize the eggs in the archegonia. The resulting zygote grows into a small sporophyte, which produces spores that germinate and give rise to a new gametophyte generation—the thallus already described.

Fig. A.11. *Marchantia polymorpha*, a common thallus liverwort. Upper left, gametophyte with antheridial heads; lower left, gametophyte with gemma cups from which asexual buds (gemmae) are issuing; right, gametophyte with archegonial heads. (*Photos by Prof. E. B. Mains.*)

In addition to this reproductive cycle, Marchantia reproduces asexually in two ways. One results from the mode of growth; the growing point advances and from time to time divides, while the plant dies from the rear. When death reaches a fork, two separate thalli are formed from one. The second method is the production of tiny, oval, flat buds in small cups on the upper surface. These buds, called *gemmae* (Fig. A.11), break free and are splashed away by rain to grow into new gametophyte plants.

The *leafy liverworts* look like mosses but have definite upper and lower surfaces like the thallus types, instead of stems with radial structure like mosses. They also differ from mosses in having no vascular tissues, in having leaves without midribs, and in the fact that the spore capsule (sporophyte generation) is either retained within the archegonium or, if emergent, lacks a cap. In the temperate zones leafy liverworts are not numerous; but in the perpetually moist cloud forests of tropical America (Fig. 33.16) they and other similarly delicate plants cover the tree trunks, lianas, and rock surfaces with an inches-thick growth that holds water like a sponge.

The Mosses (Musci) represent a higher level of bryophyte organization. They have been described in Chap. XIII, and their life cycle was discussed in Chap. XVII (Fig. 17.4). They are world-wide in distribution and grow in every kind of habitat from aquatic to dry. Like the liverworts most of them are small, but they tend to

Fig. A.12. Representative mosses. Left, a true moss, *Aulacomnium palustre*, showing the leafy gametophyte and the bare stalks and capsules of the sporophyte. Right, a bog moss, Sphagnum. In this group the gametophyte plant includes not only the leafy stems but also the sporophyte-bearing stalks; the small sporophytes are ovoid capsules with a very short foot. When the spores are mature, the round lid of the capsule pops off. (*Left, courtesy General Biological Supply House, Inc.; right, photo by Prof. E. B. Mains.*)

grow in dense masses which may, as in the case of sphagnum, form hummocky growths covering a large expanse. Those that grow on the ground have no underground parts except the rhizoids, so that moss mats may easily be stripped from the substratum. Mosses have true leaves and a stem with a central strand of vascular tissue. Although many of them occur in dry situations, they require water for sexual reproduction, since—like the liverworts—they have swimming sperms. The sporophyte generation is more conspicuous than in the liverworts, but it is parasitic on the gametophyte; it produces a spore case with a cap that pops off to release the spores.

Phylum III. TRACHEOPHYTA (trāk ē of′ it a; Greek, *trachia,* "trachea," "windpipe," and *phyton,* "plant"). The Vascular Plants.

This phylum includes all those plants in which the sporophyte is the dominant generation, with the gametophyte reduced, and in which the sporophyte has a well-developed vascular system. It is the latter characteristic which gives the name to the group. The old divisions Pteridophyta and Spermatophyta are included.

Subphylum I. **Psilopsida** (sĭ lŏp' sĭ da). This group includes the most primitive of vascular plants, the extinct psilophytes and two surviving tropical related genera. The oldest known true land plants are psilophytes from the lower Devonian of Canada, but the group is better known from the middle Devonian of Scotland, where a number of species of several genera have been found. Two of these, *Rhynia and *Asteroxylon, are shown in Fig. 26.9. The simplest were merely erect, sparsely branched green stems 8 to 10 inches tall, that grew thickly clustered on swampy ground. They lacked roots and leaves. The tips of some of the branches were enlarged into hollow, oval structures in which were formed numerous spores. The undiscovered gametophyte generation was probably, as in the fern, a delicate and ephemeral structure.

The stem of Rhynia contained a central strand of vascular tissue, surrounded by cortical parenchyma, and a cutinized, stomata-bearing epidermis. In these respects the psilophytes resembled ferns, but they were more primitive than any fern, for there were no true roots; the stem continued under the ground as a branching rhizome furnished with rhizoids, as in the bryophytes. Asteroxylon was more advanced than Rhynia in that it possessed small scalelike leaves densely covering the stem. The remaining subphyla of the vascular plants probably developed from various psilophytes, and the lycopods in particular may well have come from plants of Asteroxylon type.

Subphylum II. **Sphenopsida** (sphēn ŏp' sĭ da).

The Horsetails and Their Allies. In this group the sporophytes have roots, rhizomes, aerial stems, and leaves that are generally small, often wedge-shaped, and arranged in whorls at the nodes of the stems and branches. The stems are usually jointed. The spores are all alike and are borne in sporangia on sporophylls that may be clustered or may form a compact cone.

The subphylum includes the single class Equisetinae, with three orders, of which only the Equisetales have living representatives. These all belong to the genus Equisetum (horsetails or scouring rushes, Fig. A.13), of which there are about 30 species. Most of them are less than 18 inches tall, though in Central America and Cuba there is a giant form that grows in dense stands to a height of 40 feet; its stem diameter, however, is never more than an inch. All the members of this genus have a subterranean rhizome (stem), from which arise aerial stems and true roots. The aerial stems are vertically grooved and jointed at the nodes with a whorl of small leaves or branches at each node.

The horsetails were formerly much more important than they are today. In Paleozoic times (Devonian to Permian, and especially in the Carboniferous) there lived a great variety of treelike plants of this group, belonging to the order *Calamitales and the genus *Calamites. Some of these are shown in Figs. 26.12 and 27.20, and their structure and mode of reproduction are indicated in Fig. A.14. They attained a height of 60 and sometimes 90 feet, with a diameter up to 15 inches. The stem had a thick bark and a ring of xylem enclosing a large central pith. It was abundantly branched, with a crowded tuft of leaf whorls at the apex of the main stem and at the nodes of the branches. Calamites differed chiefly from its small modern relatives in its much larger size and in the fact that its stems showed secondary thickening.

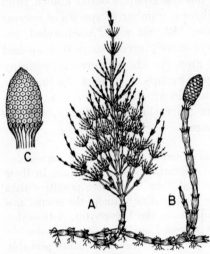

A third order, *Sphenophyllales, included many small herbaceous or vinelike undergrowth plants in the coal forests of Carboniferous time; the whorled leaves were wedge-shaped. *Sphenophyllum appears in Fig. 27.20.

Subphylum III. **Lycopsida** (lī cop′ sĭ da).

The Club Mosses and Their Allies. Like the last, this suborder also contains but a single class, the Lycopodinae, better represented in the past than today. One of the four orders, the *Lepidodendrales, is extinct; the other three have living representatives.

Fig. A.13. The common field horsetail or scouring rush, *Equisetum arvense. A*, the sterile sporophyte plant. *B*, a spore-bearing shoot. *C*, sporangia in a conelike structure at the shoot tip. (*Courtesy General Biological Supply House, Inc.*)

The best-known group includes the ground pines, running pines, or club mosses, of the order Lycopodiales. Most of these belong to the largest of the two surviving genera, Lycopodium, which has about 300 species. They have a sprawling stem with erect branches, all parts of the stem and branches being covered with small, generally sharp-pointed leaves. The spores are produced in sporangia borne by sporophylls that may be distributed along the branches or grouped into conelike apical structures. All the spores are alike, each capable of producing a minute but generally free-living gametophyte that bears both antheridia and archegonia, as in most other primitive vascular plants.

Selaginella (order Selaginellales) is a genus of about 600 species, some of which are called little club mosses (Fig. A.15). It includes plants similar to but more delicate than Lycopodium; many of them grow in moist tropical forests, but a few live in very dry places. The resurrection plant of the southwestern United States and Mexico is a xerophytic Selaginella, which can dry and curl up into a ball and lie dormant for months until the return of moist conditions.

This group is of peculiar interest because of the fact that its reproductive processes show an advance over Lycopodium in the direction of the higher plants. Instead of all its spores being alike (homosporous condition) as in Lycopodium, they are of two sorts (microspore and megaspore) as in all the higher forms, including the seed plants. The microspore produces a minute male gametophyte that remains completely enclosed in the spore wall; the megaspore germinates into a much larger but still minute female gametophyte that remains within the megasporangium. The microspores, with their contained male gametophytes,

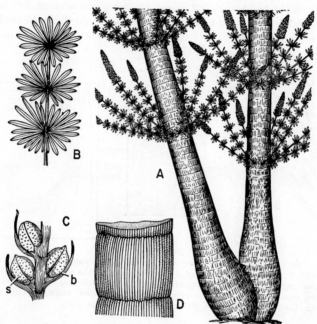

Fig. A.14. The extinct Carboniferous horsetail Calamites, which grew to a height of 50 feet and a diameter of 2 feet. The leaves were borne in whorls of 6 to 20, encircling the branches. A, base of plant showing whorled branching. B, leaves. C, section of cone with (s) sporangium and (b) enclosing bract. D, part of stem. (*Courtesy General Biological Supply House, Inc.*)

are shed in large numbers. In the presence of moisture they liberate swimming sperms, some of which find their way to the egg cells in the gametophytes and fertilize them. Here is obviously the first stage in the mechanism that has reached its culminating development in the spermatophytes. A similar life cycle occurs in the peculiar genus Isoetes (order Isoetales), which comprises small grasslike plants that grow partly submerged in swampy land and pond margins; each of the slender leaves bears a sporangium near the base, and the megaspore is large and seedlike.

The lycopods have had a long geological history. The present-day orders are the descendants of the Paleozoic *Lepidodendrales, which are first known from the Devonian. They became the dominant plants of the late Paleozoic era and formed a large proportion of the trees of the coal forests. Some of these trees were rather small; but others grew to giant size, with massive trunks supported at the base by four to seven spreading branches (*stigmaria*), which penetrated the soil and bifurcated again and again, and to which were attached the short true roots. There were two chief types of these trees—*Sigillaria and *Lepidodendron.

*Sigillaria (Figs. 26.11 and A.16) had an unbranched or few-branched trunk which in some species attained a height of 70 to 100 feet. The top 10 feet of the trunk surface was clothed with erect or drooping grasslike leaves, only a few inches long in some species but several feet long in others. Where the leaf bases dropped from the trunk they left a scar, the form and arrangement of the scars differing with the species. In Sigillaria the scars are typically in vertical rows, and look like repeated impressions of the same seal or stamp, whence the name seal tree (Latin, *sigilla*, "a seal or mark").

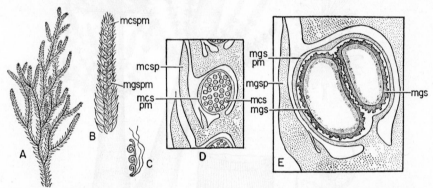

FIG. A.15. The "little club moss" Selaginella. *A*, the sporophyte plant. *B*, a sporangia-bearing shoot. *C*, the swimming sperm. *D*, section through the microsporangium. *E*, section through the megasporangium. *mcs*, microspore; *mcsp*, microsporophyll; *mcspm*, microsporangium; *mgs*, megaspore; *mgsp*, megasporophyll; *mgspm*, megasporangium. (*Modified from Turtox chart, courtesy General Biological Supply House, Inc.*)

Lepidodendron (Figs. 26.11 and A.17) means scale tree (Greek, *lepis*, "scale," and *dendron*, "tree"), referring to the fact that the leaf scars were arranged in spirals to give a fish-scalelike pattern. Over 100 species of this genus are known; some of them had trunks which rose well over 100 feet to the base of the 20 foot crown of forking branches. The leaves were usually only a few inches long and covered the upper parts of the trunk and branches. Both Sigillaria and Lepidodendron produced microspores and megaspores, borne on sporophylls grouped into conelike structures. The microspores were shed in such vast numbers that they make up a considerable part of the carbonized plant material that is coal.

Subphylum IV. **Pteropsida** (ter ŏp' sĭ da). The Ferns and Seed Plants.

The reasons for including the ferns and seed plants in one subphylum are too technical to elaborate upon; they include such considerations as the position of the sporangia on the lower instead of the upper surface of the leaves or sporophylls, the presence of leaf gaps in the vascular cylinder, etc. Broadly speaking the Pteropsida are the large-leaved plants, though there are many exceptions. Three classes are recognized: the ferns (Filicinae), the lower seed plants (Gymnospermae), and the flowering plants (Angiospermae). In the older classification the ferns are included in the division Pteridophyta along with the Lycopsida, and

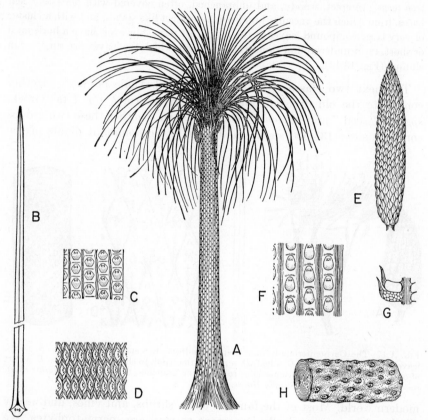

Fig. A.16. The Carboniferous lycopod Sigillaria, a massive tree which grew to be 100 feet tall and 6 feet in diameter. It reproduced by spores, borne on cones up to a foot long and an inch or two in diameter. The gametophyte generation produced from these spores is unknown. *A*, the entire tree. *B*, a leaf. *C*, *D*, and *F*, portions of trunks of different species. *E*, a spore-bearing cone. *G*, section of part of cone, showing sporophylls, spore chambers, and spores. *H*, a piece of one of the stigmaria, or subterranean branches, from which the true roots issued, as shown by the root scars. (*Modified from Turtox chart, courtesy General Biological Supply House, Inc.*)

the gymnosperms and angiosperms together make up the division Spermatophyta.

The Ferns (Filicinae) are said to have some 8,000 living species, most of which fall into the order Filicales, or true ferns. We have already discussed their structure and mode of reproduction in Chaps. XIII and XVII and will not repeat what was given there. As a group the ferns are widely distributed but are most at home in tropical regions. They prefer moist, shady habitats, although some of the species such as the bracken fern and the resurrection fern may grow in very dry situations. Ferns attain their greatest size in the tropics, where certain species are trees (Fig. 13.15) that may reach a height of 50 to 80 feet. The stems of such tree ferns are erect, woody, and unbranched, often covered with persistent leaf bases, from which the vascular bundles may project like spines, and with a cluster of very large compound leaves at the top. Most ferns, however, have a horizontal or short, erect underground stem (rhizome) from which the leaves rise singly or in clumps (Fig. 13.14).

The next two classes (Gymnospermae and Angiospermae) together constitute the old division **Spermatophyta** (sperm ă tŏf′ ĭ ta; Greek, *sperma*, "seed," and *phyton*, "plant"). Taken together these two groups comprise some 133,500 species and include the dominant plants of the

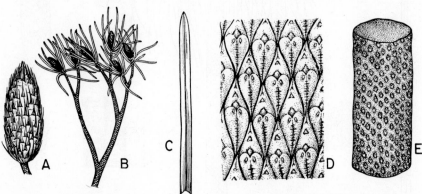

Fig. A.17. The Carboniferous lycopod Lepidodendron. *A*, a spore-bearing cone. *B*, twigs, leaves, and terminal cones. *C*, a leaf. *D*, a part of the trunk to show the leaf scars. *E*, a part of one of the subterranean stigmaria or root-bearing branches. (*Modified from Turtox chart, courtesy General Biological Supply House, Inc.*)

modern world. Most of the familiar trees, shrubs, and vines, and nearly all the plants economically important to man are spermatophytes. We have already described in some detail (Chaps. IX–XII and XVII) the structure and functioning of a seed plant and here need mention only those features of the various groups that represent departures from the basic pattern there discussed.

Class Gymnospermae

THE LOWER SEED PLANTS

The gymnosperms form the second class of the subphylum Pteropsida, or the first subdivision of the division Spermatophyta. The plants of this group are distinguished from other seed plants chiefly by a difference in their reproductive mechanism. The name *gymnosperm* means "naked seed" and refers to the fact that the seeds are not formed in the ovaries of flowers. Instead the seeds are borne on the faces of scalelike leaves (sporophylls), which are generally arranged spirally on an axis so as to form a structure called a *cone*. The group includes the modern pines, spruces, firs, junipers and yews,[1] sequoias, ginkgoes, and cycads. It also includes various extinct groups, among which are the seed ferns. In structure the members of the Gymnospermae do not differ greatly from the flowering plants. One feature in which they are unlike angiosperms is the usual presence of resin or mucilage ducts in the wood. In the pines

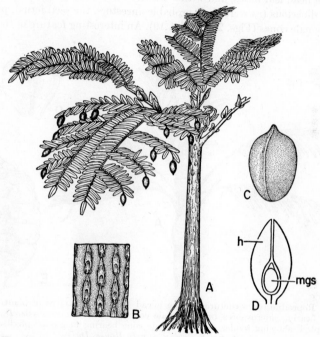

Fig. A.18. The Carboniferous seed fern Neuropteris. *A*, reconstruction of the whole plant. *B*, part of trunk with leaf scars. *C*, a seed. *D*, section of unmatured seed, showing the megaspore (*mgs*) and husk (*h*). (*Modified from Turtox chart, courtesy General Biological Supply House, Inc.*)

and their allies, also, the xylem is composed only of tracheids, and the phloem sieve tubes do not have companion cells. All gymnosperms are woody in structure.

The Gymnospermae fall into two main series—the *cycad line*, which includes the extinct seed ferns and the cycads; and the *conifer line*, to which are assigned the extinct large-leaved evergreen trees, the ginkgoes, the conifers, and a few other aberrant forms.

The Seed Ferns (Cycadofilicales) were common in the late Paleozoic (Figs. 26.11 and A.18). Most of them were undergrowth plants or small trees, with large

[1] The cone is often berrylike in the junipers and yews.

fernlike leaves bearing well-developed ovules at their tips or along the midribs; the ova were probably fertilized by swimming sperms. They had all the appearance of ferns and were originally classified as such, but discovery of their seeds revealed their true position.

The Cycads (*Bennettitales, fossil; Cycadales, recent) were important during the Mesozoic era but are represented today by only nine genera and about 90 species. The plants are like palms or tree ferns in appearance (Figs. 26.14 and A.19), with a thick columnar stem that rarely branches and is often covered by an armor of dead leaf bases, and with a crown of thick, feathery, stiff leaves. The cycads are dioecious (as were their probable ancestors, the seed ferns), producing male and female cones (Figs. 25.2 and A.19). An interesting feature of the cycads,

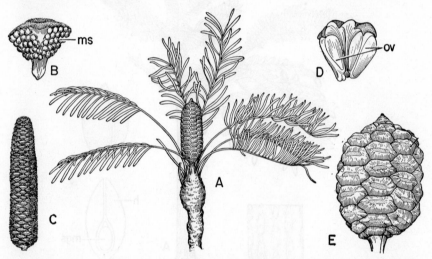

FIG. A.19. Reproductive structures of the cycad Zamia. A, habitus of plant. B, microsporophyll bearing microspores (ms). C, male cone with microsporophylls. D, section of megasporophyll showing ovules (ov). E, female cone bearing megasporophylls. (Modified from Turtox chart, courtesy General Biological Supply House, Inc.)

shared with the ginkgoes and doubtless with the seed ferns, is the fact that the sperms developed in the pollen tube are ciliated and able to swim, like those of the bryophytes, lycopods and ferns. In those lower groups motile sperms are necessitated by the method of fertilization; but in plants that have a pollen tube the development of ciliated sperms is unnecessary and can only represent a survival of ancestral characteristics. Motile sperms, and the leaflike structure of the cone scales of some species indicate that the cycads are the most primitive of existing seed plants.

Cycads are characteristically very slow-growing and long-lived plants. Individuals of some species certainly reach an age upwards of a thousand years, and probably much more. Modern representatives of the order are practically confined to tropical and subtropical regions, although some of the fossil forms were much more widely distributed during the Mesozoic. Four native species of the genus

Zamia occur in Florida, where they are known as "coonties," "compties," or Florida arrowroots. They have subterranean stems, the crown of leaves growing apparently from the soil, giving a fernlike appearance to the plant. The cones are stalked, the staminate one more slender than the ovulate one. A larger species

FIG. A.20. Representative conifers. *A*, arborvitae or white cedar, Thuja. *B*, red cedar or juniper, Juniperus or Sabina, with male cones. *C*, red cedar with female cones or "juniper berries." *D*, tamarack or larch, Larix. *E*, yew, Taxus, with female cone. *F*, yew with male cones. *G*, hemlock, Tsuga. (*From Miller and Blaydes, Methods and Materials for Teaching Biological Sciences.*)

(*Cycas revoluta*, Fig. 26.14) has been introduced and is cultivated in many parts of the south as an ornamental plant.

The Large-leaved Evergreen Trees (*Cordaitales) were the commonest gymnosperms of the late Paleozoic. They were tall, slender trees that formed extensive forests, or grew among the lycopods of the coal swamps. Some of the largest were as much as 120 feet tall and 3 feet in diameter at the base, with the lower two-thirds or three-fourths of the trunk unbranched, and the dense crown of branches bearing many large, simple leaves. In one genus, *Cordaites (Fig. 26.12 and 27.20) the leaves sometimes reached a length of 6 feet and a width of 6 inches. In other genera the leaves were smaller, sometimes strap-shaped with blunt or sharp tips, and sometimes grasslike, ½ inch in breadth and 20 inches long. The leaves were thick and parallel-veined.

Separate male and female catkinlike cones were borne on the same tree. The female cones generally matured only a single large seed with a hard seed coat and fleshy rind. The wood of the trunk was much like that of modern pines but had a large central pith. Members of this group showed a combination of the features of seed ferns, cycads, ginkgoes, and conifers, and are thought to have been ancestral to the latter.

The Maidenhair Trees (Ginkgoales, pronounced ging kō ā′ lēz in spite of the spelling) are an ancient group of which there is today but a single survivor. The

FIG. A.21. Male cones of the red pine, *Pinus resinosa*, surrounding a terminal cluster of young leaves ("needles"). (*Photo by Prof. E. B. Mains.*)

maidenhair tree (*Ginkgo biloba*, Fig. 26.15) is almost unknown in the wild state, though extensively in cultivated form. It grows to a height of 90 feet, with freely branched crown. The leaves are flattened and usually bilobed, resembling those of the maidenhair fern. The small, inconspicuous male and female cones are borne on separate trees. Members of this order are known as early as the Carboniferous, and the genus Ginkgo had its origin as early as Triassic time.

The Conifers (Coniferales). The needle-leaved evergreen trees constitute by far the most conspicuous group of living gymnosperms. This is true whether one considers number of individuals, number of genera (46), number of species (nearly 500), size of individuals (many large, the sequoias among the most gigantic living things, with trunks almost 400 feet tall), or economic importance. Conifers provide the softwoods of the lumbering industry, pulpwood for paper mills, resin, and turpentine. The group includes the Auracarian pines, now confined to the southern hemisphere but formerly widespread; the sequoias or California "big trees," the ancestry of which can be traced back to the Permian; and the pines, spruces, firs, junipers ("red cedars"), larches ("tamaracks"), cypresses, and yews. In all the conifers, pollen is produced in small male cones and is broadcast on the wind in great amounts; it reaches the female cones wholly by accident. The leaves are needle- or scalelike, and the wood lacks vessels and generally possesses resin ducts.

Class Angiospermae
THE HIGHER SEED PLANTS

The Angiosperms form the third class of the subphylum Pteropsida, or the second subdivision of the division Spermatophyta. These are the flowering plants, in which the seeds develop within the ovary of a flower. The group comprises about 133,000 species, which include herbs, shrubs, vines, and trees. Most of the plants important to man as sources of food, clothing, and industrial materials are angiosperms. The group is often characterized as "the broad-leaved plants," by contrast with the conifers.

Gymnosperms and angiosperms are similar in producing seeds, as opposed to the three lower divisions. The angiosperms differ from the gymnosperms, however, in the following respects: (1) the presence of *vessels in the xylem;* (2) the production of *flowers* and *fruit;* (3) the formation of a *pistil,* to the apex of which pollen adheres and through which the pollen tube must grow to reach the ovule;[1] (4) the predominance of *insect pollination* (though wind pollination also occurs in several large groups); and (5) *the further reduction of the gametophyte* to merely a few cells existing but a few days.

The angiosperms include some 300 families of plants, but these can be grouped into two main subdivisions—*monocotyledons* and *dicotyledons.* The principal distinctions between these two groups are as follows:

1. The leaves of monocotyledons are generally parallel-veined and almost always have smooth, even margins, whereas the leaves of dicotyledons are generally net-veined and are very often toothed, lobed, or divided.

2. The flowers of the monocotyledons are generally built on a plan of three; *i.e.,* the number of flower parts of any one kind (petals, sepals, etc.) is three or some multiple of three. In the dicotyledons the number of parts of each kind is generally four or five or some multiple of four or five.

3. In the stems of the monocotyledons the conducting tissue is in numerous vascular bundles scattered through the stem but not arranged in a single ring; in dicotyledonous stems the conducting or vascular tissue either is a hollow cylinder surrounding the pith and increasing in width as the stem grows older or is distributed in separate bundles arranged in a single circle.

4. The embryos of the seeds of monocotyledons have only one seed leaf (cotyledon), while in the dicotyledons there are almost always two.

The Monocotyledons (subclass Monocotyledoneae, commonly called *monocots*) number about 27,000 species. Only four of the more important families can be mentioned.

The *Gramineae* (grass family) includes a number of species that are of preeminent economic importance. In the tropics bamboo is one of the most valuable of plants, being used for a great variety of purposes. In the temperate regions

---

[1] In the gymnosperms, the wind-borne pollen falls into the angles between the cone scales and is thence drawn up through the neck of the ovule by a sticky secretion first extruded from the ovule and then resorbed; the pollen tube has merely to penetrate the inner layer of ovule tissues and is very short.

MONOCOTYLEDON	DICOTYLEDON
Flower parts in threes or multiples of three	Flower parts in fours or fives
Leaves usually parallel veined	Leaves usually net veined
Stems with scattered (closed) vascular bundles	Stems with regularly arranged (open) vascular bundles
One cotyledon (seed leaf)	Two cotyledons (seed leaves)
Roots with many xylem elements	Roots with three, four, or five xylem elements

FIG. A.22. A comparison of some characteristic features of dicots and monocots. (*Modified from Turtox chart, courtesy General Biological Supply House, Inc.*)

hay and forage for cattle are provided chiefly by small grasses. Sugar cane is one of the two chief sources of sugar (the other being the sugar beet, a dicotyledon). Most important of the grasses are the cereals—wheat, corn, oats, rice, rye, and barley. All members of the grass family are wind-pollinated.

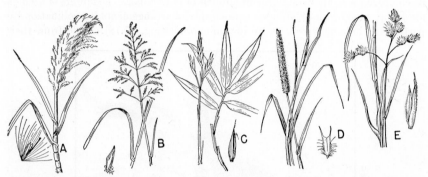

Fig. A.23. Representative grasses. All are shown in flower, with an enlarged floret. *A*, sugar cane, Saccharum; *B*, bluegrass, Poa; *C*, large cane, Arundinaria; *D*, timothy, Phleum; *E*, orchard grass, Dactylis. (*Modified from Turtox chart, courtesy General Biological Supply House, Inc.*)

Fig. A.24. Representative lilies. Left, the Japanese lily, *Lilium speciosum;* right, the dog-tooth violet or adder's-tongue, *Erythronium americanum.* (*Left, courtesy Ward's Natural Science Establishment; Inc.; right, photo by Prof. E. B. Mains.*)

The *Palmaceae* (palm family) is chiefly tropical; the appearance of its members is familiar to all. In this group a large number of simple flowers develop within a single leaflike bract. The coconut palm, date palm, sago palm, and others are put to a variety of uses by inhabitants of the tropical and subtropical regions.

The *Liliaceae* (lily family) includes some of the most typical and easily recognized of monocotyledons. Here the floral parts are separate and occur in threes or in multiples of three, with the petals generally brightly colored, and often the sepals as well. The plant is generally herbaceous and is usually provided with a bulb or some other form of underground stem. Asparagus, onion, trillium, lily-of-the-valley, true lilies, tulip, and dogtooth violet are members of this family.

The *Orchidaceae* (orchid family) is the most advanced and specialized of all the families of monocotyledons and is largest in number of species, though not to be compared with the Gramineae in number of individuals. The flowers of orchids are highly modified in relation to various special arrangements for pollination by particular kinds of insects or by hummingbirds (Fig. 17.18). Aside from their

Fig. A.25. A native orchid, the yellow lady's-slipper, *Cypripedium calceolus.* (*Photo by Prof. E. B. Mains.*)

value as ornamental plants, orchids are of little economic importance; the only one that plays a part in ordinary commerce is a Mexican species from which vanilla is obtained.

The Dicotyledons (subclass Dicotyledoneae, commonly called *dicots*) are a much larger assemblage than the monocots, with about 106,000 known species. Two great sections or series can be distinguished, based upon the characteristics of the flower. In Series I (Archichlamydeae) the petals are either separate (Polypetalae) or absent (Apetalae). In Series II (Metachlamydeae) the petals are partly or completely fused into a tube around the stamens and pistils (Sympetalae). The two series are also distinguished by various other differences.

Series I. Among the families of this assemblage are several small ones that include some of our common hardwood trees with wind-pollinated, inconspicuous flowers—the Juglandaceae with the walnuts, hickories and pecans; the Salicaceae with the willows and aspens; the Fagaceae with the oaks, beeches and chestnuts; the Betulaceae with the birches and alders; the Ulmaceae with the elms and hackberries; and the Aceraceae with the maples. Only a few of the larger families can be mentioned.

The *Ranunculaceae* (buttercup family) includes herbs that have five petals, numerous stamens and numerous separate pistils; it includes such well-known plants as clematis, anemone, hepatica, marsh marigold, peony, larkspur, and columbine. In many of the cultivated species, so-called "double" flowers have been produced by transformation of stamens and pistils into petals.

Fig. A.26. Extremes of flower form among the dicots. Left, the male catkin or ament of willow, Salix. The imperfect staminate and pistillate catkins are borne on different plants, making the willows dioecious. The flowers are wind-pollinated. Center, the perfect and complete but simple flowers of the spring beauty, *Claytonia virginica*. This is a regular but unsymmetrical flower, with two sepals, five petals, five stamens, and three-celled ovary. Right, the perfect, complete, and complicated passion flower or maypop, Passiflora. This has five sepals united into a calyx throat crowned with a double or triple fringe, five petals attached to the calyx throat, stamen filaments united into a tube that sheathes the long stalk of the ovary but separate above, and a one-celled ovary with three or four club-shaped styles. (*Photos by Prof. E. B. Mains.*)

The *Cruciferae* (mustard family) includes plants with a pungent taste and with four sepals, four petals in a single circle, four long and two short stamens, and two pistils. Included in this family are stock, water cress, horse-radish, mustard, cabbage, turnip, and radish.

The *Rosaceae* (rose family) includes many useful as well as beautiful plants, among which are roses, strawberries, raspberries, blackberries, peaches, apricots, plums, cherries, apples, pears, and quinces.

The *Leguminosae* (legumes) is the largest family of Series I. It is characterized by irregular flowers (which are highly adapted, like those of orchids, to insect pollination) and by the ripening of the ovary into the well-known "pod." The legumes include such plants as sweet pea, wisteria, lupine, sensitive plant, locust, honey locust, coffee tree, clover, alfalfa, Crotalaria, beans and peas, peanuts, and acacias, as well as many tropical trees.

The *Umbelliferae*, in which the flowers form distinctive clusters (Fig. 17.12 *G, H*), is the most advanced family of the series. Examples are carrot, celery, and parsnip.

Other well-known plants belonging to the first series but not included in any of the preceding families are tulip tree, magnolia, bay, basswood, sycamore, ash, buckeye, horse chestnut, box elder, sweet gum, black gum, violets, pinks, geranium, nasturtium, fuchsia, cotton, flax, hemp, currants, gooseberries, grapes, citrus fruits, tea, and cacao.

Series II. The plants of this assemblage, with tubular corollas, include the highest dicotyledonous families, only a few of which can be mentioned here.

The *Ericaceae* (heath family) has flowers with two sets of five stamens each, so that there are five circles of flower parts. The members of this family are mostly shrubs; included in it are trailing arbutus, bearberry, heather, rhododendron, azalea, mountain laurel, wintergreen, huckleberries, blueberries, and cranberries.

The *Labiatae* (mint family) can be recognized by the two-lipped corolla, square stems, opposite leaves, and four-lobed ovary. It includes many strongly scented

FIG. A.27. Representative dicot flowers. Left, the shooting star, Dodecathion; center, a composite, *Actinella grandiflora;* right, the pasqueflower, *Anemone pulsatilla.* (*Photos by Prof. Alexander H. Smith.*)

plants, among which are pennyroyal, lavender, mint, horehound, savory, marjoram, thyme, sage, rosemary (but not the "rosemary" of the Florida scrub), and catnip.

The *Solanaceae* (nightshade family) includes plants with conspicuous, regular corollas and with floral parts arranged in four circles. Here are included nightshade, red pepper, ground cherry, belladonna, Jimson weed, Irish potato, tomato, and tobacco.

The *Compositae*[1] (composites), the highest of the families of Series II, is characterized by having numerous small flowers compacted into a head that looks like a single large flower (Fig. 17.13). The composites are mostly herbaceous plants, abundant in the temperate regions. Among the better known members of this family are dandelion, sunflower, goldenrod, thistle, beggar ticks, blazing star, daisies, asters, everlasting, ragweed, cockle burr, zinnia, dahlia, cosmos, marigold, chrysanthemum, sagebrush, burdock, and lettuce. The family is noteworthy for the number of noxious weeds that it includes.

Other well-known dicotyledons with tubular flowers that do not belong to any of the preceding families are the coffee plant, cinchona (from which quinine is obtained), sweet potato or yam, olive, and the gourd fruits (watermelon, muskmelon, cucumber, pumpkin, squash).

[1] In recent classifications often broken into several families.

THE ANIMAL KINGDOM

In our treatment of the varied patterns of animal life (Chap. XIII) we were not concerned with classification as such but merely with showing how animals meet their common functional requirements by a variety of structural patterns. It was sufficient for that purpose to group animals under only four divisions—Protozoa, simple Metazoa at the cellular level, intermediate Metazoa at the tissue level, and complex Metazoa at the organ-system level of construction. This could be done only by ignoring many important differences in structure. When these are taken into consideration, it becomes necessary to recognize at least 11 animal phyla of major importance: Protozoa, Porifera, Coelenterata, Ctenophora, Platyhelminthes, Nemathelminthes, Mollusca, Echinodermata, Annelida, Arthropoda, and Chordata. These 11 sharply distinguished phyla contain by far the greater number of all animals. There are in addition a number of lesser groups, some of which are clearly of phylum rank, others of uncertain status; those that will require brief mention are the Nemertinea, Rotifera, Bryozoa, Brachiopoda, and Onychophora.

Characteristics used in classifying animals. The phyla are distinguished from one another not so much by the possession of unique characteristics as by unique combinations of characters. Among the important features in which they may differ are the following:

1. *Degree of Cell Differentiation.* Animals are either (*a*) unicellular (or composed of a relatively small number of undifferentiated cells) or (*b*) composed of many cells exhibiting various degrees of differentiation and division of labor. Those of the first category are the Protozoa; those of the second, the Metazoa.

2. *Number of Germ Layers.* Metazoa develop either two or three germ layers (embryonic cell layers). Those with two germ layers are said to be *diploblastic;* those with three germ layers are *triploblastic.* The three layers are, beginning with the outermost, *ectoderm, mesoderm,* and *entoderm.* Mesoderm is lacking in diploblastic animals.

3. *Kinds of Symmetry.* Although a few animals are asymmetrical, possessing no plane of symmetry, the great majority are built on a symmetrical plan, with spherical, radial, or bilateral arrangement of body

parts. *Spherical symmetry* is that of a ball, any section through the center dividing the organism into symmetrical or mirrored halves. *Radial symmetry* is that of a wheel or cylinder, any one of several sections through the main axis dividing the organism into symmetrical halves. *Bilateral symmetry* is that of a boat or wagon, there being only one section, a vertical one that passes through the longitudinal axis, that will divide the organism into mirrored halves.[1]

4. *Metamerism.* Several phyla are characterized by the fact that their members have bodies composed of linear series of segments, each segment being built on the same basic structural plan and repeating, in more or less modified form, the structure of the segments anterior and posterior to it. This condition is known as *metamerism*, and each segment is a *metamere* or *somite*.

5. *Body Cavities or Internal Spaces.* Any metazoan has either one or two body cavities. In the *lower Metazoa* the body is saclike in general plan; *i.e.*, the two-layered body wall surrounds a single large space that has but one opening. The cavity may be a true digestive cavity and the single opening a mouth (as in the Coelenterata), or it may be a cloaca or water cavity and the single opening an excurrent pore (as in the Porifera). In the *higher Metazoa* the body is constructed according to the tube-within-tube plan. The alimentary canal is a tube open at both ends (mouth and anus), lined with digestive cells (entoderm). In addition, a new cavity lined with mesoderm separates the body wall from the digestive tube; this is the coelom.

6. *Special Features and Combinations of Features.* A number of phyla and certain subphyla are characterized by the possession of structures that are not found in any other group. Among examples that might be cited are the pores and canal system of the Porifera, the stinging cells (nematocysts) of the Coelenterata, the water-vascular system of the Echinodermata, the hollow dorsal nervous system and notochord of the Chordata, and the vertebral column of the subphylum Vertebrata.

Even when structures are shared by more than one phylum (for instance, metamerism by Annelida, Arthropoda, and Chordata; a ventral ladderlike nervous system by Annelida and Arthropoda), they occur in combinations that are distinctive and diagnostic of each phylum. Thus the combination of metamerism, ventral ladderlike nervous system, soft skin, and unsegmented appendages, with other features, is peculiar to

---

[1] Just as there may be minor departures from complete bilateral symmetry in a boat or wagon, bilaterally symmetrical animals may show imperfect symmetry in details of their structure. Thus in man the intestine, though essentially a bilaterally symmetrical structure, is so long that it is assymetrically coiled in the abdomen; and the originally symmetrically paired aortic arches have been reduced in number to a single unpaired arch that lies on the left side of the median line of the body.

the Annelida. In the Arthropoda the first two characteristics are combined with the presence of an exoskeleton and jointed appendages. In the Chordata metamerism occurs in combination with a hollow dorsal nervous system, notochord, and other peculiar features.

7. *Habitat.* The environment in which an animal lives is *not* a criterion for its classification; but information concerning the major habitat or habitats of the members of a phylum aids in forming a conception of the group. Thus all the Echinodermata are inhabitants of the ocean; the greater number of the Platyhelminthes and at least half of the Nemathelminthes are parasitic; and very few of the Porifera occur in fresh water, though all are aquatic.

In the accompanying table of the chief groups of animals and in the discussion of them that follows, extinct groups are starred.

The Animal Phyla and Some of Their Subdivisions

SUBKINGDOM I. PROTOZOA

The Unicellular Animals

PHYLUM I. PROTOZOA. Animals composed of a single cell or of a colony of similar cells.

SUBKINGDOM II. METAZOA

Multicellular Animals with Specialized Tissues

(1) *Metazoa without a true digestive cavity*

PHYLUM II. PORIFERA. The Sponges. Diploblastic, phagocytic.

(2) *Metazoa with a true digestive cavity with mouth but no anus; coelom absent*

PHYLUM III. COELENTERATA. The Coelenterates: Hydra, corals, jellyfishes, sea anemones, etc. Dipoblastic; with stinging cells.

PHYLUM IV. CTENOPHORA. The Comb Jellies or Sea Walnuts. Transitional between diplo- and triploblastic; without stinging cells.

(*All remaining phyla triploblastic*)

PHYLUM V. PLATYHELMINTHES. The Flatworms: Planaria, liver flukes, tapeworms, etc.

(3) *Metazoa with coelom in addition to digestive cavity; mouth and anus present; body built on tube-within-tube plan*

(Body unsegmented = non-metameric)

PHYLUM VI. NEMATHELMINTHES. The Roundworms: Nematodes, etc.

PHYLUM VII. ECHINODERMATA. The Echinoderms. Radially symmetrical or with secondary bilateral symmetry.

Class 1. STARFISHES. (Asteroidea.)

Class 2. SERPENT STARS OR BRITTLE STARS. (Ophiuroidea.)

Class 3. SEA URCHINS AND SAND DOLLARS. (Echinoidea.)

Class 4. SEA CUCUMBERS. (Holothuroidea.)

Class 5. SEA LILIES OR FEATHER STARS. (Crinoidea.)

PHYLUM VIII. MOLLUSCA. The Mollusks. Bilaterally symmetrical or twisted. Body enclosed in a shell (with rare exceptions).
Class 1. CHITONS. (Amphineura.)
Class 2. SNAILS. (Gastropoda.)
Class 3. TOOTH SHELLS. (Scaphopoda.)
Class 4. BIVALVE MOLLUSCS. (Pelecypoda or Lamellibranchiata.) Clams, etc.
Class 5. CEPHALOPOD MOLLUSCS. (Cephalopoda.) Squids, octopus, etc.
(Body segmented = metameric)
PHYLUM IX. ANNELIDA. The Segmented Worms: earthworms, leeches, etc.
PHYLUM X. ONYCHOPHORA. Peripatus, etc. Annelid and arthropodlike features.
PHYLUM XI. ARTHROPODA. The Arthropods. Body enclosed in jointed armor.
Class 1. *TRILOBITES. (Trilobita.) Primitive arthropods.
Class 2. CRUSTACEANS. (Crustacea.) Lobsters, crabs, water fleas, barnacles, etc.
Class 3. ARACHNIDS AND KIN. (Chelicerata.) King crabs (Xiphosurida), sea spiders (Pycnogonida), *eurypterids (Eurypterida), spiders, mites, scorpions (Arachnida).
Class 4. MILLIPEDES AND KIN. (Diplopoda, Pauropoda, Symphyla.)
Class 5. CENTIPEDES. (Chilopoda.)
Class 6. INSECTS. (Insecta or Hexapoda.) Springtails, bristletails, grasshoppers, dragonflies, bugs, beetles, flies, butterflies, bees, etc.
PHYLUM XII. CHORDATA. The Chordates. With notochord, hollow dorsal nerve cord, and gill pouches or slits in pharynx.
Subphylum A. **Primitive Chordates.** Protochordata: acorn worms, sea squirts or tunicates, Amphioxus. Without cranium, jaws, backbone, or paired appendages.
Subphylum B. **Vertebrates.** (Vertebrata or Craniata). With cranium and backbone.
Class 1. JAWLESS FISHES. (Agnatha.) Without true jaws or paired appendages.
Subclass 1. *Ostracoderms. (Ostracodermata.) Bony, armored.
Subclass 2. Lampreys and Hagfishes. (Cyclostomata.) Bone lost.
Class 2. *PRIMITIVE JAWED FISHES. (Placodermi.) Bony; primitive jaws.
Subclass 1. *Acanthodians. (Acanthodii.) "Spiny sharks."
Subclass 2. *Arthrodires. (Arthrodira.) Joint-necked fishes.
Subclass 3. *Antiarchs. (Antiarchi.) Flippered fishes.
Subclass 4. *Stegoselachians. (Stegoselachii.) The remaining placoderms, sometimes called "the funny fishes."
Class 3. SHARKS AND RAYS. (Chondrichthyes.) Bone lost, skeleton cartilaginous; jaws advanced in structure; scales placoid.
Class 4. BONY FISHES. (Osteichthyes.) Bone retained; jaws advanced in structure; scales various.
Subclass 1. Choanate (Internal-nostrilled) Fishes. (Choanichthyes.) Includes the lungfishes (Dipnoi), *lobe-finned fishes (Crossopterygii), and coelacanths (Coelacanthi).
Subclass 2. Ray-finned Fishes. (Actinopterygii.) Includes the "ganoids" and the modern teleosts (Teleosti), the dominant fishes of the recent fresh waters and seas.

The Tetrapod Series

Four-legged "Land" Vertebrates

Class 5. AMPHIBIANS. (Amphibia.) Primitive tetrapod vertebrates; eggs without a shell, embryo without amnion, larvae typically aquatic, respiring by gills; adults with highly glandular, usually scaleless skin, typically terrestrial and respiring by lungs; digits very rarely clawed.

Subclass 1. *Stegocephalians, Frogs, and Toads*. (Apsidospondyli.) Includes the *Labyrinthodontia, of which *Seymouria* is one, and the modern frogs and toads (Salientia or Anura).

Subclass 2. *Salamanders, Blindworms, and Their Kin*. (Lepospondyli.) Includes several extinct orders, the modern salamanders (Urodela), and blindworms (Apoda or Gymnophiona).

Class 6. REPTILES. (Reptilia.) Typically terrestrial tetrapods (some secondarily aquatic), respiring by lungs; with a shelled egg, dry cornified skin usually covered by scales or bony scutes, and toes usually clawed.

Subclass 1. *Cotylosaurs and Turtles*. (Anapsida.) Includes the primitive stem reptiles (*Cotylosauria) and the turtles and tortoises (Chelonia or Testudinata).

Subclass 2. *Pelycosaurs and Mammal-like Reptiles*. (*Synapsida.) Includes the fin-backed reptiles (*Pelycosauria) and the mammal-like reptiles (*Therapsida).

Subclass 3. *Ichthyosaurs*. (*Parapsida or Ichthyopterygia.) Includes the fish lizards (*Ichthyosauria).

Subclass 4. *Plesiosaurs and Their Kin*. (*Euryapsida or Synaptosauria.) Includes several groups of extinct aquatic reptiles, chief among which are the plesiosaurs (*Plesiosauria).

Subclass 5. *Scaly Reptiles and Archosaurs*. (Diapsida.) Includes two main divisions: (1) the scaly reptiles (Lepidosauria), with the *eosuchians, tuataras, lizards, and snakes; (2) the ruling reptiles or archosaurs (Archosauria), with the *phytosaurs, crocodilians, *pterosaurs, and *saurischian and *ornithischian dinosaurs.

Class 7. BIRDS. (Aves.) Body covered with feathers; forelimbs modified for flight; with a shelled egg, warm blood, and completely four-chambered heart.

Subclass 1. *Reptilian Birds*. (Archaeornithes.) Includes *Archaeopteryx and *Archaeornis (Jurassic.)

Subclass 2. *True Birds*. (Neornithes.) Includes the toothed birds (*Odontognathae, with *Hesperonis and *Ichthyornis); the ratite birds (Palaeognathae, with ostriches, rheas, emus, casuaries, "elephant-birds" (*Aepyornis), moas (*Dinornis), kiwis, and tinamous); and the carinate birds (Neognathae, with loons, grebes, albatrosses and petrels, penguins, pelicans and allies, herons and allies, ducks and allies, hawks and allies, pheasants and allies, marsh birds, *Diatryma, gulls and shore birds, doves and pigeons, parrots, cuckoos and road runners, owls, goatsuckers and whippoorwills, swifts and hummingbirds, African colies, trogons, kingfishers and hornbills and allies, woodpeckers and toucans, and perching or passerine birds—the last group including about half the modern bird population).

Class 8. MAMMALS. (Mammalia.) Body usually covered with hair; warm blood and completely four-chambered heart; young nourished on milk from mammary glands of female.

Subclass 1. *Egg-laying Mammals.* (Prototheria.) Includes the monotremes (duckbill, Ornithorhynchus; spiny anteater, Tachyglossus).

Subclass 2. *True Mammals.* (Theria.) The classification of this group is considered in some detail in the treatment which follows.

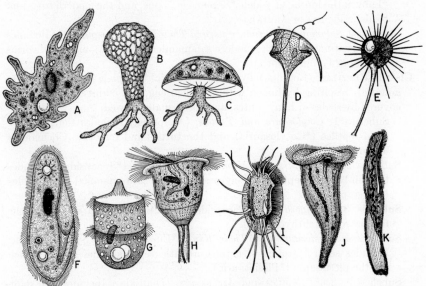

FIG. B.1. Representative Protozoa. *A* to *C*, class Sarcodina, order Amoebina. *A*, *Amoeba proteus*, a naked type. *B*, *Difflugia oblonga*, which makes a shell of sand grains. *C*, *Arcella vulgaris*, which secretes a shell. *D*, class Mastigophora; Ceratium, a flagellate. *E*, class Suctoria; Ephelota, with feeding "tentacles" through which it sucks the cell contents of other protozoans. *F* to *K*, class Ciliata. *F*, Paramecium. *G*, Didinium, predatory on other protozoans. *H*, Vorticella, a stalked food strainer. *I*, Euplotes, a "walking" species with "legs" (cirri) made up of fused cilia. *J*, Stentor, a food strainer. *K*, Spirostomum, a large free-swimming type. (*Courtesy General Biological Supply House, Inc.*)

Phylum I. PROTOZOA (pro′ to zo′ a; Greek *protos*, "first," and *zoon*, "animal").

Single-celled animals or colonies of relatively loosely aggregated cells exhibiting little or no cell differentiation or division of labor, though some colonies, like Volvox,[1] have differentiated germ cells. Minute, mainly microscopic forms. Examples: Amoeba (Fig. 13.1), Paramecium (Fig. 15.2), etc.

[1] Euglena, Volvox, and Stentor may be regarded as Algae, since they contain chlorophyll; but since they possess a number of animal characteristics, they are often included among the Protozoa by zoologists. These organisms are excellent examples of the Protista.

The Protozoa are the simplest of all animals. Because of their microscopic size, they do not come within our everyday experience, and one who for the first time sees them swarming in a drop of pond water under the microscope feels as though he were discovering a new world. Protozoa are unable to live under permanently dry conditions, but they may occur in fabulous numbers in moist or aquatic situations. Fresh-water ponds, lakes, and streams have many of them; uncountable numbers live in the sea; and there is a great protozoan fauna in the soil. Many species of Protozoa are parasitic, living on or within the bodies of other

FIG. B.2. Model of a marine protozoan, *Lychnosphaera regina*. This is a member of the class Sarcodina, order Radiolaria. The skeleton is composed chiefly of silicious spicules. (*Courtesy American Museum of Natural History.*)

animals. Among the more interesting and important parasites are the species that live within the red blood cells of man and produce malaria.

Approximately 15,000 species of Protozoa have been described.

Phylum II. PORIFERA (po rĭf′ er a; Latin, *porus*, "pore," and *ferre*, "to bear").

The *sponges*. Primitive aquatic Metazoa, mostly marine and invariably sessile; usually colonial or consisting of many individuals indistinguishably fused; exhibiting the following characters (Figs. 13.4 and B.3):

Body wall diploblastic, consisting in the adult of an outer dermal epithelium and an enclosed gastral epithelium, between which there is usually a noncellular layer, the mesoglea. The mesoglea is a jellylike substance, in which occur the germ cells and a skeleton of spicules or spongin. Embryological data indicate that the two germ layers are not homologous with the ectoderm and entoderm of higher phyla. Symmetry radial or lacking. No metamerism. Possessed of a generalized body cavity, the cloaca, reached from the outside by way of many small incurrent pores and opening to the outside by a single large excurrent pore, the osculum. Body cavity not homologous with that of the coelenterates, which it superficially resembles.

Fig. B.3. Representative sponges. Left, the spongin fiber skeleton of a Florida glove sponge, Hippospongia. Right, the redbeard sponge, *Microciona prolifera*. (*Courtesy U.S. Fish and Wildlife Service and American Museum of Natural History, respectively.*)

Among the features peculiar to this group are the presence of pores in the body wall, forming part of a canal system, and the presence in the gastral epithelium of collared cells, the flagella of which create a current of water through the canals that brings in food particles and oxygen and carries away waste products.

Sponges are an aberrant group that belongs near the bottom of the animal series and outside the main line of metazoan evolution; hence they are often separated from the rest of the Metazoa and are called Parazoa. A very few species of sponges live in fresh water. The majority, found in the shallow waters of the ocean, are encrusting or weakly erect; those occurring in the deeper portions of quiet seas include stemmed, foliate, and ramifying forms, such as finger and cup sponges, the Venus'-flower-basket, and the bath sponge of commerce. Many sponges consist of indistinguishably fused individuals and may weigh hundreds of pounds.

About 3,000 species of sponges have been described.

Phylum III. COELENTERATA (sēl en' ter ā' ta; Greek, *koilos*, "hollow," and *enteron*, "intestine").

The *hydroids, jellyfishes, sea anemones,* and *corals* (Fig. B.4). Simple Metazoa, mostly marine. Exhibiting usually the following characters:

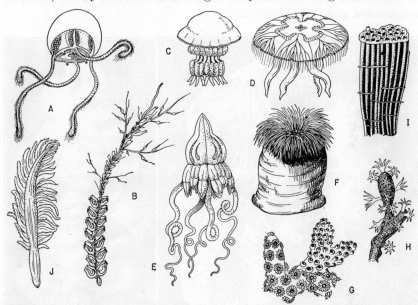

FIG. B.4. Representative coelenterates. *A* and *B*, Hydrozoa. *A*, Petasus, a medusa or jellyfish. *B*, Halistemma, a colony of differentiated polyps related to the Portuguese man-of-war. *C* to *E*, Scyphozoa; three types of medusae. *F* to *J*, Anthozoa. *F*, Metridium, a sea anemone. *G*, Madrepora, a coral. *H*, Corallium, the precious red coral of the Mediterranean. *I*, Tubipora, the organ-pipe coral. *J*, Pennatula, one of the sea pens. (*Modified from Turtox chart, courtesy General Biological Supply House, Inc.*)

Body wall diploblastic, with an outer germ layer, the ectoderm, and an inner, the entoderm, enclosing a third jellylike, noncellular layer, the mesoglea, which may become very thick in some forms (jellyfish). Somatic cell differentiation marked. Radial symmetry, modified by an increasing tendency toward bilateral symmetry in the higher species of the phylum. No metamerism. Possessed of a coelenteron—a single body cavity lined with entoderm and opening to the outside by a mouth but lacking an anus. The typical sac-type of body organization occurs throughout but is modified to form either a tubular polyp or a bell- or umbrella-shaped medusa (jellyfish).

Among the features peculiar to this group is an alternation of generations, called *metagenesis*, whereby a usually sessile and colonial asexual polyp generation produces, by budding, the sexual, often free-swimming medusa or jellyfish generation. The presence of tentacles furnished with highly specialized stinging cells known as *nematocysts* is another unique characteristic.

The coelenterates are divided into three classes. With the exception of the Portuguese man-of-war and a few other showy forms, the first class, Hydrozoa, comprising the freshwater Hydra (Figs. 13.5 and 32.9), the marine colonial hydroids (Obelia, etc.), small jellyfishes, and the hydrocorals, is known chiefly to students of aquatic life. The group consists of thousands of species, some very common and many very beautiful.

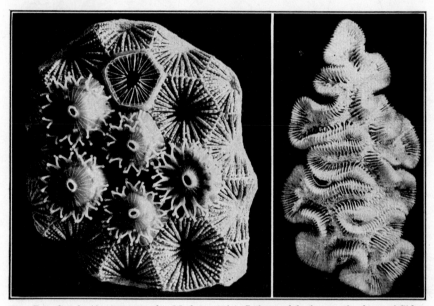

FIG. B.5. Corals (Anthozoa, order Madreporaria). Left, model of part of colony of Siderastraea, showing expanded polyps, a polyp in cross section (upper center) and empty polyp cups or thecae. Right, the skeleton of the common rose coral, *Manicina areolata*, showing elongate thecae formerly occupied by fused, many-mouthed polyps. (*Courtesy American Museum of Natural History and University of Miami Department of Biology, respectively.*)

To the second class, Scyphozoa, belong practically all the large jellyfishes (Fig. 32.2), familiar seashore sights, their often vivid coloring and brilliant phosphorescence making them conspicuous.

Sea fans, sea feathers, most of the corals (Fig. 33.19), and all the sea anemones make up the last class, Anthozoa, some members of which are familiar to all visitors to the seashore.

Approximately 4,500 species of this phylum are known.

Phylum IV. CTENOPHORA (tē nŏf' or a; Greek, *ktenos*, "comb," *phoros*, "bearing").

The *sea walnuts* or *comb jellies*. Relatively simple marine Metazoa, exhibiting the following characters:

Body wall of adults primarily diploblastic. However, the jellylike mesoglea, separating the ectoderm from the entoderm, contains some muscle cells that originate embryologically in such a manner as to suggest that they are mesodermal. Hence the Ctenophora is often placed as the most primitive of the triploblastic phyla. Radial combined with bilateral symmetry (sometimes called *biradial symmetry*). A highly specialized coelenteron consisting of one cavity that connects with a system of tubes and canals, and another cavity (reached through the single opening, the mouth), each cavity flattened on a plane at right angles to the other.

Among the features peculiar to the phylum are the tentacles equipped with adhesive cells instead of nematocysts and the possession of eight meridionally arranged rows (combs) of swimming plates.

The Ctenophora is a minor phylum composed of exclusively marine jellyfishlike animals, formerly classified as Coelenterata. Ctenophora differ from coelenterates in their general body form (bell-shaped or ribbonlike), their tendency toward the triploblastic type of organization, the absence of nematocysts, and biradial symmetry. There is no mistaking ctenophores seen in life: they are remarkably transparent and are among the most beautiful of all sea animals. During the day, the plate rows are irridescent with reflected light, and at night, the entire animal may be vividly phosphorescent.

One hundred species are known.

Phylum V. PLATYHELMINTHES (plat′ e hel min′ thēz; Greek, *platys*, "broad," and *helminthos*, "worm").

The *flatworms*. Intermediate Metazoa, exhibiting the following characters.

Body triploblastic, much flattened dorsoventrally. Flatworms possess a definite third layer of cells, the mesoderm, and have developed from this layer various systems of organs. Bilateral symmetry. No true metamerism, unless the tapeworm be considered an "individual" rather than a colony of individuals.

Digestive system essentially a coelenteron, with a single opening, the mouth. In many species, however, the coelenteron has been modified into a highly branched gastrovascular system. No coelom; no anus. Digestive system entirely lacking in the tapeworms, which absorb through the body wall food already digested in the intestine of their host.

Among the special features of the phylum are the presence of "flame cells" in the excretory system and the fact that individuals are for the most part hermaphroditic, having both male and female reproductive systems.

The Platyhelminthes include both free-living and parasitic species. The former, of which Planaria (class Turbellaria, Fig. 13.6) is an example, are the less numerous and occur principally in fresh or salt water. The parasites include the flukes (class Trematoda) and the tapeworms (class Cestoidea, or Cestoda). Most of

FIG. B.6. Free-living flatworms (Platyhelminthes, class Turbellaria). Left, the fresh-water triclad Planaria; right, the marine polyclad *Yungia aurantiaca*. (*Courtesy General Biological Supply House, Inc., and American Museum of Natural History, respectively.*)

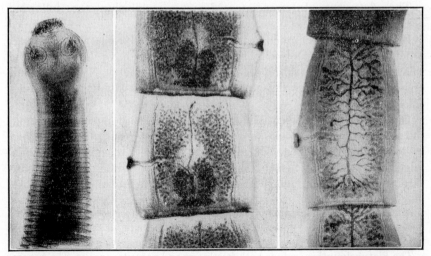

FIG. B.7. The dog and cat tapeworm, *Taenia pisiformis* (Platyhelminthes, class Cestoda.) The larvae encyst in the liver of rabbits; the adults occur in the intestines of rabbit-eating mammals. Left to right: the attaching "head" (scolex); young segments (proglottids) from the middle of the worm; mature egg-filled segments from the end of the worm, ready to be shed. (*Courtesy General Biological Supply House, Inc.*)

these live within the bodies of other animals, and many of them cause diseases of man and domestic animals. As in the instance of other parasitic animals, they show great specialization related to their peculiar mode of life, such as enormously increased powers of reproduction and extremely complicated life cycles that in certain cases involve three or four different larval forms, each requiring a different host.

Approximately 5,000 species of the phylum are known.

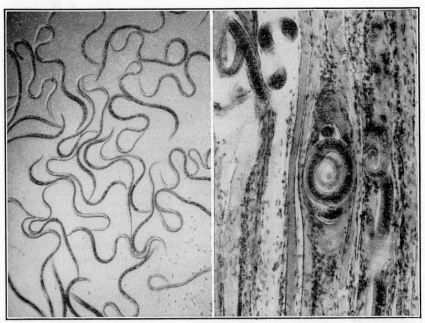

Fig. B.8. Roundworms (Nemathelminthes, class Nematoda). Left, the vinegar eel, Turbatrix, a free-living form. Right, the larvae of *Trichinella spiralis*, the trichina worm, encysted in muscle. If meat containing encysted larvae is eaten by a susceptible mammal (including man) the larvae are freed by digestion of the meat, grow to maturity and mate in the intestine. The female worm produces as many as 1,500 minute larvae. These enter the lymphatics in the intestinal wall, pass to the blood, and are carried to various parts of the body of the host, where they burrow into the tissues and encyst. Heavy infestation causes the sometimes fatal disease trichinosis. (*Courtesy General Biological Supply House, Inc.*)

Phylum VI. NEMATHELMINTHES (něm′ a thel min′ thēz; Greek, *nematos,* "thread," and *helminthos,* "worm").

The unsegmented *roundworms* or *threadworms.* Intermediate Metazoa, exhibiting for the most part the following characters:

Triploblastic; bilateral symmetry; no metamerism. Digestive tract complete, both mouth and anus being present. Body cavity or coelom present, though incomplete or atypical in not being lined throughout with mesoderm. Body elongated, cylindrical, usually pointed at both ends. Body organization of the most primitive tube-within-tube type.

These smooth, glistening, slender worms occur in large numbers, both as regards species and individuals, in soil and in fresh and salt water and as parasites in plants and animals. The common vinegar eel (Fig. B.8) is an example of the free-living roundworms; the horsehair "snake" is typical of others that spend part of their lives as parasites and another part as free-living organisms. The hookworms (Fig. B.9) and Ascaris are roundworms completely adapted to parasitic existence.

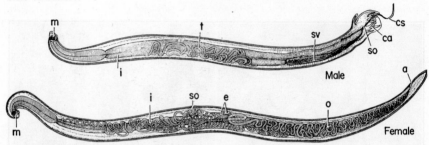

Fig. B.9. A roundworm *Necator americanus*, the commoner of the two chief human hookworms in the United States. The adults live in the intestine, feeding on blood from the intestinal walls. The eggs are passed with feces; they hatch into small larvae that can penetrate exposed skin, causing "ground itch." In the body they travel in the blood and lymph vessels to the lungs, thence to the trachea and esophagus, and so to the intestine. This figure shows the anatomy of the male and female worms, which is fairly typical of that of nematodes in general. *a*, anus; *ca*, copulatory appendages; *cs*, copulatory setae; *e*, eggs in oviduct; *i*, intestine; *m*, mouth; *so* sex openings; *sv*, seminal vesicle; *t*, testes. (*Courtesy General Biological Supply House, Inc.*)

Approximately 80,000 species of Nemathelminthes have been described. Partly because of the extreme difficulty of recognizing species in this group, it is probable that many more thousands remain to be discovered.

ANIMALS OF UNCERTAIN RELATIONSHIP

A number of groups of animals are considered together here because their relationships to other animals and to each other, as well as their position in an evolutionary sequence, are uncertain. All are triploblastic and bilaterally symmetrical, and all show a degree of organization at least as complex as that of the Platyhelminthes and Nemathelminthes.

NEMERTINEA (nĕm′ er tin′ e a). *Worms,* mostly marine, probably related to the flatworms. Important characteristics: a protrusible proboscis that lies in an anterior sheath (the latter considered by some the coelom); digestive tract tube-like, with both mouth and anus; a blood-vascular system. They are the most primitive animals with a circulatory system.

ROTIFERA (ro tĭf′ er a). *Rotifers* or wheel animalcules. Minute but complex animals, most of which live in fresh water, although some are marine and a few parasitic. Movements of cilia at the anterior end suggest rotating wheels. Digestive tract tubelike, with both mouth and anus; easily visible chitinous jaws present within pharynx; 1,000 species.

BRYOZOA (brī′ o zo′ a). *Moss animals.* Small, sessile, unsegmented, mostly colonial animals, living in both fresh and salt water, though more abundant in the latter. Mouth enclosed in a crown of tentacles, the lophophore, a characteristic structure; intestine U-shaped, with anus near the mouth. Bryzoan colonies often bear a superficial resemblance to hydroid colonies, and many secrete coral-like skeletons. This group is sometimes combined with the following one to constitute the phylum Molluscoidea. About 1,200 known species.

BRACHIOPODA (brak′ i op′ o da). *Lamp shells* (Fig. 27.1). Body unsegmented and covered by a calcareous (limy) two-valved shell, which often has the appearance of an ancient form of lamp. The shells cover the dorsal and ventral

FIG. B.10. Rotifers and other minute organisms in a tiny portion of a pond. Above, center, a trap bladder of the flowering plant Utricularia, ready for victims. Left, a spherical (radiating) colony of the rotifer *Conochilus hippocrepis*. Lower left, a large solitary rotifer, *Dicranophorus forcipatus*. Diatoms and other algae are lodged on the Utricularia branches. (*Courtesy American Museum of Natural History.*)

surfaces instead of the lateral surfaces, as in the clams and mussels (phylum Mollusca). The mouth is situated between two looped ciliated arms (*lophophore*), which lie coiled within the shell; the ciliated food canal may end blindly or be provided with an anus near the mouth; the body may be directly moored to the substratum or be attached by a stalk (*pedicel*) from the posterior region. More abundant in past geological periods than at present, thousands of fossil species being known; 500 living species, all marine.

Phylum VII. ECHINODERMATA (e kĭn′ o der′ ma ta; Greek, *echinos*, "hedgehog," referring to the spines, and *derma*, "skin").

Starfishes, brittle stars, sea urchins, sea cucumbers, sea lilies. Complex Metazoa, typically with the following characters:

Triploblastic. No marked metamerism. Adults radially symmetrical (usually on a plan of five repeated parts). Inasmuch as larval echinoderms are bilaterally symmetrical, the phylum has probably been derived from bilaterally symmetrical ancestors. A large coelom and distinct alimentary canal that usually, but not always, terminates in an anus.

The following special features of the phylum are notable: skin usually spiny; body wall with calcareous plates (much reduced in the sea cucumbers) that form a protective exoskeleton; a peculiar water-vascular system that, in most forms, constitutes a hydrostatic pressure system that regulates movements of the tube

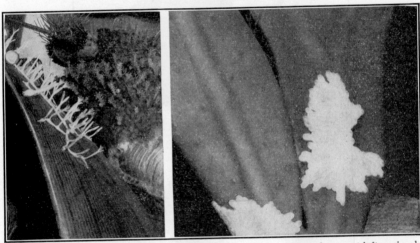

Fig. B.11. Marine bryozoans or moss animals, greatly enlarged. On eel grass at left, a simply branched creeping colony (Pedicellina) and an encrusting colony; on kelp at right, Membranipora in large encrusting colonies. (*Courtesy American Museum of Natural History.*)

feet (locomotor organs characteristic of this phylum). Circulatory and nervous systems poorly developed.

The echinoderms are all marine and constitute a considerable portion of the animal life of the seashore. Among the objects most likely to attract the attention of the shore visitor, particularly if the coast is somewhat rocky, are the five-armed starfishes (class Asteroidea). These are often found in abundance, when the tide is low, clinging to rocks and seaweeds. Among the seaweeds that grow below the tidal zone there may be found somewhat similar animals called serpent stars (class Ophiuroidea), which have five slender, wriggling, snakelike arms. Just below the reach of low tide there occur other related animals, of rounded form, covered with long, coarse spines; these are commonly known as sea urchins (class Echinoidea). The flattened sand dollars are also members of this class. And if one digs in the sand exposed between tides, he may encounter pink or whitish worm-like animals, without distinct appendages but nevertheless able to cling to the hand; some of these belong to a group of the echinoderms known as sea cucumbers (class Holothuroidea). The sea lilies, or feather stars (class Crinoidea), live mostly in deep water; they were more abundant in the past than they are today (Fig. 25.2).

These five classes of animals, different as they may seem at first glance, are included in this one phylum because they possess in common the features specified above. Certain indications from the developmental stages of echinoderms suggest that these animals and the chordates had a common ancestry.

Approximately 6,000 modern species of echinoderms are known.

Phylum VIII. MOLLUSCA (mol lus' ka; Latin, *molluscus*, "soft").

Snails, clams, squids, and *octopuses*. Complex Metazoa, typically exhibiting the following characters:

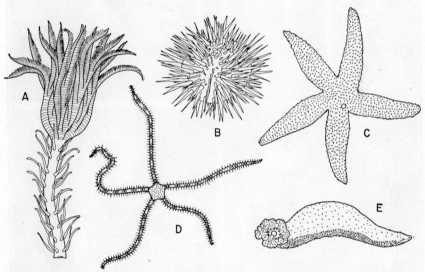

Fig. B.12. Some echinoderms. *A*, a crinoid or sea lily, class Crinoidea. *B*, Arbacia, a sea urchin, class Echinoidea. *C*, Asterias, a starfish, class Asteroidea. *D*, Ophiura, a serpent star, class Ophiuroidea. *E*, a sea cucumber, class Holothuroidea. (*Courtesy General Biological Supply House, Inc.*)

Triploblastic. Bilateral symmetry, tending toward asymmetry (snails). Soft-bodied, unsegmented animals without jointed appendages.

Coelom present. Complex respiratory (gills), circulatory, reproductive (monoecious or dioecious) and nervous systems. Digestive system complete with anus. Nervous system variable, not of the ladder or dorsal cord types, exhibiting strong cephalization in certain groups that have very complex organs of sight.

Usually a shell of lime carbonate is present, secreted from the outer surface of an enveloping layer of tissue called the *mantle;* a space, the mantle cavity, separates the main body from the mantle. The shell may be: (1) of *one piece*, pyramidal or coiled (in snails); (2) composed of *two lateral valves* (in clams, etc., called *bivalves);* (3) composed of a series of small *plates* (in Amphineura); (4)

reduced or wanting (in the squid, octopus, some snails). Even when the shell is rudimentary or absent, the mantle and its cavity are still present. All Mollusca possess a fleshy organ called the *foot*, which, in the snail, is usually a flat sole used for creeping over surfaces; in the clam, is generally a wedge-shaped organ used for plowing in mud or sand; and in the squid, is divided into arms provided with sucking disks and used for seizing prey.

Fɪɢ. B.13. Snails and tooth shells, phylum Mollusca. The tooth shell, *Dentalium entale*, class Scaphopoda, is in the center above. All the others are snails, class Gastropoda. Upper left, a small whelk, *Cyclonassa neritea*. Upper right, a conch, *Fusus syracusanus*. Lower left, a periwinkle, Littorina. Lower right, *Helix nemoralis*, an air-breathing European tree snail naturalized in the United States. All the others are marine. (*Courtesy American Museum of Natural History.*)

Mollusks are among the more abundant of animals. Many snails and slugs crawl about on land, breathing by means of a sort of lung. Fresh-water ponds and streams are the haunts of numerous species of snails, both lung breathers and gill breathers, as well as of the fresh-water mussels and clams. The sea, however, is the home of the greatest variety of mollusks. The principal classes of this phylum are easily distinguished; they are as follows:

Class 1. *The Chitons* (Amphineura). These are flattened or wormlike mollusks with obvious bilateral symmetry. The commonest type has the back covered with a shell composed of a longitudinal row of eight curved plates, the joints between which allow the animal to roll up like an armadillo. Chitons are all marine, living mostly on rocky coasts. There are several hundred existing and about 100 known fossil species.

Class 2. *The Snails and Slugs* (Gastropoda). In this class, there is a well-defined head, and the bilateral symmetry is usually obscured by a one-piece spiral shell, which is sometimes absent (Fig. 32.3). The foot has a flat, crawling sole. Most snails are marine, and many of the most attractive sea shells of our beaches are made by members of this group, some of which live among rocks and others in sand or mud. Some of the marine snails have become pelagic and swim at the

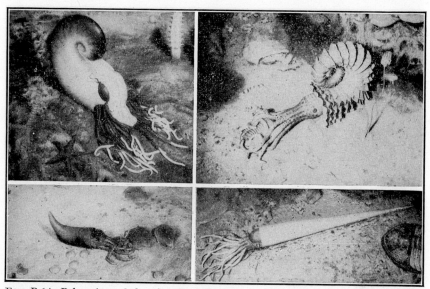

Fig. B.14. Paleozoic cephalopod mollusks. From straight-shelled flat-partitioned types (lower right) there developed various curved (lower left), coiled (upper left) and ornate (upper right) types with flat or simply waved internal partitions in the shell. Eventually from some of these came the Mesozoic ammonites with their complexly frilled and wrinkled partitions. (*From a restoration of Devonian marine life in New York, courtesy Rochester Museum.*)

surface by flapping their two-winged foot. Most are herbivorous, but many live on decomposing animal matter, and some are predacious. A relatively small number of kinds inhabits fresh water, and the land snails (Pulmonata) have a sort of lung developed from the mantle cavity.

Class 3. *The Tooth Shells* (Scaphopoda). A small group of marine mollusks with a conical shell, straight or curved, and open at both ends; marine, burrowing in sand and mud.

Class 4. *The Bivalve Mollusks* (Pelecypoda, or Lamellibranchiata). A very large group of mollusks, which lack a head, have bilateral symmetry, a shell composed of two lateral valves, and a mantle of two lobes (Fig. 32.5). Largely marine, but some occur in fresh water.

Class 5. *The Cephalopods* (Cephalopoda). Squids, octopods, nautiloids, ammonites, etc. These mollusks have a well-developed head with prominent eyes, the latter closely analogous to but not homologous with the eyes of vertebrates; mouth with horny jaws and a rasping tongue like that of the snails; foot transformed into a ring of arms or tentacles surrounding the mouth, prehensile and often furnished with sucking disks and hooks; the mantle muscular, its cavity so arranged that the water contained in it can be squirted out through a "funnel" or "siphon," thus propelling the animal backward. The earlier forms all covered with a straight-conical or coiled, chambered shell; shell reduced or absent in most modern forms.

The fossil record of this group is unusually complete (Figs. 27.7 and B.14). Surviving cephalopods are the squids, cuttlefishes, nautilus and octopus. These

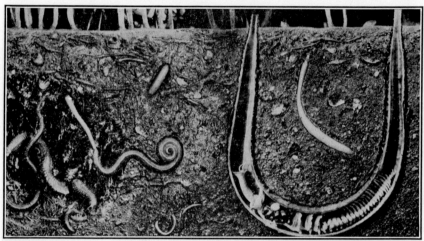

Fig. B.15. Burrowing and tube-dwelling marine worms in a section of sandy sea floor at Woods Hole, Mass. In the cavity at the left are the clamworm, *Nereis virens* (stout-bodied), and Arabella (slender); the proboscis worm, Rhynchobolus or Glycera, is also seen with its four-fanged pharyngeal proboscis extended as in catching prey. At the right is the U-shaped tube of the parchment worm Chaetopterus. This worm has some of its segments shaped like pump valves, and by means of them pumps a food-and-oxygen-bearing stream of water through the tube. Within the loop of the tube is Phascolosoma, one of the Sipunculida, a group of uncertain zoological relationships. All the others are Annelida. (*Courtesy American Museum of Natural History.*)

are among the most peculiar and fascinating of animals. Some of the deep-sea squids are the largest of all invertebrates.

Many of the mollusks are of economic importance. Some are eaten (oysters, clams, scallops); the shells of others are used for making buttons and for other commercial purposes; and the pearl oysters are the basis for an important industry. About 80,000 modern species of mollusks have been described, and fossil forms are extremely numerous. The snails appear to be the largest group in existence today and are now at the climax of their development.

Phylum IX. ANNELIDA (an nĕl' i da; Latin, *annelus*, "ring").

Segmented worms such as earthworms, marine worms, and leeches. Highly developed intermediate Metazoa, typically exhibiting the following characters.

Triploblastic; bilateral symmetry; metamerism well developed, each metamere (somite or segment) more or less similar to the others. Blood vessels, excretory organs (nephridia), and nervous system segmentally arranged. Tube-within-tube type of organization; alimentary canal differentiated into organs; distinct coelom present, lined with mesoderm and often divided into chambers by transverse metameric partitions.

A complex circulatory system present, operating with respiratory organs (external gills) in some of the marine Annelida (Fig. B.16); ventral double nerve cord with nerve centers (ganglia) in each metamere, constituting a "ladder type" of central nervous system, in front encircling the alimentary canal to form a

Fɪɢ. B.16. The plankton-straining marine annelid Amphitrite. The gill-bearing heads of two individuals are seen protruding from their tubes; a third is partly retracted. Encrusting bryozoan colonies are also shown. (*Courtesy American Museum of Natural History.*)

"brain" above it. When present, the appendages are not jointed or segmented but in the form of spines (earthworms), fleshly flaps (marine Annelida), or suckers (leeches).

Most annelids are marine, but many live in fresh water or in the soil or other moist places. A few are parasitic, notably the leeches, many of which are external parasites on the bodies of aquatic animals and a few on terrestrial animals.

The common earthworm (Lumbricus, Fig. 13.7 and 15.6) is the most frequently studied annelid. Earthworms are soft-bodied and "slimy." They live in moist earth and venture out of their burrows chiefly on damp nights. The burrows usually extend about 2 feet beneath the surface. The worms can force their way through soft ground but must eat their way through harder soil. The earth eaten passes through the alimentary canal and is deposited on the surface of the ground as "castings." Decaying vegetable matter in the soil provides food; the worms also eat leaves and other surface vegetation, which they drag into their burrows at night. Thus earthworms continually honeycomb the soil, making it more porous, permitting better penetration of air and moisture, and increasing its fertility.

About 8,000 species of Annelida have been described. The Annelida are closely related to and presumably the ancestors of the Arthropoda.

Phylum X. ONYCHOPHORA (ŏn' i kŏf' o ra; Greek, *onyx*, "claw," and *phoros*, "bearing"). Soft-bodied, wormlike creatures up to a few inches long, discontinuously distributed in the tropics. They show some features like those of Annelida, such as the paired excretory nephridia and the flexible cuticle covering the body; in other respects they suggest Arthropoda, having respiratory organs resembling the tracheae of insects, and a series paired legs showing weak segmentation. The most ancient known type was found in Cambrian marine sediments and had a pair of gills near the head; all living species are terrestrial. Example: Peripatus.

Phylum XI. ARTHROPODA (ar thrŏp' o da; Greek, *arthron*, "joint," and *podos*, "foot").

Crustaceans, centipedes, insects, spiders, and their allies. Complex Metazoa, typically exhibiting the following characters:

Triploblastic; bilaterally symmetrical; metameric. Although the body cavity is continuous and without transverse septa, metamerism is shown internally in the arrangement of the nervous system, muscles, heart, and other organs. Groups of segments tend to fuse or specialize into larger regions, such as head, thorax, and abdomen, or into combinations of these (cephalothorax). With the exception of the vertebrates, arthropods are the most highly developed metameric animals. Coelom present but much reduced, its place being taken by an extensive blood space, the hemocoele.

Jointed appendages. Usually a hard exoskeleton. Ladder type of nervous system (as in Annelida), with a tendency toward cephalization (concentration of ganglia at anterior end). Usually with well-developed and segmented head appendages (antennae, mouth parts, etc.). A main longitudinal blood vessel ("heart") dorsal to the alimentary canal. Respiration by gills or tracheae.

The arthropods comprise about four-fifths of all the known species of animals. Many occur in marine and fresh-water habitats, but they are best represented on land. They may be regarded as the dominant animals of today, if numbers of different species and numbers of individuals are accepted as criteria of dominance. Approximately 650,000 living species are known, of which 600,000 are insects. This huge assemblage of animals may be divided into classes, as follows:

Class 1. *The Trilobites* (*Trilobita). Primitive marine arthropods of the Paleozoic era (Figs. 25.2, 27.2 and B.17), with flattened, segmented bodies, covered above with a carapace; with an anterior head region, a segmented thorax, and a tail plate or telson; and with a pair of longitudinal grooves dividing the body into a central and two lateral lobes. Head region with a pair of slender antennae, a pair of compound eyes, and paired ventral appendages; thoracic segments each with a pair of two-branched ventral appendages. The group has been discussed in Chap. XXVII.

Class 2. *The Crustaceans* (Crustacea). Mostly aquatic; usually with gills; chitinous exoskeleton usually stiffened with limy deposits into a carapace. Head (of five fused segments) with two pairs of antennae, a pair of jaws, and two pairs of maxillae; segmental appendages usually two-branched (biramous). This large group of some 25,000 existing species includes marine, fresh-water, and terrestrial

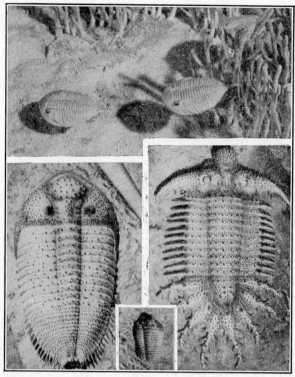

Fig. B.17. Some Paleozoic trilobites. Upper, the Silurian Dalmanites, swimming. The rest are Devonian species. Lower left, Arctineurus; center, Calymene; right, *Terataspis grandis*, which reached a length of 18 inches and is one of the largest known trilobites. (*Courtesy University of Michigan Museums.*)

types with a wide range in form and size. The principal groups are the Branchiopoda (brine shrimps, fairy shrimps, water fleas, etc.), the Ostracoda (minute bivalved crustaceans), the Copepoda (small forms important in the plankton), the Cirripedia (goose barnacles and rock barnacles, Fig. 32.6), and the great subclass Malacostraca, which includes by far the majority of crustaceans. Among the malacostracans are included various shrimplike forms, the flattened isopods (pill bugs, wood lice, and various free-living and parasitic aquatic forms), the compressed amphipods (sand fleas, etc.), the mantis shrimps (Squilla, etc.), and the decapods (true shrimps, prawns, lobsters, crayfishes, crabs).

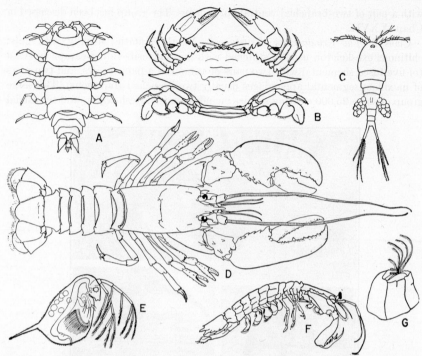

FIG. B.18. Representative crustaceans. *A*, Asellus, a fresh-water isopod about half an inch long. *B*, Callinectes, the edible blue crab. *C*, Cyclops, a minute plankton copepod. *D*, Homarus, the lobster. *E*, Daphnia, a small plankton phyllopod. *F*, Squilla, the mantis shrimp, several inches long. *G*, Balanus, a rock barnacle. (*Modified from Turtox chart, courtesy General Biological Supply House, Inc.*)

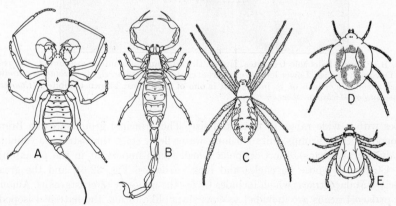

FIG. B.19. Representative arachnids. *A*, Mastigoproctus, a nonpoisonous though formidable-looking whip scorpion. *B*, a true scorpion with stinging tail. *C*, a typical spider, order Araneae. *D*, a water mite, order Acarina. *E*, a tick, order Acarina. (*Modified from Turtox chart, courtesy General Biological Supply House, Inc.*)

Class 3. *The Arachnids and Allies* (Chelicerata). No antennae; body consisting of a cephalothorax and abdomen, the former furnished with six pairs of appendages—pincerlike chelicerae and pedipalps, and four pairs of legs. Respiration by book lungs or tracheae in terrestrial forms, by book gills in aquatic ones. This varied class includes the marine eurypterids (*Eurypterida, Figs. 25.3 and 27.6) and king crabs (Xiphosurida, Limulus), the sea spiders (Pycnogonida), the water bears (Tardigrada), and the parasitic tongue worms (Pentastomida), in addition

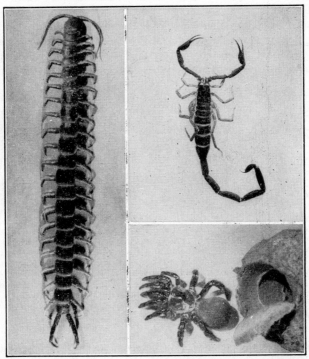

Fig. B.20. Three poisonous arthropods, the bite or sting of which is painful but not dangerous to man. Left, Scolopendra, a large centipede common in the southern United States. Upper right, *Centruroides gracilis*, the slender scorpion. Lower right, *Pachylomerus audouini*, a southern trap-door spider, with its silk-lined, hinge-lidded tube nest removed from the ground. (*Courtesy Ward's Natural Science Establishment, Inc., except scorpion, U.S. Department of Entomology and Plant Quarantine.*)

to the great group Arachnida, the subclass which includes most living chelicerates. These true arachnids include the scorpions, the whip scorpions, about 20,000 species of spiders, the harvestmen or "daddy longlegs," and the mites and ticks, in addition to other less well known types of organisms.

Class 4. *The Millipeds and Allies* (Diplopoda, Pauropoda, Symphyla). The diplopods are the *millipedes*, or thousand-legged worms. They have long subcylindrical bodies with from 25 to more than 100 segments, most segments bearing two pairs of appendages; the head has one pair of antennae and a pair of mandibles and of maxillae. The sex openings are anterior. The pauropods and symphylans are small creatures of similar general aspect, not closely related but grouped here for convenience.

Class 5. *The Centipedes* (Chilopoda) are similar in general form to the diplopods, but each segment bears a single pair of legs, the sex openings are posterior, and the anterior pair of legs is modified into poison fangs.

Class 6. *The Insects* (Insecta or Hexapoda) are air-breathing arthropods with bodies divided into head, thorax, and abdomen, each body division formed by fusion of segments. The head bears one pair of antennae, the thorax three pairs of legs. The mouth parts are formed from the appendages of three segments, grouped into a complicated chewing or sucking apparatus. Wings are present on the thorax in most groups. Insects breathe by means of tracheae or tracheal gills. The class is mainly terrestrial, with certain groups secondarily adapted to life in fresh water; marine forms are very few. A high degree of social development

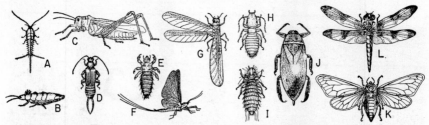

Fig. B.21. Representative lower insects. *A* and *B* are primitive wingless insects, Apterygota; all the rest belong to the winged group, Pterygota, though some have lost wings. *A*, Lepisma, a bristletail or silver fish. *B*, a collembolan or springtail. *C*, a grasshopper, Orthoptera. *D*, an earwig, Dermaptera. *E*, a body louse, Anoplura. *F*, a mayfly, Ephemeroptera. *G*, a winged (sexual caste) termite or white ant, Isoptera. *H*, a book louse or bark louse, Corrodentia. *I*, a biting louse or bird louse, Mallophaga. *J*, a giant water bug or electric-light bug, Hemiptera. *K*, a cicada or harvest locust, Homoptera (often treated as a suborder of Hemiptera.) *L*, a dragonfly, Odonata. (*Modified from Turtox chart, courtesy General Biological Supply House, Inc.*)

has been reached by the termites, ants, bees, and wasps. Insects are more numerous in species and probably in individuals than all other animals taken together; something over 600,000 species are said to have been described, and thousands of previously unknown species are named each year. Many of man's most serious competitors and enemies are insects. The essential roles of some of the flower-visiting insects in pollination are well-known, and members of this group form the basic food supply for numberless food chains. The principal subclasses and orders of insects are as follows:

Subclass 1. *Apterygota*, primitively wingless insects with little or no metamorphosis. Includes the bristletails (Thysanura) and springtails (Collembola). Members of the latter group are the oldest known insects, fossils having been found associated with psilophytes in Devonian rocks.

Subclass 2. *Pterygota*, the winged insects. Wings usually present, sometimes reduced or lost; no abdominal appendages except at tip. Among the winged insects two grades or divisions may be recognized—a lower and a higher—distinguished chiefly by their mode of development.

The lower insects (Paurometabola and Hemimetabola) show a gradual development; the young stages are *nymphs* with compound eyes, and the wings develop externally[1], increasing in size at successive molts. The nymphal form is not very different from that of the adult, and metamorphosis is gradual, there being no

Fig. B.22. Representative lower insects. Upper: left, a lantern fly, Homoptera; right, a cicada, Homoptera. Center: left, the introduced Chinese mantis, Orthoptera; center, a winged termite, Isoptera; right, a tropical walking stick, Orthoptera. Lower: left, a grasshopper, Orthoptera; center, a dobson fly, Megaloptera; right, a squash bug, Hemiptera. (*Courtesy Ward's Natural Science Establishment, Inc., except the grasshopper, photo by J. W. McManigal, Gendreau, New York.*)

well-defined pupal stage. There are at least 12 orders of this group. It includes the cockroaches, mantids, walking sticks, grasshoppers and locusts, katydids, and crickets (Orthoptera); the earwigs (Dermaptera); the stone flies (Plecoptera); the termites or white ants (Isoptera); the embiids (Embioptera); the dragonflies,

[1] For this reason the included orders are often grouped as the Exopterygota, meaning "externally winged."

some of which are sometimes called damsel flies (Odonata); the mayflies (Ephemeroptera); the biting lice (Mallophaga); the sucking lice (Anoplura); the book lice (Corrodentia); the true bugs (Hemiptera); the cicadas, aphids or plant lice, scale insects, tree hoppers, white flies, etc. (Homoptera); and the thrips (Thysanoptera).

The higher insects (Holometabola, or Endopterygota) show a sudden metamorphosis which takes place in the stage just preceding maturity. The young

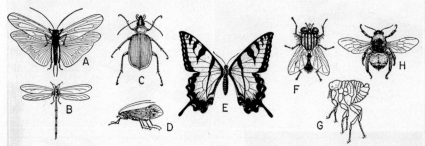

FIG. B.23. Representative higher insects (except *A*). *A*, a stone fly, Plecoptera. *B*, an ant lion, Neuroptera, adult of the doodlebug (ant lion larva) that digs pit traps in powdery soil. *C*, a ground beetle, Coleoptera. *D*, a caddis fly, Trichoptera; the aquatic larvae of this group make cases of sticks or pebbles. *E*, the tiger swallowtail butterfly, Lepidoptera. *F*, the house fly, Diptera. *G*, a flea, Siphonaptera. *H*, a bumblebee, Hymenoptera. (*Modified from Turtox chart, courtesy General Biological Supply House, Inc.*)

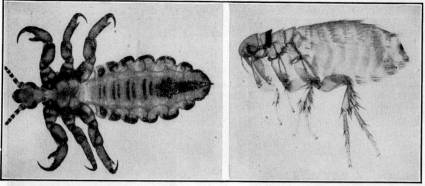

FIG. B.24. Insect parasites of mammals. Left, the body louse, *Pediculus humanus*, order Anoplura; right, a flea, order Siphonaptera. (*Courtesy of Ward's Natural Science Establishment, Inc.*)

stages are *larvae* without compound eyes and without external signs of wings; there is a pupal stage in the life history in which the larva takes on the adult form and in which the wings are everted from their internal position. The larvae are very different in form and in mode of life from the adults. There are at least ten orders of this group. It includes the scorpion flies (Mecoptera); the dobson flies (Megaloptera); the antlions, or "doodle bugs," and their allies (Neuroptera); the caddis flies (Trichoptera); the moths and butterflies (Lepidoptera); the crane flies, mosquitoes, midges, gnats, and other true flies (Diptera); the fleas (Siphonaptera); the beetles and weevils (Coleoptera); the stylopids, parasitic in bees and a few other insects (Strepsiptera); and the horntails, sawflies, ichneumon flies, gall wasps, chalcid egg parasites, ants, velvet ants, wasps, and bees (Hymenoptera).

Phylum XII. CHORDATA (cor dā′ ta; Greek, *chorde*, "cord," *i.e.*, the notochord).

The backboned animals and their allies. The *vertebrates* constitute the majority of the chordates and include man and all his nearest rela-

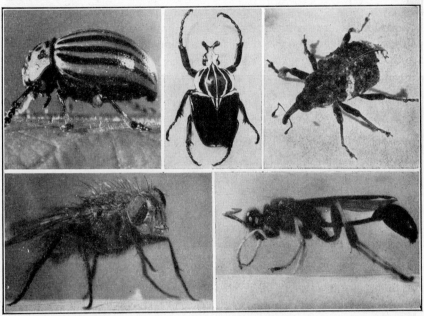

FIG. B.25. Representative higher insects. Upper: left, the Colorado potato beetle, Coleoptera; center, a large African scarab beetle, Coleoptera; right, the plum curculio, a snout beetle, Coleoptera. Lower: left, the house fly, Diptera; right, a mud dauber wasp, Hymenoptera. (*Courtesy Ward's Natural Science Establishment, Inc.*)

tives. The chordates are the most highly developed of all animals. Among their general characteristics are the following:

Triploblastic. Bilateral symmetry. Metamerism evident. Coelom present; organ systems highly developed. Endoskeleton always present at some stage. Its characteristic form is the notochord, a longitudinal dorsal rod, replaced to varying degrees in higher forms by the centra of a series of vertebrae, which together constitute a vertebral column (backbone). Respiration always involving the pharynx; gill clefts or pouches present in this region at some stage of development (these persistent as functional gill clefts only in the classes below Amphibia). Central nervous system composed of a dorsal hollow nerve cord, the anterior portion of which forms the brain in the vertebrates.

There are about 70,000 existing species of Chordata, of which all but a relatively small number are vertebrates. Four subphyla are commonly recognized, but the first three of these may be combined under the name Protochordata. The remaining subphylum, the Vertebrata, may be conveniently divided into eight classes, though more than eight are often made.

Subphylum *A*. **The Primitive Chordates** (Protochordata). This subphylum includes the lower chordates, for the most part unrecognizable as such except on the basis of their embryology. They possess, in some stage, what are believed to be the homologues of notochord, gill slits, and hollow dorsal nerve cord; but they lack a brain case, vertebral column, paired appendages, true ventral heart, and hemoglobin in the blood. There are three classes:

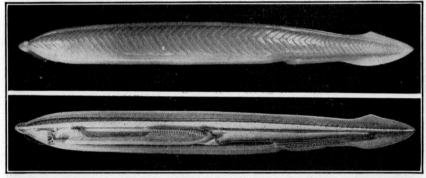

Fig. B.26. Models of the primitive chordate Amphioxus (Branchiostoma). Upper, side view showing the external appearance; lower, the left half mostly removed to show internal structures. Note the perforated walls of the large pharynx. (*Courtesy American Museum of Natural History.*)

Class 1. *The Acorn Worms* (Hemichordata). Wormlike marine animals with a muscular proboscis and collarlike neck region; without typical notochord, that structure possibly represented by a short blind tube extending forward into the proboscis from the dorsal wall of the alimentary canal; paired lateral gill slits present. Some students of the chordates would exclude this group from the phylum. Example: Balanoglossus.

Class 2. *The Sea Squirts, or Tunicates* (Urochordata). Solitary or colonial marine animals (Fig. 27.5) with a saclike covering called the *tunic*. Notochord absent in adult, present in the tail of the tadpolelike larva. Adult either fixed (sessile) or in a few forms free-swimming and pelagic.

Class 3. *The Lancelets* (Cephalochordata). Amphioxus, a small fishlike marine animal, with elongated body in which metamerism is evidenced by the V-shaped muscle segments of the trunk. Notochord well developed, extending practically the full length of the body. Gill slits numerous. Without true head or brain. A good swimmer but spending most of time buried in sand with anterior and posterior ends protruding. Beating cilia cause a stream of water to flow into the mouth and out the gill slits, food particles being retained by entanglement with a gelatinous secretion of the pharynx.

Subphylum *B*. **The Vertebrates** (Vertebrata). Notochord, if persistent, surrounded by cartilage; if not persistent, replaced by a vertebral column made of cartilage or bone. A brain case (cranium) present and, typically, two pairs of appendages (forelimbs and hind-limbs), each arising from several somites and supported by an internal skeleton. Front end of neural tube enlarged into a brain, the remainder forming the spinal cord. Includes the following classes, the first six of which are cold-blooded, the last two warm-blooded:

Class 1. *The Jawless Fishes* (Agnatha). Primitive vertebrates with a single median nostril; the mouth an opening without hinged jaws; without paired fins. Includes two subclasses, the ostracoderms and the cyclostomes.

Subclass 1. The *ostracoderms* (*Ostracodermata) are the most ancient known vertebrates. They had heavily armored heads and fishlike tails. The group has been described and illustrated (Fig. 27.4) in Chap. XXVII.

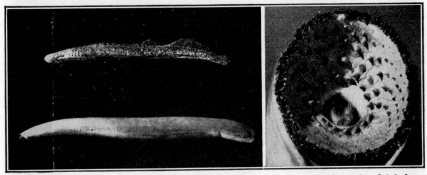

Fɪɢ. B.27. Cyclostomes, the most primitive living fishes. Left, lamprey above, hagfish below. Right, much enlarged view of the mouth disk and rasping "teeth" of the lamprey. (*Courtesy American Museum of Natural History.*)

Subclass 2. The *lampreys and hagfishes* (Cyclostomata) are eel-like forms with circular mouths armed with rasping "teeth," numerous gill slits, and a persistent notochord covered with a cartilaginous sheath; they lack bone and scales. The lampreys are world-wide in distribution in fresh and salt waters. They attach themselves to fishes, turtles, etc. by the sucking mouth, and rasp away the flesh, eventually killing the prey. The hagfishes are all marine. They are nocturnal, spending the day buried in the mud of the sea floor at depths of over 2,000 feet; at night they attack fishes, boring their way into the body by means of a special drilling apparatus and cleaning it out so as to leave only a shell. These two types seem to be descendants of different groups of ostracoderms.

Class 2. *The Primitive Jawed Fishes* (*Placodermi). The principal types of placoderms have been described and illustrated in Chap. XXVII.

Class 3. *Sharks, Rays, and Chimaeras* (Chondrichthyes). These are the cartilaginous fishes. All surviving types are marine. In this class bone has been lost; the notochord is persistent, though partially replaced by the centra of the vertebrae. The jaws are advanced in structure, and armed with many pointed or flattened teeth. There are numerous gill slits, exposed or covered only by a flap of skin. The fins are paired. The skin has imbedded denticles or "placoid scales" that have the general structure of a tooth. The heart is two chambered.

There are two subclasses, of which the Elasmobranchii is by far the largest. This group is known back to the Devonian, and includes the extinct *Cladoselachii (Fig. 27.12) and the order Selachii. To the latter belong many extinct and all modern elasmobranchs, including the sharks, skates, sawfishes, sting rays, or

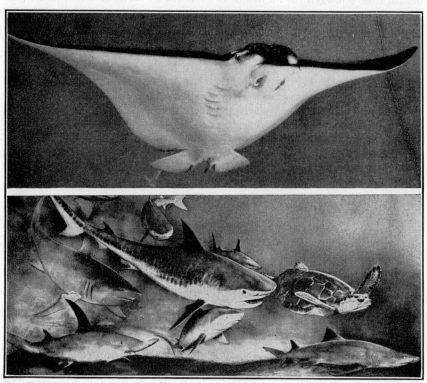

Fig. B.28. Sharks and rays, class Chondrichthyes. Above, an eagle ray, *Aetobatus marinari*. Below, a group of sharks, including the white, hammerhead, southern ground, spot-fin ground, and tiger sharks. Also shown is the marine loggerhead turtle. (*Courtesy American Museum of Natural History*.)

stingarees, electric rays, and the giant mantas (also called eagle rays or sea vampires). To the second subclass, Holocephali, belong only the strange chimaeras.

Class 4. *The True or Bony Fishes* (Osteichthyes). Cold-blooded aquatic vertebrates with internal skeleton bony or partly bony; gills covered by a bony flap (operculum); scales usually present, of "ganoid" or "cosmoid" type in primitive forms, in modern teleost fishes thin and horny (cycloid or ctenoid), never of "placoid" type. Paired fins usually present. Heart two-chambered, approaching the three-chambered condition in Dipnoi.

Subclass 1. The *choanate fishes* (Choanichthyes) have internal nostrils (choanae) enabling them to breathe air without opening the mouth. This subclass includes the lungfishes (Dipnoi, Fig. 27.16), with fan-shaped tooth plates, without maxillary and premaxillary bones in the upper jaw, and with elongate leaflike paired fins having a central skeletal axis; the *lobe-finned fishes (Crossopterygii, Figs. 27.15 and 17), with marginal teeth on the maxillary and premaxillary bones and fins with a fleshy base that contains the skeletal elements of the pentadactyl limb, extinct but ancestral to Amphibia; and the coelacanths (Coelacanthi).[1]

Subclass 2. The *ray-finned fishes* (Actinopterygii) have no internal nostrils; fins with a very short base and consisting chiefly of a membranous web supported by slender horny rays. The principal group of the ray fins is the order Teleosti, the modern fishes (Fig. B.30), which comprises more than 90 per cent of all living species of fishes. In this order the scales are thin and horny or absent altogether,

FIG. B.29. The northern longnose gar, *Lepisosteus osseus oxyurus*, a primitive "ganoid" ray-finned fish. (*Courtesy Institute of Fisheries Research, Michigan Department of Conservation.*)

and the swim bladder is no longer used as a lung but is purely a hydrostatic organ.

The first four classes of vertebrates, above, are sometimes all grouped into the single category of Fishes (Pisces).

Class 5. *The Amphibians* (Amphibia). "Stegocephalians," salamanders, frogs, toads, and blindworms. Cold-blooded vertebrates partially adapted to land life, with two pairs of pentadactyl limbs except when these have been lost through degeneration. Skull with double occipital condyle. Skin smooth or rough and rich in glands that keep it moist, modern amphibians almost always without skin plates or scales, extinct types with dermal bony plates buried in the skin. Respiration usually by gills in the young, by lungs and skin in the adult. Heart three-chambered in adult. Eggs, with few exceptions, laid in water and larval stages aquatic; most adults partly or completely terrestrial but some aquatic throughout life.

Subclass 1. The *Apsidospondyli* have "arch vertebrae" in which the centra are formed by fusion of an anterior and a posterior cartilage block. Includes the

---

[1] The coelacanths, an offshoot of the lobe fins, were supposed to have been extinct since the Cretaceous. But in 1938, a South African fisherman seined up a 5-foot long, blue-scaled marine fish from a depth of 40 fathoms, which proved to be a surviving coelacanth. It was named *Latimeria*.

FIG. B.30. Some fresh-water bony fishes. *A*, northern brook silversides, *Labidesthes s. sicculus*. *B*, round whitefish, *Prosopium cylindraceum*. *C*, lake sturgeon, *Acipenser fulvescens*, with primitive form of tail. *D*, Iowa darter, *Etheostoma exile*. *E*, American eel, *Anguilla rostrata*. *F*, slimy sculpin, *Cottus cognatus*. *G*, topminnow or mosquito fish, *Gambusia a. affinis*. *H*, largemouth bass, called "trout" in Florida, *Micropterus salmoides*. *I*, American smelt, *Osmerus mordax*. *J*, brook trout, *Salvelinus fontinalis*. *K*, madtom, *Schilbeodes eleutherus*. *L*, common shiner, *Notropis cornutus chrysocephalus*. *M*, carp, *Cyprinus carpio*. *N*, nine-spine stickleback, *Pungitius pungitius*. (*Courtesy Institute of Fisheries Research, Michigan Department of Conservation, except* (*H*), *New York State Biological Survey, and* (*M*), *Illinois State Natural History Survey.*)

majority of the Paleozoic "stegocephalians" (*Labyrinthodontia, Figs. 27.17 and 19, so named because of the complex infolding of the enamel layer of their large teeth), and the modern frogs (Fig. B.13) and toads (Figs. 15.8 and 9) (Salientia or Anura).

Subclass 2. The *Lepospondyli* have "husk vertebrae" in which the centra are formed by deposition of bone directly around the embryonic notochord. Includes a few groups of small Paleozoic stegocephalians and the modern orders Urodela (salamanders, Fig. B.31) and Apoda (blindworms or caecilians). The salamanders are lizardlike in form; as adults some are aquatic while others live in moist terrestrial habitats. The blindworms are small, burrowing, wormlike tropical animals; some are oviparous, the male possessing a copulatory organ, unlike most amphibians.

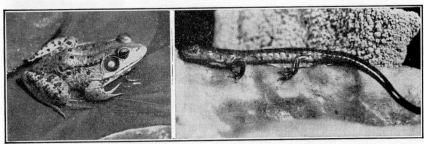

Fig. B.31. Representative amphibians. Left, the grass frog, *Rana pipiens;* right, the cave salamander, *Eurycea lucifuga. (Courtesy Ward's Natural Science Establishment, Inc., and American Museum of Natural History, respectively.)*

Class 6. *The Reptiles* (Reptilia). Lizards, snakes, turtles, alligators and crocodiles, Sphenodon, and numerous *extinct groups of the Paleozoic and Mesozoic. Cold-blooded, fully terrestrial vertebrates (except for secondary adaptations to aquatic existence), without gills at any time; independent of the water for breeding, through possessing a shelled egg along with internal fertilization; oviparous or ovoviparous; skin with few glands, covered by horny epidermal scales unlike the dermal scales of fishes, making it dry and waterproof; with two pairs of pentadactyl limbs except when these have been lost through degeneration, the toes usually armed with claws—the forerunners of the claws, hoofs, and nails of birds and mammals; lung breathing aided by ribs; heart three-chambered, the ventricle partly subdivided, thus tending toward the four-chambered condition and complete double circulation; third eyelid, pineal eye, and depressed eardrum developed; skull with a single median occipital condyle. The classification of the reptiles has been dealt with in detail in Chap. XXVIII.

Class 7. *The Birds* (Aves). Warm-blooded, air-breathing vertebrates, with primary adaptations for flight; body covered with feathers; forelimb three-fingered, modified into a wing (in a few groups it is secondarily specialized for swimming, or vestigial); heart four-chambered, with complete double circulation, single right aortic arch preserved; respiration by means of highly perfected lungs, their capacity increased by accessory air sacs that penetrate the coelomic cavity and the interior of the bones, reducing relative weight and thus aiding in flight; all modern birds with a syrinx or voice-organ situated at the junction of the

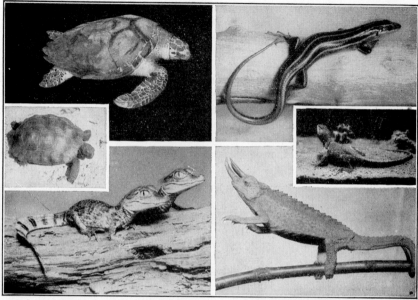

FIG. B.32. Representative reptiles. Left: upper, the marine hawksbill turtle, *Eretmochelys imbricata;* center, the desert tortoise or "gopher," *Gopherus agassizii;* lower, two young alligators, *Alligator mississippiensis.* Right: upper, the five-lined skink, *Eumeces quinquelineatus;* center, the collared lizard, *Crotaphytus collaris;* lower, the horned African chameleon, Chameleo. (*Courtesy Zoological Society of Philadelphia, except right center, General Biological Supply House, Inc.*)

FIG. B.33. One of the largest of the snakes, the anaconda *Epicrates cenchria.* (*Photo by Isabelle deP. Hunt.*)

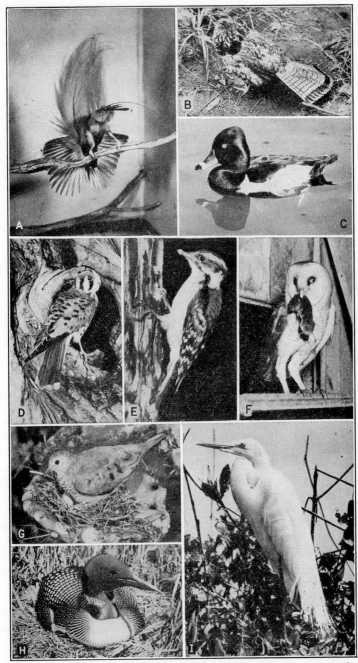

FIG. B.34. Some representative birds. *A*, Count Salvadori's bird of paradise in display. *B*, ruffed grouse. *C*, ring-necked duck. *D*, sparrow hawk. *E*, downy woodpecker. *F*, barn owl with prey. *G*, ground dove on nest. *H*, common loon. *I*, American egret. [*Photos by Allan D. Cruickshank* (*C, E, I*), *Hugh M. Halliday* (*B, D, H*), *Lee S. Crandall* (*A*), *and John H. Gerard* (*F*). *All courtesy National Audubon Society, except* (*A*), *New York Zoological Society*.]

trachea with the two bronchi, taking the place of the larynx as a sound-producing structure; skeleton made rigid by fusion of many of its bones, the breastbone in all strong fliers enlarged for insertion of massive flight muscles; body streamlined; a single left ovary and oviduct retained in most forms; eggs and egg membranes essentially reptilian, but the eggs usually incubated by the heat of the parent's body, and parental care highly developed in the majority of modern forms.

The birds form a large and highly successful group, which is apparently not even yet at its zenith. Relationships among modern birds are so close and the assemblage is so homogeneous that it is not easy to subdivide the existing species into numerous well-defined groups. The differences that distinguish the orders and families are much less pronounced than in the other classes of vertebrates.

Class 8. *The Mammals, or Hairy Vertebrates* (Mammalia). Warm-blooded, air-breathing vertebrates with bodies more or less covered with hair. The skin contains sweat, oil, and mammary glands, the secretion of the latter (milk) serving to nourish the young. The skull has two occipital condyles; the lower jaw consists of a single bone, the dentary, which articulates with the squamosal bones; the articulate and quadrate bones of the ancestral jaw hinge are transformed into the malleus and incus bones of the middle ear, the third ear bone (stapes) being inherited from the reptiles. The teeth are imbedded in sockets in the jawbone and are of two sets (milk teeth and permanent teeth); they are differentiated into incisors, canines, premolars, and molars. The ear is usually furnished with an external trumpet, the tympanic membrane lies at the bottom of a tube, and the cochlea of the inner ear (the auditory sense organ) is spirally coiled except in the monotremes. There are fleshy cheeks and lips covering the edges of the jaws and teeth (replaced by horny plates in monotremes).

The neck nearly always has only seven vertebrae; the centra of the vertebrae are separated by cartilaginous disks; usually the ribs articulate with the vertebrae by two heads; the first digit of forelimbs and hind limbs has two bones, all the remaining digits three (a lower number than in the reptiles). The thoracic and abdominal cavities are separated by a muscular diaphragm that aids in breathing. The brain is relatively large, the cerebrum and especially the cerebral cortex (neopallium) greatly enlarged, and the two cerebral hemispheres are connected by the corpus callosum, a massive bundle of fiber tracts (rudimentary in marsupials and absent in monotremes). The cerebellum is large, complex, and solid.

A cloaca (combined anal and urinogenital opening) is absent except in monotremes and some insectivores; a urinary bladder is present. A penis is always present. The eggs are alecithal, microscopic (except in monotremes); they develop in a uterus (except in monotremes), to the walls of which the embryo is attached by a placenta (except in the monotremes and most marsupials); the young are "born alive" (except in monotremes).

The classification of the mammals is given below in somewhat more detail than was done for the other classes of vertebrates, with special attention to the primates.

Class Mammalia

Subclass I. THE EGG-LAYING MAMMALS. (Prototheria or Monotremata.) Includes the duckbill (Ornithorhynchus) and spiny anteater (Tachyglossus).

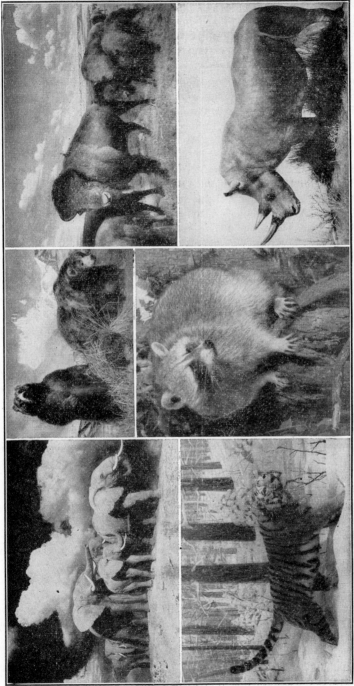

Fig. B.35. Some representative mammals. Upper: left, a herd of African elephants; center, Alaskan brown bears; right, a herd of American bison. Lower: left, a Siberian tiger; center, the eastern raccoon; right, the African white rhinoceros. [Courtesy American Museum of Natural History, University of Michigan Museum of Zoology (lower center), and Chicago Natural History Museum (lower right).]

Subclass II. THE TRUE MAMMALS. (Theria.) Viviparous.

A. PRIMITIVE MESOZOIC AND PALEOCENE GROUPS.* (Triconodonta, Symmetrodonta, Multituberculata, Pantotheria.)

B. THE MARSUPIAL MAMMALS. (Metatheria, with one order, Marsupialia.) Includes the American opossums and extinct South American carnivorous types, some of bear size and one similar to the placental saber-toothed tiger; also the Australian marsupials discussed in Chap. XXVIII, as well as extinct Australian types up to the size of a rhinoceros.

C. THE PLACENTAL MAMMALS. (Eutheria.)

Order 1. The Insectivores. (Insectivora.) Moles, shrews, "flying lemurs," etc.

Order 2. The Bats. (Chiroptera.)

Order 3. **The Primates.** (Primates.) See Chap. XXIX.

Suborder 1. The Lemurs. (Lemuroidea.)

Suborder 2. The Tarsioids. (Tarsioidea.) Tarsius.

Suborder 3. The Anthropoids. (Anthropoidea.)

Series 1. The New World Monkeys. (Platyrrhini.)

Families Hapalidae (marmosets) and Cebidae (South American monkeys).

Series 2. The Old World Catarrhines. (Catarrhini.)

Family 1. The baboons, monkeys, apes, etc. (Cercopithecidae.)

Family 2. The manlike apes. (Simiidae.)

? Family 3. The South African man-apes. (*Australopithecidae.)

Family 4. **Ancient and modern men.** (Hominidae.)

? Genus 1. Java Man. (*Pithecanthropus.) ⎫ ⎛Placed under
? Genus 2. Peking Man. (*Sinanthropus.) ⎬ ⎨Homo by many re-
? Genus 3. Piltdown Man. (*Eoanthropus.) ⎭ ⎝cent authorities

Genus 4. **Modern Man.** (Homo.)

Order 4. The Carnivores. (Carnivora.)

Suborder 1. The Creodonts. (*Creodonta.) Primitive carnivores.

Suborder 2. The Fissipedes. (Fissipedia.) Modernized carnivores. Includes the terrestrial carnivores: civets, hyenas, cats, weasels, otters, dogs, wolves, bears, etc.

Suborder 3. The Seals and Walruses. (Pinnipedia.)

Order 5. The Amblypods. (*Amblypoda.) Pantolambda, Coryphodon, etc.

Order 6. The Uintatheres. (*Dinocerata.) Uintatherium, etc.

Order 7. The Hyraxes. (Hyracoidea.)

Order 8. The Proboscidians. (Proboscidea.) Includes the *dinotheres, *mastodons, *mammoths, and modern elephants.

Order 9. The Dugongs or Manatees. (Sirenia.)

Order 10. The Aardvarks. (Tubulidentata.)

Order 11. The Condylarths. (*Condylarthra.)

Order 12. The Litopterns. (*Litopterna.)   ⎫Groups of strange South
Order 13. The Notungulates. (*Notoungulata.) ⎭American mammals.

Order 14. The Odd-toed Ungulates. (Perissodactyla.)

Superfamily 1. Horselike Animals. Includes the horses (Equidae), titanotheres (*Titanotheridae), and chalicotheres (*Chalicotheridae).

Superfamily 2. Tapirlike Animals. Includes the tapirs (Tapiridae) and rhinoceroses (Rhinocerotidae), with other families.

Order 15. The Even-toed Ungulates. (Artiodactyla.)

Suborder 1. The Swine Series. (Suina.) Includes the swine (Suidae), peccaries (Tayassuidae), hippopotamuses (Hippopotamidae), and other families.

Suborder 2. The Ruminant Series (Ruminantia).

Infraorder 1. The Camel Series. (Tylopoda.) Includes the camels and llamas (Camelidae), oreodonts (*Oreodontidae), giant "pigs" (*Agriochaeridae), and other families.

Infraorder 2. The Deer Series. (Pecora.) Includes the mouse deer (Tragulidae), deer (Cervidae), giraffes (Giraffidae), prongbucks (Antilocapridae), and antelopes, musk oxen, mountain sheep, true sheep, goats, cattle and bison (Bovidae).

Order 16. The Edentates. (Edentata or Xenarthra.) Includes the groundsloths, sloths, anteaters, and armadillos.

Order 17. The Scaly Anteaters. (Pholidota.)

Order 18. The Cetaceans. (Cetacea.) Includes the dolphins, toothed whales, and whalebone whales.

Order 19. The Rodents. (Rodentia.)

Suborder 1. The Squirrel Series. (Sciuromorpha.) Includes the squirrels, flying squirrels, chipmunks and woodchucks (Sciuridae), beavers (Castoridae), pocket gophers or "salamanders" (Geomyidae), pocket mice and kangaroo rats (Heteromyidae), and others.

Suborder 2. The Porcupine Series. (Hystricomorpha.) Includes the porcupines (Erythizontidae), cavies or guinea pigs and capybaras (Caviidae), chinchillas (Chinchillidae.)

Suborder 3. The Rats and Mice. (Myomorpha.) Includes the jumping mice (Zapodidae) and the true rats and mice (Muridae.)

Order 20. The Rabbits and Hares. (Lagomorpha.) Treated as a suborder of the Rodentia in older classifications. Includes the pikas or conies (Ochotonidae) and the hares and rabbits (Leporidae).

LIST OF VISUAL AIDS

The visual materials listed below and on the following pages may be used to supplement the subject matter of this book. We recommend, however, that each film be reviewed before using in order to determine its suitability for a particular class or group.

Both motion pictures and filmstrips are included in this list of visual materials, and the character of each one is indicated by the self-explanatory abbreviations "MP" or "FS." Immediately following this identification is the abbreviated name of the producer and distributor, given in full with addresses at the end of the bibliography.

Unless otherwise indicated, the motion pictures listed in this bibliography are 16-mm. sound films and the filmstrips are 35 mm., silent.

Alternation of Generations in Plants (FS, Macmillan, 52 fr). Shows how a fern, a selaginella, and a flowering plant solve the problems of fertilization and dispersal by an alternation of the sporophyte and gametophyte generations.

The Amoeba (MP, UWF, 10 min). Shows by photomicrography and animated drawings the structure and life of a single-celled organism. Contains the following principal sequences: production of pseudopodia, amoeba pursuing and capturing prey, process of ingestion, and reproduction by fission.

Beginning of History (MP, IFB, 46 min). The prehistory of Great Britain, from the ice age to the coming of the Romans. Produced for the British Ministry of Education by the Crown Film Unit.

Body Defenses against Disease (MP, EBF, 10 min). The body's three levels of defense against infection—skin and mucous membranes, lymphatic system, and blood circulatory system including liver and spleen.

The Brain (MP, Brandon, 75 min, silent). Shows structure, cranial nerves, embryonic development, ventricles, fissures and convolutions, cerebral hemispheres, etc. Approved by the American College of Physicians and Surgeons.

Cell Division (MP, Brice, 11 min). The living cell is shown by photomicrography during a 21-hour division cycle. All parts of parent cell and daughter cells are identified.

Cells and Their Functions (MP, Athena, 14 min). Shows by means of photomicrography and time-lapse photography mitosis, beating cilia, blood cells engulfing bacteria, and the proliferation and growth of cardiac and other tissue.

Circulation (MP, UWF, 16 min). Animated diagrams of the human body and its circulatory system; systemic and pulmonary circulation of the blood; functions of heart, lungs, arteries, veins, and capillaries.

Development of the Bird Embryo (MP, EBF, 14 min, silent). Development of chick and wren embryos, showing by photomicrography the establishment of circulation, action of the heart, and formation of yolk sac, amnion, and allantois.

Development of a Frog (MP, OSU, 10 min). Shows through time-lapse photography and photomicrography the cell division of a frog egg.

Digestion (MP, UWF, 2 parts). *Part* 1 (15 min). Mechanical and muscular processes involved in the digestion of food. *Part* 2 (18 min). Chemical changes involved in the digestion of carbohydrates, proteins, and fats; secretion and action of saliva, gastric, pancreatic, intestinal juices, and bile on each type of food.

Elimination (MP, UWF, 12 min). A study of the human body's methods of elimination—through the skin, kidneys, lungs, and colon.

Endocrine Glands (MP, EBF, 11 min). Points out the effects of improper functioning of the endocrine glands, and the causes and remedies of faulty glandular action.

The Earth's Rocky Crust (MP, EBF, 10 min). Dynamic aspects of geology, including the formation and destruction of rocks and land forms, illustrative of the content of chapter XXV.

The Earthworm. (MP, UWF, 11 min). Study of an animal organized on a simple organ-system plan, skillfully dissected to show its structure, and with included material on its role in aeration and enrichment of the soil, and its reproductive mechanisms and behavior.

Fingers and Thumbs (MP, Lib F, 20 min). Traces the development of man's hands from prehuman stages to the present. Produced under the supervision of Julian Huxley.

Heredity (MP, EBF, 11 min). Presents by animated charts and animal picturization the Mendelian laws of inheritance.

Heredity and Prenatal Development (MP, McGraw, 21 min). Step-by-step picturization of growth, subdivision, and union of male and female sex cells, including explanation of chromosomes and genes.

Heredity Variations in Coleus (MP, OSU, 11 min). Photographic record of experiments conducted over a period of time showing the variety of offspring derived from the coleus plant.

How Animals Defend Themselves (MP, YAF, 10 min). Adaptations for protection, including speed and agility, armor, defensive weapons, camouflage, and mimicry.

How Seeds Germinate (MP, USDA, 9 min, silent). Through time-lapse photography, shows the germination of crimson clover and spring vetch over a period of a week.

How the Organs of the Body Function (MP, Bray, 30 min). Presents the important organs of the body; visualizes the structure of the body by X-rays; and shows the contraction of muscles, movement of bones and joints, and action of heart and lungs. Condensed version of a series entitled "The Human Body" consisting of silent films with following titles:

Human Skeleton (38 min)
Circulatory System (30 min)
Respiratory System (15 min)
Digestive Tract (22 min)
Urinary System (15 min)
Human Development (22 min)

Human Reproduction (MP, McGraw, 20 min). Describes the human reproductive system and the process of normal human birth; the anatomy and physiology of male and female reproductive organs; and the process of ovulation, fertilization, and development of the human embryo. Supplementary filmstrip, same title, also available.

The Hydra (MP, UWF, 10 min). The general structure and behavior of Hydra, and the functioning of its parts.

In the Beginning (MP, USDA, 17 min). Portrays the ovulation, fertilization, and early development of the mammalian egg.

Kidneys, Ureters, and Bladder (MP, Bray, 11 min). Description by animated drawings of the important anatomical features of the kidneys, ureters, and urinary bladder; relationship of constituent parts of the urinary system; and the process of elimination.

Life Cycle of Moss (MP, UWF, 10 min). Reproduction of mosses, showing production of sex organs, gametes and fertilization, growth of sporophyte, spore production, and protonema.

Life in a Pond (MP, Coronet, 10 min). A class field trip to a pond, where plants and animals ranging from microscopic to the size of fishes are seen and their food chain relationships noted.

Life through the Ages (FS, Macmillan, 49 fr). Shows how plants and animals have left a record of their past in the fossils which are examples of life in the Paleozoic, Mesozoic, and Cenozoic eras.

A Lost World (MP, EBF, 10 min). Glimpses into the world of dinosaurs and prehistoric monsters. Based on a story of the same title by A. Conan Doyle.

Marine Animals and Their Food (MP, Coronet, 10 min). Food supply and food-getting adaptations of marine animals, illustrative of contents of pages 550–553 and 565–576.

Meiosis—In Spermatogenesis of the Grasshopper, Psophus stridulus (MP, Brice, 19 min). Scenes of living cells, primary and secondary spermatocytes going through prophase, metaphase, anaphase, and telophase cycles.

Muscles (MP, EBF, 15 min, silent). Nature, structure, and use of muscles, contraction, fatigue, arrangement in antagonistic groups.

Nine Basic Functional Systems of the Human Body (MP, Bray, 11 min). Shows by animated drawings the skeletal, muscular, excretory, circulatory, nervous, sensory, digestive, lymphatic, and endocrine systems of the human body.

Plant Physiology (FS, Macmillan, 47 fr). Shows the parts of a plant; traces the flow of water through the plant; and illustrates food-making and respiratory activities and various kinds of tropism.

Plant Reactions (MP, Academy, 11 min). Shows through time-lapse photography the reactions of plants to water, light, gravity, and chemicals.

Plant Survival (MP, UWF, 10 min). Shows the protective devices of plants by means of close-up photographs of roots, seeds, buds, leaves, and flowers.

Protoplasm—The Beginning of Life (MP, Bray, 15 min). Traces through the study of geology the earliest forms of life, and explains their characteristics of movement, irritability, assimilation, and reproduction.

The Protozoa (MP, EBF, 27 min, silent). Life of various Protozoa, including means of locomotion, food getting, reproduction, waste elimination, and reactions to environment.

Pygmies of Africa (MP, EBF, 20 min). Life and customs of Pygmies of the Ituri Forest, showing the dominance of food-gathering activities in their primitive society.

Reactions in Plants and Animals (MP, EBF, 10 min). A study of reactions to stimuli.

Reptiles (MP, EBF, 14 min, silent). Characteristics and adaptations of various species.

Rodents (MP, ICS, 10 min). Covers many types of rodents, including the lagomorphs, and may be useful in connection with the section on taxonomy.

Root Development (MP, UWF, 9 min). Shows by photomicrography the details of root structure and growth, and by animation the moisture absorption of roots.

Seashore Oddities (MP, YAF, 20 min, color). Marine invertebrate life, including many species of each of four phyla—coelenterates, echinoderms, arthropods, and molluscs, with good discussions of their characteristics, food habits, and reproduction.

Sea Urchin (MP, UWF, 18 min). Life history of the sea urchin, with special reference to it early embryology.

Tiny Water Animals (MP, EBF, 10 min). Protozoa and small metazoan inhabitants of water, shown by photomicrography.

Water Life Series (FS, JH, 7 strips, 60 fr. each). Color photos of many freshwater and marine organisms.
1. Life in Ponds, Lakes, and Streams
2. Small Freshwater Animals and Insects
3. Freshwater Shellfish and Amphibians
4. Freshwater Turtles and Fish
5. Keeping an Aquarium
6. Plants and Strange Animals of the Sea
7. Shellfish of the Seashore

DIRECTORY OF SOURCES

Academy—Academy Films, Box 3088, Hollywood, Calif.

Athena—Athena Films, Inc., 165 W. 46th St., New York 19.

Brandon—Brandon Films, Inc., 200 W. 57th St., New York 19.

Bray—Bray Studios, Inc., 729 Seventh Ave., New York 19.

Brice—Arthur T. Brice, P.O. Box 423, Ross, Calif.

Coronet—Coronet Instructional Films, Coronet Building, 65 E. South Water St., Chicago 1.

EBF—Encyclopaedia Britannica Films, Inc., 1150 Wilmette Ave., Wilmette, Ill.

ICS—Institutional Cinema Service, 1560 Broadway, New York 19.

IFB—International Film Bureau, 6 N. Michigan Ave., Chicago 2.

JH—Jam Handy Organization, 2821 E. Grand Blvd., Detroit 14.

Lib F—Library Film Distributors and Producers, P.O. Box 1104, Hollywood 28, Calif.

Macmillan—The Macmillan Company, 60 Fifth Ave., New York 11.

McGraw—McGraw-Hill Book Company, Inc., Text-Film Department, 330 W. 42d St., New York 36.

OSU—The Ohio State University, Columbus 10.

USDA—U.S. Department of Agriculture, Motion Picture Service, Washington 25. D.C.

UWF—United World Films, Inc., 1445 Park Ave., New York 29

YAF—Young America Films, Inc., 18 E. 41st St., New York 17.

INDEX

Omission of the seldom-used glossary and reading lists has permitted much more complete indexing than in the previous edition. Technical terms have been held to a minimum throughout the book. Those used are explained by definition, context, or illustration. Text references are in roman type, those to footnotes followed by *n*. Illustrations accompanying text are not separately indexed, but if on other pages are given in *italic* type. •

A